HEINEMANN
ADVANCED
SCIENCE

Physics

PATRICK FULLICK

Heinemann Educational Publishers
Halley Court, Jordan Hill, Oxford, OX2 8EJ
a division of Reed Educational & Professional Publishing Ltd
Heinemann is a registered trademark of Reed Educational &
Professional Publishing Ltd

OXFORD MELBOURNE AUCKLAND
JOHANNESBURG BLANTYRE GABARONE
IBADAN PORTSMOUTH NH (USA) CHICAGO

© First edition Patrick Fullick, 1994
© This edition Patrick Fullick, 2000

First published 2000

ISBN 0 435 57097 8

04 03 02 01 00
10 9 8 7 6 5 4 3 2 1

Edited by Patrick Bonham

Designed and produced by Gecko Limited, Bicester, Oxon

Original illustrations © Heinemann Educational Publishers, 2000

Printed and bound in Spain by Mateu Cromo

Acknowledgements
The author and publishers would like to thank the following for permission to use
photographs:

Cover photos: Science Photo Library/Mehau Kulyk

p2 SPL/NASA; **p8** Bureau International Des Poids et Mesures; **p13** Quadrant Picture
Library; **p14** Mark Powell; **p15 M and contents** SPL/Prof. Harold Edgerton; **B** Peter
Gould; **p16** J. Allan Cash; **p21** SPL/Dr Jeremy Burgess; **p23 L** Philip Parkhouse;
R Ford; **p25** SPL/NASA; **p36** Colorsport/Sipa Press; **p37** Robert Harding Picture
Library; **p39 T** Ben Schott **M** Roger Scruton; **p41** SPL; **p42 all** Philip Parkhouse;
p43 Allsport/Simon Bruty; **p46** MIRA; **p49** MIRA; **p50 T** Robert Harding Picture
Library; **B** SPL/Stephen Dalton; **p51 T** Colorsport; **M** SPL/Roger Ressmeyer,
Starlight; **B** Action Plus; **L** SPL/Roger Ressmeyer, Starlight; **p62 all** Philip
Parkhouse; **p63 all** Philip Parkhouse; **p66** Ford; **p67** Oxford Scientific Films/Lon
Lauber; **p78** Allsport; **p79** Peter Gould; **p82** Quadrant Picture Library; **p83** Action
plus; **p85** SPL/European Space Agency; **p86** SPL/Cern, P Loiez; **p92** Kobal;
p104 Memtek International; **p115** HE; **p116 TL** SPL/John Sanford; **BL** Robert
Harding Picture Library; **TR** Philip Parkhouse; **BR** J Allan Cash Ltd; **p122** SPL/Bill
Sanderson; **p125 TR** Robert Harding Picture Library; **BR** Philip Parkhouse;
p128 Impact/Ken Graham; **p129 T** SPL; **M** SPL/Prof. H Hashimoto, Osaka
University; **B** SPL/G Muller, Struers GMBH; **p130 all** Peter Gould; **p131 L, M, R**
Peter Gould; **p134 L** Robert Harding Picture Library;
M Zefa; **R** Action Plus; **p137** Reed International Books Ltd/Peter Laughran;
p138 L Robert Harding Picture Library; **R** SPL/CNRI; **M** SPL/Francis Leroy
Biocosmos; **p146** Courtesy Central Library for Physics in Vienna; **p151** Corbis;
p152 T The Science Museum; **B** Vivien Fifield Picture Library; **p156** American
Association for Advancement of Science; **p158 all** Peter Gould; **p160** Allsport/Mike
Powell; **p162 T** Rex Features; **B** SPL/Richard Lawenberg; **p166** Trip/H Rogers;
p170: L SPL/NOAO; **R** Philip Parkhouse; **p171: both** Vivien Fifield Picture Library;
p173: L Mary Evans Picture Library; **R** SPL/NASA; **P176: all** Peter Gould; **p178:
both** Philip Parkhouse; **p179: T** Philip Parkhouse; **B** SPL/Tony Craddock; **p180: L,
R** Philip Parkhouse; **B** Mark Powell; **p181 T x 3** Mark Powell; **BL** Peter Gould; **BR**
Philip Parkhouse; **p182** Mansell Collection; **p190 T** Robert Harding Picture Library,
BL SPL/Tommaso Guicciardini, **BR** SPL/Alex Bartel; **p193: T** SPL/World View/
ELST; **B** SPL/Bruce MacKie; **p202** Action Plus; **p203** SIPA Press; **p210 L** Comstock
Photo Library; **R** SPL/Alfred Pasieka; **p213 T** Colorsport; **M and contents** Action
Plus; **p215 T** Philip Parkhouse, **B** Peter Gould; **p220 both** Peter Gould; **p221 both**
Education Development Center; **p222 both** Peter Gould; **p225 L, TR, and R both**
Philip Parkhouse; **TM and BR** Peter Gould; **p229 both** Peter Gould; **p230** Peter
Gould; **p233 T** SPL/Science Source, **M** SPL/A Barrington Brown, **BL** SPL, **BR**
Corbis; **p235** SPL/CNRI; **p238** Corbis; **p243: a** Vivien Fifield; **b** Mansell Collection;
c, d and e Vivien Fifield; **p244:** Peter Gould; **p246** HE; **p247:** Peter Gould; **p250**
SPL; **p251** SPL/Dr Jean Lorre; **p252** SPL/Hale Observatories; **p253 T** SPL/Space
Telescope Science/NASA, **B** SPL/Hale Observatories; **p254 T** SPL/NASA CSFC,
B Corbis; **p259** HE; **p262 T** both Roger Scruton, **M1** SPL/Carl Schmidt-Luchs **M2**
SPL/David Parker, **B** SPL/Alex Bartel; **p263: a** Philip Parkhouse, **b** SPL/Martin
Dohrn; **c, d and e** Philip Parkhouse; **p265** SPL; **p276** SPL/Adam Hart-Davis; **p277
T** SPL, **B** BBC Photograph Library; **p278** Crown Copyright/The National Physical
Laboratory; **p279** Peter Gould; **p281** Courtesy of Samsung; **p285** Mansell
Collection; **p286: L** Peter Gould; **R** Philip Parkhouse; **p287: T** NASA; **B (and
contents)** SPL/Peter Menzel; **p295 all** Peter Gould; **p299** Patrick Fullick;

p300 Peter Gould; **p301** Peter Gould; **p305 L** Mark Powell/Roland Caldecutt,
University of Southampton; **R** Peter Gould; **p306** SPL/David Parker; **p315** Peter
Gould; **p317** Patrick Fullick; **p318 all** Peter Gould; **p320** Peter Gould; **p332** Peter
Gould; **p336** Peter Gould; **p341** SPL/Adam Hart-Davis; **p350: T** Picturepoint, **others**
Peter Gould; **p351** Peter Gould; **p352** Peter Gould; **p353 p355** Peter Gould; **p357**
Peter Gould; **p360 T** Ronald Grant Archive, **B** INS News Group; **p361** Peter Gould;
p374 SPL/Simon Terrey; **p377 TL** Barnaby's Picture Library, **BL** SPL/NOAO,
M Allsport, **R** University of Southampton, Department of Teaching Media; **p378**
Robert Harding Picture Library; **p379 T and R** Mary Evans Picture Library; **L** Derby
Museums; **p380** The Royal Society; **p382** SPL/NASA; **p400 L** Mary Evans Picture
Library, **R** SPL/NASA; **p403** SPL/NASA; **p410 both** Peter Gould; **p411** Ann Ronan
at Image Select; **p416** Peter Gould; **p417 T and contents:** ACE Photo Agency,
B Berger and Vogelsganger, Bull. Sev. 57: 1-22 (1966); **p423** Peter Gould; **p427**
Peter Gould; **p430 T** Teslav, **M and B** Andre Geim, Nijemgen University; **p444**
SPL/Jack Finch; **p445 both** Peter Gould; **p457 T** Mary Evans Picture Library,
B Trip/N Ray; **p472** SPL/CERN; **p473 a and c** Ann Ronan at Image Select, **b, i and j**
SPL, **d** Associated Press, **e, g, h, k and l** Mary Evans Picture Library, **f** Bettman
Archive; **p474 T** Mary Evans Picture Library; **B and contents** SPL/Prof. Erwin
Mueller; **p477** Vivien Fifield; **p483** The Science Museum; **p485** Associated Press;
p486 a Ann Ronan at Image Select, **b, c and d** Mary Evans Picture Library; **p487**
Corbis; **p488 L** SPL/Tim Beddow; **R** SPL/US Department of Energy; **p489 T** Peter
Gould; **B** SPL; **p491** Peter Gould; **p509** Mary Evans Picture Library; **p510 T**
SPL/Patrick Blackett; **B** The Science Museum; **p511 L** Science Photo Library; **R** SPL;
p514 SPL; **p515** SPL/Novosti; **p516** Corbis; **p517** Popperfoto; **p518 T** SPL/Will
McIntyre; **B** SPL; **p520** SPL/NASA; **p527 T** Mary Evans Picture Library **B** Reprinted
by permission from *Nature 3* Feb 2000 © Macmillan Magazines Ltd; **p528** Associated
Press; **p538** SPL; **p539** SPL/NOAO, **p543** Laser Fantasy International; **p547 T** The
Wellcome Institute Library, London, SPL/Ouellette & Theroux, Publiphoto
Diffusion; **p551** SPL; **p552** SPL; **p556 T and contents** SPL/CERN; **B** SPL/Patrice
Loiez, CERN; **p557** SPL; **p558** SPL/Lawrence Berkeley Lab; **p559** OSF; **p565**
California Institute of Technology.

Picture research by Thelma Gilbert

The authors and publishers would like to thank the AQA, Edexel and OCR
Examination Boards for permission to reproduce their material.

The authors and publishers would like to thank the following for permission to
reproduce copyright material:

p290 and **p398** Maps reproduced from Ordnance Survey mapping with the
permission of the Controller of Her Majesty's Stationery Office, © Crown copyright,
Licence no. 398020; **p563** Jutta Waloshek for the drawings of George Zweig and
Murray Gell-Mann; **p375** the Bouguer map is reproduced by permission of the
British Geological Survey (IPR/3-21). © NERC. All rights reserved.

The publishers have made every effort to trace the copyright holders, but if they
have inadvertently overlooked any they will be pleased to make the necessary
arrangements at the first opportunity.

Tel: 01865 888058 www.heinemann.co.uk

How to use this book

Heinemann Advanced Science: Physics has been written to accompany your AS and A2 physics course, and contains all the core specification material you will need during your period of study. The book is divided into six sections of associated material which have been made easy to find by the use of colour coding.

Within each chapter a Physics Focus explores the real-life context of an area relevant to the physics in the chapter. You may use this to whet your appetite for physics, or read it when you have made some progress with the physics to emphasise the relevance of what you are doing. However you use it, I hope it will make you want to read more!

In addition to the main text, the chapters of the book contain two types of boxes.

The *blue information boxes* contain basic facts or techniques which you need to know. This often includes key facts you will have already met at GCSE – the boxes then carry these ideas forward to AS or A2 level. Information boxes are sometimes referred to in the main text, and can be read either as you meet them or when you have finished reading the chapter.

The *pink headed extension boxes* contain more advanced information which is not referred to in the main text. You do not need to address the content of these extension boxes until you have really got to grips with the rest of the material in the chapter or are studying the subject at A2 level.

When you have completed the work in a chapter of the book, there are questions to help you find out how much of the material you have understood and to help you with your revision. Many chapters also have a Key Skills question. These are designed to help you develop the Key Skills needed to complete your studies successfully, particularly in the areas of Communication [C], Application of Number [A] and Use of IT [IT]. These Key Skills often refer to the Focus material as well as the chapter contents. The summaries at the end of each chapter provide further help with revision, while at the end of each section of the book there is a selection of AS and A2 level questions. In addition, the end of each section has a concept map to help you see how the ideas you have met in that section are related to each other and to other sections of the book.

This book has been written to be an accessible, clear and exciting guide to AS and A2 physics. I hope that it will help to maintain your interest in the subject you have chosen to study, and that it will play a valuable role in developing your knowledge of physics – and with it, an increased understanding of the way the universe works.

Acknowledgements

I should like to thank the team at Heinemann who helped get this new edition into print, particularly Lindsey Charles who has been stalwart in her support and Pat Bonham for his superb editing skills.

Finally, I should like to thank my family, friends and professional colleagues for their continuing advice, support and encouragement with all aspects of the revision. Special thanks go to my wife Ann, my sons, and Ann's mother for their many and varied contributions.

Patrick Fullick, 2000

Dedication
For William, Thomas, James and Edward

CONTENTS

1 | FORCES AND MOTION

2 | MATTER AND ENERGY

3 | WAVES

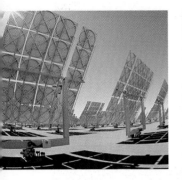

4 | ELECTRICITY

5 | FIELDS

6 | ATOMIC & NUCLEAR PHYSICS

1 FORCES AND MOTION

Introduction

We live in a world that is constantly changing and moving. The movements of animals, of the clouds in the sky, of rivers and seas are easily observed. Less obvious, but just as important, are the motion of plants as they grow and respond to light and other stimuli, the motion of atoms, and the movement of stars and planets in space. To understand movement is to understand something important about our universe.

One of the first people to set out to describe how and why things move was Aristotle, who lived in Greece almost 2500 years ago. He argued that stones fell because they were made of the element earth, which naturally belonged below our feet. By the same reasoning, smoke rose because it contained the element fire, which belonged in the heavens along with the Sun. Aristotle's explanations seem strange and amusing to us now, but they lasted for nearly 2000 years, until Galileo and then Isaac Newton set about carefully describing motion that they saw, and devising theories to explain their observations.

In this first section, our look at motion will be based on ideas that Newton first put forward more than three hundred years ago. You have already met many of the ideas central to understanding motion, like *distance*, *speed*, *time* and *force*. We shall look carefully at these in a little more depth, and build up explanations using some reasonably straightforward mathematics. By doing this one step at a time, we shall put together a simple 'physics toolkit' containing tools to help us as we meet more complicated situations in chapters to come.

We shall also think carefully about the idea of *energy*. This important and powerful concept is a vital part of the physicist's toolkit, capable of simplifying problems that are otherwise difficult to crack. All of the ideas in this section crop up again later in the book, and a thorough understanding of them early on will give you a sound base on which to build.

Figure 1.1 Space shuttle Atlantis blasts off. Each of the solid rocket boosters produces a thrust of more than 10^7 N.

FOCUS THE PHYSICS OF BUNGEE JUMPING

Figure 1.1.1 A bungee jump may be made from a specially adapted crane, or from a bridge or other tall structure.

If you have ever been to a fair or other large outdoor event, you may have seen someone bungee jumping. This hazardous activity involves flinging yourself off a tall structure, with your legs fastened to a long rubber cord, or bungee. The bungee stretches and breaks your fall, stopping you a safe distance above the ground before you are bounced back up into the air again.

But how does the person organising a bungee jump know that the person jumping is not going to hit the ground? A little careful thought about the situation suggests that there are four important *variables* about which we must know something if we are going to predict how far the jumper will fall before the bungee brings them to a halt.

The length of the bungee
It is common sense that the longer the bungee, the further the person will fall.

The 'stretchiness' of the bungee
A bungee that is easily stretched will allow someone to fall further than a bungee that is difficult to stretch.

The weight of the person
A heavy person will stretch the bungee more than a light person.

Where the upper end of the bungee is fastened
This will determine how far the jumper falls before the cord becomes taut and begins to slow them down. Normally the bungee is fastened to the platform from which the person jumps.

As well as knowing something about these four variables, there is an *assumption* that we need to make. Figure 1.1.3 shows the situation immediately after the jumper leaves the jumping platform. As they fall, the amount of bungee cord below them gets less and less. This means that the downward pull of the cord will also decrease, until it becomes zero once the cord is taut. This will make our calculations very difficult, unless we can assume that the weight of the cord is so small compared to the weight of the jumper that we can safely ignore it.

Figure 1.1.2 The effect of weight and 'stretchiness'. Cords A and B are identical, and have the same unstretched length as cord C.

The physicist's toolkit

The problem of the bungee jumper is an example of the kind of problem that physics enables us to solve. To solve these problems, physicists use a variety of different tools. During your physics course you will steadily build up your own physics toolkit, enabling you to tackle problems using the appropriate techniques. One such tool is *simplification*, which we have seen used here, when we decided that we could neglect the weight of the cord because it is small compared to the weight of the jumper. This simplification will enable us to put together a simple *model* of the bungee jump which can then be used to predict what will happen to a person who uses it. You will learn more about these and other tools in the toolkit as we go through the course.

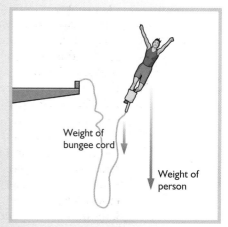

Weight of bungee cord

Weight of person

Figure 1.1.3 The forces acting on the jumper the instant after they have jumped. As well as their own weight, the bungee is also pulling down on them.

Measuring and representing motion

Describing motion – speed and distance

Before we can attempt to understand movement and what causes it, we need to be able to *describe* it. Let us look at the most obvious aspect of motion – **speed**, or how fast something is moving.

An object's speed is calculated by dividing the distance moved by the time taken to move that distance. In the language of physics, we say that speed is *distance moved in unit time*:

$$\text{Speed} = \frac{\text{distance travelled}}{\text{time taken}}$$

What was your speed on your way home last night? If you travelled 3 km in 15 minutes (0.25 hour), your answer to this might be 12 km/h (3 km ÷ 0.25 h). But this is not the whole story, as figure 1.1.4 shows.

It is clearly unlikely that anyone will cycle at a constant speed, even without hills and stops at a shop to cope with. So the calculation of speed as distance divided by time in the example above tells us simply the **average speed** for the journey. It does not tell us anything about the speed at any given instant, as it would be measured by a speedometer, for example. In fact, this **instantaneous speed** is often more important than average speed. If you drive at a speed of 40 m.p.h. along a street with a 30 m.p.h. speed limit and are stopped for speeding, the police officer will not be impressed by the argument that your average speed in the last 5 minutes was only 30 m.p.h.!

Figure 1.1.4 Average speed does not describe the speed at any particular instant.

Graphs of motion

It is often useful to represent motion using a graph, for example plotting distance against time or speed against time. Figure 1.1.5 shows two graphs for a journey.

Look at the shapes of the two graphs. The second graph shows the distance travelled away from home, while the first graph shows the instantaneous speed of the person. Where the speed–time graph is horizontal between two points, the distance–time graph has a steady slope between the same points because the distance travelled per unit time is constant. Where the speed–time graph has a value of zero, the distance–time graph is horizontal because the person is stationary. In other words, the **slope** or **gradient** of a distance–time graph represents the speed at that particular point, the **instantaneous speed**.

Because speed is found by dividing distance by time, another way of describing speed is as 'rate of change of distance with time' – so the greater the object's speed, the further it travels in a given time.

Notice that a **steady speed** corresponds to a **straight line** on the distance–time graph. Where an object has a steady speed, the slope of the distance–time graph is constant, and the object's average speed and its instantaneous speed are the same.

In the world of physics, speed is usually measured in metres per second, although we often use miles per hour in our everyday lives.

O left home
O–A accelerating
A–B travelling at steady speed
B–C slowing down as going uphill
C–D travelling at steady speed, slower than between A and B
D–E slowing down
E–F stopped
F–G accelerating again
G–H travelling at steady speed, faster than between A and B
H–J slowing down
J reached destination

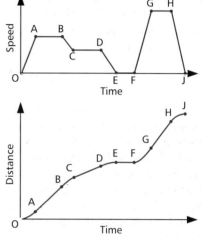

Figure 1.1.5 Speed–time and distance–time graphs for the same journey.

Straight-line graphs

Graphs are extremely useful in physics for finding and confirming relationships between different variables (for example, the stretching of a piece of metal wire and the load applied to it). The simplest type of relationship is **linear**, where a graph of one variable against another is a straight line.

Figure 1.1.6 is an example of a linear relationship, showing how the speed of an object varies with time. Speed is plotted on the vertical axis (referred to as the 'y-axis' or the 'ordinate'), and time is plotted on the horizontal axis (referred to as the 'x-axis' or the 'abscissa').

The general form of the equation for a straight line is:

$$y = mx + c$$

where:

m is the *slope* or *gradient* of the line

and:

c is the *intercept* on the y-axis (the point where the line crosses the y-axis)

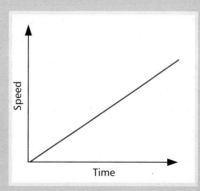

Figure 1.1.6

Distance and displacement

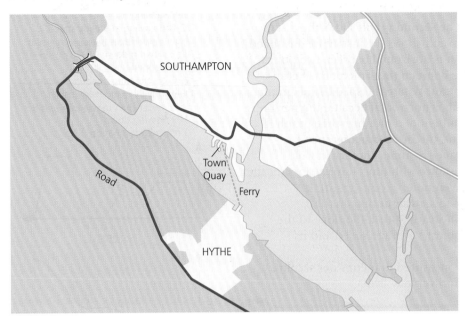

Figure 1.1.7 The distance between two places depends on the route you take. The displacement of one relative to the other does not vary.

Look at the map of the Southampton area in figure 1.1.7. How far is it from Hythe to Southampton Town Quay? Of course, the distance depends on the route you take. By ferry the journey is only 1.5 miles, but by road you would need to travel 12 miles between the two places.

Clearly we need a way of distinguishing between these two measurements of distance. In physics we use the terms **distance** and **displacement** to do this. If you travel from Hythe to Town Quay by road, the *distance* you have travelled is defined as the *length of path* you have taken, as measured by the mileometer in your car. However, your *displacement* is defined as the *straight line distance* between Hythe and Town Quay, as if you had taken the ferry.

To describe fully the distance travelled, we only need to say how far you have gone. To describe your displacement, we need to specify not only how far you are from where you started, but also in what direction you have travelled. Distance is a **scalar** quantity – it has only size or *magnitude*. Displacement is a **vector** quantity – as well as magnitude, it has *direction*.

Displacement and velocity

We have seen that speed is defined as distance moved in unit time. In the same way, we can now use the definition of displacement to calculate a new quantity, velocity:

$$\text{Velocity} = \frac{\text{displacement}}{\text{time taken}}$$

Like speed, velocity has magnitude. Velocity is the rate of change of displacement, so like displacement, it also has a direction – it is a vector.

Speeding up and changing velocity

We are quite used to saying that an object **accelerates** when it increases its speed. However, the word 'accelerate' has a very precise meaning in physics. As we have just seen, velocity is the rate of change of displacement. Acceleration is the rate of change of velocity, so it too is a vector.

A car moving away from rest increases its speed – it accelerates. Approaching traffic lights at red, the car slows down – this is also an acceleration, but a *negative* one, because speed is taken away as the car slows down.

Imagine the model train in figure 1.1.8 moving round the track from point A through points B, C and D and back to A again at a steady speed of 0.25 m/s. Although its speed is the same at A, B, C and D its velocity is not, because the direction in which it is moving is different. So although its speed is constant, the train's velocity is changing – and under these circumstances we also say that it is accelerating.

Acceleration is defined as *the rate of change of velocity with time*, and happens when there is:
- a change in speed, or
- a change in direction, or
- a change in speed *and* direction.

$$\text{Average acceleration} = \frac{\text{final velocity} - \text{initial velocity}}{\text{time taken for change}}$$

Notice one other thing about the model train. Although its average speed between two points is always 0.25 m/s, its average velocity as it goes round the track from A and back to A again is zero, because its displacement is zero.

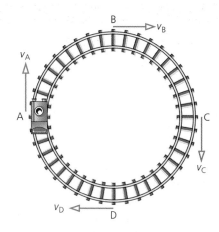

Figure 1.1.8

Units

A great deal of science is based on measuring physical quantities, such as length and mass. The value of a physical quantity consists of two things – a number, combined with a unit. For example, a length may be quoted as 2.5 km or 2500 m. In order that scientists and engineers can more easily exchange ideas and data with colleagues in other countries, a common system of units is now in use in the world of science. This system is called the **Système Internationale** (**SI**), and consists of a set of seven **base units**, with other **derived units** obtained by combining these. The base SI units are the metre (m), kilogram (kg), second (s), ampere (A), kelvin (K), candela (cd) and mole (mol). Each of these base units relates to a standard held in a laboratory somewhere in the world, against which all other measurements are effectively being compared when they are made. Figure 1.1.9 shows the standard kilogram.

The units of distance, speed and acceleration show how the base units and derived units are related:
- Distance is a length, and therefore has units of *metres* in the SI system.
- Speed is distance travelled in unit time, so the units of speed (and of velocity too) are *metres per second*. This may be written as metres/second, m/s or m s^{-1}. Each of these means the same thing: metres ÷ seconds. Because s^{-1} = 1/s, m s^{-1} means the same as m/s.
- Acceleration is change in velocity in unit time, and is measured in (m/s)/s, written as m/s^2 or m s^{-2}.

Because the value of a physical quantity consists of a number multiplied by a unit, the heading for a column in a table or the scale for the axis of a graph may be written as (for example) 'length/m' or 'velocity/m s^{-1}'.

Since the description tells the reader that the value of the physical quantity has been divided by the unit, it is then only necessary to write down the numerical part of the physical quantity, since, for example, $3\text{ m} \div \text{m} = 3$.

For vector quantities like displacement, direction must also be considered. A direction in which displacement is to be measured in a given situation is decided, and displacements in this direction are then taken as positive. Velocities and accelerations then take the same sign as displacement. The choice of direction is quite arbitrary – when solving problems, the direction is usually chosen so that the mathematics involved in the solution is as simple as possible.

Figure 1.1.9 This platinum–iridium cylinder is the standard kilogram – it is defined as having a mass of exactly 1 kg. When you buy 1 kg of apples at the supermarket you are effectively comparing their mass with the mass of this cylinder!

Velocity–time graphs

Velocity–time graphs are particularly useful in providing information about motion. The slope of a distance–time graph gives us information about an object's speed, because speed is rate of change of distance with time. In the same way, the slope of a velocity–time graph gives us information about the magnitude of an object's acceleration, although it tells us nothing about changes of direction.

Look at the velocity–time graph in figure 1.1.10. It tells us that:
- the object accelerates from rest to 8 m s^{-1} between 0 s and 4 s. So:

$$\textbf{Acceleration} = \frac{\textbf{change in velocity}}{\textbf{time}} = \frac{\textbf{8 m s}^{-1} - \textbf{0 m s}^{-1}}{\textbf{4 s} - \textbf{0 s}} = \textbf{2 m s}^{-2}$$

- there is no change of velocity between 4 s and 9 s – the acceleration is zero.
- the object accelerates to rest between 9 s and 17 s. So:

$$\textbf{Acceleration} = \frac{\textbf{change in velocity}}{\textbf{time}} = \frac{\textbf{0 m s}^{-1} - \textbf{8 m s}^{-1}}{\textbf{17 s} - \textbf{9 s}} = \textbf{-1 m s}^{-2}$$

Where a velocity–time graph is a straight line, the acceleration is uniform. Just as speed is rate of change of *distance* with time, acceleration can be described as 'rate of change of *velocity* with time'.

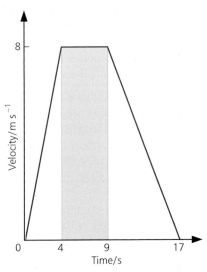

Figure 1.1.10 Velocity–time graph showing acceleration, a steady velocity and then negative acceleration.

The graph in figure 1.1.10 also gives information about the distance travelled. Between 4 s and 9 s the object travelled with a uniform (constant) velocity of 8 m s⁻¹ in the direction of positive displacement. We can use this information to work out how far it travelled (its change in displacement) in this time:

$$\text{Velocity} = \frac{\text{change in displacement}}{\text{time taken}}$$

so: **Change in displacement** = velocity × time taken
= 8 m s⁻¹ × 5 s
= 40 m

If you look carefully, you will see that this change in displacement represents the shaded area under the flat part of the graph. Because the area under the graph is calculated by multiplying together a velocity (in m s⁻¹) and a time (in s):

$$\frac{\text{m}}{\text{s}} \times \text{s} = \text{m}$$

the answer is in metres, and so represents a displacement.

In the same way, the areas under the other parts of the graph represent displacement too:

Change in displacement during initial acceleration = ½ × 8 m s⁻¹ × 4 s = 16 m

Change in displacement during final acceleration = ½ × 8 m s⁻¹ × 8 s = 32 m

The total displacement for the whole 17s is 16 m + 40 m + 32 m = 88 m

Direction of acceleration

Velocity–time graphs can give information about more complicated situations too, as figure 1.1.11 shows. The graph shows the motion of a ball thrown upwards, and falling back to Earth again to be caught. The ball starts from rest at time = 0. The graph is a straight line with a positive slope between O and A – this is because the person throwing the ball gives it a uniform upwards acceleration between these two points. The graph is a straight line with a negative slope between A and B – between these points the ball moves upwards but accelerates negatively (slows down) at a steady rate, until it comes to rest at B, the highest point of its trajectory.

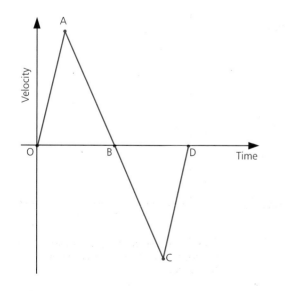

The ball is thrown upwards in this direction. Displacements, velocities and accelerations in this direction are counted as positive in this example.

O The ball is thrown from here.

Displacements, velocities and accelerations in this direction are counted as negative in this example.

Figure 1.1.11 Velocity–time graph for a ball being thrown upwards and then caught again.

Physics and models

A biologist, a chemist and a physicist are asked to suggest ways of increasing the milk production of a dairy farm. After some research, they report to the farmer. The biologist says 'The cows' barn should be painted green instead of brown, to make it more like their natural environment, and trees should be planted to make the fields more interesting for them.' The chemist says 'The balance of chemical nutrients in the cows' food is wrong – if this is corrected, they will produce more milk.' The physicist asks for a chalkboard, draws a circle on it and begins: 'Assume that a cow is a perfect sphere …'.

The point about this story is that physicists simplify situations in order to make simple models of them. If a model works, it can then be made more complex to make it work better, should that be necessary. Just as a real cow is not a perfect sphere, the motion of a real ball being thrown will not be quite as simple as figure 1.1.11 suggests. How will it differ?

Non-linear graphs

Measuring the area under a graph can be used to determine the distance travelled for graphs which are non-linear (not straight lines), though the method is not as straightforward as for linear graphs.

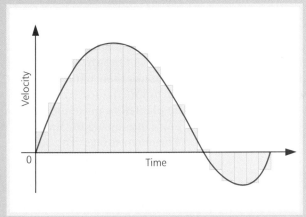

Figure 1.1.12 Finding the area under a non-linear velocity–time graph.

The area under the line in figure 1.1.12 can be calculated by adding together the areas of all the strips under the line, each of which is a rectangle. The narrower the strips, the more accurately they represent the area under the line – but the more of them there are to add up. It is important to remember to take into account whether a strip is above or below the *x*-axis when adding its area to the area of the other strips between the line and the axis.

As an example, consider the graph in figure 1.1.12 again. The area between the *x*-axis and the line above it is the sum of the areas of all the strips, say 350 m. (Remember the area represents a displacement.) The area between the *x*-axis and the line below it is once more the sum of the strips, say –50 m. The area is negative because it represents a displacement in the opposite direction to the first displacement. So the total displacement is the total area between the *x*-axis and the line, which is 350 m + –50 m = 300 m.

Between B and C the graph has the same slope as it did between A and B, but its velocity is increasingly negative – it is steadily accelerating downwards (speeding up) between these points on the graph. At C the ball is caught. Between C and D the graph has a large positive slope as the person gives the ball a large upward acceleration to bring it back to rest.

Notice how the slope of each part of the graph tells us about the acceleration of the ball, while the line itself shows how the velocity of the ball changes. Careful measurement of the two areas of the graph OAB and BCD shows that they are equal, although area OAB is positive and area BCD is negative. Since the area under the line represents the ball's displacement, this shows that the ball's displacement upwards (in a positive direction) is equal to its displacement downwards (in a negative direction) – in other words, the ball falls back to Earth the same distance as it rises, and finishes up where it began.

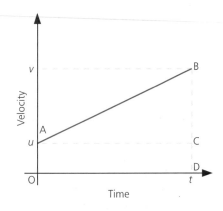

Figure 1.1.13 Velocity–time graph showing initial velocity *u* and final velocity *v* after time *t*.

Equations of motion *(for constant acceleration)*

Figure 1.1.13 enables us to write a set of four equations which can be applied in virtually all situations when objects are moving with a constant acceleration.

1 The slope of the graph tells us the acceleration of the object. If we use the symbol *a* for acceleration, then we can write:

$$a = \frac{v - u}{t} \quad \left(\text{i.e. } \frac{\textbf{final velocity – initial velocity}}{\textbf{time taken for change}} \right)$$

which we can rewrite as:

$$v = u + at \qquad \textbf{(equation 1)}$$

2 The area under the graph is the area of the rectangle OACD (which has height *u* and length *t*), plus the area of triangle ABC on top of it. This area is the object's displacement, *s*:

$$s = ut + \tfrac{1}{2}(v - u)t$$

Acceleration

Using mathematical notation, we can represent 'the change in the value of *x*' much more simply by writing it as Δx. In this way we can write acceleration as $\frac{\Delta v}{\Delta t}$.

We shall meet this kind of notation later on in the book in a number of different situations.

Equation 1 gives us a relationship between u, v, t and a, so we can substitute at for $(v - u)$ in the new equation:

$$s = ut + \tfrac{1}{2}(at)t$$

or
$$s = ut + \tfrac{1}{2}at^2 \qquad \text{(equation 2)}$$

3 Since the object's average velocity can be calculated from its displacement and time, we can also calculate its displacement from its average velocity:

$$\textbf{Average velocity} = \frac{v + u}{2}$$

So:
$$s = \frac{(v + u)t}{2} \qquad \text{(equation 3)}$$

4 Finally, equations 1 and 3 can be combined. Rearrange equation 1:

$$t = \frac{v - u}{a}$$

Substitute this expression for t into equation 3:

$$s = \frac{(v + u)}{2}\frac{(v - u)}{a}$$

Multiply each side by $2a$: $\quad 2as = (v + u)(v - u)$

Multiply out the brackets: $\quad 2as = v^2 - u^2$

which gives: $\quad v^2 = u^2 + 2as \qquad \text{(equation 4)}$

Equations of motion – worked examples

The four equations of motion are used in a wide range of situations, and it is therefore very important to know how to apply them. There are five symbols in the equations – if you know the numerical values of any three of these, you can always find the numerical values of the other two. Always begin problems by writing down the numerical values you know.

Example 1

A girl running in a race accelerates at 2.5 m s^{-2} for the first 4 s. How far does she travel in this time?

Information known:

$u = 0$ (athlete starts from rest) $\qquad v = ?$

$a = 2.5$ m s^{-2} $\qquad t = 4$ s

$s = ?$

Use equation 2:

$$s = ut + \tfrac{1}{2}at^2$$
$$= 0 \text{ m s}^{-1} \times 4\text{s} + \tfrac{1}{2} \times 2.5 \text{ m s}^{-2} \times (4 \text{ s})^2$$
$$= 20 \text{ m}$$

Example 2

The driver of a train travelling at 40 m s^{-1} applies the brakes as the train enters a station. The train slows down at a rate of 2 m s^{-2}. The platform is 400 m long. Will the train stop in time?

$u = 40$ m s^{-1} $\qquad\qquad\qquad v = 0$

$a = -2$ m s^{-2} (acceleration negative as $\qquad t = ?$
  in opposite direction to
  positive displacement)

$s = ?$ (actual stopping distance
  of train not known – only
  length of platform)

Use equation 4:

$$v^2 = u^2 + 2as$$
$$(0 \text{ m s}^{-1})^2 = (40 \text{ m s}^{-1})^2 + 2 \times -2 \text{ m s}^{-2} \times s$$

so: $0 \text{ m}^2 \text{ s}^{-2} = 1600 \text{ m}^2 \text{ s}^{-2} - 4 \text{ m s}^{-2} \times s$

and: $\quad s = \dfrac{1600 \text{ m}^2 \text{ s}^{-2}}{4 \text{ m s}^{-2}} = 400 \text{ m}$

So the train stops just in time.

Moving in more than one dimension

Using vectors

So far we have confined ourselves to simple situations which are real enough, but which do not cover every type of motion found in our everyday lives. Think carefully about all the examples of motion you have seen so far and you will realise that they have all been concerned with movement in a straight line. Whilst some things do move in one dimension, more often than not motion is more complex than this.

Vectors give us a fairly simple way of handling motion when it is not in one dimension. Vectors can be represented by arrows drawn to scale. The *length* of the arrow represents the *magnitude* of the vector, while the *direction* of the arrow represents the *direction* of the vector.

Combining vectors – the triangle rule

The triangle rule can be applied whenever one vector acts followed by another. For example, suppose you travel 30 m due south, and then 40 m due east – what is your displacement from your starting position?

The way of calculating your final displacement is to draw out the vectors involved. The diagrams in figure 1.1.14 show the following process:

1 Move 30 m south.

2 Move 40 m east.

3 Combine these two movements.

4 The vector joining your starting point to your finishing point is your displacement from your starting point.

If you have drawn a scale diagram, you can measure the distance and direction of the displacement. Alternatively, you can use trigonometry to calculate the displacement. In the case of figure 1.1.14 the final displacement is 50 m at an angle of 53° east of the first displacement. The sum of two or more vector quantities is called their **resultant**.

Combining vectors – the   elogram rule

The parallelogram rule can be applied whenever vectors act at the same time or from the same point. If you have ever walked or run up a down escalator, you will have some idea of what **relative motion** is. When an object is moving, it is often important to give some information about what its motion is relative to. For example, someone travelling along a moving walkway may have a velocity of 2 m s^{-1} relative to the walkway, but if the walkway has a velocity of –2 m s^{-1} (note the negative sign, showing that the walkway is moving in the opposite direction to the person), the person will get nowhere fast with respect to the ground!

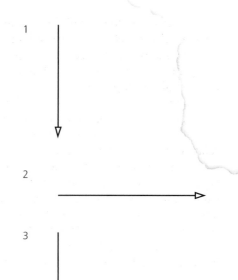

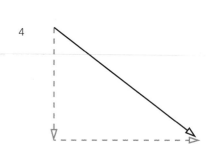

Figure 1.1.14 Addition of displacement vectors. 1 cm represents 10 m.

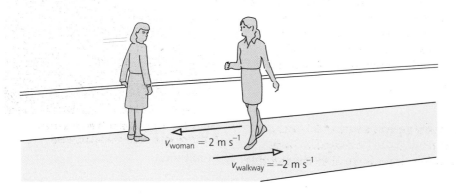

Figure 1.1.15 Getting nowhere fast!
$v_{woman} + v_{walkway} = 0$.

The resultant velocity of the woman in figure 1.1.15 is the sum of the vector for her velocity relative to the walkway and the vector for the velocity of the walkway relative to the ground. Adding vectors is easy when both vectors act along the same line, as here – but a slightly different method is needed when they act along different lines.

Think about a man on a ship walking from one side of the ship to the other. If the ship is steaming forwards with a speed of 4 m s⁻¹ and the man walks from one side to the other with a speed of 3 m s⁻¹, what will be the man's movement relative to the Earth's surface?

As the man walks across the ship in figure 1.1.16, the ship carries him to the right. In 1 s the man moves 3 m across the ship, and in this time, the ship also carries him 4 m to the right. The vector diagram shows his displacement 1 s and 5 s after starting to walk. The man's resultant velocity relative to the Earth is the vector shown. This is the resultant of the ship's velocity relative to the Earth's surface and the man's velocity relative to the ship. The resultant velocity is 5 m s⁻¹ in a direction making an angle of 37° with the velocity of the ship.

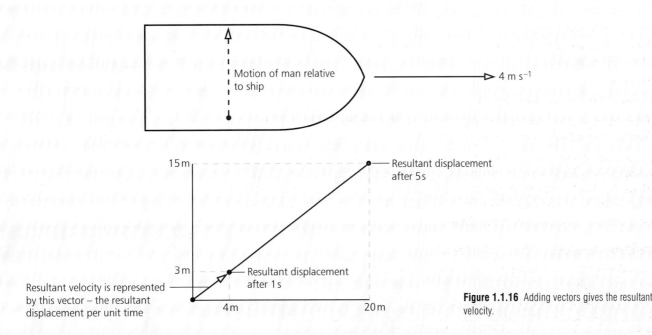

Figure 1.1.16 Adding vectors gives the resultant velocity.

Measuring motion

A variety of practical methods is available for investigating the motion of moving objects. The precise method chosen will depend on several factors – for example, whether the investigation is to be carried out in a laboratory or outside, the size of the object to be investigated and its likely speed are all factors that may influence the method to be used. Here we shall deal with the principles behind the main methods of measuring motion that you may meet as part of your physics course.

Ticker timer

A **ticker timer** produces dots on a piece of ticker tape at a rate of 50 dots per second. The tape is attached to the object which is to be investigated, so the speed at which the tape moves through the ticker timer is equal to the speed of the object.

Figure 1.1.17 One situation in which accurate knowledge about relative motion is essential.

Using ticker tapes

The tape produced by a ticker timer may be used to calculate speed and acceleration, as figure 1.1.18 shows.

Ticker timer methods are reasonably simple and are inexpensive. However, they can only measure straight line motion, and are only suitable for use where the considerable friction forces generated between the tape and the timer itself can easily be overcome.

The space between successive dots increases as the tape moves through the ticker timer, showing that the speed of the tape was increasing. The timer makes 50 dots each second, so the time interval between two successive dots is $\frac{1}{50}$ second.

Tape moved in this direction

Average velocity between these two points $= \dfrac{\text{distance}}{\text{time}} = \dfrac{\text{distance}}{0.02 \text{ s}} = v_1$

Average velocity between these two points $= \dfrac{\text{distance}}{\text{time}} = \dfrac{\text{distance}}{0.02 \text{ s}} = v_2$

v_2 is calculated from two dots which are $5 \times 0.02\text{s} = 0.1\text{s}$ later than the dots used to calculate v_1. So the average acceleration between these two points on the tape can be calculated:

$$\text{Average acceleration} = \frac{\text{change in velocity}}{\text{time for change}} = \frac{v_2 - v_1}{0.1 \text{ s}}$$

Figure 1.1.18

Light gate and microcomputer

A **light gate** consists of a source of light and a light detector. Light from the source falls on the detector, which produces an electrical signal. The change in signal when an object interrupts the beam may be used to trigger a timer. A light gate can be connected to a microprocessor chip, either in a self-contained unit or in a microcomputer, to carry out the timing. Such chips can typically measure times down to around 0.001 s.

Using light gates

Light gates and microprocessors make the measurement of motion easy, since they can do some of the calculations for you, as figure 1.1.19 shows.

The vehicles have cards attached to them which break the light beams.

This card breaks each light beam once. The vehicle's velocity is calculated by dividing the length of the card by the length of time for which it breaks the light beam.

This card breaks each light beam twice, so that two velocities can be calculated. From these two velocities and the time between them, the vehicle's acceleration can be calculated.

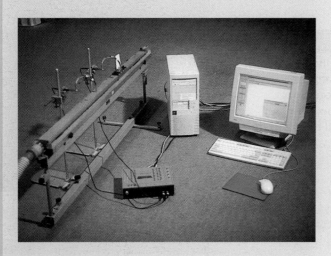

Figure 1.1.19 Two ways of measuring motion using microprocessors. One uses a computer to measure and display the information on a screen. The other uses a portable 'data-logger' – you may need to connect this type of unit to a computer to display and process the data after the investigation, or it may be able to process and display the results independently.

Methods using light gates and microprocessors, once set up, are quick and powerful. Although they are not limited to measuring motion in a straight line, they can only give information about distance and speed, not direction. They may be used with a wide range of objects, since they do not interact directly with the moving objects as ticker tape does.

Multiflash (stroboscopic) photography

A series of pictures of a moving object may be obtained by leaving the shutter of a camera open while the object moves past the camera, lit only by a rapidly flashing light. The photograph can then be examined to measure the motion of the object. The time interval between flashes may be used to calculate velocities and accelerations.

Using multiflash photography

The calculation of velocity and acceleration using multiflash photography is much the same as for ticker tapes, as figure 1.1.20 shows.

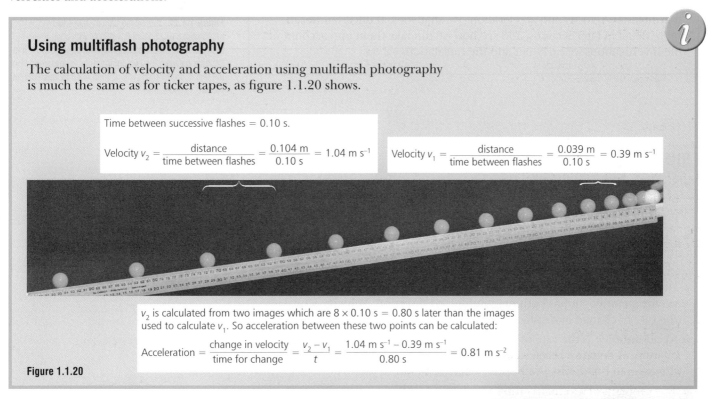

Time between successive flashes = 0.10 s.

$$\text{Velocity } v_2 = \frac{\text{distance}}{\text{time between flashes}} = \frac{0.104 \text{ m}}{0.10 \text{ s}} = 1.04 \text{ m s}^{-1}$$

$$\text{Velocity } v_1 = \frac{\text{distance}}{\text{time between flashes}} = \frac{0.039 \text{ m}}{0.10 \text{ s}} = 0.39 \text{ m s}^{-1}$$

v_2 is calculated from two images which are 8×0.10 s = 0.80 s later than the images used to calculate v_1. So acceleration between these two points can be calculated:

$$\text{Acceleration} = \frac{\text{change in velocity}}{\text{time for change}} = \frac{v_2 - v_1}{t} = \frac{1.04 \text{ m s}^{-1} - 0.39 \text{ m s}^{-1}}{0.80 \text{ s}} = 0.81 \text{ m s}^{-2}$$

Figure 1.1.20

Multiflash photography is useful in a wide range of situations. It can give information about direction as well as distance and speed, and can be used for motion in more than one direction, as the photograph in figure 1.1.21 shows.

How precise are measurements of speed and acceleration?

Errors and mistakes are a fact of lofe – although that one was deliberate! The methods of measuring speed and acceleration just described all have limits to how precisely they measure these quantities. Whenever we make measurements using instruments there is some error or **uncertainty** in the result. Sometimes the uncertainty may be due to the experimenter (for example, reading a scale wrongly) and sometimes it may be due to the equipment (for example, a wrongly calibrated ammeter). The word 'uncertainty' is used because the problems which arise in making measurements are not always due to mistakes – they may often be due to the limits of the equipment being used, or of the experiment itself.

Figure 1.1.21

Consider the limitations of the methods described for measuring speed. Each of them depends on measuring speed over a small time interval, as little as 0.02 s in the case of ticker timer investigations or as much as 0.5 s in the case of an experiment using light gates. What we are actually measuring here in each case is *average* velocity over a fairly small time interval. Since we cannot actually *measure* instantaneous velocity (because we need to divide a distance by a time in order to calculate it) the best we can do is to calculate the average speed over a very small distance or a very small time. The smaller we make this distance, the closer the result will be to the true value of instantaneous speed.

Of course, there are other limits to the precision with which these methods may measure velocity and acceleration. We shall look at uncertainties in more detail in later sections, and see how we can take them into account in the investigations we carry out and the calculations we do.

Figure 1.1.22 This speed camera takes two photographs of a speeding vehicle, with a set time between them. The distance the vehicle has travelled in the time between the two photographs is measured from the marks on the road. This is then used to calculate the vehicle's speed.

SUMMARY

- **Speed** is distance moved in unit time. **Average speed** = distance travelled/time taken. This equation does not give the speed at a particular point in time, the **instantaneous speed**.

- The gradient of a **distance–time graph** at a particular point represents the instantaneous speed at that point. Instantaneous speed is dx/dt, or the rate of change of distance with time.

- Distance is a **scalar quantity** – it has only magnitude. **Displacement** s is a **vector** quantity – it has both magnitude and direction. **Velocity** u or v is the rate of change of displacement with time t and is a vector quantity.

- **Acceleration** a is the rate of change of velocity with time, and is a vector quantity. A negative acceleration is an acceleration in the opposite direction to that taken as a positive displacement.

- The gradient of a **velocity–time graph** at a point represents the acceleration at that point. The area under a velocity–time graph gives the change in displacement.

- Four **equations of motion** can be derived from a velocity–time graph showing constant acceleration:

$$v = u + at$$
$$s = ut + \tfrac{1}{2} at^2$$
$$s = \frac{(v + u) t}{2}$$
$$v^2 = u^2 + 2as$$

- **Vectors** can be used to represent vector quantities, where the length of the arrow represents the magnitude of the quantity and the direction of the arrow the direction of the quantity. The **resultant**, the effect of combining vectors, can be found using the triangle rule or the parallelogram rule.

EXAMPLES

1 *In a test of a safety restraint, a test car was slowed from 50 m s⁻¹ to rest in a time of 0.40 s.*
  a *What acceleration was this?*
  b *How far did the car travel in this time?*

We are given the following data:
$u = 50$ m s⁻¹ $v = 0$ $t = 0.40$ s

a We are asked to find the acceleration a and the distance travelled s.
  For acceleration:
$$v = u + at$$
  Substituting the known values into this:
$$0 = 50 \text{ m s}^{-1} + a \times 0.40 \text{ s}$$
  Rearranging:
$$a = \frac{0 - 50 \text{ m s}^{-1}}{0.40 \text{ s}}$$
$$= -125 \text{ m s}^{-2}$$
  The acceleration is *negative*, showing that the car *slows down* at a rate of 125 m s⁻².

b For the distance travelled in this time, we know that:
$$s = ut + \tfrac{1}{2}at^2$$
  Substituting known values into this:
$$s = 50 \text{ m s}^{-1} \times 0.40 \text{ s} +$$
$$\tfrac{1}{2} \times -125 \text{ m s}^{-2} \times (0.40 \text{ s})^2$$
$$= 20 \text{ m} - 10 \text{ m}$$
$$= 10 \text{ m}$$
  The car travelled 10 m in the time taken to slow from 50 m s⁻¹ to rest.

2 *A hunter shoots an arrow at a target moving directly away from him. When the arrow is shot the target is 60 m away, and when it strikes the target is 80 m away. If the arrow travels at 70 m s⁻¹:*
  a *How long did the arrow take to hit the target?*
  b *How fast was the target moving?*
  What assumptions did you make in solving this problem?

a The arrow strikes the target after travelling a distance of 80 m at a speed of 70 m s⁻¹. Therefore we know that:
$s = 80$ m $v = 70$ m s⁻¹ (see comments at end of solution)
  Therefore:
$$v = s/t \text{ which gives } t = s/v$$
  Thus:
$$t = 80 \text{ m}/70 \text{ m s}^{-1}$$
$$= 1.14 \text{ s}$$
  The arrow takes 1.14 s to reach the target.

b In this time the target travels (80 m – 60 m) = 20 m, so:
$s = 20$ m $t = 1.14$ s
  Thus:
$$v = s/t$$
$$= 20 \text{ m}/1.14 \text{ s}$$
$$= 17.5 \text{ m s}^{-1}$$
  The target moves with a velocity of 17.5 m s⁻¹.

Comments: To answer this question with the information we are given, we need to assume that:
i the arrow travels horizontally
ii we can neglect air resistance
iii we can also neglect the small time it takes the arrow to accelerate from rest to 80 m s⁻¹.

QUESTIONS

1 Nerve impulses travel at about 100 m s⁻¹. If a woman 1.8 m tall steps on a drawing pin:
  a roughly how long is it before she knows about it?
  b if she is walking along with a speed of 2 m s⁻¹, how far will she have travelled in this time?

2 The cheetah is the fastest land animal in the world. It can accelerate from rest to 20 m s⁻¹ in 2 s, and has a top speed of about 30 m s⁻¹, although it can only maintain this for a distance of about 450 m before it has to stop to rest. In contrast, an antelope can run at around 22 m s⁻¹ for long periods.
  a What is a cheetah's average acceleration between rest and 20 m s⁻¹?
  b Assume that a cheetah accelerates up to its top speed with the acceleration in your answer to **a**.
    i How far will the cheetah travel while it accelerates from rest up to its top speed?
    ii How long does this acceleration take?
  c If the cheetah continues at top speed, how long will it be before it has to stop to rest?

  d For how long can a cheetah run, starting from rest?
  e If an antelope starts from rest and accelerates to its top speed at the same rate as a cheetah, how far will it travel in the time obtained in your answer to **d**?
  f If a cheetah chases an antelope and both start from rest, what is the maximum head start the cheetah can allow the antelope?

3 The world record for the women's 100 m sprint in 1993 stood at 10.49 s.
  a What average speed does this represent?
  b If the athlete accelerates to a steady speed in the first 1.5 s of the race and then runs at this speed until reaching the finishing line, at what steady speed does she run? (*Hint:* Try drawing a velocity–time graph to solve this.)
  c How is this *model* of the runner's behaviour likely to differ from her real behaviour?

4 A car is travelling along a road at 30 m s⁻¹ when a pedestrian steps into the road 55 m ahead. The driver applies the brakes of the car after a reaction time of 0.5 s, and the car slows down at a rate of 10 m s⁻². What happens?

5 Astronomers use a unit of length called the **light year** – the distance light travels in 1 year. Given that the speed of light in a vacuum is almost 3×10^8 m s^{-1}, what is the length of 1 light year in kilometres?

6 A ball on a snooker table is hit by another ball and travels a distance of 50 cm due south. It is then hit again, and travels a distance of 25 cm due south west. What is its displacement from its initial position?

7 An aircraft has a velocity of 90 m s^{-1} with a bearing of N20°E. There is a wind of 30 m s^{-1} blowing from the west. What is the resultant velocity of the aeroplane with respect to the ground?

8 Why do aircraft take off and land against the wind?

9 Figure 1.1.23 shows the shortest stopping distances for cars as given in the *Highway Code*.
  a Convert the figures in the table to SI units. What is the relationship between:
   i thinking distance and speed
   ii braking distance and speed?
  b Explain why thinking distance and braking distance vary in the way that they do.
  c 'Only a fool breaks the two-second rule' is a saying designed to help drivers leave a large enough gap between their car and the car in front.
   i What distances does a 'two-second gap' between two cars give?
   ii How do these distances compare with the distances from the *Highway Code*?

Figure 1.1.23

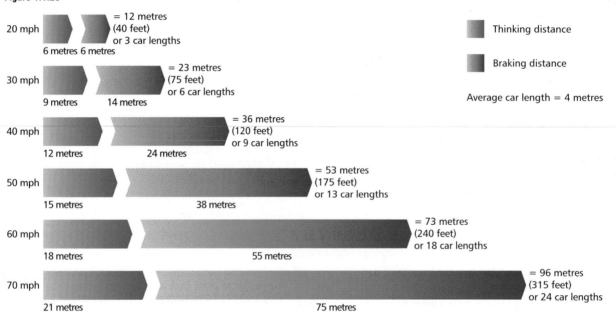

20 mph = 12 metres (40 feet) or 3 car lengths
6 metres 6 metres

30 mph = 23 metres (75 feet) or 6 car lengths
9 metres 14 metres

40 mph = 36 metres (120 feet) or 9 car lengths
12 metres 24 metres

50 mph = 53 metres (175 feet) or 13 car lengths
15 metres 38 metres

60 mph = 73 metres (240 feet) or 18 car lengths
18 metres 55 metres

70 mph = 96 metres (315 feet) or 24 car lengths
21 metres 75 metres

Thinking distance

Braking distance

Average car length = 4 metres

Developing Key Skills

One of the major causes of road accidents is drivers driving too close to the car in front of them.

You have been commissioned to design a hard-hitting advertisement to be placed in a motoring magazine as part of a national campaign to encourage car drivers to behave more responsibly on the roads. Use the information in figure 1.1.23 together with the physics in this chapter to help you produce your design.

[Key Skills opportunities: C, A, IT]

Causes of motion

Having looked at ways of describing motion, let us look at what *causes* motion. Aristotle said that the answer to this question was simple – motion was maintained by forces. A force made something move. When the force stopped acting, the object came to a standstill. In modern contexts, this idea seems quite reasonable when you think about pulling a heavy box along the floor, or pushing a car along a flat road. But what about the situation when you kick a football, for example? Once your foot ceases to be in contact with the ball, it can no longer exert a force on it, and yet the ball carries on moving for some considerable time before it eventually comes to rest.

The Italian scientist Galileo Galilei thought about problems like this, nearly 2000 years after Aristotle (Galileo was born in 1564). Galileo understood that the idea of force is central to the understanding of motion, but realised that Aristotle's explanation was incomplete. According to one story, Galileo's interest in moving objects began as a result of attending a mass in the cathedral at Pisa. During the sermon, he noticed that a cathedral lantern suspended from the roof by a long chain always took the same time to swing, whether it was swinging through a large arc or a small one. (Not having a clock, he used his own heartbeat to time the swings.) Galileo then carried out further experiments with a pendulum. He noticed that if he released a pendulum bob from a measured height, the bob always rose to an equal height on the opposite side of its swing. Carrying this investigation further, he fixed a pin below the point of support of a simple pendulum, as shown in figure 1.2.1. He raised the bob to one side and released it. The bob still rose to the height from which it was released.

Galileo then extended this experiment by carrying out a 'thought experiment', that is an experiment carried out in his head. He reasoned that if a ball rolls down a slope onto an infinitely long flat surface, by simple analogy with the pendulum experiment it will continue moving until something else causes it to stop. This is explained further in the box below.

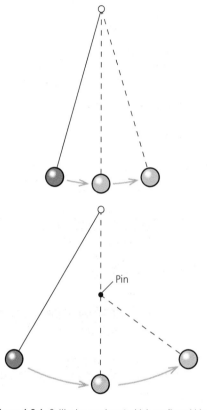

Figure 1.2.1 Galileo's experiment which confirmed his ideas on forces and motion.

The ball and the pendulum

By careful analogy with his pendulum experiment, Galileo reasoned that the ball would always tend to rise to the height it had been released from, even if it had to travel a greater horizontal distance to do so – diagrams (a) and (b) in figure 1.2.2 show this happening. When the rising track on the right-hand side is replaced by a flat track (c), the ball carries on moving indefinitely in an attempt to rise to its original height. This is in direct conflict with Aristotle's explanation of the motion of objects.

It took the work of Newton to carry forward Galileo's explanation and put it on a basis that we would today recognise as being 'scientific'. Galileo had realised the importance of distinguishing between motion horizontally and vertically in a gravitational field, and had laid the foundations of thought that made possible the journey to the Moon, over 300 years later.

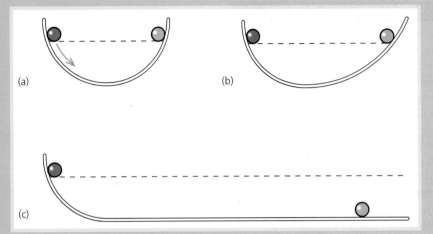

Figure 1.2.2 The diagrams show Galileo's thought experiment. The tracks and balls are perfectly smooth, so that there are no frictional forces between them.

Newton's first law of motion

Forces and changing motion

The key to understanding motion is to understand forces and their interactions. The reason why we appear to need to push something to keep it moving steadily is because the motion of any object here on Earth is opposed by **frictional forces** – and in many cases these are quite considerable. If there were no frictional forces then one push would cause an object to move indefinitely along a flat surface at a steady speed. Galileo had noticed that the concept of force was important when thinking about *changing* motion rather than about motion in its own right. Galileo's work was taken up and developed by Isaac Newton, born in Lincolnshire, England in 1642, the year of Galileo's death. Building on Galileo's work, Newton framed three simple rules governing the motion of objects, which he set out as his three **laws of motion** in his work the *Principia*, published in 1687.

Although we now know that Newton's laws of motion break down under certain conditions (in particular, as the velocity of an object approaches the velocity of light), the laws are so very nearly correct under all common circumstances that they can be regarded as precise to all intents and purposes.

The *Principia* was written in Latin, the language of scholarship of the time. Translated into modern English, the **first law of motion** can be stated as:

Every object continues in its state of rest or uniform motion in a straight line unless made to change by the total force acting on it.

In other words, an object has a constant velocity (which may be zero) until a net force acts on it. So the first law of motion defines for us what a force *is*, or rather what it *does* – a force is something which can cause acceleration.

Newton's first law in mathematical terms

Newton's first law expresses motion in terms of the total force acting on a body. The law can be written down in mathematical terms. If we wish to write down 'the sum of all the forces acting on a body' we can use the mathematical expression ΣF ('sigma F') to do this. So to state Newton's first law we can say:

If a point mass has a number of forces $F_1, F_2, \dots F_n$ acting on it, it will remain in a state of constant motion only if

$$\sum_{i=1}^{i=n} F_i = 0$$

(that is, if the sum of all the forces from F_1 to F_n is equal to zero). Note that in adding the forces together we must treat them as vectors.

This condition is both necessary and sufficient for a point mass to remain in a state of constant motion. However, in the case of a solid object, the condition is still necessary but is no longer sufficient, since rotation has to be taken into account. We shall deal with this in section 1.3.

Free body diagrams

Before considering the first law further, it is worth looking at how we can represent clearly the forces acting on a body.

Because a force can cause acceleration, it is a vector quantity, with both magnitude and direction. We therefore need a way of representing both magnitude and direction on a diagram in order to represent forces. A diagram which shows all the forces acting on a body in a certain situation is called a **free body diagram**. A free body diagram shows only the forces acting on the object under consideration, not those acting on other objects. Figure 1.2.3 shows a free body diagram.

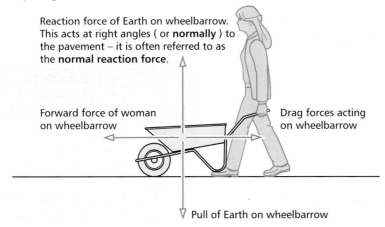

Reaction force of Earth on wheelbarrow. This acts at right angles (or **normally**) to the pavement – it is often referred to as the **normal reaction force**.

Forward force of woman on wheelbarrow

Drag forces acting on wheelbarrow

Pull of Earth on wheelbarrow

Figure 1.2.3 A simplified free body diagram of a wheelbarrow being pushed at a steady speed along a flat surface. Notice how each force acting is cancelled out by a force exactly equal in size but opposite in direction to it. This is what Newton's first law tells us – the resultant force acting on an object which has constant velocity is zero.

Drag forces

Once we see the situation represented in a free body diagram like that in figure 1.2.3, it becomes quite obvious why an object stops moving when you stop pushing it. Remove the forward force acting on the wheelbarrow and the forces on it are no longer balanced. The resultant force now acts backwards, so the wheelbarrow accelerates backwards – that is, it slows down and eventually stops.

An obvious question is why doesn't an object start moving backwards once it has stopped if there is now a resultant force acting on it? The answer to this question is because of the way drag forces work. Drag forces are made up of two types of force, both due to matter in contact with other matter. These are *frictional forces* and *air resistance*.

Frictional forces

Where two solid surfaces rub on each other (for example in a wheel bearing or axle) **friction** always occurs. This friction is caused as atoms in one surface form bonds with atoms in the other surface. Even apparently perfectly smooth surfaces are very rough. When two such surfaces rub over one another, it is rather as if we had turned the Cairngorm Mountains upside down and rubbed them across Snowdonia – only the very tips of the mountains will touch. During sliding, the tiny areas at the top of the ridges of the two surfaces become instantaneously 'spot welded' together, making the two surfaces stick. As the surfaces slide across one another these welds then break, new welds are formed, and so on.

Figure 1.2.4 Even the smoothest of surfaces is rough, as this high magnification photograph shows. Oil between the surfaces pushes them apart, and so stops the tops of the ridges becoming 'spot welded' together.

Measuring the frictional force

Experiments between surfaces rubbing together show that the frictional force behaves in a predictable way. Consider the situation shown in figure 1.2.5, in which a block resting on a flat surface is pulled harder and harder until it is just about to move.

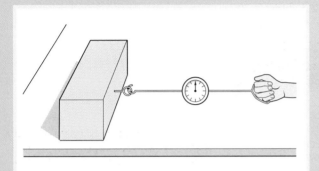

Figure 1.2.5

As the block is pulled harder and harder, the force acting on it increases. The force pulling the block along the surface is exactly opposed by the frictional force between the block and the surface, so that the resultant force acting on the block is zero and it remains in a state of rest. As the pulling force increases, it eventually reaches a value where the box is just about to slide. At this point the frictional force has its **limiting value** – the maximum possible value it can have for this particular situation. If the pulling force on the block increases any further, the resultant force acting is no longer zero, and the block begins to move. The way in which the limiting value of the frictional force varies can be investigated, and figure 1.2.6 suggests some ways of doing this.

Investigations like this show that the limiting value of the frictional force:
(1) varies depending on the surfaces in contact
(2) is independent of the *area* of the two surfaces in contact
(3) is proportional to N, the normal reaction force of the plane on the block.

This can be summarised as follows:

> For any pair of surfaces in contact there is a limiting value of the frictional force which depends only on the normal reaction force between the two surfaces, so that

$$\frac{\text{Limiting value of frictional force}}{\text{normal reaction force}} = \text{constant}$$

This constant depends only on the two surfaces in contact, and is called the **coefficient of friction** μ for the two surfaces. μ has no units – it is obtained by dividing one force by another force, so the units simply cancel out.

If μ and N are known it is then a simple matter to calculate F, the limiting value of the frictional force, from the relationship:

$$F = \mu N$$

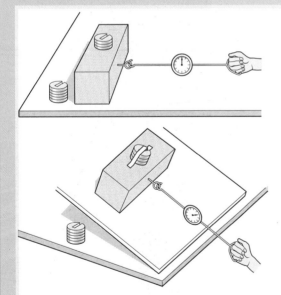

If the block is pulled with a force F_{pull} using a forcemeter, as long as the box remains stationary, F_{pull} and $F_{friction}$ must be equal in size and opposite in direction. The limiting value of $F_{friction}$ will thus be the largest value of F_{pull} recorded on the forcemeter.

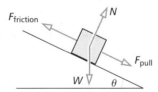

On a slope there is a component of the gravitational pull of the Earth on the block acting down the slope. If angles are measured in the way shown here, this component is $W \sin \theta$ (see section 1.3 for more details about adding and resolving forces). So in this case $F_{friction}$ and ($F_{pull} + W \sin \theta$) will be equal in size and opposite in direction as long as the box is stationary. The limiting value of $F_{friction}$ will be $W \sin \theta$ plus the largest value of F_{pull} recorded on the forcemeter.

Figure 1.2.6

Air resistance

The other drag force which acts on the wheelbarrow is not important in this example, but is very important in many other examples. Air resistance or **aerodynamic drag** acts when a body moves through air. It is caused by the fact that an object has to push air out of the way in order to move through it, and this requires a force. The force that is exerted by two surfaces rubbing together does not depend on the speed at which the two surfaces move over each other. However, the aerodynamic drag caused by an object moving through air *does* depend on speed – the faster the object moves, the greater the aerodynamic drag, as figure 1.2.8 illustrates. In fact, the drag increases as the square of the velocity.

Figure 1.2.7 Air resistance becomes more important the faster you want to go. Careful design can reduce aerodynamic drag, using air tunnels to explore very precisely the flow of air around a new shape.

Because aerodynamic drag increases greatly as an object's velocity increases, objects tend to reach a **terminal velocity** as their velocity increases – whether they are a parachutist falling through air or a car travelling along a race track (see question 9 on page 29).

Free fall and terminal velocity

A man who jumps out of a tethered balloon some way above the ground will obviously accelerate towards the ground under the influence of the gravitational force exerted by the Earth. The acceleration with which he falls is called the **acceleration of free fall** or the **acceleration due to gravity**. At the surface of the Earth the approximate value of this acceleration is 10 m s^{-2}. The acceleration of a falling object is not uniform, because the resultant force decreases as the velocity increases, as figure 1.2.8 shows.

Figure 1.2.8 Free fall and terminal velocity.

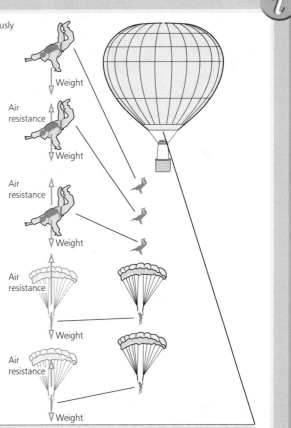

At the top of the jump, the man is instantaneously stationary, so his air resistance is zero. The resultant force acting on him is greatest at this point, so his acceleration at this point has its maximum value.

A little later the man is moving more rapidly and his air resistance is now significant. The magnitude of his weight is still greater than his air resistance, so he is still accelerating downwards, but not as quickly as at first.

Later still his velocity has reached a point where his air resistance is equal to his weight. Now the resultant force acting on him is zero – and he is no longer accelerating. The velocity at which this happens is called the **terminal velocity.** For a human being without a parachute, terminal velocity is about 56 m s^{-1}.

On opening the parachute, the air resistance increases dramatically due to the parachute's large surface area. Now the air resistance is greater than the weight – so the resultant force on the man is upwards. The man accelerates upwards and his velocity decreases.

Eventually the man's velocity decreases to a new terminal velocity. This terminal velocity is much lower than the previous terminal velocity – about 10 m s^{-1}. Hitting the ground at this speed still requires some care – it is like jumping off a wall 5 m high!

FOCUS DRAG FORCES AND THE BEAUTIFUL GAME

How much physics do footballers know? Although the answer to this question is probably 'not a lot', that doesn't stop the best footballers making spectacular use of physics when it comes to playing the game.

As an example of this, take a situation in which a player takes a free kick from just outside the penalty area (figure 1.2.9). Players from the opposing team line up to form a wall between the ball and the goal. Despite this, the player taking the free kick manages to curve the ball around the end of the wall, into the top of the goal mouth. The diagrams show how this is done.

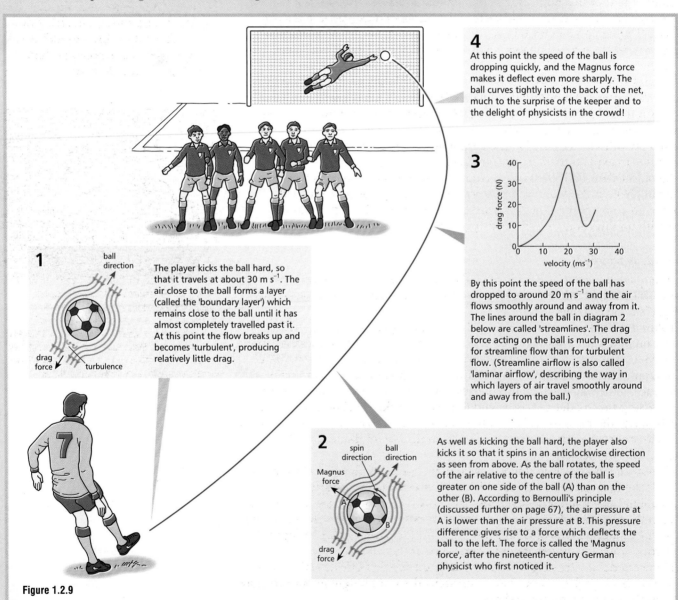

4 At this point the speed of the ball is dropping quickly, and the Magnus force makes it deflect even more sharply. The ball curves tightly into the back of the net, much to the surprise of the keeper and to the delight of physicists in the crowd!

3 By this point the speed of the ball has dropped to around 20 m s^{-1} and the air flows smoothly around and away from it. The lines around the ball in diagram 2 below are called 'streamlines'. The drag force acting on the ball is much greater for streamline flow than for turbulent flow. (Streamline airflow is also called 'laminar airflow', describing the way in which layers of air travel smoothly around and away from the ball.)

1 The player kicks the ball hard, so that it travels at about 30 m s^{-1}. The air close to the ball forms a layer (called the 'boundary layer') which remains close to the ball until it has almost completely travelled past it. At this point the flow breaks up and becomes 'turbulent', producing relatively little drag.

2 As well as kicking the ball hard, the player also kicks it so that it spins in an anticlockwise direction as seen from above. As the ball rotates, the speed of the air relative to the centre of the ball is greater on one side of the ball (A) than on the other (B). According to Bernoulli's principle (discussed further on page 67), the air pressure at A is lower than the air pressure at B. This pressure difference gives rise to a force which deflects the ball to the left. The force is called the 'Magnus force', after the nineteenth-century German physicist who first noticed it.

Figure 1.2.9

Inertia, mass and weight

Newton's first law of motion is useful in considering what we mean by the term force – but it has other applications.

The tendency of an object to stay in its state of rest or uniform motion is called its **inertia**. Inertia is something that we all experience in our everyday lives.

- A large, massive object like a car is harder to get moving than a relatively small, light one like a bicycle.
- Without the help of a seatbelt, it can be hard for someone sitting in a moving car to stop moving when the driver applies the brakes sharply.

These are both examples of inertia.

Inertia and mass

An object's inertia depends only on its *mass*. The definition of mass is very difficult, and you will probably have met the idea that 'mass is a measure of the amount of matter in a body'. While this statement is not false, it is not the whole truth either. The most satisfactory definition of mass uses the idea of inertia. If two objects A and B have the same acceleration, but the resultant force on object A is $2F$ while that on object B is F, then object A must have twice the mass of object B. Figure 1.2.10 shows an application of this.

The resistance of objects to changes in their motion is not something that Newton's first law of motion can explain – in fact, it is not something that physics can explain. Inertia is not the *explanation* for this behaviour – it is just another name for it. Objects behave like this because they behave like this! Physics provides laws to predict the behaviour of objects, but does not guarantee to explain them to our satisfaction.

An object's inertia is the same no matter where it is – it is just as hard to stop a moving ball on the Moon or in deep space as it would be here on Earth. The mass of an object is therefore the same no matter where it is. Mass has only size, with no direction – it is a scalar quantity.

So what is weight?

We often use the term 'weight' in everyday life – sometimes we mean mass, rather than weight, while at other times we really do mean weight. An object's **weight** is a force acting on it.

Following Galileo's work, in Book III of the *Principia*, Newton set out his theory on how masses attract one another in a process termed **gravitation**. Our modern interpretation of this theory says that all masses have a **gravitational field** around them. A field is a model which physicists use to explain 'action at a distance' – the way in which two objects not in contact exert a force on each other. Using this model, a mass is said to have a gravitational field around it which causes the mass to attract another mass which is close to it. The size of the field around a particular mass depends on the size of the mass and whereabouts in the field you are.

If another mass is brought into this field, it experiences a force which pulls it towards the first mass. The size of this force varies with the strength of the gravitational field, and as we shall see later, this varies with the position of the mass in the field. So while mass is constant no matter where it is measured, the force due to a gravitational field acting on a given mass varies according to the strength of the gravitational field that the mass is in.

Physicists define the weight of an object as the force of gravity acting on it. However, this is probably not what we mean by the word weight in our everyday lives, as the following example shows.

Inertia

If the standard kilogram requires a force F to change its motion in some way, and an object with unknown mass requires a force of $2F$ to change its motion in exactly the same way, then the mass of the object must be 2 kg. How do we know this? Since the object requires twice as much force as the standard kilogram to change its motion in exactly the same way, it must have twice the inertia. And since inertia depends on the mass of an object, the object must have twice the mass of the standard kilogram, that is, 2 kg.

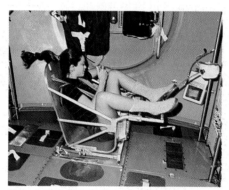

Figure 1.2.10 Newton's first law in action. It is important to know about changes in body mass of astronauts during long periods in orbit. Obviously bathroom scales are useless in this situation. This device uses the inertia of the astronaut's body to affect the way in which oscillations happen – the oscillations are then timed and used to calculate the mass of the astronaut.

Think about an astronaut orbiting the Earth. Seeing them floating around their spacecraft, we commonly say that an astronaut is 'weightless'. But if the force of the Earth pulling on the spacecraft and astronaut really was zero, it would not be possible for them to orbit the Earth, as Newton's First Law tells us that they would continue moving in a straight line at constant speed.

The confusion comes about because what we really mean by weight in our everyday lives is brought about by the force our bodies (the soles of our feet if we are standing up) exert downwards on whatever solid surface we are standing on. But it is not this force that we experience – instead, it is the *upward* push of the solid surface on us. It is the size of this upward force that we measure when we weigh ourselves or any other object! This is why we think of the astronaut as being weightless, since they are not exerting any force on the spacecraft. However, this is *not* because the Earth is not exerting a force on them – as we shall see later, it is because both the spacecraft and the astronaut are falling freely towards the Earth under the influence of the Earth's gravitational field.

In this book we shall use the physicists' definition of weight as being the gravitational force acting on an object – and when we use this term, we must always be careful to ensure that we understand the difference between 'physicists' weight' and 'everyday weight'!

Gravitational field strength g and weight

Because the weight of an object varies according to the strength of the gravitational field it is in, this enables us to define the strength of a gravitational field.

Gravitational field strength g at a point in a gravitational field is defined as the *force per unit mass* acting at that point. In mathematical terms:

$$g = \frac{F}{m}$$

where F is the force acting on the object with mass m, that is, its **weight**. Gravitational field strength has SI units of N kg^{-1}, and is a vector quantity. The weight of an object may be calculated from this relationship, giving an expression that you will certainly have used before:

$$W = mg$$

There is a relationship between acceleration due to gravity g and gravitational field strength g, and the two can be taken to be numerically equal. We shall explore this relationship in more detail in section 5.1, where we shall see that the relationship between the two g's is not quite so straightforward.

Newton's third law of motion

Forces come in pairs

Our everyday experience tells us that forces come in pairs. Push a laden supermarket trolley and you can feel it pushing backwards against you. Lift a heavy bag and you can feel it pulling down on you.

Newton realised this, and stated it in his **third law of motion**. (We shall come to Newton's second law in section 1.4.) Newton's third law is probably the most widely known and quoted of his laws – and it is also the most widely misunderstood! Nowadays, the law is stated as:

If body A exerts a force on body B, then body B exerts a force of the same size on body A, but in the opposite direction.

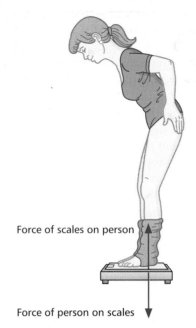

Force of scales on person

Force of person on scales

Figure 1.2.11 There is a contact force between the soles of the person's feet and the scales acting downwards. This is opposed by an upward force due to the spring in the scales. It is the size of this upward force that the scales measure.

It is vital to realise that these **third law pairs** of forces act on *different* bodies, so that a free body diagram will only ever contain one of a given pair.

In the situation shown in figure 1.2.12, only the forces F_{TP} and F_{PT} (representing the force of the trolley on the person and the force of the person on the trolley respectively) are a third law pair. The 'missing force' is the other member of the pair to which F_{GP} (the force of the ground on the person) belongs. This would be shown on a free body diagram for the Earth, as in figure 1.2.13, and would be represented by F_{PG} using this terminology.

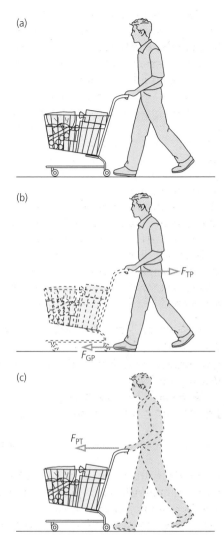

Figure 1.2.12 Think about the forces acting as you do the weekly shopping. Diagram (b) shows the free body diagram for *you* as you start the trolley moving, while diagram (c) shows the free body diagram for the *trolley*. In this situation only those forces which act in a horizontal direction have been shown - we shall look at those acting in a vertical direction shortly.

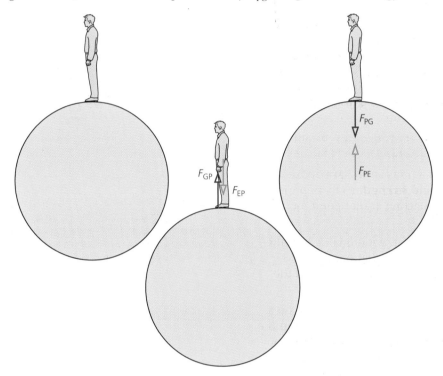

Figure 1.2.13 These diagrams show the vertical forces acting on someone standing still on the Earth.

It is tempting to assume that the push of the ground upwards on our feet, F_{GP}, is the other member of the third law pair involving the pull of the Earth downwards on us, F_{EP} – but the free body diagrams show that this is not so. Notice that the two third law pairs in this case are different types of force pairs. F_{EP} and F_{PE} are a gravitational pair, while F_{GP} and F_{PG} are a pair caused by contact between two surfaces. If you jump in the air, the contact pair cease to exist while you are airborne – but the gravitational pair continue to exist, to bring you (literally) back to Earth. Both members of a third law pair of forces are always of the same type – gravitational, electrostatic, contact, etc.

Types of forces

Forces are often labelled to help us understand how they arise. In this section we have been closely concerned with gravitational forces, which arise due to gravitational fields. We have also considered two types of contact forces, which arise when two surfaces touch – normal contact forces (acting perpendicularly to a surface) and frictional contact forces (acting along a surface). In other parts of this book we shall look at other types of forces, which will include electric, magnetic and nuclear forces.

As we shall see in section 5.1, all forces can be classified as being one of the four types of fundamental forces – the gravitational force, the electromagnetic force, the 'strong' force and the 'weak' force.

SUMMARY

- **Newton's first law of motion** states that every object continues in its state of rest or uniform motion in a straight line unless made to change by a resultant force acting on it. A **force** F may therefore cause a change in movement – an acceleration.

- A **free body diagram** is used to analyse the forces acting on a body.

- **Drag** forces oppose motion, and act to stop motion when the pushing or pulling force on a moving object no longer acts. Drag forces include **frictional forces** and **air resistance**.

- **Air resistance** or **aerodynamic drag** acts when a body moves through the air. To a good approximation the aerodynamic drag on a body increases as the square of its velocity. A falling body reaches a **terminal velocity**, when the acceleration due to gravity equals the aerodynamic drag, so the resultant force is zero and the velocity is constant.

- **Inertia** is the tendency of an object to stay in its state of rest or uniform motion, and depends only on the mass of the object.

- **Weight** is the force which acts on a mass at a point in the **gravitational field** of another mass. The **gravitational field strength** g at a point in a gravitational field is the force per unit mass acting at that point, or $g = F/m$.

- The **acceleration due to gravity** at a point in a gravitational field is the rate of change of velocity of a mass falling freely at that point. The numerical value of the gravitational field strength g at a point and the acceleration due to gravity at the same point are equal.

- **Newton's third law of motion** states that if a body A exerts a force on a body B, then body B exerts a force of the same size on body A, but in the opposite direction. This gives rise to **third law pairs** of forces acting on different bodies.

QUESTIONS

(Assume $g = 10$ m s^{-2}.)

1 If a coin is placed on a piece of card resting on top of a jar, it is possible to flick the card away sharply so that the coin falls into the jar. Explain why this is so.

2 A person standing on a bus is thrown towards the rear of the bus as it begins to move, and to the front of it as it slows down. Why?

3 A car is being towed by means of a rope connected to another car. Draw free body diagrams showing the horizontal forces acting on:
a the car being towed
b the car doing the towing
c the rope.
Identify the Newton third law pairs of forces.

4 Lewis Carroll posed a question about a monkey on a rope. The rope is weightless and perfectly flexible, and passes over a frictionless pulley. On the other end of the rope is a weight, which exactly counterbalances the monkey. Figure 1.2.14 shows the situation. If the monkey begins to climb, what happens to the weight?

(After Sam Loyd)

Figure 1.2.14

5 The stones making up the circle of stones at Stonehenge have a mass of around 30 tonnes each. If the stones were dragged over land without any rollers, how many men would be needed to drag each stone? Assume that $\mu = 0.6$ for a stone sliding over earth, and that a man can exert a constant horizontal force of 400 N.

6 An aeroplane makes an emergency landing on a runway without landing gear. If the aeroplane lands at 40 m s^{-1} and the coefficient of friction for the aeroplane sliding on the runway is 0.5, how far will the aeroplane slide before coming to rest?

7 A person standing on the side of ship drops a coin and sees it splash into the water 2 s later. How far above the water is the person standing?

8 A window cleaner drops an apple as he is cleaning a window at the top of the Canary Wharf tower, 220 m above the ground.
   a If air resistance is neglected, how long will the apple take to reach the ground?
   b Assuming that he can shout loudly enough, will it be any use if the window cleaner shouts to warn people below? (Speed of sound in air = 340 m s^{-1}.)

9 The aerodynamic drag on an object moving through air is proportional to Av^2, where A = area of cross-section and v = velocity. The terminal velocity of a person without a parachute falling through air is about 56 m s^{-1}.
   a Estimate the area of cross-section of a person seen from the front.
   b Using this estimate, obtain a figure for the area that a parachute must have in order to reduce a person's terminal velocity to 5 m s^{-1}.

10 The acceleration of a body may be measured by comparing it with the acceleration due to gravity at the surface of the Earth – an acceleration of 9.81 m s^{-2} = 1g. The nearest star to the Earth is Proxima Centauri, 4.3 light years away (see section 1.1, page 18, question 5 for the definition of the light year). It has been suggested that a spacecraft could travel to Proxima Centauri, accelerating at 1g until the midpoint of the journey and then slowing down to rest at 1g for the remainder of the journey.
   a What forces would the astronauts feel on such a journey?
   b How long would the journey take?
   c What would be maximum speed of the spaceship?
   (This is an example where the model we are using to understand something breaks down. At speeds close to that of light (about 3 x 10^8 m s^{-1}) classical Newtonian physics cannot be used, and the relativistic physics of Einstein must be used instead. According to the theory of relativity, no object can travel faster than the speed of light.)

Developing Key Skills

A local football club has asked you to produce a poster for the club's changing rooms. This is aimed at telling players in the club's youth team how to take an effective corner, curving the ball into the box for the forwards to head it into the goal. Use the focus information on page 24 to help you to produce this poster.

[Key Skills opportunities: C, IT]

1.3 Statics

So far we have looked at motion and the way forces cause changes in motion. Motion and forces can be connected in another way too – that is, where forces cancel each other out and the object on which they act is stationary or moving with a constant velocity. Under these conditions we say that the forces on the object are **in equilibrium**. The branch of physics concerned with the study of forces in equilibrium is called **statics** – the study of bodies which are not accelerating.

Statics is obviously important to civil engineers designing a structure (for example, a large bridge), but surprisingly, it is also important to aeronautical engineers ensuring the stability of a new design of aircraft in flight. In both cases a good understanding of the forces acting is needed in order to ensure the strength and stability of the object being designed.

Getting started – adding and resolving forces

Statics is about analysing the effect that forces have when they act on a body, so we need to have the right tools to carry out the analysis. These tools are essentially mathematical, and we shall look at them first.

Simple trigonometry

Much of physics makes use of trigonometry, and we shall meet it on many occasions in this and later sections of this book. Although it is possible to obtain solutions to many problems by using scale drawings, it is much preferable to use trigonometry, since this does not depend on the ability to draw accurate diagrams and take measurements from them.

Figure 1.3.1 shows a right-angled triangle in which angle BOA is θ. The lengths of the sides and the size of angle θ are related by the trigonometrical functions sine ('sin'), cosine ('cos') and tangent ('tan') as follows:

$$\sin \theta = \frac{AB}{OB}$$

$$\cos \theta = \frac{OA}{OB}$$

$$\tan \theta = \frac{AB}{OA}$$

From these definitions it follows that:

$$\tan \theta = \frac{AB}{OA} = \frac{(AB/OB)}{(OA/OB)} = \frac{\sin \theta}{\cos \theta}$$

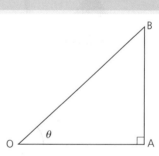

Figure 1.3.1

For the moment, the variation of these functions with angle is less important than the ability that they give us to carry out accurate calculations. You should however note that:
(1) When $\theta = 90°$, OA = 0 and OB = AB.
   At this angle, $\cos \theta = 0$, and $\sin \theta = 1$ (this is the largest value that $\sin \theta$ can have).
(2) When $\theta = 0$, AB = 0 and OB = OA.
   At this angle, $\sin \theta = 0$, and $\cos \theta = 1$ (this is the largest value that $\cos \theta$ can have).
(3) When $\theta = 45°$, OA = AB.
   At this angle $\tan \theta = 1$. The smallest value of $\tan \theta$ is zero, which occurs when $\theta = 0$. As θ gets closer to 90°, OA approaches zero. This means that $\tan \theta$ tends to infinity as θ tends to 90°.

Adding forces

Since force is a vector quantity, when we add forces together we must be careful to take into account both their magnitude and their direction. To do this easily we draw vector diagrams, like those used in section 1.1, page 12, to analyse motion in more than one direction.

When adding two forces together we use the **parallelogram rule**, as the forces act at the same point, like the example of adding two velocities in section 1.1. In this case we use a **parallelogram of forces**. Figure 1.3.2 shows a ball which has two forces acting on it at right angles to each other (the forces are not balanced, so the ball is accelerating).

The sum of the 4 N force acting horizontally and the 3 N force acting vertically is the **resultant force** acting on the ball – in this case 5 N at an angle of 37° to the horizontal. You can find the resultant force by using the methods described for combining vectors in section 1.1.

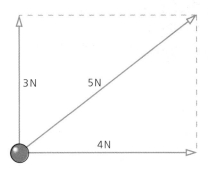

Figure 1.3.2 Example of a parallelogram of forces.

Work it out (1)

In the example in figure 1.3.2, it is not too difficult to work out the resultant force, because the two forces acting are at right angles to each other and are simple numbers. We can find out the size and direction of the resultant force by using a scale drawing. For example, a scale drawing with 1 N = 1 cm shows that the length of the line representing the resultant force is 5 cm, so the resultant force is 5 N. The angle θ can be measured as 37°.

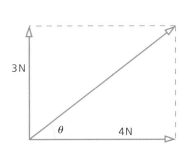

Figure 1.3.3

Alternatively, we can use trigonometry. Pythagoras' theorem relates the length of the hypotenuse to the lengths of the other two sides in a right-angled triangle. In this case it tells us that:

$$\textbf{(Resultant force)}^2 = \textbf{(3 N)}^2 + \textbf{(4 N)}^2$$
$$= \textbf{9 N}^2 + \textbf{16 N}^2 = \textbf{25 N}^2$$

so that:

$$\textbf{Resultant force} = \sqrt{\textbf{(25 N}^2\textbf{)}} = \textbf{5 N}$$

To find out the angle θ we can use the fact that:

$$\tan \theta = \textbf{3/4 (from the property of the right-angled triangle)}$$

so:

$$\theta = \tan^{-1}(0.75) = 37°$$

Although it is not always as easy as this, the principle of adding two forces (or any other vector quantity) acting at a point is always the same:

- Draw the two forces acting at the same point.
- Construct the parallelogram.
- Draw in the diagonal from the point at which the forces act to the opposite corner of the parallelogram.
- Measure or calculate the size and direction of the resultant.

Where two forces act in the same direction, the parallelogram of forces 'collapses' to become a straight line, and the resultant force is simply the size of the two forces added together, acting in the same direction, as it was in the case of the two velocities acting in the same direction. Figure 1.3.4 shows this happening.

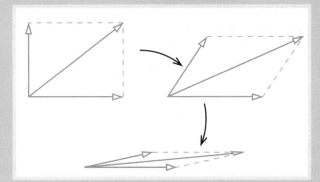

Figure 1.3.4 The resultant of two forces acting in the same direction is simply the sum of the forces.

Three or more forces

Adding more than two forces is not difficult – but it can be tedious! The idea is to start by adding two forces together to find their resultant. This force is then added to the next force to find the resultant of this pair. The process is repeated until all the forces have been added together. The forces may all act in the same plane (when they are said to be **coplanar**) or they may act in different planes. The method will work in either case, since any *pair* of forces can always be drawn as acting in the same plane. Figure 1.3.5 shows the process for five forces acting at a point.

Forces in one plane

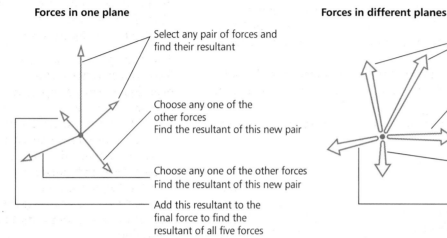

Select any pair of forces and find their resultant

Choose any one of the other forces
Find the resultant of this new pair

Choose any one of the other forces
Find the resultant of this new pair

Add this resultant to the final force to find the resultant of all five forces

Forces in different planes

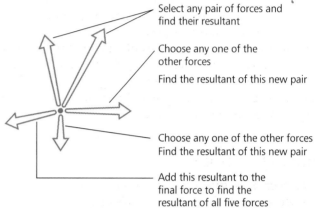

Select any pair of forces and find their resultant

Choose any one of the other forces
Find the resultant of this new pair

Choose any one of the other forces
Find the resultant of this new pair

Add this resultant to the final force to find the resultant of all five forces

Figure 1.3.5 The process can be carried out for any number of forces acting in any number of different directions.

Resolving forces

There are times when it is necessary to break down the resultant action of a force into its effects in a particular direction or pair of directions. This is called **resolving** a force into its **components**.

Figure 1.3.6

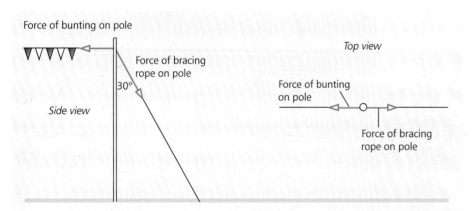

Figure 1.3.6 shows a pole with a line of bunting attached to it, together with a bracing rope. For simplicity we shall assume that the bunting is horizontal, even though this is actually impossible – question 2 on page 44 explores this situation further. The bunting and the rope pull on the pole as a result of being pulled tight. (In section 2 we shall look in more detail at why pulling on something exerts a force.) The bunting pulls the pole horizontally to the left, while the bracing rope pulls it downwards and to the right. This becomes obvious if we resolve the forces into their components acting at right angles to each other. In this case we shall use components which act horizontally and vertically.

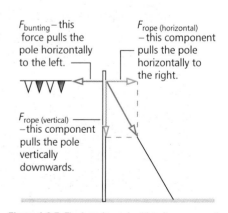

Figure 1.3.7 The force is resolved into its components by drawing a parallelogram of forces in which the angles between the sides are all 90° – in other words, a rectangle.

By resolving the forces as shown in figure 1.3.7 it becomes clear that the tension in the bunting and the rope has two effects:

1 pulling the pole sideways
2 pulling the pole downwards.

We shall see shortly how this method can be used in calculations about the forces acting on an object.

The concept of static equilibrium

The example of the bunting provides us with a good opportunity to gain an understanding of the idea of static equilibrium. Look again at figures 1.3.6 and 1.3.7. As the pole is at rest, Newton's first law of motion tells us that the sum of the forces acting on it must be zero.

If this were not the case, for example if one of the ropes attached to the pole were to snap, then the pole would be pulled to one side and would fall over as a result. This means that $F_{\text{bunting}} = -F_{\text{rope (horizontal)}}$ and that $F_{\text{rope (vertical)}}$ must also be balanced by an equal and opposite force – supplied by the ground pushing upwards on the base of the pole.

Frames of reference

In this section we shall concern ourselves only with systems we shall think of as being at rest. However, Newton's first law of motion tells us that this situation of balanced forces applies equally when objects are moving with constant velocity. Strictly we should therefore say that we are dealing in this section with situations in which the system under investigation is moving with a constant velocity which may be zero. The system will appear to be at rest to an observer looking at the system who has the same velocity as the system, in other words, a velocity relative to the system of zero. In this case we say that the observer and the system are in the same **frame of reference**. As far as the investigator is concerned, the system is stationary, although to another observer in a different frame of reference the system may appear to be moving, if the two frames of reference are moving with respect to each other. Figure 1.3.9 illustrates the point.

Figure 1.3.9 This seems to be a fairly clear-cut situation – B knows that A is moving because she can observe his movement. From A's point of view, B may *appear* to be moving, but he knows that this cannot be because he is the one on the train! A and B are in different frames of reference. We usually think of B's frame of reference as being stationary, and judge all motion relative to this frame. But what would the situation appear to be to another observer in space whose frame of reference had zero velocity relative to the Sun – who would appear to be moving then?

Work it out (2)

Scale drawing and trigonometry can be used to calculate the components of a force in the same way as when adding forces. Figure 1.3.8 shows how trigonometry can be used to resolve the components of the force exerted by the bracing rope in figure 1.3.6.

The principle of resolving a force (or any other vector quantity) into two components is always the same:

- Decide on the two directions in which the components are to lie (these directions must *always* be at right angles to each other, and can be chosen to make analysing the situation as straightforward as possible).
- Draw the force acting.
- Construct the rectangle of forces with the components in the chosen directions.
- Measure or calculate the size of each component.

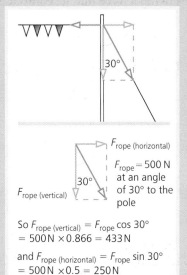

So $F_{\text{rope (vertical)}} = F_{\text{rope}} \cos 30°$
$= 500 \text{ N} \times 0.866 = 433 \text{ N}$

and $F_{\text{rope (horizontal)}} = F_{\text{rope}} \sin 30°$
$= 500 \text{ N} \times 0.5 = 250 \text{ N}$

Figure 1.3.8 Finding the components of a force by trigonometry.

The simple example of the bunting and pole illustrates the important physical idea of **equilibrium**, when an object has balanced forces acting on it and is in a state of rest as a result. (The word 'equilibrium' comes from two Latin words meaning 'even balance'.) The pole in the example has two sorts of equilibrium when it is at rest – **translational equilibrium** and **rotational equilibrium**, that is to say, it is not moving up, down or sideways, neither is it rotating. We shall go on to look at these two kinds of equilibrium in more detail.

Translational equilibrium

The pole supporting the bunting is not moving up, down or sideways, so it is in **translational equilibrium**. Let's look briefly at what this means.

For simplicity, start by imagining a simple object like a ball. At rest supported by a person's hand, the forces acting on the ball can be represented in a free body diagram, figure 1.3.10.

Obviously the two forces must be equal and opposite if the ball is in translational equilibrium. What about the case where three forces act on a ball – how can we tell whether it is in translational equilibrium? Figure 1.3.11 shows this.

Using a polygon of forces to analyse translational equilibrium

In general, when n forces act like this at a point, a closed **polygon of forces** with n sides can be drawn if the body on which the forces act is in translational equilibrium, as shown in figure 1.3.12.

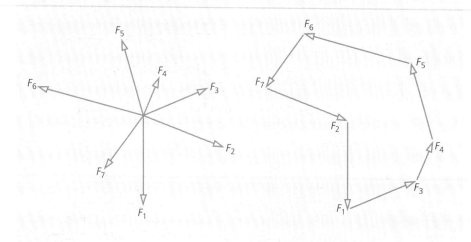

Figure 1.3.12 Free body diagram representing seven forces acting at a point.

Using a polygon of forces like this is similar to the triangle of vectors used to calculate the effect of several successive displacements in figure 1.1.13 (page 10). In both cases we are really asking 'What is the effect of vector **A**, followed by vector **B**, followed by vector **C** ... ?', and the diagram showing the vectors acting one after the other, nose to tail, provides us with a simple answer to the question. If, as a result of going round the vector polygon we get back to where we started, then the net effect of the vectors is ... zero! If the vectors represent displacements, this tells us we are literally back where we started, while if they represent forces, it tells us that the sum of the forces is zero, and we have a situation in which there is translational equilibrium. Figure 1.3.13 shows how the analysis of the bunting and the pole indicates that the pole is in translational equilibrium.

Figure 1.3.10 Free body diagram representing two forces acting on a ball.

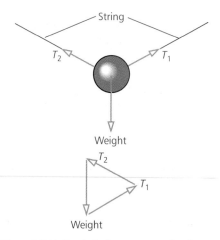

Figure 1.3.11 Free body diagram representing three forces acting on a ball.

Figure 1.3.13 Translational equilibrium as demonstrated by the polygon of forces.

Analysis of translational equilibrium using a polygon of forces

As an example, consider the stationary cable car shown in figure 1.3.14. The car is supported by a cable, which provides the force necessary to oppose the downward pull of the Earth on the car. If the weight of the car and its load is 1.1×10^4 N and the cable each side of the car makes an angle of 10° with the horizontal, what is the tension in the cable?

A scale drawing of the forces enables us to answer this question.

Careful measurement of T_1 and T_2 shows that they have a value of around 3.2×10^4 N. Alternatively, trigonometry could be used to find T_1 and T_2.

Figure 1.3.14 Note that the cable is stationary, so the tension in all parts of it must be the same – otherwise it would accelerate.

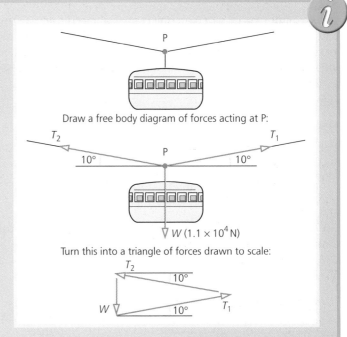

Draw a free body diagram of forces acting at P:

Turn this into a triangle of forces drawn to scale:

Powers of 10, standard form and logarithms

There are several different ways of referring to quantities. Physicists often use powers of 10 to express very large or very small numbers. For example, the approximate distance travelled by light in one year is 10^{16} m, or 10 000 000 000 000 000 m. In this example, 16 is called the **index** – the power to which 10 is raised, and 10 is the **base**. Similarly, the approximate size of an atom is 10^{-10} m, or 0.000 000 000 1 m.

The use of powers of 10 saves writing out all the zeros. Note that the *sign* of the index tells you which way the decimal point moves.

Numbers are very often written in **standard form**, as a number between 1 and 10 multiplied by 10 raised to the appropriate power. So, for example, the speed of sound in air at 0°C is 3.31×10^2 m s^{-1}, the radius of the Earth is 6.4×10^6 m, and the mass of an electron is 9.109×10^{-31} kg. In each case here, the number of significant figures is different – how to decide on the precision with which to quote a quantity is dealt with in the box 'Precision' on page 36.

A further use of powers is in **logarithms**. Two types of logarithms are in common use:
- base 10 logarithms, written as $\log_{10}$ (or sometimes just lg)
- base e logarithms or **natural logarithms**, written as $\log_e$ (or sometimes just ln).

The logarithm of a number in a given base is the power to which the base must raised in order to equal the number. So:

$$\log_{10} 10\,000 = 4, \text{ since } 10\,000 = 10^4$$

Tables of logarithms can be used to carry out calculations, although most people now prefer to use calculators. However, logarithms can still be very useful in exploring relationships between quantities. Natural logarithms occur when dealing with the mathematics of certain situations, in particular where the rate of change of a quantity is proportional to the quantity itself. Such changes are called **exponential** changes, and we shall meet and explore these further in sections 3.4, 4.3 and 6.2.

Resolving forces to analyse translational equilibrium

An alternative approach to using a vector polygon of forces is to resolve the forces into components. Newton's first law tells us that for equilibrium the sum of the components in each direction must be zero, and so we have a simple way of calculating the forces required for equilibrium.

Analysis of translational equilibrium by resolving forces

Consider once again the stationary cable car, shown in figure 1.3.15.

The horizontal components of the tension in the cable cancel each other out, so the resultant horizontal force is zero. The vertical components of the tension provide the force required to oppose the gravitational attraction of the Earth for the car and its load. Using trigonometry to calculate these rather than a scale drawing, and T to represent either T_1 or T_2, we can write:

$$T \sin 10° + T \sin 10° = -1.1 \times 10^4 \, \text{N}$$

so:

$$2T = \frac{-1.1 \times 10^4 \, \text{N}}{\sin 10°} \quad \text{and} \quad T = \frac{-1.1 \times 10^4 \, \text{N}}{2 \sin 10°}$$

Calculation of T gives a value of $3.17 \times 10^4 \, \text{N}$ to three significant figures.

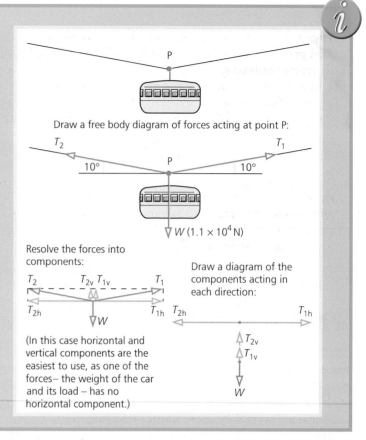

Draw a free body diagram of forces acting at point P:

Resolve the forces into components:

Draw a diagram of the components acting in each direction:

(In this case horizontal and vertical components are the easiest to use, as one of the forces– the weight of the car and its load – has no horizontal component.)

Figure 1.3.15 Translational equilibrium as demonstrated by resolving forces.

Determining whether a body is in translational equilibrium

For a body to be in translational equilibrium, the vector sum of all the forces acting on it – that is, the resultant force – must be zero (this is simply another way of stating Newton's first law of motion). It is possible to find out whether a body is in translational equilibrium by using a polygon of forces, or by resolving the forces acting into components and adding them.

Precision

As we have seen, we may obtain answers to the same problem in different ways, using either drawing or calculation. Depending upon the scale of the drawing you use to solve a problem, you may obtain an answer within limits of say 2%. (This will also depend on how good you are at drawing accurate force diagrams.) This represents an uncertainty of 640 N in the value of $3.2 \times 10^4 \, \text{N}$ measured from the diagram in the example of the cable car, since:

$$\text{Uncertainty of 2\%} = \frac{2}{100} \times 3.2 \times 10^4 \, \text{N} = 640 \, \text{N}$$

This means that the tension in the cable lies somewhere between 31 360 N and 32 640 N. On the other hand, if a calculation using trigonometry is done with an eight-digit scientific calculator, we get an answer of 31 673.273 N.

Figure 1.3.16 This ice skater is not in translational or rotational equilibrium.

What is a reasonable answer to give? The weight of the cable car and its load given was 1.1×10^4 N – that is, to two significant figures. We can therefore reasonably assume that the load lies between 1.05×10^4 N and 1.14×10^4 N, since if it lay outside these values it would then have been given as either 1.0×10^4 N or 1.2×10^4 N respectively. The uncertainty in the known value of the weight can be calculated as approximately:

$$\frac{0.05 \times 10^4\,\text{N}}{1.1 \times 10^4\,\text{N}} \times 100\% \approx 4.5\%$$

Since the tension in the cable depends directly on the weight of the cable car and its load, it is obviously absurd to be any more precise in our answer than the data allow. We should not quote our answer to any greater precision than the data supplied – so we should not give an answer to more than two significant figures, that is 3.2×10^4 N.

In solving numerical problems it is generally bad practice to give a solution to a greater number of significant figures than the most precise item of data given. Similar rules govern the way in which experimental data are treated – these are dealt with later.

Rotational equilibrium

As well as translation, it is necessary to consider **rotation** when thinking about objects in equilibrium. An object is in **rotational equilibrium** when its angular acceleration is zero – in other words, it is either not rotating or is rotating at a constant rate. Rotational equilibrium is important in a situation such as a crane on a building site, as shown in figure 1.3.17. The crane lifts a load at a point on its jib, and in order to prevent the jib rotating about the fulcrum (to preserve rotational equilibrium), there is a counterbalance on the jib, the other side of the fulcrum. Just like translational equilibrium, there are some conditions that must be met for an object to be in rotational equilibrium.

Possibly the simplest situation where rotational equilibrium may be observed is in a simple beam or lever balance like that shown in figure 1.3.18, where W represents weight and l the perpendicular distance of the weight from the fulcrum. Such a beam is often used to investigate rotational equilibrium.

Investigations show that a uniform beam pivoted at a point can be balanced – in other words, it may be in rotational equilibrium. For this to be so in both cases shown in figure 1.3.18, the condition is that:

$$W_1 l_1 = W_2 l_2$$

The quantity $W_1 l_1$ is the **moment** M of W_1 about the pivot or fulcrum. The moment of a force is calculated by multiplying together the force and the perpendicular distance between the fulcrum and the line of action of the force. The SI unit of moment is the newton metre (N m).

This mathematical statement about the moments of forces acting about a point is sometimes called the **law of the lever** or the **principle of moments**, and is sometimes expressed in words as:

The sum of the clockwise moments equals the sum of the anticlockwise moments

Figure 1.3.17 The jib of this crane is maintained in a state of equilibrium by the counterbalance.

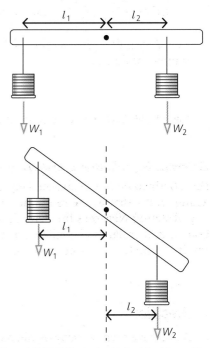

Figure 1.3.18 Taking moments about the fulcrum. The beam is pivoted at its mid-point.

The principle of moments in mathematical terms

Just as we wrote Newton's first law as $\Sigma F = 0$ (page 20), we can write the principle of moments as

$$\Sigma M = 0$$

Notice that we do not need to know the weight of the beam and the reaction force of the fulcrum on the beam. Since the moments of all the forces are being measured about the point through which the weight and reaction forces act, these two forces do not exert a turning effect on the bar – their moments are zero, since l is zero.

The building site crane in rotational equilibrium – worked example

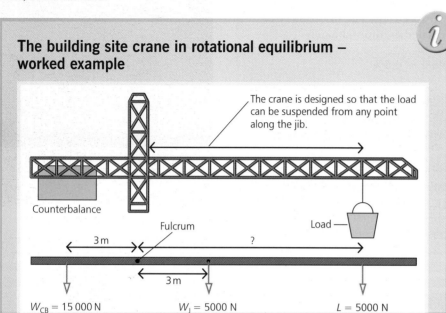

The crane is designed so that the load can be suspended from any point along the jib.

Counterbalance

Fulcrum

Load

3 m

?

3 m

$W_{CB} = 15\,000$ N $W_J = 5000$ N $L = 5000$ N

Figure 1.3.19

The force diagram in figure 1.3.19 shows the situation when a load of 500 kg is being lifted. The jib of the crane itself has a mass of 500 kg, and a counterbalance of 1500 kg is used to counteract the turning effect of the load. Where must the load hang from in order for the crane's jib to be in rotational equilibrium?

Let us look at the turning force acting on the jib in this situation, assuming $g = 10$ N kg^{-1}:

$$\sum(\text{clockwise moments}) = 5000 \text{ N} \times 3 \text{ m} + 5000 \text{ N} \times ? \text{ m}$$

$$\sum(\text{anticlockwise moments}) = 15\,000 \text{ N} \times 3 \text{ m} = 45\,000 \text{ N m}$$

For rotational equilibrium, these two moments must be equal in size, so:

$$5000 \text{ N} \times 3 \text{ m} + 5000 \text{ N} \times ? \text{ m} = 45\,000 \text{ N m}$$

so:

$$15\,000 \text{ N m} + 5000 \text{ N} \times ? \text{ m} = 45\,000 \text{ N m}$$

and:

$$? \text{ m} = \frac{45\,000 \text{ N m} - 15\,000 \text{ N m}}{5000 \text{ N}} = \frac{30\,000 \text{ N m}}{5000 \text{ N}} = 6 \text{ m}$$

The jib is 20 m long. Does the crane seem reasonably well designed to lift loads in the range 500 kg to 1000 kg?

THE PLAYFUL PHYSICIST

Figure 1.3.20 Yong Mao (left) and Thomas Fink

The skills of analysis learned and applied by physicists can sometimes be used to solve problems in a very light-hearted way. During the late 1990s two physicists from Cambridge University, Thomas Fink and Yong Mao, became interested in finding out how many ways there are of tying a tie. 'I've been interested in ties for some time,' said Fink, 'and the more we played around with them, the more it became apparent that there was a mathematical elegance behind knotting a tie.'

Carrying out their research in their spare time, the two researchers constructed a model of tying a tie based on a triangular lattice (figure 1.3.22). Each movement of the tie in making the knot is regarded as a move along one of the l, c or r axes of the lattice. The number of moves made in tying the tie is limited by the size of the knot and the length of the tie, so Fink and Mao reckon that there are no more than 85 ways of tying a knot in a tie. However, many of these knots are rather unattractive, so in practice there are just 10 knots that are likely to be used. These were selected on the basis of their symmetry and what the researchers call their 'balance'. A knot is symmetric if it contains equal numbers of left and right moves, while a well-balanced knot is one that contains a good mixture of left and right moves, without which the knot becomes easily deformed.

Of the 10 knots selected, four were already in use before this study. The simplest of these is a knot called the 'four-in-hand', which has the movements l–r–l–c. If you have worn a tie at any time, this will almost certainly be the knot you have used. Of the six new knots produced, Fink usually ties his tie using a knot he calls the '7–3'.

Despite the interest generated by their study of ties, Fink and Mao are keen to stress the serious side of their work, in protein folding and polymer physics – for even though physics has a light side, it doesn't do to be better known for your contributions to tie knotting than your work on more important topics.

Figure 1.3.21 This is the 'four-in-hand', the simplest kind of knot used for a tie.

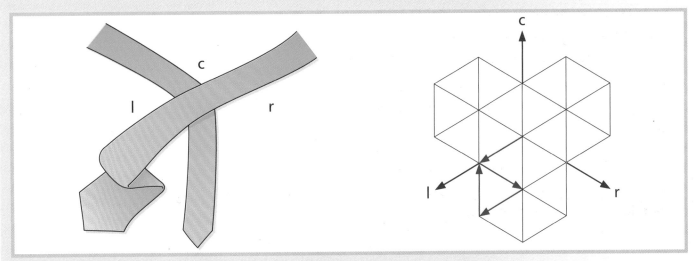

Figure 1.3.22 The three possible movements in knotting a tie are represented by the axes of a triangular lattice. The letters c, l and r stand for centre, left and right.

Taking moments about different points

Surprisingly, the point about which moments are taken is not important, as the following example shows.

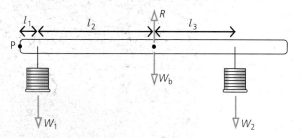

Figure 1.3.23 Taking moments about P.

The physical situation in figure 1.3.23 is identical to the one in figure 1.3.18, but this time we take moments about the left-hand end of the bar rather than about the fulcrum. In the previous case we ignored W_b, the weight of the beam, and R, the reaction force of the fulcrum on the beam, because their moments were zero. This is not the case here, and so we must include them in our calculation.

Σ(**clockwise moments**) =
$$W_1 l_1 + W_b(l_1 + l_2) + W_2(l_1 + l_2 + l_3)$$

Σ(**anticlockwise moments**) $= R(l_1 + l_2)$
$$= (W_1 + W_2 + W_b)(l_1 + l_2)$$

(Since the bar is in translational equilibrium,
$$R = W_1 + W_2 + W_b)$$

The beam is in rotational equilibrium, so
Σ(clockwise moments) = Σ(anticlockwise moments):

$$W_1 l_1 + W_b(l_1 + l_2) + W_2(l_1 + l_2 + l_3) = \\ (W_1 + W_2 + W_b)(l_1 + l_2)$$

Multiplying out the brackets gives:

$$W_1 l_1 + W_b l_1 + W_b l_2 + W_2 l_1 + W_2 l_2 + W_2 l_3 \\ = W_1 l_1 + W_1 l_2 + W_2 l_1 + W_2 l_2 + W_b l_1 + W_b l_2$$

and this then becomes:

$$W_2 l_3 = W_1 l_2$$

which is equivalent to the expression we had when taking moments about the fulcrum.

Using forces to maintain static equilibrium

Forces, couples and moments

In the vacuum of space, it is important to understand how to use forces to cause rotational and translational equilibrium – one miscalculation could send millions of pounds' worth of spacecraft careering out of control, not to mention putting human lives at risk.

(a)

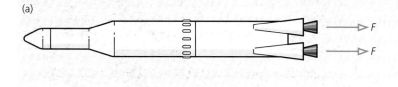

Figure 1.3.24 Three different situations in deep space, far away from any gravitational fields. The arrows show the forces caused by the craft's rockets firing in each case.

(b)

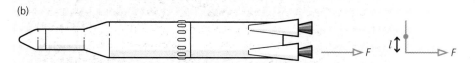

(c)

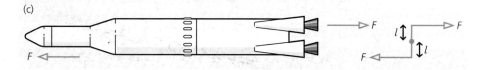

In diagram (a) in figure 1.3.24, the two small rockets at the rear of the craft are firing backwards, each exerting the same force. Obviously the sum of the forces is not zero, so the craft will accelerate forwards. However, the sum of the moments is zero, so the craft is in rotational equilibrium.

In diagram (b), only one of the small rockets at the rear of the craft is firing. In this case, neither the sum of the forces nor the sum of the moments is zero, so the craft is in neither translational nor rotational equilibrium. It will accelerate forwards, rotating in a clockwise direction at the same time.

In diagram (c), one rocket at the rear of the craft is firing, together with another at the front. Both exert the same size force on the craft, but in opposite directions. Here the sum of the moments is not zero, so the craft will rotate in an anticlockwise direction. However, the sum of the forces is zero, so the craft is in translational equilibrium.

Diagram (c) shows an example of a **couple** – a pair of forces equal in size but opposite in direction which act on a body to cause rotation about the centre of mass, but not translation. The turning moment provided by a couple is known as its **torque**. Like moment, the SI unit of torque is the newton metre (N m).

Centre of gravity and centre of mass

In problems involving solid objects, like that of the crane, we often draw the weight of an object as acting through a single point. This point is called the **centre of gravity**, and the justification for doing this is quite straightforward.

If we think of a ruler balanced at its midpoint, we would draw a free body diagram of the forces acting on the ruler like that shown overleaf in figure 1.3.27. This diagram assumes that we can think of the weight of the ruler as acting at its midpoint. The justification for this is to think of the Earth pulling vertically downwards on each particle of the ruler. As each particle on one side of the ruler has a similar particle on the other side of the ruler exactly the same distance away from the ruler's centre, the sum of the moments of all the particles in the ruler about the midpoint of the ruler is zero. The ruler will therefore be in rotational equilibrium when it is suspended at its midpoint, as figure 1.3.28 overleaf shows.

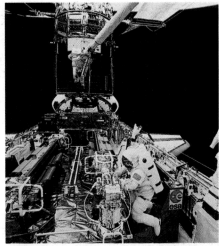

Figure 1.3.25 Astronaut Kathy Thornton carries out routine servicing work on the Hubble Space telescope. The telescope uses gyroscopes which serve as a balancing 'inner ear', detecting changes in rotation. Conventional gyroscopes use a rapidly spinning, heavy mass, require lubrication and eventually wear out. A new gyroscope designed for space operation has now been developed which will not require servicing. Its dimensions are 4 mm by 4 mm, and its mass is less than 1 g.

The torque of a couple – worked example

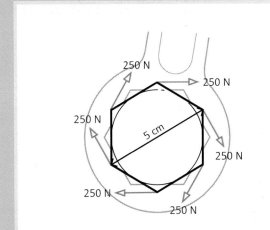

Figure 1.3.26

A nut being turned by a spanner has three equal couples acting on it. The total torque on the nut is found by adding together the torque due to each of these couples.

Torque of couple = 2 × 250 N × 0.025 m = 12.5 N m

Each force in the couple has a moment of 250 N × 0.025 m about the point of rotation of the nut, so the torque exerted by the couple is 2 × 250 N × 0.025 m. In general, the torque exerted by a couple is calculated by multiplying one of the forces in the pair by the perpendicular distance between them. This is equivalent to combining the moments of each force in the couple:

250 N × 0.05 m = 2 × 250 N × 0.025 m

Total torque acting = 3 × 12.5 N m = 37.5 N m

The centre of gravity of an object is simply the point about which the sum of the moments of all its particles of mass is zero. In practical terms, this is the point at which the weight of the object appears to act.

An object's **centre of mass** has a similar definition – it is the point at which all the object's mass may be considered to be concentrated. In most common circumstances, an object's centre of mass and centre of gravity are at the same place, although this is not always so. We shall return to the concept of centre of mass when we look at gravitational fields in section 5.

Stability

Figure 1.3.29 The thing these all have in common is – stability!

Stability is important in many everyday objects – without it, they would be in danger of toppling over. Toppling occurs when the centre of gravity of an object falls outside its base, because it is then impossible to balance moments.

A low centre of gravity and/or a wide base helps to make an object more stable, by making as large as possible the angle through which the object must tilt in order to cause the centre of gravity to fall outside the base (figure 1.3.30).

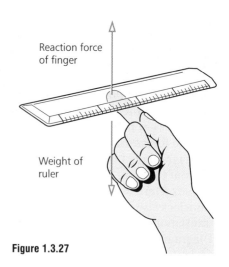

Reaction force of finger

Weight of ruler

Figure 1.3.27

This point has an identical point on the other side of the finger. The moments of the two points cancel out exactly.

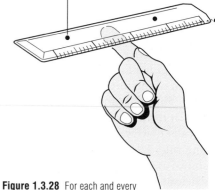

Figure 1.3.28 For each and every point on the ruler there is another point which has a moment which is equal and opposite.

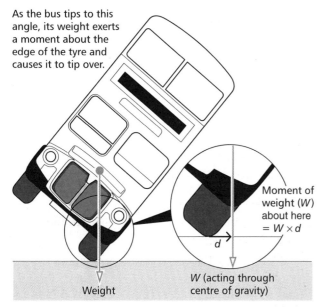

As the bus tips to this angle, its weight exerts a moment about the edge of the tyre and causes it to tip over.

Moment of weight (W) about here = $W \times d$

Weight

W (acting through centre of gravity)

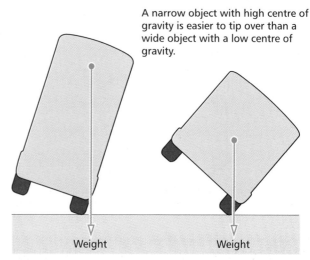

A narrow object with high centre of gravity is easier to tip over than a wide object with a low centre of gravity.

Weight

Weight

Figure 1.3.30 Why are standing passengers not allowed on the upper deck of a double decker bus?

Forces in the gym – a matter of balance

Consciously or unconsciously, we make use of statics when taking part in almost any sporting activity. The reason why the boxer stands as shown in figure 1.3.31 is concerned with stability – he has made his centre of gravity as low as possible and has placed his feet wide apart. This means that the moment of a force caused by his opponent hitting him is unlikely to be large enough to rotate his body to make his centre of gravity fall outside the 'base' formed by his feet.

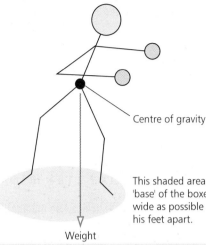

Centre of gravity

This shaded area shows the 'base' of the boxer, made as wide as possible by keeping his feet apart.

Weight

Figure 1.3.31

SUMMARY

- **Statics** studies the forces acting on an object which is not accelerating – an object in **equilibrium**. Since the object is not accelerating, the forces on it are balanced.

- Forces can be added by finding the resultant of their vectors using the parallelogram rule.

- Forces can be **resolved** into components acting perpendicular to each other by drawing a rectangle around the force vector.

- An object that is not moving is in **translational equilibrium** and **rotational equilibrium**.

- For an object in **translational equilibrium**, a closed polygon of forces can be drawn.

- The **moment** M of a force F which causes rotation about a point P is $M = Fl$ where l is the perpendicular distance from point P to the line of action of the force.

- For an object in **rotational equilibrium**, the sum of the clockwise moments equals the sum of the anticlockwise moments.

- A **couple** is a pair of forces equal in size but opposite in direction which act on a body to cause rotation. The turning force provided by a couple is known as its **torque**. The torque of a couple is found by multiplying the magnitude of one of the forces in the couple by the perpendicular distance between the forces.

- The **centre of gravity** of an object is the point about which the sum of the moments of the downwards pull of the Earth acting on all its particles is zero – the point at which the weight of the object appears to act.

- The **centre of mass** of an object is the point at which an object's mass appears to be concentrated, and is usually at the same point as the centre of gravity.

- **Stability** is the resistance of an object to toppling when displaced from its stable position. Stable objects tend to have a low centre of gravity and a wide base. An object topples when its centre of gravity falls outside the area enclosed by its base.

EXAMPLE

A person with a weight of 650 N stands on the ball of one foot with the heel slightly raised as shown in figure 1.3.32. The bones of the foot act as a lever with forces acting at the points shown. Calculate the force exerted by the Achilles tendon.

To solve this problem we can treat the foot as a lever with the ball of the foot as the fulcrum. The weight of the person acts perpendicularly to the lever 14 cm from the fulcrum, exerting a clockwise moment. The Achilles tendon exerts a force F perpendicular to the lever 19 cm from the fulcrum, producing an anticlockwise moment. For equilibrium, these two moments must be equal and opposite.

Thus:

$$\text{Clockwise moment} = 650 \text{ N} \times 1.4 \times 10^{-1} \text{ m} = 91 \text{ N m}$$
$$\text{Anticlockwise moment} = F \times 1.9 \times 10^{-1} \text{ m}$$

Since:

$$\text{Clockwise moment} = \text{anticlockwise moment}$$

then:

$$91 \text{ N m} = F \times 1.9 \times 10^{-1} \text{ m}$$

so:

$$F = \frac{91 \text{ N m}}{1.9 \times 10^{-1} \text{ m}}$$
$$= 480 \text{ N (to 2 SF)}$$

In order for the person to balance on the ball of one foot, the Achilles tendon must exert an upwards force of 480 N.

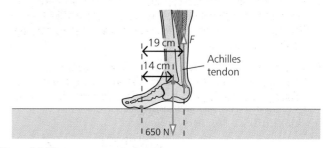

Figure 1.3.32

QUESTIONS

1 A mirror weighs 30 N. It hangs from a wire which passes over a nail in the wall. The wire on each side of the nail makes an angle of 30° with the horizontal. What is the tension in the wire?

2 A party trick involves tying a piece of string around a book and challenging a person to pull on the ends of the string so that it becomes horizontal (see figure 1.3.33).
   a Write down an expression for the component of tension in the string which supports the book.
   b Explain why the string can never be made exactly horizontal.

Figure 1.3.33

3 A car bonnet weighs 200 N and is 1.8 m long. The bonnet's weight acts at its midpoint. If the bonnet is freely hinged at one end and is supported by a vertical force at the other end, what size must this force be in order to support the bonnet at an angle of 30° to the horizontal?

4 A mechanic tests the tension in a car fan belt by pushing on its midpoint with a force of 80 N (see figure 1.3.34). If the free length of the belt between the pulleys is 50 cm, what is the tension in the belt when the mechanic pushes on it?

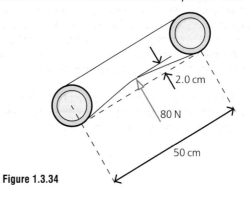

Figure 1.3.34

5 The 'sport' of arm wrestling requires two competitors to sit opposite one another at a table while clasping opposite hands. Each competitor then attempts to force the other competitor's hand down onto the table. The rules state that each competitor must keep the elbow in contact with the table while doing this. Why does raising the elbow from the table give a competitor an unfair advantage?

6 Estimate the mass of one of your **i** legs **ii** arms.

  a How is it possible for a high jumper to jump over a bar while her centre of mass passes *below* the bar?

  b What body position is necessary to do this?

7 A car maintenance manual specifies that the cylinder head bolts on an engine should be tightened to a torque of 69 N m. What force must be applied to the end of a spanner 30 cm long in order to achieve this?

8 A railway engine weighing 7.5×10^5 N is 40 m across the centre span of a bridge consisting of an iron girder 120 m long, weighing 1.0×10^7 N (see figure 1.3.35). Calculate the load on the support at each end of the bridge.

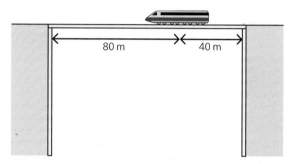

80 m   **40 m**

Figure 1.3.35

9 A rectangular box 2 m tall and with a base 1 m × 1 m is filled with matter of uniform density. It stands on the back of a flat-bed truck. What is the maximum acceleration that the truck can have if the box is not to topple over? (Assume that the friction between the box and the truck is such that the box does not slide.)

(*Hint*: Start by drawing a free body diagram for the box showing the situation when it begins to topple and so only makes contact with the truck along its rear edge.)

10 Figure 1.3.36 shows a load hanging from a loading boom. The load weighs 5000 N. Assuming that the loading boom has negligible mass, calculate:

  a the tension in the stay

  b the compressional force acting on the boom.

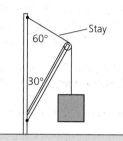

Stay

60°

30°

Figure 1.3.36

Developing Key Skills

A physicist and an artist have read about the work on ties described in the focus on page 39. They are using these ideas to produce an exhibit which is intended to increase people's interest in science. They intend to display this exhibit in an art gallery, in order to reach an audience who may not normally have much interest in science.

To support their work, they have applied for a government grant. The Chair of the committee which allocates these grants has asked you for your opinion about whether a grant should be awarded for this work. Write a short letter explaining your point of view.

[Key Skills opportunities: C, (IT)]

1.4 Measuring forces and their effects

We have established a connection between force and acceleration which is **qualitative** – we know that a force can cause acceleration. However, we must find a **quantitative** connection between force and acceleration in order to understand motion and its causes in any depth.

The link between force, mass and acceleration

The investigation of the relationship between force, mass and acceleration is a fairly straightforward matter in the laboratory, where we can use the techniques of measuring and determining velocity such as ticker timers, light gates and multiflash photography which we saw in section 1.1.

Figure 1.4.1 Measuring the effect of large forces on the safety of a car. Tests like this are used to provide consumers with information to help them make choices when buying a car in which they and their family will travel.

Investigating the relationship between *F*, *m* and *a*

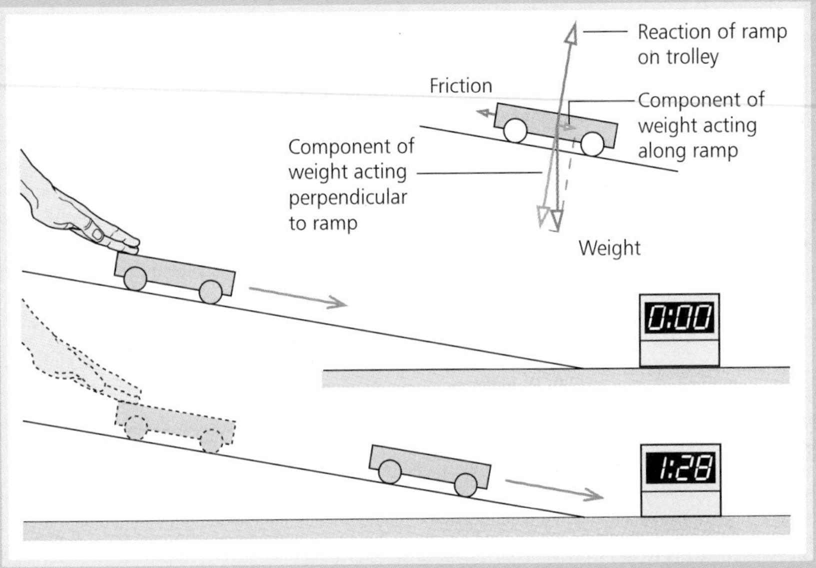

Reaction of ramp on trolley

Friction

Component of weight acting along ramp

Component of weight acting perpendicular to ramp

Weight

0:00

1:28

Figure 1.4.2 A sloping ramp is used so that a component of the weight of the trolley acts down the ramp. The slope is adjusted so that this component exactly cancels out the force of friction acting up the slope – and so the trolley has zero resultant force acting on it when moving, and is **friction compensated**. The trolley therefore moves at a steady speed down the slope.

An investigation may be carried out using a dynamics trolley, as shown in figure 1.4.2, or an air track may be used (see figure 1.1.19 on page 14). In either case, the motion of the vehicle is measured when a resultant force acts on it, for example when it is pulled using an elastic band to provide a constant force. Graphs of velocity versus time are plotted for various values of the resultant force (different numbers of elastic bands) while the mass of the vehicle is kept constant, and graphs are also plotted for varying masses of vehicle while the resultant force is kept constant. Figure 1.4.3 shows the results.

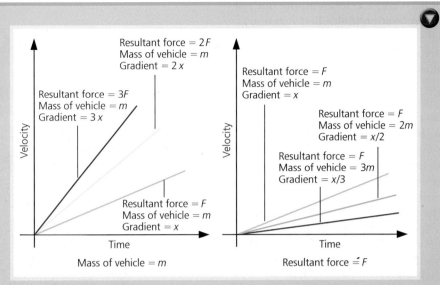

Figure 1.4.3 Velocity–time graphs for constant mass and for constant resultant force.

Since the slope of a velocity–time graph represents acceleration (dv/dt), the results can be represented as in table 1.4.1.

Mass of vehicle = m		Resultant force = F	
Force	Acceleration	Mass	Acceleration
F	a	m	a
2F	2a	2m	a/2
3F	3a	3m	a/3

Table 1.4.1

It is clear from the first set of results that there is a direct relationship between F and a, and that a is proportional to F (that is, as F increases by a factor x, so does a. This can be represented as $F \propto a$). The second set of results shows that there is a different relationship between a and m. Here $a \propto 1/m$ (that is, as m increases by a factor x, a changes by a factor of $1/x$ – we say that 'a is inversely proportional to m').

These two relationships can now be combined:

$$\left.\begin{array}{l} a \propto F \\ a \propto 1/m \end{array}\right\} \quad a \propto \frac{F}{m} \quad \text{or} \quad F \propto ma$$

An investigation using simple laboratory apparatus such as dynamics trolleys or air tracks can quickly lead us to the conclusion that a simple relationship between force, mass and acceleration exists, so that we can write:

$$F \propto ma$$

or:

$$F = kma$$

where k is a constant.

By using SI units for our measurements of mass and acceleration, the units of force become kg m s^{-2} (the units of mass and acceleration multiplied together). If we *define* the unit of force in such a way that *one* unit of force accelerates a mass of *one* kilogram at a rate of *one* metre per second per second, then the constant in the equation must also have a value of one, and so:

$$F = ma$$

Both *F* and *a* are vector quantities – the acceleration takes place in the direction in which the force acts. Notice that the *units* on each side of the relationship are the same (because we are comparing physical quantities), and that the effect of defining the unit of force in this way is not only to make *k* equal to 1 but also to make it **dimensionless** – with no units.

The unit of force in this system is of course better known as the **newton**. This equation defines the newton as being the resultant force which produces an acceleration of one metre per second per second when it acts on a mass of one kilogram. The mathematical statement *F* = *ma* is sometimes referred to as **Newton's second law of motion**. Neither this definition of the newton nor the statement *F* = *ma* is the whole story, as we shall see.

Using *F* = *ma* – worked examples

Example 1

A runner in a sprint race reaches 9 m s^{-1} in 3 s from the start of the race. If her mass is 50 kg, what force must she exert in order to do this?

$u = 0$ m s^{-1}	$v = 9$ m s^{-1}
$a = ?$	$t = 3$ s
$s = ?$	

Use equation of motion 1 (see page 10):

$$v = u + at$$

Substitute values:

$$9 \text{ m s}^{-1} = 0 \text{ m s}^{-1} + a \times 3 \text{ s}$$

so:

$$a = \frac{9 \text{ m s}^{-1} - 0 \text{ m s}^{-1}}{3 \text{ s}}$$

$$= 3 \text{ m s}^{-2}$$

Now apply *F* = *ma*:

$$F = 50 \text{ kg} \times 3 \text{ m s}^{-2}$$

$$= 150 \text{ N}$$

So the athlete needs to exert a force of 150 N in order to accelerate at this rate. (Will she exert this force constantly over the first three seconds of the race? Why?)

Example 2

An aeroplane lands with a velocity of 55 m s^{-1}. 'Reverse thrust' from the engines is used to slow it to a velocity of 25 m s^{-1} in a distance of 240 m. If the mass of the aeroplane is 3×10^4 kg, what is the size of the reverse thrust supplied by the engines?

$u = 55$ m s^{-1}	$v = 25$ m s^{-1}
$a = ?$	$t = ?$
$s = 240$ m	

Use equation of motion 4:

$$v^2 = u^2 + 2as$$

Substitute values:

$$(25 \text{ m s}^{-1})^2 = (55 \text{ m s}^{-1})^2 + 2 \times a \times 240 \text{ m}$$

so:

$$a = \frac{625 \text{ m}^2 \text{ s}^{-2} - 3025 \text{ m}^2 \text{ s}^{-2}}{2 \times 240 \text{ m}}$$

$$= \frac{-2400 \text{ m}^2 \text{ s}^{-2}}{480 \text{ m}}$$

$$= -5 \text{ m s}^{-2}$$

Now apply *F* = *ma*:

$$F = 3 \times 10^4 \text{ kg} \times -5 \text{ m s}^{-2}$$

$$= -1.5 \times 10^5 \text{ N}$$

The reverse thrust of the engines is 150 000 N (or 150 kN). (Why was the answer obtained from the equations negative?)

FOCUS — SAFETY IN CARS

Newton's laws of motion can be applied to any object that is accelerating, and can help us to understand some important aspects of passenger safety in cars.

When a car collides with another car (or with a stationary object), injuries to an occupant of the car are usually caused by the occupant colliding with the inside of the car, such as the steering wheel, the dashboard, the windscreen or some other part of the vehicle's structure. To minimise the injury to the driver and passengers in collisions, two basic techniques are used.

First, car occupants are restrained so that secondary collisions with the car interior are avoided as far as possible. Second, careful design is used to provide a rigid passenger cell. Around this cell, energy-absorbing features are built into the car body, so that the kinetic energy of the moving car or cars may be dissipated in inelastic processes during the collision.

Restraining measures

Secondary collisions between the car occupants and the car body may be prevented through the use of seat belts alone, or by a combination of seat belts and air bags. These safety devices are shown in figures 1.4.4 and 1.4.5. An air bag is a plastic bag contained in a small compartment within the steering wheel or the glove compartment. A control system inflates the bag explosively (using nitrogen gas) in the event of a deceleration greater than a preset level. The bag inflates into the face and chest of the driver and front seat passenger in about one second, braking the forward motion of both occupants.

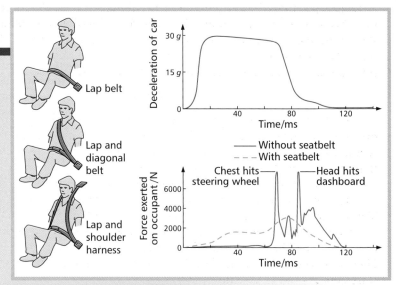

Figure 1.4.4 The lap and diagonal belt represents a good compromise between the lap and shoulder harness, which is the most effective practical restraining harness for ordinary cars, and the simple lap belt. Although a lap belt does restrain a passenger in the event of a collision, it does not prevent the upper part of the body moving forwards, which may lead to the passenger's head striking the interior of the car. The graph shows the force acting on a car occupant in a collision with and without belts.

Figure 1.4.5 An air bag inflates just as the car begins to decelerate, braking the forward motion of the occupants reasonably gently. Many cars also use belt tensioners in conjunction with air bags. At the same time as the air bags inflate, the tensioners take up any slack in the seat belts, further reducing the likelihood of secondary collisions.

Newton's second law and momentum

'Unstoppability'

What makes an object hard to stop? Is it harder to stop a bullet fired from a gun than to stop a lorry travelling along a motorway? Or are they both as difficult to stop as each other? What differences are there between these two situations?

The bullet will be hard to stop because it is travelling very fast (several hundred metres per second). The lorry will be hard to stop because it has a very large mass (30 000 kg or more). It might be reasonable to expect that a bullet travelling at 400 metres per second will be twice as hard to stop as one travelling at 200 metres per second. In the same way, a 30-tonne lorry might well be expected to be twice as hard to stop as a 15-tonne lorry. So our quick thought experiment leads us to suspect that 'unstoppability' could be related to mass and velocity like this:

$$\text{'Unstoppability'} \propto \text{velocity}$$

$$\text{'Unstoppability'} \propto \text{mass}$$

Combining these two relationships gives us:

$$\text{'Unstoppability'} \propto \text{mass} \times \text{velocity}$$

'Unstoppability' is not a very scientific term, although the idea seems quite reasonable in the context of our thought experiment. The scientific name for this quantity is **momentum** and it has the symbol p. An object's momentum is defined simply as the product of its mass and its velocity. Once again the constant of proportionality becomes one if we choose the right units. Using the SI system of units, mass is in kilograms and velocity is in metres per second, so the units of momentum are kilograms metres per second (kg m/s or kg m s^{-1}). Because velocity is a vector quantity, momentum is also a vector quantity.

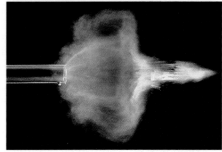

Figure 1.4.6 Which one of these would you rather stop?

Calculating momentum – worked example

Momentum is very significant in Newton's laws of motion, and is a useful quantity to be able to calculate – we shall see why shortly.

Consider two people travelling in opposite directions along the pavement, as in figure 1.4.7.

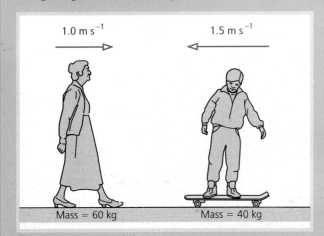

1.0 m s^{-1} 1.5 m s^{-1}

Mass = 60 kg   Mass = 40 kg

Figure 1.4.7

Calculating their momenta is quite straightforward. For the woman:

$$\text{Momentum}_{\text{woman}} = \text{mass}_{\text{woman}} \times \text{velocity}_{\text{woman}}$$
$$\text{to right} \qquad\qquad\qquad\qquad \text{to right}$$
$$= 60 \text{ kg} \times 1.0 \text{ m s}^{-1} = 60 \text{ kg m s}^{-1}$$

For the boy:

$$\text{Momentum}_{\text{boy}} = \text{mass}_{\text{boy}} \times \text{velocity}_{\text{boy}}$$
$$\text{to right} \qquad\qquad\qquad\qquad \text{to right}$$
$$= 40 \text{ kg} \times -1.5 \text{ m s}^{-1} = -60 \text{ kg m s}^{-1}$$

Notice that although the two people have different masses and different velocities, the *magnitude* of the woman's momentum is the same as the *magnitude* of the boy's momentum. But because they are moving towards each other, each person has momentum in the opposite *direction* to the other one, shown by the boy's velocity and momentum being negative. In this case we have chosen left to right to be the positive direction; we could equally have well have chosen right to left.

What do you think will happen if the two collide?

Rewriting Newton's second law

As we have seen, we may write acceleration as $\Delta v/\Delta t$. Using this, we can rewrite Newton's second law, the equation $F = ma$, as:

$$F = m \frac{\Delta v}{\Delta t}$$

This rewritten form of the equation is important because it allows us to generalise the equation to deal with a greater range of circumstances.

If we rearrange the equation it becomes:

$$F\Delta t = m\Delta v$$

$m\Delta v$ represents a change in momentum which happens when the velocity of an object changes. $F\Delta t$ is the force which acts to cause this change in momentum, multiplied by the time for which the force acts – this is called the **impulse**. The equation can now be simply stated in words or mathematical symbols:

Impulse = change in momentum

or:

$$F\Delta t = \Delta(mv) \quad \text{(sometimes called the \textbf{impulse momentum equation})}$$

or:

$$F = \frac{\Delta(mv)}{\Delta t}$$

= rate of change of momentum with time

Now our equation gives us a feel for what Newton's second law of motion is really about. Rather than thinking in terms of mass and acceleration, we should think in terms of *change of momentum* when considering the law. Although this may seem a small point, it means that the law can apply to situations where a change in mass as well as a change in velocity occurs, such as those in figure 1.4.9.

This form of Newton's second law now results in the proper definition of the newton as:

The force which causes a rate of change of momentum of one kilogram metre per second per second.

Figure 1.4.8 'Follow through' is important when hitting a golf ball. The impulse momentum equation helps us to understand why. Make Δt as large as possible (that is, have the club head in contact with the ball for as long as possible), and you can maximise $m\Delta v$ for a given value of F.

Figure 1.4.9 In all these situations a change in mass occurs together with a change in velocity. In which of them is the change in mass not negligible?

$F = ma$ and dimensions

Whenever we write down the value of a physical quantity, we represent it as the product of a number and a unit. Thus a distance may be 2 m (which means '2 multiplied by metres'), while a force may be 1.5 N ('1.5 multiplied by newtons').

Rather than confine ourselves to the SI system of units, it is sometimes useful to consider the **dimensions** that a physical quantity has. For example, length may be measured in metres, inches or miles, but it will always have the dimensions of *length*. Similarly mass may be measured in kilograms, stones or tons, but it will always have the dimensions of *mass*. By using a small number of base dimensions, we can examine the way in which physical quantities combine to form other quantities.

Restricting ourselves to the base dimensions of length and time (represented by the symbols L and T respectively), we can examine the way that distance and time combine to produce the quantities velocity and acceleration, for example:

$$[\text{Velocity}] = \frac{\text{distance}}{\text{time}} = \frac{L}{T} = L\,T^{-1} \quad \text{('velocity has dimensions } L\,T^{-1}\text{')}$$

$$[\text{Acceleration}] = \frac{\text{change in velocity}}{\text{time}}$$

$$= \frac{L\,T^{-1}}{T} = L\,T^{-2} \quad \text{('acceleration has dimensions } L\,T^{-2}\text{')}$$

These two examples tell us that, no matter what system of units we use, velocity is always found by dividing a length by a time, and that acceleration will always be found by dividing a change in velocity by a time.

In this way, force has the dimensions of momentum divided by the dimensions of time – in other words:

$$[\text{Force}] = \frac{M\,L\,T^{-1}}{T} = M\,L\,T^{-2}$$

Notice that the dimensions of force are the same as the dimensions of 'mass × acceleration', so that although the simplified form of Newton's second law $F = ma$ is just that – a simplification – there is no problem with the units or dimensions involved in the simplification. If this were not so, then the relationship would not be comparing like with like – rather like saying 'there are four apples in a kilogram of bananas'!

Using Newton's second law – worked examples

The impulse momentum equation is especially helpful where it may be difficult to calculate the acceleration involved in a change, as the following examples show.

Example 1

A jet of water from a hosepipe hits a wall perpendicular to the surface of the wall, as figure 1.4.10 shows. If 10 kg of water hit the wall each second, and the jet has a velocity of 25 m s^{-1}, what horizontal force does the water exert on the wall?

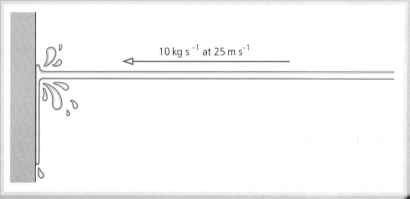

10 kg s^{-1} at 25 m s^{-1}

Figure 1.4.10

Use $F = \Delta(mv)/\Delta t$. To calculate $\Delta(mv)$ we shall need to make an assumption about the velocity of the water immediately after it has hit the wall. For simplicity, let us assume that the water simply falls vertically to the ground, so that its velocity has no horizontal component, and therefore its momentum can be taken as zero in this direction.

In 1 s, 10 kg of water hit the wall, and its velocity changes from 25 m s^{-1} to zero. Therefore:

$$\frac{\Delta(mv)}{\Delta t} = \frac{10 \text{ kg} \times (0 - 25 \text{ m s}^{-1})}{1 \text{ s}} = \frac{-250 \text{ kg m s}^{-1}}{1 \text{ s}} = -250 \text{ kg m s}^{-2}$$

Since $F = \Delta(mv)/\Delta t$, the wall must exert a force of 250 N on the water in order to cause this change of momentum, and Newton's third law tells us that the water must exert a force on the wall equal in size to this but opposite in direction. (The negative sign shows that the change of momentum is in the opposite direction to the initial velocity of the water. The wall exerts a force on the water to cause this change.) What would the force be if the water rebounded from the wall with a horizontal velocity of -12.5 m s^{-1}?

Example 2

A tennis player plays a ball which reaches her with a velocity of 20 m s^{-1}, figure 1.4.11. If the maximum force she can exert on the ball is 200 N, how long must the ball be in contact with the racquet in order for the player to return it to her opponent with a velocity of -30 m s^{-1}? (Mass of a tennis ball = 0.058 kg.)

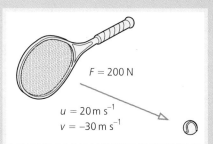

$F = 200 \text{ N}$

$u = 20 \text{ m s}^{-1}$
$v = -30 \text{ m s}^{-1}$

Figure 1.4.11

Use $F\Delta t = \Delta(mv)$, the impulse momentum equation:

$$\Delta(mv) = 0.058 \text{ kg} \times (-30 \text{ m s}^{-1} - 20 \text{ m s}^{-1})$$
$$= 0.058 \text{ kg} \times -50 \text{ m s}^{-1} = -2.9 \text{ kg m s}^{-1}$$

The negative sign here shows that the final momentum of the ball is in the opposite direction to its momentum before being struck. To find how long the ball was in contact with the racquet we need consider only the magnitude of the quantities, so $200 \text{ N} \times \Delta t = 2.9 \text{ kg m s}^{-1}$ and:

$$\Delta t = \frac{2.9 \text{ kg m s}^{-1}}{200 \text{ N}} = 0.0145 \text{ s}$$

So the ball must be in contact with the racquet head for at least 0.0145 s for the player to return it at -30 m s^{-1}. In practice the time will need to be longer than this – why?

Calculus and the impulse momentum equation

In a situation where a force causes a change of momentum (for example, where a tennis ball is hit by a tennis racquet), it is very rare for a constant force to be exerted. In this case, we may plot a graph of the force acting against time. For the real case and the 'ideal' case, the graphs might look like those in figure 1.4.12.

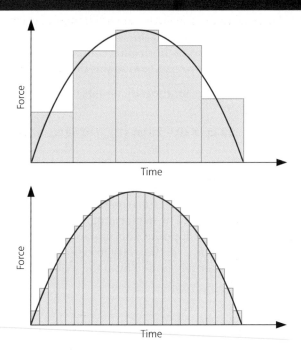

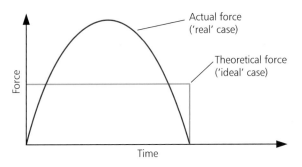

Figure 1.4.12

The impulse causing the change in momentum is $F\Delta t$, which is the area under the graph. We have already seen how dividing the area under a non-linear graph into a series of strips enables us to calculate the area under the graph, in the case of velocity–time graphs on page 10. This principle can be applied here too, but it can be made more useful by taking it a bit further.

By dividing the area under the graph into thin strips, as in figure 1.4.13, F is approximately constant for Δt, the thickness of the strip. The area of the strip is then $F\Delta t$, and the area under the graph is $\Sigma(F\Delta t)$. If we now let $\Delta t \rightarrow 0$ (the '→' means 'tend to' or 'approach'), this approximation becomes even better, and we can write:

$$\text{Change in momentum} = \int F \, \text{d}t$$

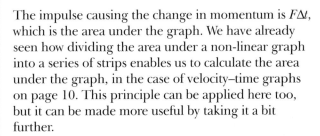

Figure 1.4.13

In doing this, we have effectively made the strips as thin as possible. The summation of the area of these strips is shown by using the symbol $\int$ (an elongated S for summation) rather than the Greek symbol Σ.

No obvious mathematical relationship exists between F and t in this example, and it serves only to underline the need to make Δt small enough to ensure that F is constant for the duration of each strip. We can then laboriously calculate the area of each strip individually and then add the whole lot together. But in cases where a mathematical relationship can be shown to exist, the technique of **integral calculus** is very powerful indeed, as we shall see later.

Conservation of momentum

Newton's second law of motion tells us about the way in which momentum changes when a force acts. Newton's third law of motion tells us about the forces that act on different bodies. Combining these two laws provides us with another law – the **law of conservation of momentum**.

Think about the Newton's third law pair of forces acting in the situation in figure 1.4.14. The law says that:

Force of man on boat = – force of boat on man

Figure 1.4.14 She knows what's about to happen here! But *why* does it happen?

Newton's second law tells us about the rate of change of momentum in each case:

Force of man on boat = rate of change of momentum of boat

and:

Force of boat on man = rate of change of momentum of man

Since the two forces are equal in size, we can write:

$$\textbf{Rate of change of momentum of boat} = \textbf{– rate of change of momentum of man}$$

or:

$$\frac{\textbf{Change of momentum of boat}}{\textbf{time taken}} = \frac{\textbf{– change of momentum of man}}{\textbf{time taken}}$$

The forces act for the same time (they are a pair – when one force ceases to act, so does the other), so this becomes:

Change of momentum of boat = – change of momentum of man

In symbols this can be written:

$$m_{\text{boat}} \times \Delta v_{\text{boat}} = m_{\text{man}} \times \times -\Delta v_{\text{man}}$$

A little thought shows that in this case, as m_{boat} and m_{man} are similar, the two move with $\Delta v_{\text{boat}} = -\Delta v_{\text{man}}$; in other words, with equal speeds but in opposite directions. (How does this compare with the situation if $m_{\text{boat}} \gg m_{\text{man}}$?)

Investigating the conservation of momentum

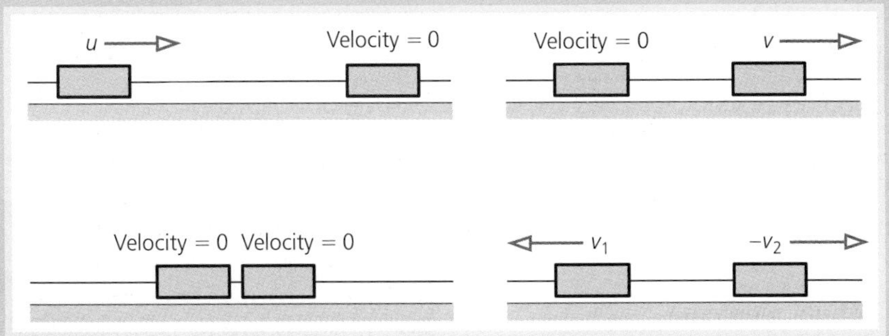

Figure 1.4.15

The investigation of conservation of momentum can be carried out using dynamics trolleys, although an air track is probably easier to use (figure 1.4.15). The ends of the experimental vehicles may be covered with Plasticine, or they can be fitted with magnets. If the end of each vehicle carries a magnet with (say) the north pole exposed, the vehicles will repel each other, whereas vehicles with Plasticine on the ends will stick together after colliding. Investigations may be done in which vehicles collide with each other, or in which two vehicles, held together against the repulsive force of two magnets, are released. The effect of varying the masses of the vehicles and their collision speeds can be studied. One such set of results is shown in table 1.4.2 and figure 1.4.16. For simplicity, all the vehicles used are identical.

	Collision – vehicles with magnets		Collision – vehicles with Plasticine		Explosion	
	Vehicle A	Vehicle B	Vehicle A	Vehicle B	Vehicle A	Vehicle B
Initial velocity/m s^{-1}	+0.13	0	+0.24	0	0	0
Final velocity/m s^{-1}	0	+0.13	+0.12	+0.12	+0.08	−0.08

Table 1.4.2

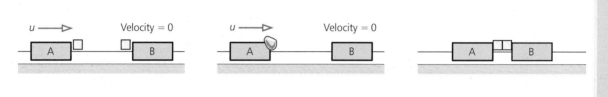

Figure 1.4.16

As a result of such investigations, a rule emerges which relates the masses and velocities of objects before and after interactions between them. Initially expressed in terms of mass and velocity, such a rule looks something like:

$$m_1u_1 + m_2u_2 = m_1v_1 + m_2v_2$$

where:

m_1 = **mass of object 1**

m_2 = **mass of object 2**

u_1 = **initial velocity of object 1**

v_2 = **final velocity of object 2**

and so on.

Investigations with dynamics trolleys or air track vehicles lead us to conclude that the relationship:

sum of initial momenta = sum of final momenta

can be applied, whether we are talking about *colliding* objects or about *explosions*, where an initially stationary set of objects is set in motion at one instant. This relationship is usually referred to as the law of conservation of momentum.

In general, the law of conservation of momentum can be stated as:

The total momentum of an isolated set of bodies acting on each other remains constant.

This applies whether we are considering two or more bodies in contact which begin to move apart, or two or more bodies which move together and collide – momentum is *always* conserved. Take care that when you apply the law you include *all* the bodies that are interacting. The motion of two vehicles colliding on an air track can be understood by applying the law – but if someone touches one of the vehicles just before or after the collision, the person becomes part of the system of interacting objects too, and must be included in the calculations!

Conservation of momentum in mathematical terms

Once again, we can write our expression for conservation of momentum as

$$\Sigma p_{\text{initial}} = \Sigma p_{\text{final}}$$

Applying the law of conservation of momentum – worked examples

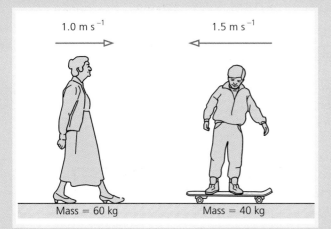

1.0 m s^{-1} 1.5 m s^{-1}

Mass = 60 kg   Mass = 40 kg

Figure 1.4.17

Some careful thought about the situation in figure 1.4.17 which you met earlier may have told you what happens next – but the law of conservation of momentum makes it easy.

The sum of the momenta here is zero (60 kg m s^{-1} + –60 kg m s^{-1}), so if the two people collide they will come to a dead halt, at least until they recover from the shock and use their leg muscles to exert a force on the pavement to move themselves apart!

Example 1

A car and van travelling in opposite directions along a road collide and stick together. From the marks on the road, police officers are able to work out that:
(1) the car was travelling due west at 12 m s^{-1}
(2) the two vehicles locked together and travelled due east along the road with an initial combined velocity of 20 m s^{-1}.

Given that mass$_{car}$ = 750 kg and mass$_{van}$ = 2000 kg, was the van driver breaking the 30 m.p.h. (= 13.6 m s^{-1}) speed limit before the collision?

Total momentum before collision = total momentum after collision

so:

$$m_{car} \times u_{car} + m_{van} \times u_{van} = (m_{car} + m_{van}) \times v_{combined}$$

Substituting values:

$$(750 \text{ kg} \times 12 \text{ m s}^{-1}) + (2000 \text{ kg} \times u_{van})$$
$$= (750 \text{ kg} + 2000 \text{ kg}) \times -20 \text{ m s}^{-1}$$

(Note the negative signs – after the collision the two vehicles travelled in the opposite direction to that in which the car was travelling and in the direction in which the van was travelling.)
Solving for u_{van}:

$$u_{van} = \frac{(750 \text{ kg} + 2000 \text{ kg}) \times -20 \text{ m s}^{-1} - (750 \text{ kg} \times 12 \text{ m s}^{-1})}{2000 \text{ kg}}$$

$$= -32 \text{ m s}^{-1}$$

In other words, the van was travelling due east at 32 m s^{-1} (about 70 m.p.h.) before the collision.

Example 2

A bullet with a mass of 50 g is fired from a gun with a mass of 5 kg. The bullet leaves the muzzle of the gun with a velocity of 300 m s^{-1} relative to the ground. What is the recoil velocity of the gun?

Total momentum before collision
= total momentum after collision

so:

$$0 = m_{bullet} \times v_{bullet} + m_{gun} \times v_{gun}$$

Substituting values:

$$0 = 0.05 \text{ kg} \times 300 \text{ m s}^{-1} + 5 \text{ kg} \times v_{gun}$$

Rearranging:

$$v_{gun} = \frac{-0.05 \text{ kg} \times 300 \text{ m s}^{-1}}{5 \text{ kg}}$$

$$= -3 \text{ m s}^{-1}$$

So the gun recoils (in the opposite direction to that in which the bullet travels) with a velocity of 3 m s^{-1} relative to the ground.

SUMMARY

- Practical investigations show that the relationship between force, mass and acceleration is $F = kma$, or $F = ma$ if SI units are used. This is **Newton's second law of motion**.
- The SI unit of force is the *newton*.
- The **momentum** p of an object is the product of its mass and its velocity, $p = mv$.
- Newton's second law can be written as $F\Delta t = \Delta(mv)$, sometimes called the **impulse momentum equation**. $F\Delta t$ is the **impulse**, or the force that acts to change the momentum ($\Delta(mv)$), multiplied by the time for which the force acts.
- The **newton** is defined as the force which causes a rate of change of momentum of 1 kg m s^{-2}.
- The **law of conservation of momentum** states that the total momentum of a closed set of bodies acting on each other remains constant.

EXAMPLE

A cardboard box and its contents (total mass = 30 kg) are pushed across a rough floor at a steady 0.8 m s^{-1}. When the box is no longer pushed, it comes to rest in a distance of 0.5 m. What frictional force acts on the box while it is being pushed?

Once the push on the box is removed, the only force acting on the box is the frictional force. This opposes the motion of the box and causes it to slow down. As we know the mass of the box we can calculate the size of the frictional force if we know the acceleration of the box. We know that:

$u = 0.8$ m s^{-1} $v = 0$ $s = 0.5$ m

Therefore we can use:

$$v^2 = u^2 + 2as$$

Substituting known values:

$$0^2 = (0.8 \text{ m s}^{-1})^2 + 2 \times a \times 0.5 \text{ m}$$

Rearranging:

$$a = \frac{0 - (0.8 \text{ m s}^{-1})^2}{2 \times 0.5 \text{ m}}$$
$$= -0.64 \text{ m s}^{-2}$$

The box slows down (indicated by the negative sign) at a rate of 0.64 m s^{-2}. This acceleration is caused by the frictional force between the box and the floor. Applying Newton's second law to this gives:

$$F = ma$$
$$= 30 \text{ kg} \times -0.64 \text{ m s}^{-2}$$
$$= -19.2 \text{ N}$$

The frictional force acting on the box is 19 N to 2 SF (any greater precision than this would not be justified from the data we have). The negative sign for this force shows that it acts in the opposite direction to the initial velocity of the box.

QUESTIONS

(Assume $g = 10$ m s^{-2}.)

1 A railway locomotive with a mass of 70 tonnes accelerates at a rate of 1 m s^{-2}. What force does the engine of the locomotive exert?

2 A 60 kg woman involved in a car accident is accelerated by her seat belt from 14 m s^{-1} to rest in 0.15 s.
   a What is the average horizontal force acting on her?
   b How does this force compare with her weight?

3 An archer pulls back the string of a bow with a force of 200 N.
   a If the two halves of the string on either side of the archer's hand make an angle of 120° with each other, what is the tension in the bow string?

   b What acceleration will this cause if the archer uses an arrow with a mass of 75 g?

4 A rocket is about to blast off from a space station in deep space. At lift-off, the mass of a rocket is 2.45×10^6 kg, while at burn-out, all the rocket's fuel is spent and its mass has fallen to 7.5×10^4 kg. Assuming that the rocket's engines develop a constant thrust of 3.3×10^7 N:
   a What is the acceleration of the rocket at lift-off?
   b What is the acceleration of the rocket just before burn-out?

5 A car runs out of fuel while travelling at a steady 25 m s^{-1} up a slope which makes an angle of 30° to the horizontal. How far up the slope does the car travel before coming to rest and then rolling down again?

6 The Earth has a mass of approximately 6.0×10^{24} kg and travels round the Sun with an instantaneous velocity of about 3.0×10^{4} m s^{-1}. What is the momentum of the Earth?

7 a What is the momentum of a 1200 kg car travelling at 30 m s^{-1}?

  b What velocity would a football with a mass of 0.45 kg need in order to have the same momentum?

8 In an unlikely situation, a bird with a mass of 0.1 kg lands on a roller skate with a mass of 0.4 kg. If the velocity of the bird as it lands is 2 m s^{-1} at an angle of 45° to the vertical, with what speed do the bird and the roller skate move off together?

9 Multiflash photography suggests that when a golf club hits a golf ball (mass = 0.045 kg) the two remain in contact for about 10^{-3} s while the ball acquires a speed of about 70 m s^{-1}. Estimate the force exerted by the club on the ball.

10 A ship with a mass of 3.0×10^{4} tonnes steaming at 5 m s^{-1} due north strikes an iceberg with a mass of 6.0×10^{6} tonnes drifting due east with a velocity of 0.5 m s^{-1}. If the ship and the iceberg remain locked together after the collision, what is their velocity after colliding?

11 A fire hose sprays out water in a jet at a rate of 5 kg s^{-1} with a velocity of 30 m s^{-1}. What is the recoil force on the hose?

12 A pile driver is used to drive steel piles or girders into the ground. One such machine consists of a 100 kg piece of steel which is raised to a height of 3.0 m above the top of a pile having a mass of 1000 kg, and then released. On hitting the pile the steel drives it 0.25 m further into the ground. Calculate:

  a the speed of the steel just before it strikes the pile

  b the speed with which the pile starts to move

  c the frictional force of the ground acting on the pile.

13 Inside a Mexican jumping bean is a small insect larva which jumps up and down. How does this make the bean jump?

So far we have examined the laws of motion described by Newton, and used these ideas together with those which began their development with Galileo to describe and explain the motion of objects.

The laws and rules which come from these sources are powerful tools to use in the investigation of the interactions between objects. No description of the tools that physicists use in this way would be complete without an introduction (at this stage a short and incomplete one, to which we will return in section 2) to one of the most powerful ideas that physicists have devised – the concept of **energy**.

The concept of energy

The law of conservation of energy

We commonly think of energy as coming in a number of forms, such as chemical, electrical, kinetic, and so on. Simple investigations of energy and its forms lead us to conclude that although energy may appear in different forms when a change occurs (for example, when a battery containing stored chemical energy causes an electric current containing electrical energy to flow through a wire, lighting a light bulb and producing thermal energy and light energy), the total amount of energy remains constant. Figure 1.5.1 illustrates this point. This rule has the status of a law in physics, and is called the **law of conservation of energy**. This is often expressed as:

Energy cannot be created or destroyed.

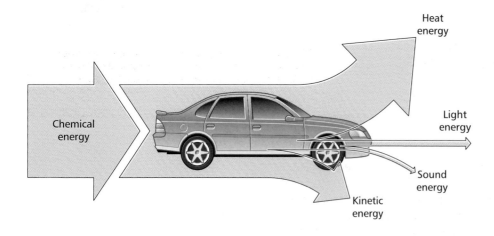

Figure 1.5.1 Energy transfers in an accelerating car. The total amount of energy in a system remains constant – note that the car here is *not* the whole system but a part of it. Where does the energy from the fuel eventually end up?

The law of conservation of energy, together with the idea of energy existing in different forms, make up an area of physics that is the most powerful and the most misunderstood of all. Essentially, the concept of energy is a *tool* for understanding and explaining the way the Universe behaves – just like any other law or theory of physics.

Laws and theories

At its simplest, a **law** of physics can be thought of as a summary of observations that physicists have made. A law is of course built on a limited number of observations, so that it is necessary for physicists to *assume* that it is possible to predict the behaviour of the Universe in the future based on observations made in the past. This is an assumption common to the whole of science, and the success of science as an area of study certainly seems to justify it.

A law supplies us with information about *how* the physical world may be expected to behave based upon past experience, but it does not tell us anything about *why* the physical world behaves in this way. For example, the 'energy law' we have just met says that we cannot create or destroy energy, but does not explain very much about what energy actually is or why it cannot be created or destroyed.

It is the job of *theories* in science to tell us about the behaviour of things in rather more depth. Strangely, scientists and philosophers find it very hard to agree on the way in which scientific theories come about, although most would accept that they are best described as being 'invented' (that is, made up by people) rather than simply 'discovered'.

One way in which theories are produced, based on the ideas of the philosopher Sir Karl Popper, runs as follows. A scientist wishing to explain something about the behaviour of the world will formulate a tentative idea, called at this stage a *hypothesis*. This hypothesis must be based on existing scientific knowledge, but as long as it does not contradict this knowledge, it can be as bold and imaginative as the scientist wishes. The scientist then tests the hypothesis by carrying out a number of *experiments*.

If it survives this testing, an account of the hypothesis and the tests it has survived is then published in a scientific journal so that other scientists can read about it and decide whether it is true or not – a process called *peer review*. Hypotheses that survive the process of peer review become accepted scientific knowledge – that is, they become theories.

It is important not to confuse the use of the term 'theory' in a scientific context with its use in everyday life, where it is often used to mean 'guess'. (For example, I may have a 'theory' about why a particular football team is unlikely to win any competitions next year.) A theory in science is not a guess, but a very well-established framework that explains many observations and experimental results. A good theory will produce new hypotheses that can be tested, and so on.

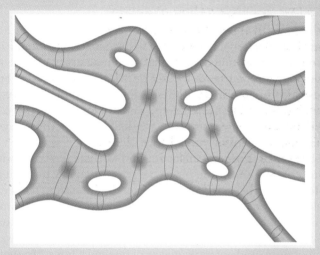

Figure 1.5.2 Superstring theory suggests that we live in a universe in which there are 10 dimensions, six of which are 'coiled up' on each other. This is a very bold and imaginative theory, but it is based on far more than simple guesswork.

Energy transformations

The ideas behind the concept of energy represent a model for understanding the way the world (and the whole Universe) behaves. We talk about chemical energy being transferred to kinetic energy by a petrol engine. This is a quick way of saying that the petrol – because of the way the bonds in its molecules are arranged – may be burnt in an engine to produce movement, and that in doing this there is a relationship between the amount of petrol used and the movement produced. We do not mean that the engine literally, as if by magic, takes something out of the petrol and uses it to turn the wheels.

Consider the example of winding a grandfather clock shown in figure 1.5.3. The clock is driven by a descending weight. This weight can be regarded as a source of energy, in just the same way as the spring in an old-fashioned watch or the battery in a modern digital watch. Where does this energy come from in the case of the grandfather clock?

A scientific understanding of the situation (that is, one that fits with physicists' current understanding of the Universe) is that once the weight has been raised the person's muscles contain *less* of the chemicals that can be used to do something useful (like raise a weight). The raised weight, however, now has something which will let it do *more* than it could before. Energy is simply the 'accounting system' which we use to keep track of a system's ability to do something useful – rather like we use money to keep track of our ability to buy things.

An alternative explanation says that *chemical energy* in the person's muscles has been used to lift the weight, and that as a result, the chemical energy has been transformed into *potential energy* stored in the raised weight. This implies that something has gone from the person's muscles into the weight and has changed in some way – 'chemical energy has been transformed into potential energy'. Whilst this might seem to be a satisfactory explanation, it is not, because of the idea of energy transformation that it uses. A much better term to use is **energy transfer**. Figure 1.5.4 shows how energy transfers can be compared to transferring money.

Figure 1.5.3

Energy, work and power

Transferring energy – heating and working

Transferring energy is compared with transferring money in figure 1.5.4. There are many ways of transferring money (cash, cheque, credit card, postal order, etc.), but far fewer ways of transferring energy. In this section we are concerned only with *two* of these – the ways of transfer which physicists call *heating* and *working*. (In section 2 we shall look much more closely at heating and working, while in section 3 we shall look at a third way of transferring energy – by means of waves.)

The difference between heating and working lies in the way that energy is transferred. If we heat an object, we transfer energy to it using a temperature difference, perhaps by means of a flame. If we wish to transfer energy without making use of a temperature difference, we do it by doing work – for example, by lifting an object off the floor onto a table. The terms 'heat' and 'work' therefore describe energy which has been transferred in a particular way – by means of a temperature gradient or by means of moving a force. We shall return to the topics of heat and work in section 2.4 when we look at the laws of thermodynamics.

Figure 1.5.4 When you pay a cheque into the bank you increase your ability to buy things by transferring money into your account. When you pay for something by cheque later, you decrease it again – but no actual money changes hands in the transfer. In the same way, energy may be transferred – the energy in a system can be changed without anything actually flowing into or out of it. This is why it is better to talk about energy being *transferred* rather than *transformed*.

Transferring energy using a temperature difference – heating.

Transferring energy without using a temperature difference – working.

Figure 1.5.5 In many cases it is much easier to say 'heat' than 'energy transferred by means of a temperature difference' or 'work done' rather than 'energy transferred by means of moving a force'.

Work and the units of energy

As we have just seen, when energy is transferred it may be transferred by doing **work**, for example when electrical energy drives an electric motor. The amount of work done is calculated simply as:

Work done = force × distance moved in direction of force

This simple relationship leads to the definition of the unit of energy, in the same way as Newton's second law of motion led to the definition of the unit of force. In this case, the SI unit of energy, the **joule** (J), is defined as being the energy transferred when a force of one newton is displaced a distance of one metre, that is, 1 J = 1 N m.

Although in calculating work we are multiplying two vectors together (force and displacement), the result is a scalar. Energy has magnitude only.

If the force and the displacement are in different directions, the force must be resolved in order to calculate the work done. Figure 1.5.6 shows how this is done.

Kinetic and potential energy

We are used to saying that an object has **gravitational potential energy** when it is raised through a distance Δh. In this case we write:

$$E_\text{p} = mg\Delta h$$

where m is again the object's mass and g is the gravitational field strength of the Earth. Strictly $mg\Delta h$ is the *change* in the object's potential energy – we shall return to this point in section 5.

In the same way, we talk about a moving object possessing **kinetic energy**, and write the amount of this energy as:

$$E_\text{k} = \tfrac{1}{2}mv^2$$

where m is the object's mass and v its velocity.

The idea of work as a means of transferring energy by moving a force lies behind both these expressions for the energy an object has in a particular situation. The grandfather clock example (see figure 1.5.7) can show us this.

When the weight in the clock is raised, a force equal and opposite to the gravitational force of attraction on the weight is applied to it. Therefore the

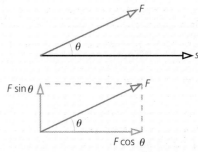

The force is resolved so that one component ($F \cos \theta$) lies in the same direction as the displacement. This is the component of the force that is involved in transferring energy. The component of the force perpendicular to the displacement does *no* work, as it does not move in the direction in which it is acting.

Figure 1.5.6 In this case, work done $= (F \cos \theta) \times s$.

The dimensions of energy

The definition of the joule enables us to calculate the dimensions of energy:

$$[\text{J}] = [\text{N m}] = [\text{kg m s}^{-2}\text{ m}]$$
$$= [\text{kg m}^2\text{ s}^{-2}] = \text{M L}^2\text{ T}^{-2}$$

So energy has dimensions $\text{M L}^2\text{ T}^{-2}$.

work done on it (the energy transferred by means of moving a force) is equal to the gravitational force on the weight multiplied by the distance it is raised.

Work done $= W \times \Delta h$
$$= mg\Delta h$$
$$= \textbf{gravitational potential energy stored in weight } (E_p)$$

This potential energy may be released slowly as the weight does work on the clock mechanism (as it transfers energy to the mechanism by means of a moving force), driving the hands round.

If the wire supporting the weight breaks, the weight will fall. Instead of doing work on the clock mechanism, the weight now does work on itself (because the weight is not connected to anything, the energy transferred by the moving force has only one place to go – it stays with the weight). The potential energy of the weight will be transferred to kinetic energy. In this case:

$v^2 = u^2 + 2as = 2a\Delta h$ **(as the weight falls from rest, $u = 0$, through Δh)**

so:

$$\Delta h = \frac{v^2}{2a}$$

Now:

Kinetic energy gained = work done on falling weight

$$= F \times \Delta h$$

$$= F \times \frac{v^2}{2a}$$

Since $F = ma$:

Kinetic energy gained $= ma \times \dfrac{v^2}{2a}$

$$= \tfrac{1}{2}mv^2$$

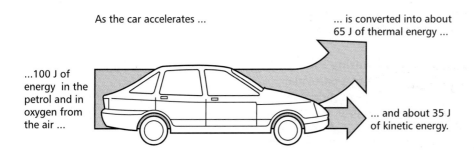

Figure 1.5.7

Efficiency

The idea of **efficiency** is useful when considering energy transfers. With some thought it comes as little surprise to find that it is often impossible to take all the energy in an energy store (for example, a litre of petrol) and transfer it so that it does something useful. (This process may involve work, but as the box on the opposite page shows, it can involve heating instead.) Figure 1.5.8 shows the energy transfer in this situation.

As the car accelerates ...

... is converted into about 65 J of thermal energy ...

...100 J of energy in the petrol and in oxygen from the air ...

... and about 35 J of kinetic energy.

Figure 1.5.8

Clearly this process is not 100% efficient, since in burning petrol in a car engine we want to end up with as much kinetic energy as possible – we certainly do not want thermal energy. The efficiency of this process can be calculated as:

$$\text{Efficiency} = \frac{\text{useful energy got out (the kinetic energy)}}{\text{energy put in}}$$

$$= \frac{35 \text{ J}}{100 \text{ J}} \times 100\%$$

$$= 35\%$$

If we think of a machine or a process as a box which has energy going into it and energy coming out of it, as in figure 1.5.9, then we define efficiency in the way we have just seen, that is:

$$\text{Efficiency} = \frac{\text{useful energy output}}{\text{energy input}} \times 100\%$$

Note that efficiency depends on the definition of 'useful energy output'. In the example of the car, the useful output was defined as kinetic energy.

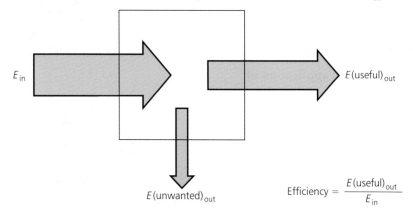

$$\text{Efficiency} = \frac{E(\text{useful})_{\text{out}}}{E_{\text{in}}}$$

Figure 1.5.9

Since efficiency is calculated by dividing one quantity in joules by another also in joules, it has no units – it is simply a ratio. It may, of course, be expressed as a percentage by multiplying the ratio by 100%.

We shall see in section 2 that there are laws of physics which govern every aspect of energy transfers and their efficiency, in the same way that Newton's laws of motion govern the behaviour of masses and forces.

Calculating efficiency – worked example

A central heating boiler supplies 250 kJ of energy to hot water flowing through the boiler. In order to supply this energy to the water, the gas burnt in the boiler must produce 400 kJ of energy. What is the efficiency of the boiler?

$$\text{Efficiency} = \frac{\text{useful energy output}}{\text{energy input}} \times 100\%$$

$$= \frac{250 \times 10^3 \text{ J}}{400 \times 10^3 \text{ J}} \times 100\%$$

$$= 62.5\%$$

Power

The physical definition of **power** relates energy transferred to time taken. So:

$$\text{Power} = \frac{\text{energy transferred}}{\text{time taken}}$$

Power may be measured in joules per second (J s^{-1}) in the SI system. The unit J s^{-1} is also known as the **watt** (W).

Since we refer in many cases to the power developed when work is done, power may also be defined as:

$$\text{Power} = \frac{\text{work done}}{\text{time taken}}$$

If a force is being moved at a steady rate, provided we know the velocity at which the force is moving and the size of the force, we can calculate the power:

Work done = force × distance moved in direction of force

and:

Power = work done/time taken

so:

$$\text{Power} = \text{force} \times \frac{\text{distance moved in direction of force}}{\text{time taken}}$$

$$= \text{force} \times \frac{\text{velocity at which the point of application of the force is moving}}{}$$

In symbols:

$$P = Fv$$

Figure 1.5.10 The idea of power is common in everyday life. Physicists use the word 'power' to mean much the same thing as we understand by this example.

Calculations involving power – worked examples

Example 1

An athlete with a mass of 75 kg runs up a steep slope, rising a vertical distance of 30 m in 50 s. Neglecting the effect of any drag forces acting on the athlete, what power must his leg muscles develop in order to do this? (Assume g = 10 N kg^{-1}.)

The athlete's muscles must supply a force to lift him through a vertical distance of 30 m. Assuming that this is done at a steady rate, then the force exerted will be equal in size to the athlete's weight. So:

Work done = weight × vertical distance raised

$$= 75 \text{ kg} \times 10 \text{ N kg}^{-1} \times 30 \text{ m}$$

$$= 22\,500 \text{ J}$$

and:

$$\text{Power developed} = \frac{22\,500 \text{ J}}{50 \text{ s}} = 450 \text{ W}$$

Example 2

A car towing a caravan travels along at a steady speed of 20 m s^{-1}. If the force exerted by the engine is 2 kN, what is the power output of the engine?

$$\text{Power} = \text{force} \times \text{velocity}$$

$$= 2000 \text{ N} \times 20 \text{ m s}^{-1}$$

$$= 40\,000 \text{ W}$$

The power output of the engine is 40 kW.

Horsepower

The power output of car engines is often expressed in **horsepower** – a method of measuring the rate of doing work dating from before the industrial revolution. 1 HP ≈ 750 W, so the power output of the car engine in this example is about 53 HP. In the first example, what is the power output of the athlete's leg muscles in HP?

THE PHYSICS OF FLYING BIRDS

People have been inspired for thousands of years by the sight of birds in apparently effortless gliding flight. But a gliding bird must support its body weight by means of the lift from its wings. Each wing has a centre of lift, through which the lift can be said to act (this is just like the idea of centre of gravity, which we met on page 41). This centre of lift acts at some distance from the bird's body (figure 1.5.12a) – so you can experience what it is like to be a gliding bird by supporting your weight using your elbows as they rest on two filing cabinets (figure 1.5.12b). A few minutes of this activity will convince you that the force needed to keep your upper arms level makes gliding far from effortless!

Figure 1.5.13 shows the vertical and horizontal forces that act on a bird in level flight. Over a whole number of wingbeats, the thrust force balances the drag force, while the bird's weight is balanced by a lift force from the wings. The magnitude of the drag force acting on a bird (or any other body) travelling through the air can be calculated from the relationship

$$\mathbf{drag} = \tfrac{1}{2}AC_D\rho v^2$$

where A is the cross-sectional area of the bird as seen from the front, v is its speed, ρ is the density of the air, and C_D is a constant called the **drag coefficient**. The drag coefficient can be calculated using fairly complex formulae (or even computer models) – measured values range from 0.25 for birds like geese and swans to 0.40 for birds like pigeons.

But a bird does not need to flap its wings in order to fly! The movement of air over the wings of a bird produces a lift force which is sufficient to oppose the bird's weight and keep it up. Figure 1.5.14 explains how this lift force comes from the way in which air flows around the bird's wing. The magnitude of the lift can be calculated from

$$\mathbf{lift} = \tfrac{1}{2}SC_L\rho v^2$$

where S is the surface area of the underside of the bird's wing, v is the bird's speed, ρ is the density of the air, and C_L is a constant called the **lift coefficient**. Wind tunnel tests show that lift coefficients for both gliding pigeons and falcons are about 1.6.

Figure 1.5.11

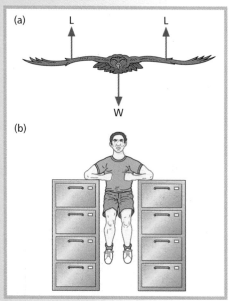

Figure 1.5.12 A gliding bird supports its weight using the lift produced by its wings.

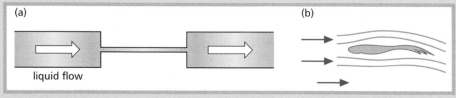

Figure 1.5.14 (a) Imagine a liquid flowing through the narrow tube between the two thicker tubes. The volume of liquid flowing through the thin tube each second must be the same as the volume flowing through the thick tube, so it must flow faster in the thin tube. To accelerate the liquid as it moves from the thick tube into the thin tube, there must be a pressure difference, with another pressure difference as the liquid travels from the thin tube into the thick tube to slow it down again. Measurements confirm that these pressure differences do indeed exist, and that the pressure in a fluid decreases as its rate of flow increases. (b) A bird's wing develops lift by deflecting the airflow over it in such a way that air above the wing is speeded up relative to air below it. The air below the wing therefore exerts a greater pressure on the wing than the air above it – and so lift is produced. This is **Bernoulli's principle**.

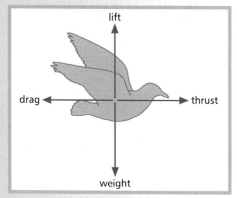

Figure 1.5.13 The forces acting on a bird in level flight.

Collisions – momentum and energy

The case of the missing energy

When two or more objects collide, energy must clearly play a part in what happens, as well as momentum. Simple investigations, such as those described in section 1.4, show that in all circumstances momentum is conserved. What about energy?

Car 1:
Mass of car and occupants = 825 kg
Velocity just prior to collision = 5 m s⁻¹
Velocity immediately after collision = 1 m s⁻¹

Car 2:
Mass of car and occupants = 1100 kg
Velocity just prior to collision = 0 m s⁻¹
Velocity immediately after collision = 3 m s⁻¹

Figure 1.5.15

In the collision in figure 1.5.15, momentum has been conserved:

$$\sum p_{\text{initial}} = 825 \text{ kg} \times 5 \text{ m s}^{-1} + 1100 \text{ kg} \times 0 \text{ m s}^{-1}$$
$$= 4125 \text{ kg m s}^{-1}$$
$$\sum p_{\text{final}} = 825 \text{ kg} \times 1 \text{ m s}^{-1} + 1100 \text{ kg} \times 3 \text{ m s}^{-1}$$
$$= 4125 \text{ kg m s}^{-1}$$
$$= \sum p_{\text{initial}}$$

Where has the energy gone in this collision?

$$E_{\text{k}}(\text{initial}) = \tfrac{1}{2} \times 825 \text{ kg} \times (5 \text{ m s}^{-1})^2 + \tfrac{1}{2} \times 1100 \text{ kg} \times (0 \text{ m s}^{-1})^2$$
$$= 10.3 \text{ kJ}$$
$$E_{\text{k}}(\text{final}) = \tfrac{1}{2} \times 825 \text{ kg} \times (1 \text{ m s}^{-1})^2 + \tfrac{1}{2} \times 1100 \text{ kg} \times (3 \text{ m s}^{-1})^2$$
$$= 5.4 \text{ kJ}$$

There is less kinetic energy after the collision than there was before. According to the law of conservation of energy, this energy cannot simply have vanished – so where has it gone? One look at the cars after the collision tells us the answer to this question. Some of the energy that the first car had before the collision has done work on the bodies of the two cars – with the inevitable result!

Collisions like this are called **inelastic collisions**. In inelastic collisions, although the total amount of momentum is conserved, the total amount of kinetic energy is not. This does not mean that energy is not conserved in inelastic collisions – simply that some of the energy that the bodies had before the collision ends up in different forms, particularly thermal energy.

The inelastic collisions resulting from careful modern car design help to make car accidents less dangerous nowadays than they were many years ago, despite greatly increased speeds and road traffic volume.

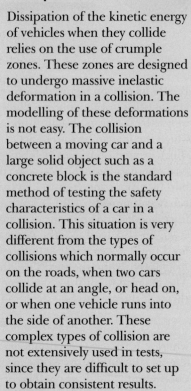

Crumple zones

Dissipation of the kinetic energy of vehicles when they collide relies on the use of crumple zones. These zones are designed to undergo massive inelastic deformation in a collision. The modelling of these deformations is not easy. The collision between a moving car and a large solid object such as a concrete block is the standard method of testing the safety characteristics of a car in a collision. This situation is very different from the types of collisions which normally occur on the roads, when two cars collide at an angle, or head on, or when one vehicle runs into the side of another. These complex types of collision are not extensively used in tests, since they are difficult to set up to obtain consistent results.

When two moving cars collide, the energy is dissipated in the two vehicles according to their mass and the 'crushability' of each car. Analysing the energy distribution in such collisions shows that the car which has the softer, more easily deformed body dissipates more energy (and so undergoes more damage). In addition, the changes in velocity during a collision between a small vehicle and a large one are much greater for the small vehicle than for the large one. Because of these facts it is desirable that a large vehicle should be designed with a soft, yielding body so that the amount of energy to be absorbed by a small vehicle in collision with it is not too great. Such a design feature has obvious advantages for pedestrian and cyclist safety as well.

Bouncing back

Again, in figure 1.5.16, momentum has been conserved:

$$\Sigma p_{\text{initial}} = 500 \text{ kg} \times 0 \text{ m s}^{-1} + 1000 \text{ kg} \times 3 \text{ m s}^{-1}$$

$$= 3000 \text{ kg m s}^{-1}$$

$$\Sigma p_{\text{final}} = 500 \text{ kg} \times 4 \text{ m s}^{-1} + 1000 \text{ kg} \times 1 \text{ m s}^{-1}$$

$$= 3000 \text{ kg m s}^{-1}$$

$$= \Sigma p_{\text{initial}}$$

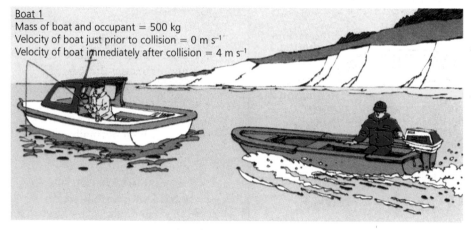

Boat 1
Mass of boat and occupant = 500 kg
Velocity of boat just prior to collision = 0 m s⁻¹
Velocity of boat immediately after collision = 4 m s⁻¹

Boat 2
Mass of boat and occupant = 1000 kg
Velocity of boat just prior to collision = 3 m s⁻¹
Velocity of boat immediately after collision = 1 m s⁻¹

Figure 1.5.16

Where has the energy gone in this collision?

$$E_k(\text{initial}) = \tfrac{1}{2} \times 500 \text{ kg} \times (0 \text{ m s}^{-1})^2 + \tfrac{1}{2} \times 1000 \text{ kg} \times (3 \text{ m s}^{-1})^2$$

$$= 4.5 \text{ kJ}$$

$$E_k(\text{final}) = \tfrac{1}{2} \times 500 \text{ kg} \times (4 \text{ m s}^{-1})^2 + \tfrac{1}{2} \times 1000 \text{ kg} \times (1 \text{ m s}^{-1})^2$$

$$= 4.5 \text{ kJ}$$

$$= E_k(\text{initial})$$

This time there is no problem tracking down the energy – as much kinetic energy is carried away from the collision by the two boats as was brought to it by the first boat. Instead of energy being dissipated as thermal energy in this collision, any work done in deforming the fenders on the boats has been returned to the boats as kinetic energy after the collision. Deformations like this are referred to as **elastic**, so this sort of collision is known as an **elastic collision** – and kinetic energy *is* conserved in elastic collisions, as we have just seen.

Elastic collisions are relatively rare outside the laboratory, though colliding snooker balls is one example. Careful design usually means that large objects such as cars are not involved in elastic collisions – question 8 on page 73 may help you to decide why this is.

Modelling elastic collisions with mathematics

Mathematics is commonly used as a tool in physics in order to model a situation so that it can be understood. A good model (one which has stood up to testing) may then be used to make predictions about new situations. One use of mathematics in this way concerns the behaviour of objects in perfectly elastic collisions.

In a perfectly elastic collision in one dimension (that is, along a straight line), conservation of momentum and conservation of energy completely determine the final velocities of the colliding bodies. The relationships between initial and final velocities, and how these are influenced by the masses of the colliding objects, can be explored using these two laws of conservation as follows.

The situation concerns two masses m_1 and m_2. Mass m_2 is initially stationary, and is then struck by mass m_1. The initial and final velocities of m_1 are u_1 and v_1 respectively, and the final velocity of m_2 is v_2.

Applying conservation of momentum:

$$m_1 u_1 = m_1 v_1 + m_2 v_2 \qquad \textbf{(equation 1)}$$

This may be rewritten as:

$$m_1(u_1 - v_1) = m_2 v_2 \qquad \textbf{(equation 2)}$$

Applying conservation of energy (the collision is perfectly elastic):

$$\tfrac{1}{2}m_1 u_1^2 = \tfrac{1}{2}m_1 v_1^2 + \tfrac{1}{2}m_2 v_2^2 \qquad \textbf{(equation 3)}$$

This may also be rewritten:

$$\tfrac{1}{2}m_1(u_1^2 - v_1^2) = \tfrac{1}{2}m_2 v_2^2$$

or:

$$\tfrac{1}{2}m_1(u_1 - v_1)(u_1 + v_1) = \tfrac{1}{2}m_2 v_2^2 \qquad \textbf{(equation 4)}$$

Dividing equation 4 by equation 2 gives:

$$\frac{\tfrac{1}{2}m_1(u_1 - v_1)(u_1 + v_1)}{m_1(u_1 - v_1)} = \frac{\tfrac{1}{2}m_2 v_2^2}{m_2 v_2}$$

or:

$$u_1 + v_1 = v_2 \qquad \textbf{(equation 5)}$$

Equations 1 and 5 form a pair of simultaneous equations:

$$m_1 u_1 = m_1 v_1 + m_2 v_2 \qquad \textbf{(equation 1)}$$

$$u_1 + v_1 = v_2 \qquad \textbf{(equation 5)}$$

Substituting $(u_1 + v_1)$ for v_2 in equation 1 gives:

$$m_1 u_1 = m_1 v_1 + m_2(u_1 + v_1)$$

or:

$$m_1 u_1 - m_2 u_1 = m_1 v_1 + m_2 v_1$$

This factorises to:

$$u_1(m_1 - m_2) = v_1(m_1 + m_2)$$

which may then be rearranged:

$$v_1 = \frac{(m_1 - m_2)}{(m_1 + m_2)} u_1 \qquad \textbf{(equation 6)}$$

In similar way, substituting for v_1 in equation 1 produces the result:

$$v_2 = \frac{2m_1}{(m_1 + m_2)} u_1 \qquad \text{(equation 7)}$$

This pair of equations shows a very important relationship between velocities and masses of colliding objects.

- Case 1: both objects have the same mass.
  If $m_1 = m_2$ then $m_1 - m_2 = 0$. This gives $v_1 = 0$ from equation 6.
  Similary, if $m_1 = m_2$ then $m_1 + m_2 = 2m_1$. This gives $v_2 = u_1$ from equation 7.
  In others words, in a perfectly elastic collision between two equal masses in which one mass is initially at rest, the stationary mass moves off with the same velocity as the incoming mass, while the incoming mass remains stationary after the collision. An example of this type of collision occurs between two snooker balls.
- Case 2: $m_1 \ll m_2$, that is, a very light object collides with a very massive stationary object. In case $(m_1 - m_2) \approx -m_2$, $(m_1 + m_2) \approx m_2$, and $m_1/(m_1 + m_2) \approx 0$. Therefore equation 6 gives $v_1 \approx -u_1$ and equation 7 gives $v_2 \approx 0$.
  This shows that the light object rebounds with a velocity equal in size and opposite in direction to its incoming velocity, while the massive object remains stationary. An example of this is a hard ball (a 'superball' for example) rebounding from a brick wall – see question 6 on page 73.
- Case 3: $m_1 \gg m_2$, that is, a very massive object collides with a very light stationary object.
  This is similar to case 2, as $(m_1 - m_2) \approx (m_1 + m_2) \approx m_1$, and $m_1/(m_1 + m_2) \approx 1$.
  Therefore equation 6 gives $v_1 \approx u_1$ and equation 7 gives $v_2 \approx 2u_1$.
  In collision, the motion of the massive object is virtually unaffected, while the much lighter object moves off with twice the velocity of the more massive one.
  There are few examples of this type of collision in everyday life – perhaps the closest approach to it is when a heavy golf club strikes a golf ball.

The use of **simultaneous equations** to obtain solutions is common in physics, and we shall meet it again later in the book.

SUMMARY

- The **law of conservation of energy** states that energy cannot be created or destroyed.
- **Energy** can be thought of as an 'accounting system' – something that has gained energy has the ability to do work.
- Energy can be transferred by heating and working. Heating transfers energy by means of a temperature difference, while working transfers energy through the motion of a force.
- **Work** W is found by multiplying a force by the distance moved in the direction of action of the force, $W = Fd$. If the force and displacement are in different directions then the force must be resolved in the direction of the displacement in order to find the work done.

- The unit of energy is the **joule**. 1 J is the energy transferred when a force of 1 N is displaced by 1 m, so 1 J = 1 N m. Energy is a scalar quantity.
- At the surface of the Earth an object raised through a small distance Δh gains **gravitational potential energy**, $E_p = mg\Delta h$ (g is the gravitational field strength of the Earth).
- A moving object has **kinetic energy**, $E_k = \frac{1}{2}mv^2$.
- The **efficiency** of a process compares the useful energy output with the energy input: efficiency = (useful energy output/energy input) × 100%.
- **Power** P is a measure of the energy transferred in unit time: power = energy transferred/time taken, or power = work done/time taken. From this it follows that $P = Fv$ for the point of application of the force moving with constant velocity v in the direction of the force.
- In an **inelastic collision**, such as between cars, momentum is conserved, but the total amount of kinetic energy of the system is not conserved. Kinetic energy is transferred to other forms of energy, so the total amount of energy *is* conserved.
- In an **elastic collision**, such as colliding snooker balls, kinetic energy is conserved.

EXAMPLE

One way of storing surplus electrical energy from a power station is to use it to raise water from a lower reservoir to an upper reservoir. This water can then be released to generate electricity again later. This is sometimes called 'pumped storage'. If the upper reservoir is 500 m above the lower reservoir and 2.5×10^6 m³ of water are pumped, how much electrical energy can be generated from this water:
a if the generation process is 100% efficient
b if the generation process is 40% efficient?
(The density of water is 1000 kg m⁻³. Take g as 10 m s⁻².)

a If the generation process is 100% efficient, all the gravitational potential energy stored in the water can be transferred to electrical energy. Thus:

$$E_p = mg\Delta h$$
$$= 2.5 \times 10^6 \text{ m}^3 \times 1000 \text{ kg m}^{-3} \times 10 \text{ m s}^{-2} \times 500 \text{ m}$$
$$= 1.25 \times 10^{13} \text{ J}$$

b If the generation process is 40% efficient, the maximum amount of electrical energy that can be generated is:

$$1.25 \times 10^{13} \text{ J} \times \frac{40}{100} = 5.0 \times 10^{12} \text{ J}$$

QUESTIONS

(Assume $g = 10$ m s⁻².)

1 A ball, initially at rest, falls from a height h and hits the ground. Assuming that air resistance may be neglected:
  a Write down an expression for the gravitational potential energy of the ball at a height h above the ground.
  b Write down an expression for the kinetic energy of the ball when its velocity is v.
  c By considering the energy of the ball
    i before it falls and
    ii just before it hits the ground, find an expression for the velocity of the ball just before it hits the ground in terms of g (gravitational field strength) and h.

  d Find v if $h = 20$ m.
  e If air resistance is not negligible, what effect does this have on the motion of the ball?

2 A crane lifts a load of 500 kg a height of 5 m in 5 s.
  a What rate of working is this?
  b If the crane is 40% efficient, what power does it develop?

3 In a human powered flying machine (the *Gossamer Albatross*) the energy for flying is supplied solely by human leg muscles. To keep the aircraft in the air, energy has to be supplied at a rate of about 200 W.
  a How much energy would be needed to keep the aircraft in the air for 2 hours?

QUESTIONS

b How many 1 MJ chocolate bars would be needed to supply this energy, assuming a person is 100% efficient at transferring energy?

4 A horse pulls a barge along a canal at 1 m s⁻¹ by exerting a force of 500 N. How many horsepower does the horse develop? (1 HP ≈ 750 W)

5 The waterfall known as the Guaíra on the Alto Paraná river between Brazil and Paraguay has an average height of 33 m with an average flow of 13 000 m³ s⁻¹. Taking the density of water as 1000 kg m⁻³:
a What mass of water goes over the falls each second?
b What rate of transfer of gravitational potential energy (in watts) does this represent?
c If 50% of this energy could be transferred to electrical energy and sold at the equivalent of 3p per kilowatt hour (1 kW h = 3.6 MJ), how much money would this earn in one year?

6 A 'superball' of mass 50 g is thrown against a hard, smooth wall, striking it with a velocity of 20 m s⁻¹ perpendicular to the face of the wall.
a Calculate the velocity of the ball after the rebound, assuming that the collision is perfectly elastic.
b Calculate the ball's change of momentum.
c In order that momentum is conserved, there must be a similar change in momentum elsewhere in this system – where?

7 Sand falls onto a conveyor belt from a hopper at a rate of 20 kg s⁻¹. The belt is moving with a steady speed of 0.8 m s⁻¹. Calculate:
a the force required to keep the belt moving at a steady 0.8 m s⁻¹
b the power required to keep the belt moving at a steady 0.8 m s⁻¹
c the kinetic energy per second gained by the sand as it falls on the belt.
d Comment on your answers to **b** and **c**.

8 This question concerns what happens when a moving car collides with one which is stationary. The moving car has a mass of 1000 kg and a velocity of 8 m s⁻¹. It collides with a similar car which is stationary.
a i Calculate the final velocity of the two cars if they lock together and travel on in the same direction as the first car's initial velocity.
ii Calculate the total kinetic energy of the two cars before the collision.
iii Calculate the total kinetic energy of the two cars after the collision.
iv Compare your answers to **ii** and **iii**. This is an example of a collision which is **totally inelastic**.
b i Now assume that instead of locking together on impact, the two cars collide **totally elastically**. Write down an expression which relates the total momentum of the two cars before and after the collision.

ii Write down an expression which relates the total kinetic energy of the two cars before and after the collision.
iii Use your expressions from **i** and **ii** to find the velocity of each car after the collision.
c Use your answers to this questions and to question **6** to suggest why cars and crash barriers are designed to absorb energy in collisions.

9 In karate the fist (or foot) is made to collide at high speed with an object, undergoing an inelastic collision with it. A large part of the kinetic energy of the fist (or foot) is then available to damage the target. A karate fighter wishes to break a piece of wood with his fist, which has a mass of 0.4 kg. The piece of wood has a mass of 2.0 kg, and the amount of energy required to break it is estimated to be around 35 J. If the fighter's fist hits the wood at a speed of 15 m s⁻¹ and makes a totally inelastic collision with it, will the wood break? Justify your answer, stating any assumptions you have made.

10 Physicists have speculated that the extinction of the dinosaurs may have been caused by the collision of a gigantic meteorite with the Earth. Calculations suggest that this meteorite may have had a mass of 5 × 10⁸ tonnes and could have been travelling at 20 km s⁻¹ before it struck the Earth. In the (inelastic) collision which followed, much of the kinetic energy of the meteorite would have been transferred to the Earth in inelastic processes, triggering what geologists have called 'the worst weekend in the history of the world'.
a What sort of effects would the inelastic processes have had?
b Calculate the kinetic energy of the meteorite before it collided with the Earth.
c Calculate the velocity acquired by the Earth (mass ≈ 6 × 10²⁴ kg) as a result of the collision.
d Calculate the kinetic energy transferred to the Earth by the collision.
e How much of the meteorite's kinetic energy was transferred to the Earth in inelastic processes during the collision?

Developing Key Skills

A social club for retired people has asked you to give a talk to members about the way in which police investigators use the laws of physics to help them determine what has happened in a road accident involving two vehicles. Prepare a presentation (using a computer presentation program if you wish) for this audience which explains the physics of collisions simply and clearly.

[Key Skills opportunities: C, A, IT]

1.6 Moving in arcs and circles

So far our introduction to the study of motion has involved the use of equations which deal with the movement of objects in a straight line. Clearly this simple approach is very limiting. However, seemingly complex motion in two or three dimensions can be analysed by resolving the movement into components, and applying simple equations of linear motion to these. In this section we shall begin by taking a look at motion in two dimensions and seeing how this can be simplified so that we can use the equations of linear motion. Following this we shall look at circular motion, and analyse it in a similar way. Like linear motion, we can also regard circular motion as a starting point – to the investigation of the behaviour of planets and satellites in their orbits.

Projectiles

Acceleration in the Earth's gravitational field

A **projectile** is an object which is **projected** – that is to say a force acts on it to start it moving and it is then subjected to a constant force while it moves. Most projectiles that we shall study are objects in free fall in the Earth's gravitational field.

An object which is dropped from rest a small distance above the surface of the Earth accelerates vertically downwards under the influence of its weight. Theoretically the acceleration of an object in free fall is independent of its mass, although this is strictly true only in a vacuum – air resistance affects the motion of objects unequally, according to their cross-sectional area.

At the surface of the Earth, the rate at which an object accelerates under the influence of the Earth's gravitational field is usually known as the **acceleration due to gravity**. As was mentioned in section 1.2, the Earth's gravitational field strength and the acceleration due to gravity are usually both represented by the symbol g, although the units of the two constants are expressed differently: $N\ kg^{-1}$ and $m\ s^{-2}$ respectively. Both constants have the same numerical value – the reason for this is explained in section 5.

Figure 1.6.1 Galileo's famous experiment in which he dropped two unequal masses from the top of the leaning tower of Pisa. The independence of an object's mass and its acceleration in free fall was first deduced by Simon Stevinus in 1586, though this observation is usually attributed to Galileo. Galileo was the first to clearly state the need for the objects in question to be falling in a vacuum for this to be true rather than an approximation.

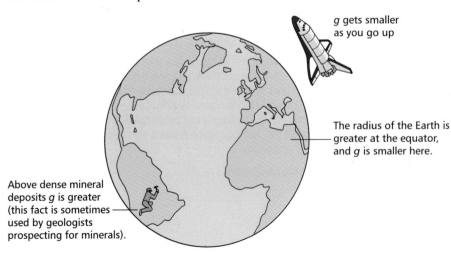

g gets smaller as you go up

The radius of the Earth is greater at the equator, and g is smaller here.

Above dense mineral deposits g is greater (this fact is sometimes used by geologists prospecting for minerals).

Figure 1.6.2 g is generally taken to be about 9.81 m s^{-2}, although it varies at different places on the Earth's surface.

Measuring *g*

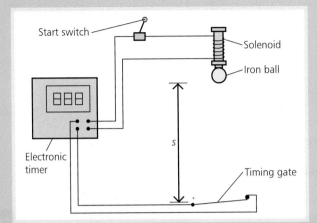

Figure 1.6.3 Apparatus for measuring *g* by free fall

Figure 1.6.3 shows one way of measuring *g*, by analysing the free fall of an object. The iron ball is released by operating the switch, which also starts the timer. The time taken for the ball to fall the vertical distance *s* is measured as it passes through the timing gate. Since:

$$s = ut + \tfrac{1}{2}at^2 \text{ and } u = 0$$

we can write:

$$s = \tfrac{1}{2}gt^2$$

This equation can be used to calculate *g* directly from one measurement of the time taken for the ball to fall. It would seem better however to take several readings, select the most consistent ones, average these and then use the average of them to calculate *g*, since this should lead to a more reliable result. Figure 1.6.4 shows an example of this process.

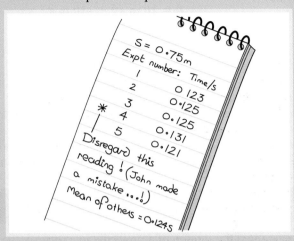

Figure 1.6.4

Even better is to notice that $s \propto t^2$, and do the investigation by varying *s* and measuring the corresponding values of t^2. A graph of t^2 (*y*-axis) versus *s* (*x*-axis) can then be plotted, the slope of which will be $2/g$:

$$s = \tfrac{1}{2}gt^2$$

so:

$$t^2 = \frac{2s}{g}$$

Compare this with $y = mx + c$ – the graph will be a straight line through the origin with slope $2/g$.

Vertical projection

What can the equations of motion tell us about the motion of the ball in figure 1.6.5? For simplicity, take *g* to be 10 m s^{-2}. So we can write:

$u = 20$ m s^{-1} $v = 0$ (taking the ball's velocity as zero at the top of its trajectory)

$a = -10$ m s^{-2} $t = ?$ $s = ?$

Using equation of motion 4:

$$v^2 = u^2 + 2as$$

Substitute values:

$$0 = (20 \text{ m s}^{-1})^2 + 2 \times -10 \text{ m s}^{-2} \times s$$

so:

$$0 = 400 \text{ m}^2 \text{ s}^{-2} - 2 \times 10 \text{ m s}^{-2} \times s$$

and:

$$s = \frac{400 \text{ m}^2 \text{ s}^{-2}}{2 \times 10 \text{ m s}^{-2}}$$

$$= 20 \text{ m}$$

The ball rises to a height of 20 m.

Initial velocity of ball = 20 m s^{-1} vertically upwards

Figure 1.6.5

We can use equation of motion 1 in the same way:

$$v = u + at$$

Substitute values:

$$0 = 20 \text{ m s}^{-1} + -10 \text{ m s}^{-2} \times t$$

so:

$$t = \frac{20 \text{ m s}^{-1}}{10 \text{ m s}^{-2}}$$

$$= 2 \text{ s}$$

The ball takes 2 s to rise to its maximum height.

Similar use of equations of motion 2 and 1 again should enable you to show that:

1 the ball takes 2 s to return to the ground from the top of its trajectory

2 its final velocity before being caught again is -20 m s^{-1}.

Projectile motion, graphs and energy

We examined the motion of a projectile in a vertical direction in section 1.1, using a graphical representation, as shown in figure 1.6.6.

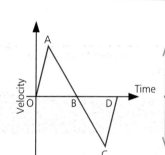

The ball is thrown upwards in this direction. Displacements, velocities and accelerations in this direction are counted as positive in this example.

The ball is thrown from here.

Displacements, velocities and accelerations in this direction are counted as negative in this example.

Figure 1.6.6 Velocity-time graph of ball being thrown upwards and caught again.

Notice that the graph gives us exactly the same information about the motion as the equations of motion, although in a different form:

- velocity at A = – velocity at C, so magnitude of initial velocity = magnitude of final velocity
- top of trajectory is at point B, where the area under the graph is maximum, and so the ball has its maximum vertical displacement here
- velocity = 0 m s^{-1} at point B.

Notice also that if the initial and final velocities have the same magnitude, the ball has the same kinetic energy just before it is caught again as it had just after it was released. This fits in with the ideas about conservation of energy that we saw in section 1.5.

Projection at an angle

Now consider an object projected at an angle, rather than vertically upwards, as in figure 1.6.7.

Figure 1.6.7 The cricket ball travels a constant horizontal distance in a given time interval, although the vertical distance travelled varies.

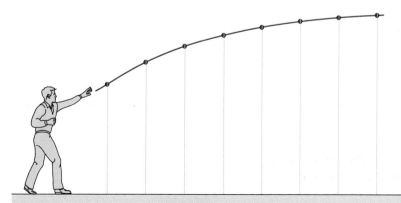

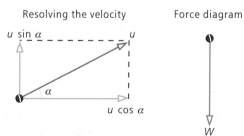

Resolving the velocity

$u \sin \alpha$ u

α

$u \cos \alpha$

Force diagram

W

The velocity of the ball can be resolved into a horizontal and a vertical component. The force diagram shows the force acting on the ball. This acts only in a vertical direction, so the ball will accelerate in a vertical direction only. As a result, the horizontal motion of the ball is not subject to any acceleration, and so the horizontal component of the ball's velocity is constant, and is $u \cos \alpha$ in this example. The vertical component of the ball's velocity is subject to an acceleration of $-g$.

The key variable that links the vertical and horizontal motion of the ball as it travels through the air is time, which is normally measured from the instant of launching the object. If we represent the horizontal displacement by the symbol s, and the vertical displacement by the symbol h, the position of the ball can be plotted as the coordinates (s,h) on a graph, as figure 1.6.8 shows. The equations of motion enable us to express s and h in terms of the other variables u and α.

Using equation of motion 2:
Horizontal motion:

$$s = (u \cos \alpha)t + \tfrac{1}{2}at^2$$

or:

$$s = ut \cos \alpha \text{ as } a = 0$$

Vertical motion:

$$h = (u \sin \alpha)t - \tfrac{1}{2}gt^2 \text{ (g is in the opposite direction to } h \text{ and } u)$$

or:

$$h = ut \sin \alpha - \tfrac{1}{2}gt^2$$

The trajectory of a projectile thrown at an angle in this way is a parabola, as drawn in figure 1.6.8. The proof of this is given in the box below.

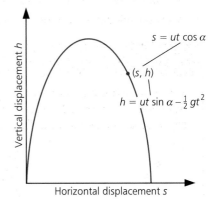

Figure 1.6.8

The parabolic trajectory

We have shown that:

$$s = ut \cos \alpha \text{ and } h = ut \sin \alpha - \tfrac{1}{2}gt^2$$

Rearranging the expression for s so that we can substitute for t in the equation for h:

$$s = ut \cos \alpha \text{ so } t = \frac{s}{u \cos \alpha}$$

Then:

$$h = ut \sin \alpha - \tfrac{1}{2}gt^2$$

Substituting:

$$h = u\left(\frac{s}{u \cos \alpha}\right)\sin \alpha - \tfrac{1}{2}g\left(\frac{s}{u \cos \alpha}\right)^2$$

$$h = s \tan \alpha - \frac{gs^2}{2u^2 \cos^2 \alpha}$$

The equation for a parabola is:

$$y = Ax^2 + Bx + C$$

In this case,

$$A = \frac{-g}{2u^2 \cos^2 \alpha}$$

$$B = \tan \alpha$$

$$C = 0$$

Therefore the trajectory is a parabola.

Projection horizontally

Figure 1.6.9 shows a projectile thrown horizontally. In this case $\alpha = 0°$, so $u \sin \alpha = 0$. This means that the equation for vertical displacement:

$$h = ut \sin \alpha - \tfrac{1}{2}gt^2$$

becomes:

$$h = -\tfrac{1}{2}gt^2$$

whilst the horizontal displacement is still:

$$s = ut \cos \alpha$$

The vertical motion and the horizontal motion can be considered quite separately. This leads to the surprising (but nevertheless true) conclusion that the time of flight (the time taken for a dropped object to reach the ground) of an object is the same whether it is dropped or projected horizontally – in both cases the initial vertical component of velocity is zero, as demonstrated in figure 1.6.10.

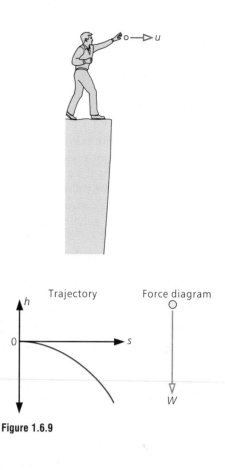

Figure 1.6.9

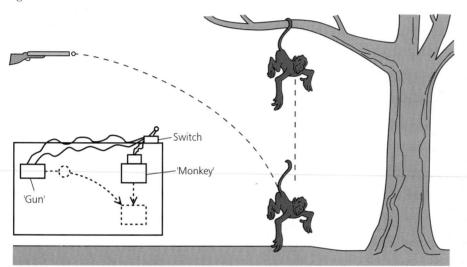

Figure 1.6.10 The 'hunter and monkey' demonstration. Operating the switch sets off the 'gun', which fires a small sphere horizontally from the same height as the 'monkey'. At the same time, the 'monkey' is released. The sphere travels downwards with the same vertical acceleration as the 'monkey', hitting it.

Motion in a circle

Newton's laws of motion

When something moves in a circle, its velocity is changing and Newton's first law tells us that a force must be acting on it. If this is so, then clearly the object must be accelerating – Newton's second law tells us that. But what exactly are the forces that act when an object moves in a circle, and how can we analyse them?

Think about the case of the athlete in figure 1.6.11 whirling the hammer, which is simply a large mass on the end of a chain. If the hammer is whirled at a constant rate in a horizontal circle, the situation seen from above could be represented as in figure 1.6.12.

At any instant, the mass will have a velocity in a direction which is a tangent to the circle, as the diagram shows. If the hammer is being whirled at a constant rate the *magnitude* of its velocity will not change, although of course its direction will constantly do so.

Because the velocity is changing, the mass is accelerating – which agrees with our understanding of the situation based on Newton's first law. The force which causes this acceleration can only be provided by the chain, which leads to the conclusion that the force that keeps the mass moving in a circle acts towards the centre of the circle. This may seem surprising at first, but the following fairly straightforward analysis shows that this is so.

Figure 1.6.11

Tangential velocity

First thoughts might lead us to conclude that if the chain holding the hammer breaks, the hammer will fly off in a direction outwards from the circle, directly away from the centre of the circle. Newton's first law of motion insists that this is not so – the instantaneous velocity of the mass is tangential to the circle, and so the mass should fly off tangentially if the chain breaks.

This can be demonstrated by whirling a rubber bung on a string and letting go of the string (or cutting it) at a suitable point. However, stroboscopic photography of a puck moving on a friction-free table as in figure 1.6.13 provides us with clearer evidence of this tangential movement.

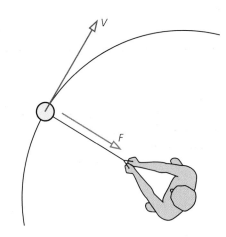

Figure 1.6.12

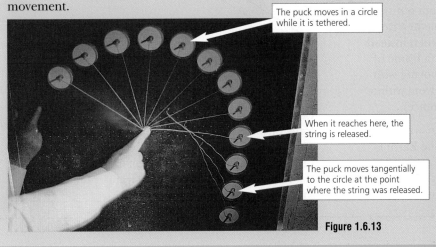

The puck moves in a circle while it is tethered.

When it reaches here, the string is released.

The puck moves tangentially to the circle at the point where the string was released.

Figure 1.6.13

Centripetal acceleration and force

Consider an object moving from A to B, two points on the circumference of a circle, as in figure 1.6.14. The object's velocity at A is v_A, and at B it is v_B. The change in the object's velocity (Δv) between point A and point B is $v_B - v_A$. This can be represented as a vector addition, since:

$$v_B - v_A = v_B + - v_A = \Delta v$$

This may be represented diagrammatically, as in figure 1.6.15. By drawing v_B and $-v_A$ in their correct orientation, it can easily be seen that Δv is directed towards O, the centre of the circle. If Δt is the time taken for the object to move between A and B, the object's acceleration is $\Delta v/\Delta t$, which, like Δv, is directed towards O.

This result agrees with the visual evidence that the chain exerts a force on the mass, forcing it to accelerate towards the centre of the circle. The direction of both the force and the acceleration is said to be **centripetal** – that is, directed towards the centre of the circle; hence the terms **centripetal force** and **centripetal acceleration**.

How big is centripetal force?

To answer this question we really need first to calculate centripetal acceleration. From this, Newton's second law will enable us to calculate the size of the force.

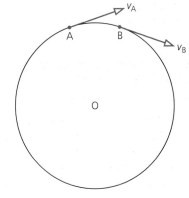

Figure 1.6.14

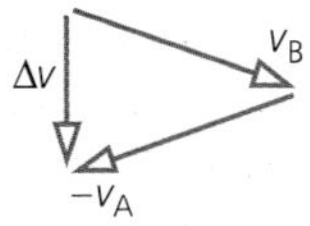

Figure 1.6.15

Centrifugal force

Many people believe that circular motion involves **centrifugal force** – that is, a force which acts radially *outwards* from the centre of the circle, in exactly the opposite direction to centripetal force. Why is this?

The careful analysis of circular motion just carried out clearly shows that an object moving in a circle accelerates towards the centre of the circle, and as a direct consequence of Newton's second law of motion, a centripetal force must be the cause of this acceleration.

The illusion of centrifugal force comes from our own experience of circular motion, for example in a car or on a fairground ride as in figure 1.6.16, when instead of viewing the situation from the outside (a frame of reference which is stationary, or at least moving with constant velocity: see page 33) we view it from within the system itself (a rotating frame of reference).

This illusion comes about by direct analogy with our own experience of weight. We know that the Earth is pulling down on us as we stand on its surface because we experience an upward push of the Earth's surface on our feet. In the same way, as we experience the

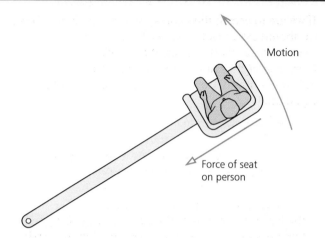

Figure 1.6.16

inward push of the seat as we rotate on a fairground ride, we believe that this must be due to centrifugal force pushing us outwards against the seat. This is another example of the principle of equivalence, the idea that gravity and acceleration are equivalent, since the rotating fairground ride is a frame of reference which is constantly accelerating.

Look once more at the situation as an object moves round a circle, as in figure 1.6.17. $\Delta v/\Delta t$ represents the *average* acceleration of the object between points A and B – in other words, the acceleration at point M. If the object travels so that the magnitude of v has a constant value, we may say that:

Distance AB = $v\Delta t$

(This is only an approximation, but it will get progressively better and better as $\Delta t \rightarrow 0$.) Now triangle OAB is similar to triangle DEF, because v_A is perpendicular to OA and v_B is perpendicular to OB. This means that:

$$\frac{DF}{DE} = \frac{AB}{OA}$$

so:

$$\frac{\Delta v}{v} = \frac{v\Delta t}{r}$$

and:

$$\frac{\Delta v}{\Delta t} = \frac{v^2}{r}$$

This is the centripetal acceleration.
Newton's second law tells us that the centripetal force must then be given by the expression:

$$F = \frac{mv^2}{r}$$

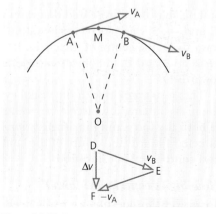

Figure 1.6.17 Note that both v_A and v_B have magnitude v.

The expression for centripetal force

If we are to accept the expression for centripetal force, we should ask ourselves (1) whether it seems reasonable, and (2) also test it to check for **homogeneity** – that is to say, whether the units/dimensions are the same on each side of the equation.

(1) $F = \dfrac{mv^2}{r}$ implies:

- the more massive an object, the bigger the force required to keep it moving in a circle
- the faster an object moves, the bigger the force required to keep it moving in a circle
- the larger the radius of the circle, the smaller the force required to keep the object moving in a circle.

All of these seem reasonable in the context of whirling a mass around your head. Do they also seem reasonable in other contexts too, for example, taking a corner in a car?

(2) Units of left-hand side of equation are newtons = kg m s^{-2} (from the definition of a newton). Units of right-hand side of equation are:

$$\frac{\text{kg } (\text{m s}^{-1})^2}{\text{m}} = \frac{\text{kg m}^2 \text{ s}^{-2}}{\text{m}} = \text{kg m s}^{-2}$$

The units on each side of the equation are the same. (Instead of checking the units of the equation, the dimensions could have been checked – see section 1.4, page 52.)

Measuring circular motion

As we have seen, circular motion can be measured in terms of straight line (linear) velocity. However, it is often much simpler to measure it in terms of **angular displacement** and **angular velocity**. An obvious situation when we would wish to do this is when considering the motion of a rotating solid object, for example the Earth. Different parts of the Earth move at different speeds as it rotates (think of the poles and the equator), so it is not possible to calculate the velocity at which it rotates. This can be overcome if we use the term angular velocity. This is defined in a similar way to linear velocity, as angular displacement/time, that is, the angle through which the object rotates in unit time. The angle may be measured in degrees or in revolutions, or more usually in a special unit called the **radian**.

The radian

If a line of length r is fixed at one end and the other end is moved around the fixed end, as in figure 1.6.18, the angle θ through which the line rotates can be defined as:

Angle of rotation $\theta = \dfrac{\text{length of arc } s}{\text{radius of arc } r}$

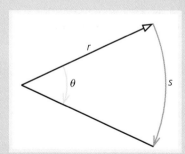

Figure 1.6.18

Since the circumference of a circle is $2\pi r$, it follows that the angle swept out when a line rotates through a complete circle must be $2\pi r/r$, that is, 2π. In this way, angles may be described in terms of units called **radians**, in much the same way as they are described in degrees. There are 2π radians in one complete rotation. When we use radians instead of degrees to measure angles we can rearrange the equation $\theta = s/r$ like this:

Length of arc s = angle of rotation θ × radius of arc r

This relationship can be very useful when we are considering circular motion. The conversion between degrees and radians is quite straightforward, as table 1.6.1 shows.

Radians	Degrees	Revolutions
$\pi/2$	90	$\frac{1}{4}$
π	180	$\frac{1}{2}$
$3\pi/2$	270	$\frac{3}{4}$
2π	360	1
4π	720	2

Table 1.6.1 Radians, degrees and revolutions

Using the radian, **angular displacement** θ is simply defined as the angle through which rotation has occurred, the direction being defined in a positive (anticlockwise) or negative (clockwise) sense. Thus a rotation of $1\frac{1}{2}$ revolutions in a clockwise direction can be represented as an angular displacement of -3π radians.

Angular velocity ω is defined in a similar way to linear velocity, that is:

$$\omega = \frac{\mathrm{d}\theta}{\mathrm{d}t}$$

$$= \frac{\theta}{t} \text{ for motion with no angular acceleration}$$

Since:

$$v = \frac{s}{t} \text{ (again, for motion that is not accelerated)}$$

and:

$$\theta = \frac{s}{r}$$

we can combine these relationships:

$$v = \frac{r\theta}{t} = \frac{r\omega t}{t} = r\omega$$

Thus $\omega = v/r$, or $v = r\omega$. The unit of angular velocity is the radian per second or rad s^{-1}.

In a similar way, since there are 2π radians in one complete revolution, the **period** of the motion T (the time for one complete revolution) is given by:

$$T = \frac{2\pi}{\omega}$$

The **frequency** of the motion, f (the number of revolutions per second) is $1/T$.

Figure 1.6.19 Circular motion is not always as spectacular as this!

The relationships for centripetal force and acceleration in terms of r and ω rather than r and v are thus:

$$a = \frac{v^2}{r} = \frac{(r\omega)^2}{r} = r\omega^2$$

and:

$$F = mr\omega^2$$

plus the relationships linking period, frequency and angular velocity:

$$T = \frac{2\pi}{\omega} = \frac{1}{f}$$

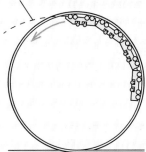

Weight of car and passengers would produce a downward acceleration of g, which would result in this trajectory.

So the track must exert a force on the car to make it accelerate downwards faster than it would do under the influence of its weight alone, in order to make it follow the circular path of the track.

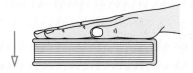

This is rather like making a book 'stick' to the palm of your hand as you accelerate it quickly downwards. This is why you cannot fall out of a roller coaster car in a similar situation.

Figure 1.6.20 This ride is a lot less dangerous than it looks! The ride is set up so that the centripetal acceleration of the car and passengers is greater than the acceleration due to gravity. At the top of the loop the track exerts a downward force on the car in order to keep it moving in a circle – so falling out is quite literally a physical impossibility.

Motion in a circle – worked example

A simple children's toy consists of a piece of cord joining a mass of 0.25 kg to a plastic loop. The toy is used as shown in figure 1.6.21.

Figure 1.6.21

Once the mass is rotating about her leg, the girl stands still so that the mass revolves in a horizontal circle about her leg, at a steady rate of 1.0 revolutions per second. Assuming that the radius of this circle can be taken as 0.80 m, find:

(1) the angular velocity of the mass
(2) its centripetal acceleration
(3) the force exerted on it by the cord.

(1) Angular velocity $\omega = \theta/t = 1.0$ rev s^{-1} = $1.0 \times 2\pi$ rad s^{-1} = 2π rad s^{-1}
(2) Centripetal acceleration = $r\omega^2$ = 0.80 m $\times (2\pi$ rad s$^{-1})^2$ = 32 m s^{-2} (to 2 SF)
(3) Force exerted on mass by cord (centripetal force) = $mr\omega^2$ = 0.25 kg $\times 0.80$ m $\times (2\pi$ rad s$^{-1})^2$ = 7.9 N

Notice how the centripetal acceleration is calculated and expressed to two significant figures – the same degree of uncertainty as the data given. This value is not used in the next part of the question however – all the original data are used, and the answer is rounded to two significant figures only at the end. Doing this makes a difference of 0.1 N in 7.9 N – over $1\frac{1}{4}\%$!

Circular motion and everyday life

Modelling motion

In practical circumstances, things rarely move at steady speeds in circles, just as few things move uniformly in straight lines. However, many motions approximate to one or other of these motions. The usefulness of the equations for both linear and circular motion is that they enable us to do calculations on everyday objects in motion in order to understand the way in which those objects behave. In the language of physics, the equations can be used to **model** the motion of objects. Even if the models are approximate, they can still be useful, not least because they can be refined and tested.

A practical example

The most common situation using an understanding of circular motion to help understand the behaviour of objects is when a car rounds a corner. For the purposes of our simple model, we shall assume that the car follows a path which is a circular arc, since this makes the mathematical relationships straightforward. Although this is an approximation, it is a reasonable one, since we shall only consider the forces acting in relation to one another, rather than doing any detailed calculations. Figure 1.6.22 shows the analysis of why camber helps a car to round a bend, and why adverse camber has the opposite effect.

Centripetal force and work

Because the centripetal force acts perpendicularly to the motion (F and v at any instant always make an angle of 90°), the centripetal force does *no work*, since work is defined as force × distance moved in the direction of the force. The centripetal force cannot therefore change the speed of the motion.

Figure 1.6.22 Camber is extremely valuable in two ways – it means that a car's tyres need to produce less friction, and also that the part of the centripetal force to make the car's occupants travel round the corner is provided by the normal reaction force of the seat on the bodies, which gives a much more comfortable ride!

In each case the car rounds a right-hand bend at a constant speed v, the path taken being a circular arc of radius r. Since the centripetal force F_c needed to make the car turn the corner is mv^2/r, this force is the same in each case.

On a flat surface, the centripetal force is provided *solely* by the friction force of the tyres on the road. $F_c = F_t$

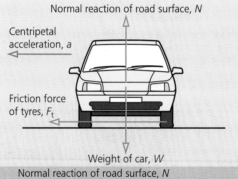

If the road is banked (the term **camber** is usually used to describe this), the normal reaction force has a component acting in the direction of the centripetal acceleration. The centripetal force is now provided by this component *plus* the component of F_t acting in a horizontal direction.

$F_c = N \sin \alpha + F_t \cos \alpha$

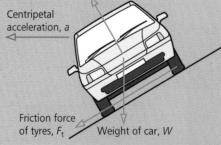

If the road has **adverse camber** (a slope in the wrong direction), the normal reaction force has a component acting in the *opposite* direction to the centripetal acceleration. Now the horizontal component of F_t must not only provide the centripetal force, it must also oppose the horizontal component of N.

$F_c = F_t \cos \alpha - N \sin \alpha$

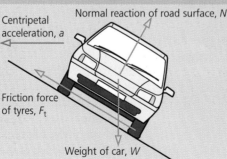

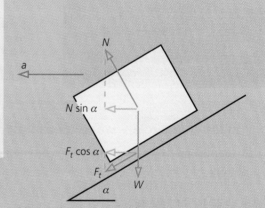

Although the component of F_t acting to provide the centripetal force is now *less* than it was above (i.e. with $\alpha = 0°$), this decrease is more than cancelled out by the component of the normal reaction force acting towards the centre of the circle when the road has a camber.

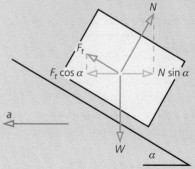

With adverse camber, the friction force must increase enormously to compensate for the component of the normal reaction acting in the opposite direction.

More assumptions and approximations

The model of the motion of the celestial bodies (the Sun, Moon and stars) was developed over many centuries, beginning with the idea that the Earth is at the centre of the Universe, generally held to have been first expounded by the Ancient Greek philosopher, Aristotle. This view was opposed subsequently by later Greek philosophers, but it was not until Copernicus published his book *De Revolutionibus Orbium Coelestium* (On the Revolutions of Celestial Bodies) in 1543 that the idea of the Earth orbiting the Sun began to be considered seriously. Copernicus assumed that the planets' orbits around the Sun were circular. This meant that he had to make elaborate modifications to his calculations in order to make them fit with observations. Over 100 years later, Newton was able to show that the orbits of the planets are in fact elliptical, not circular, and set out the arguments behind this in Book III of the *Principia*. Behind this work, however, lay Newton's initial thoughts on the orbits of celestial bodies, which began with the assumption that the orbit of the Moon around the Earth was circular. No description of the motion of projectiles and circular motion would be complete without some insight into this piece of work.

Falling towards the Earth

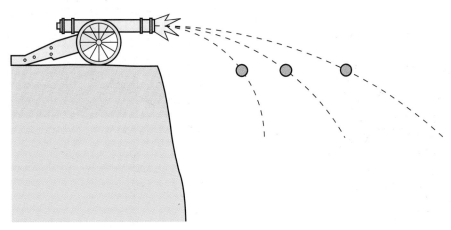

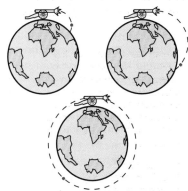

Figure 1.6.24

Figure 1.6.23 The faster the shell comes out of the mouth of a cannon, the further it travels, since $s = ut \cos \alpha = ut$ (as $\alpha = 0°$).

Newton thought carefully about the way the shell from the cannon would travel if the Earth's curvature were taken into account. His conclusion is shown in figure 1.6.24.

After the shell is fired it falls towards the Earth. Because the Earth is curved, the shell travels further than it would if the Earth were flat. Newton reasoned that if the shell were fired at just the right speed it would fall towards the Earth at exactly the right rate to ensure that its height above the Earth stayed constant. In other words, it would be in orbit. Newton applied this concept to the Earth–Moon system, assuming that the Moon's motion could be split into two components – motion in a straight line and motion towards the Earth, perpendicular to the straight line motion. This work led to far more than just an understanding of orbital motion – it resulted directly in the law of universal gravitation, to which we shall return in section 5.

Figure 1.6.25 It was nearly 300 years before Newton's predictions were demonstrated through the launch of artificial satellites.

FOCUS TRACKING SUBATOMIC PARTICLES

This spectacular photograph shows the tracks of subatomic particles through a detector called a **bubble chamber**. Bubble chambers form an essential part of experiments in which physicists probe the structure of matter by colliding subatomic particles like protons or electrons at vast energies. Spectacular pictures like this are not straightforward to interpret, but some simple physics can help us to understand what lies behind the pattern of straight lines, curves and spirals.

The tracks in the chamber are made as the subatomic particles travel through liquid hydrogen which is 'superheated' – that is, it is a liquid at a temperature above its boiling point. The particles knock electrons out of the hydrogen atoms, and cause the hydrogen to boil, thus producing a track of bubbles along their path. As they do this the particles lose some of their kinetic energy, which means that their momentum decreases.

As we shall see later, the force acting on a charge moving in a magnetic field acts at right angles to the direction in which the charge is moving. We already know that this means that the charge will move in a circle. The magnitude of the force on a charge q moving at velocity v through a magnetic field B is given by $F = Bqv$. For a particle moving in a circle, $F = mv^2/r$, so

$$F = mv^2/r = Bqv$$

and thus

$$r = mv/Bq = p/Bq$$

where p is the particle's momentum.

This simple equation explains why there are so many tracks in the bubble chamber which are spirals. As a charged particle enters the chamber, its motion through the magnetic field produces a force acting at right angles to the particle's velocity. This causes the particle to move in a circular path. At the same time, the particle is losing energy, so its momentum is decreasing. This decreases the radius of the particle's circular path, because $r = p/Bq$, and the path of a particle travelling along an arc with a decreasing radius is a spiral.

You can find out more about the behaviour of subatomic particles in section 6.

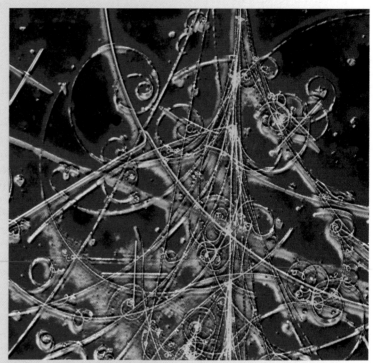

Figure 1.6.26 A bubble chamber photograph. Beautiful images like this provide physicists with deep insight into the structure of matter.

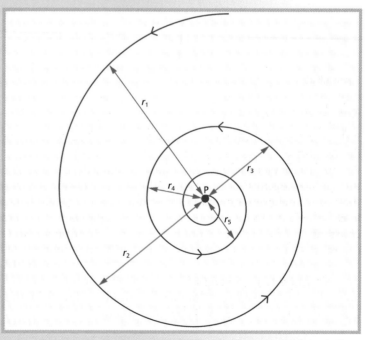

Figure 1.6.27 The particle travels around point P along an arc whose radius is constantly decreasing, so it traces out a path which is a spiral.

SUMMARY

- A **projectile** is an object which is set in motion by a force and then moves under the influence of another force.

- An object projected at an angle has the same vertical acceleration as one projected vertically, and the horizontal component of its velocity is constant.

- The motion of a projectile can be resolved to analyse the horizontal and vertical motions: **horizontal displacement** $s = ut \cos \alpha$ and **vertical displacement** $h = ut \sin \alpha - \frac{1}{2}gt^2$, where α is the angle of projection to the horizontal.

- For an object moving in a circle, the instantaneous velocity is tangential to the circle. The force that keeps the object accelerating towards the centre of the circle acts towards the centre of the circle – both the acceleration and the force are **centripetal.**

- **Centripetal force** $F = mv^2/r$ where r is the radius of the circle.

- **Angular velocity** ω is angular displacement/time. **Angular displacement** is the angle through which the object rotates, measured in **radians** where 2π radians = one revolution.

- The **period** of motion (the time for one complete revolution) $T = 2\pi/\omega$. The **frequency** of the motion is the number of revolutions per second, $f = 1/T$ or $f = \omega/2\pi$.

- Centripetal force and centripetal acceleration can be expressed in terms of angular velocity: $a = r\omega^2$ and $F = mr\omega^2$.

- An object will **orbit** the Earth in a circle if projected at an angle such that it falls towards the Earth at the same rate as the Earth's surface curves away – so that its height above the Earth remains constant.

EXAMPLE

A jet fighter flies in a vertical circle of diameter 1000 m. The speed of the aeroplane at the bottom of this circle is 185 m s⁻¹. For the aeroplane at this point, calculate:

a *the centripetal acceleration of the aeroplane*
b *the apparent weight of the pilot.*
(Take g = 9.81 m s⁻².)

a Centripetal acceleration a is given by:
$$a = \frac{v^2}{r}$$
Substituting values into this gives:
$$a = \frac{(185 \text{ m s}^{-1})^2}{10^3 \text{ m}}$$
$$= 34.2 \text{ m s}^{-2}$$
The centripetal acceleration of the aeroplane and pilot is 34.2 m s⁻².

b The centripetal acceleration is directed vertically upwards at this point. The pilot experiences a force of magnitude F from the seat of the aeroplane. F is given by:
$$F = mg + ma$$
where m is the pilot's mass, g is the acceleration due to gravity and a is the centripetal acceleration.
We can write:
$$a = \frac{34.2 \text{ m s}^{-2} \, g}{9.81 \text{ m s}^{-2}}$$
$$= 3.49g$$
Thus:
$$F = m(g + 3.49g)$$
$$= m \times 4.49g$$
The pilot thus feels the seat pushing up on him with a force some 4.5 times greater than his weight when sitting on a chair on the ground – he thus feels 4.5 times heavier.

(Assume $g = 10$ m s^{-2}.)

1 A ball is thrown with a velocity of 15 m s^{-1} at an angle of 30° to the horizontal. Calculate:
  a its time of flight (the time between launch and hitting the ground)
  b its range
  c its maximum height.

2 At Acapulco, divers jump from a cliff 36 m high into the sea. At the base of the cliff there is a ledge which sticks out a distance of 6.4 m. What must be a diver's minimum horizontal velocity in order to miss this ledge and enter the sea?

3 A stunt motorcyclist wishes to drive off a ramp angled at 45° to the horizontal and to jump over six buses, landing on a ramp the other side (see figure 1.6.28).
With what minimum speed must the motorcycle and rider leave the ramp?

20 m

Figure 1.6.28

4 One record suggests that the maximum horizontal distance an arrow has been shot on level ground is 889 m. Assuming that the arrow was shot at an angle of 45°, with what speed was it shot?

5 An aeroplane carrying out an air drop releases a parcel while travelling at a steady speed of 90 m s^{-1} at an altitude of 200 m. Calculate:
  a the time between the parcel leaving the aeroplane and it striking the ground
  b the horizontal distance travelled by the parcel in this time
  c the speed at which the parcel strikes the ground.

6 A tractor leaving a muddy field throws clumps of mud into the air from its large rear wheels. If the speed of the tractor is 8.0 m s^{-1} and the radius of the rear wheels is 1.0 m:
  a Find the maximum height that a clump of mud reaches.
  b Find where this mud lands relative to the tractor.

7 A bicycle with wheels of radius 33 cm travels along at a steady 5 m s^{-1}.
  a How many revolutions does each wheel make in 1 s?
  b What angular velocity is this?

8 The Moon travels round the Earth in a circular orbit of radius 3.8×10^8 m with a period of 27.3 days. If the mass of the Moon is 7.4×10^{22} kg, calculate:
  a the Moon's angular velocity
  b the Moon's instantaneous velocity
  c the force required to keep the Moon moving in its orbit.

9 A garden strimmer uses a piece of nylon string rotating at a rate of 100 rev s^{-1} to trim grass and other plants. If the length of the cord is 15 cm and its mass is 5 g, calculate:
  a the instantaneous velocity of the end of the cord
  b the tension in the cord at the point where the cord is attached to the spindle of the machine.

10 A swing consists of a rubber tyre of mass 20 kg suspended on a rope 5 m long. A girl with mass 40 kg sits in this swing. If her speed at the lowest point of the swing in 5 m s^{-1} calculate the tension in the rope at this point.

11 A car rounds a curve with a radius of 50 m. A coin is resting on the flat surface of the car's dashboard. If the road has no camber (is not banked), at what speed will the coin begin to slide, assuming that the coefficient of friction between the coin and the dashboard is 0.5?

12 A hump-back bridge follows an arc of a circle of radius 30 m. What is the maximum speed at which a car may be driven over this bridge if its wheels are to remain in contact with the road?

Developing Key Skills

A group of 11-year-old pupils is about to visit a theme park. One of the roller coasters in the park contains a giant vertical loop. Some of the pupils are frightened that if they go on this ride they may fall out of the roller coaster. Produce an explanation to persuade them that the ride is safe.

[Key Skills opportunities: C, (IT)]

1.7 Simple harmonic motion

Movement is an integral part of our experience – it is hard to think of anything in the world around us which does not involve motion in some way or other. All motion in the physical world can be placed in one of two simple categories: **periodic** and **non-periodic** motion. Much of section 1 has been concerned with non-periodic motion, but it is to periodic motion that we now turn in depth.

In **periodic motion**, an object repeats a pattern of movement over regular periods of time. Such motion is common in nature – for example, the beat of a butterfly's wing, the rhythmic fluctuations in blood pressure as your heart beats, the regular changes as days and seasons pass. Periodic motion is the concern of the engineer too, in complex machinery and in simple mechanical linkages like that found in a piston engine.

The pattern underlying periodic motion is often hard to discern, involving complex relationships. Motion in a circle is periodic, and quite simple to understand. However, this section will concern itself mainly with periodic motion in a straight line, and how this can be understood using the ideas introduced earlier on.

Oscillations – periodic motion in a straight line

Oscillations and displacement

We noted in section 1.2 that Galileo is reputed to have measured the time taken for the cathedral lamps at Pisa to swing, and found that the time taken for one complete swing was independent of the size of the swing. Expressing this in the more formal language of physics, we might say that Galileo's observations of an **oscillating** pendulum (the lamp) indicated that its **period** (the time taken for one complete swing from one side to the other and back again) remained the same whatever the **amplitude** of the oscillation (the distance from the centre of the swing to one extreme). Oscillators which behave in this way are termed **isochronous**.

Terms used to describe periodic motion

- **Oscillator** – any object which moves backwards and forwards in a periodic way.
- **Oscillation** – the motion of an oscillator.
- **Period** – the time taken for one complete oscillation.
- **Frequency** – the number of oscillations in a period of time.
- **Amplitude** – the maximum displacement of an oscillating object from its central position.
- **Isochronous** – motion which has a period independent of its amplitude.

Figure 1.7.1 illustrates these terms.

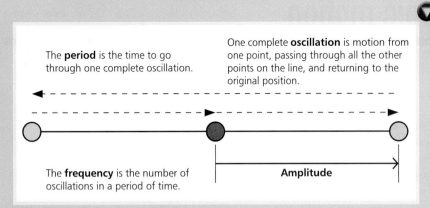

The **period** is the time to go through one complete oscillation.

One complete **oscillation** is motion from one point, passing through all the other points on the line, and returning to the original position.

The **frequency** is the number of oscillations in a period of time.

Amplitude

Figure 1.7.1

Units

- Amplitude is a displacement. It is a vector quantity, and its SI unit is the metre.
- Period is a time, whose SI unit is the second.

As we saw in section 1.6, period (T) and frequency (f) are linked. If you increase the period you decrease the frequency of motion. This is an inverse relationship.

$$f = \frac{1}{T}$$

The unit of frequency is therefore s^{-1}, which is commonly called hertz (Hz). $1\ s^{-1} = 1\ Hz$.

Investigating oscillators

In fact, Galileo's lamps were not isochronous, although he would have been hard put to discover this using the timing methods available to him. As we shall see shortly, the period of a simple pendulum *does* depend on the amplitude of its swing. The investigation of oscillations requires fairly simple equipment in the laboratory, as shown in the box opposite, but it is necessary to be able to plot reasonably accurate displacement–time graphs.

Note: although the usual symbol representing displacement is s, this can cause confusion, as this letter also represents the SI unit of time. This is especially so in this section, where links between displacement and time are continually being referred to. In this section therefore, the symbol x rather than s will be used to represent displacement.

Simple harmonic motion

Oscillations and cosine curves

Although many oscillating systems move in a complex way, there are a number of mechanical systems which are relatively straightforward to understand. These systems exhibit a type of motion known as **simple harmonic motion**. The reason for this name will become clear shortly.

A graph showing the motion of one of the examples of oscillators in the box opposite looks like figure 1.7.3.

Producing displacement–time graphs for oscillators

Figure 1.7.2 shows methods of observing the motion of oscillators. As with linear, non-periodic motion, the principle of obtaining a displacement–time graph is straightforward, and involves measuring the position of an object at known time intervals.

Moving paper and pendulum/pen

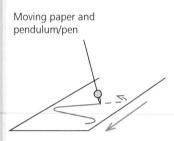

Pendulum on potentiometer connected to interface and microcomputer

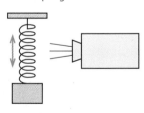

Multiflash photography of mass on spring

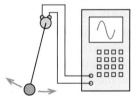

Video photography of 'wibbly-wobbly' toy

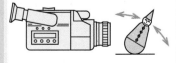

Figure 1.7.2

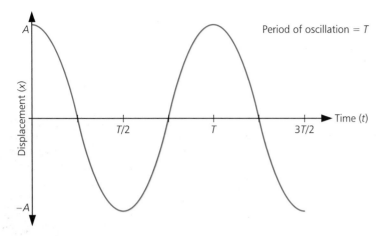

Period of oscillation = T

Figure 1.7.3 Displacement–time graph for an oscillator.

Notice several things:

1 The oscillator starts with displacement = A when $t = 0$.

2 When $t = T/2$, displacement = $-A$.

3 The displacement becomes 0 midway between $t = 0$ and $t = T/2$ (that is, at $t = T/4$) before becoming A again at $t = T$.

4 The shape of the graph is very similar to the shape of the plot of $\cos \theta$ against θ.

Clearly the last observation is an interesting one – it suggests that it may be possible to find a mathematical relationship between displacement and time.

Trigonometry – the variation of sines and cosines with angle

Figure 1.7.4 shows how $\sin \theta$ and $\cos \theta$ vary with angle (note that the angles are in radians). The values of $\sin \theta$ and $\cos \theta$ are calculated from the triangle OAB shown in the circle in the figure.

Notice that triangle OAB forms part of the segment of the circle OBC. We know that:

$$\mathbf{arc\ BC = OB \times \theta} \ \ (\theta \text{ in radians})$$

and:

$$\mathbf{AB = OB \times \sin \theta}$$

If we allow θ to become very much smaller, distance AC becomes very much smaller, triangle OAB becomes almost identical to segment OCB, and so arc BC and length AB are almost identical too. Thus, for small angles:

$$\mathbf{OB \times \theta \approx OB \times \sin \theta}$$

that is,

$$\mathbf{\sin \theta \approx \theta}$$

This called the **small angle approximation**, and is true for angles less than about $\pi/20$ (about 10°).

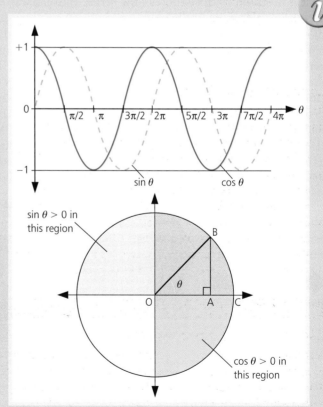

$\sin \theta > 0$ in this region

$\cos \theta > 0$ in this region

Figure 1.7.4

FOCUS TO BOLDLY GO ...

Anyone who has watched a science fiction film and who has some small knowledge of physics cannot fail to have been impressed with the ways in which people and objects in the future appear to be able to ignore the physical laws that constrain our behaviour.

For example, imagine that you are on board a spaceship just about to leave an orbiting space station and accelerate to $0.25c$ (one-quarter light-speed). We know that your body will find it difficult to cope with accelerating at more than about $3g$ (three times the acceleration due to gravity here on Earth). Since $v = u + at$, the time taken to accelerate from orbital velocity to $0.25c$ is approximately

$$t = (0.25 \times 3 \times 10^8 \, \text{m s}^{-1}) / 30 \, \text{m s}^{-2}$$

$$= 2.5 \times 10^6 \, \text{s}$$

which is about a month! And yet you manage to make the journey in a few hours ...

What is there that can protect someone from Newton's first law of motion, enabling them to accelerate at enormous rates? If the spaceship is one of the starships in the Star Trek series, the answer is 'inertial dampers', ingenious devices invented by the writers of the series. In some way these balance out the effect of acceleration on the people and objects inside a starship. Using our knowledge of physics, we can speculate about how inertial dampers must work.

You will certainly be familiar with the sensation of being pushed downwards as you travel in a lift that is accelerating rapidly upwards. This sensation is often described as 'feeling heavier' – and bathroom scales would indeed confirm this. But how would an astronaut in deep space know whether an increase in weight arose from a rapid acceleration or a strong gravitational field? As Einstein realised when he began to think about his *general theory of relativity*, it is impossible for someone in this situation to know this, and so acceleration and gravitational fields are, in some sense, exactly equivalent to one another. It is this that allows the invention of inertial dampers.

Figure 1.7.5 The writer of science fiction has to solve many problems of physics as we understand it. Not the least of these is stopping the crew of a spaceship turning into what some writers have called 'chunky salsa' as it accelerates rapidly to speeds not far from the speed of light.

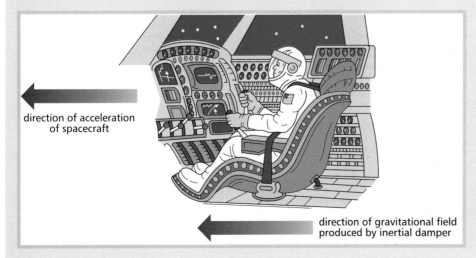

direction of acceleration of spacecraft

direction of gravitational field produced by inertial damper

Figure 1.7.6 Inertial dampers make use of the 'principle of equivalence', which tells us that it is impossible to distinguish between a force produced by acceleration and one produced by a gravitational field. In this example, the spacecraft is accelerating rapidly from right to left, so the inertial damper must produce a strong gravitational field acting from right to left.

How might such a relationship between displacement and time be shown? A first step might be to compare the relative shapes of graphs like figures 1.7.3 and 1.7.4. Such a comparison (for example, by plotting them on two pieces of overhead projector transparency which can then be superimposed) is reasonably easy to do, and shows that a similar relationship certainly appears to exist. Figure 1.7.7 shows one such comparison.

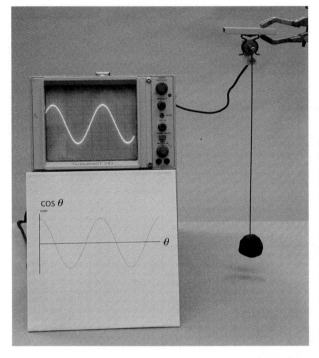

Figure 1.7.7 The pendulum in this example consists of a bob mounted on the end of a light, stiff rod. As the bob swings it turns the shaft of a variable resistor connected to a battery. By doing this, a voltage is produced which varies according to the displacement of the bob. If the bob is set swinging, an oscilloscope can be used to show how the displacement of the bob varies with time. Comparison of the oscilloscope trace with the graph of $\cos \theta$ versus θ shows the similarity. (You can find out more about using an oscilloscope in sections 4.2 and 4.4.)

Investigations do indicate agreement between the graphical representation of an oscillator's motion and a plot of $\cos \theta$ versus θ, so there is justification for assembling a mathematical model of the motion based on this similarity. This model can then be tested in order to see whether it represents the real behaviour of the system.

A model for periodic motion

A striking feature when comparing the graphs is that the displacement–time graph repeats itself with a period T, while the $\cos \theta$ versus θ graph repeats itself with a period of 2π radians.

If we wish to create a model in which displacement varies cosinusoidally with time, we obviously need to be able to relate t to an angle. We have noted that the period of the cosine graph is 2π radians, so one way of doing this is by multiplying t by $2\pi/T$ radians s^{-1}. This means that when $t = T$, the value of $2\pi t/T$ will be 2π radians.

We now have a model in which displacement x is given by the relationship:

$$x \propto \cos (2\pi /T)t$$

Now when $t = 0, T, 2T,...,$ etc., $x = A$, and $\cos (2\pi/T)t = 1$,
and when $t = T/2, 3T/2, 5T/2, ...,$ etc., $x = -A$, and $\cos (2\pi/T)t = -1$.

This means that we can write:

$$x = A \cos (2\pi /T)t$$

which expresses the relationship between the displacement and time in our example of periodic motion.

Remembering that $f = 1/T$, we can rewrite this as

$$x = A \cos (2\pi f)t$$

which could equally well be written:

$$x = A \sin (2\pi f)t$$

since the only difference between these two relationships is that the cosine relationship expresses a situation where $x = A$ when $t = 0$ (that is, the oscillating body starts from one extreme of its motion), while the sine relationship is used to show a situation where the oscillation is timed from the midpoint. Figure 1.7.8 illustrates this point.

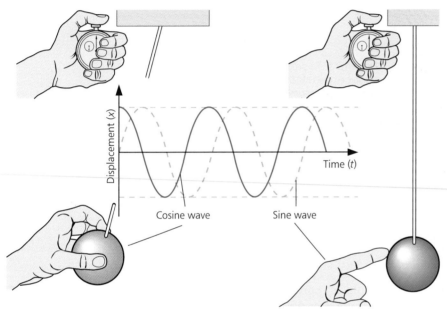

Figure 1.7.8 Pendulum oscillations may be timed from an extreme or from the centre, leading to a cosine or sine relationship respectively.

Which expression?

We have now seen two possible expressions for periodic motion:

$$x = A \cos (2\pi/T)t$$

and

$$x = A \cos (2\pi f)t$$

If we represent the quantity $2\pi/T$ by the symbol ω, we can also write

$$x = A \cos (\omega t)$$

All of these expressions are entirely equivalent, although for the sake of consistency in the rest of this chapter we shall use the expression $x = A \cos (2\pi f)t$.

Finally, since we have replaced $2\pi/T$ by ω, we can write

$$\omega = 2\pi/T$$

Models in physics

Scientists frequently use models in order to try to understand things more clearly. Sometimes this may be a model in the same sense as a 'model railway', that is, a reduced-scale version of the real thing. An example of this might be a model of a nuclear power station, designed to help people to understand what the different parts of the power station do. Other models provide a useful mental picture of something, even though they do not strictly represent it – the 'solar system' model of the atom is one of these.

The model we have used to gain a greater understanding of simple harmonic motion is yet another kind of model – a mathematical one. This is a common type of model for physicists to use, since mathematics provides a very precise way in which a model can be built to provide predictions about the future behaviour of systems, as well as providing explanations of past behaviour. This is not so very different from the ideas about theories that we met on page 61 – and in fact the terms 'model' and 'theory' can sometimes be used interchangeably.

so that

Period of oscillation $T = 2\pi/\omega$

This is the relationship between period and angular velocity we saw in circular motion in section 1.6, page 83. In the case of sinusoidal (simple harmonic) motion, ω does *not* represent angular velocity, since this term has no meaning in this context; it is merely the 'conversion factor' needed to express displacement as a function of time. A link *can* be found between sinusoidal motion and circular motion, however, as we shall see very shortly.

Simple harmonic motion – worked example

A pendulum is pulled through a small angle to one side so that its horizontal displacement is 0.10 m. It is released, and oscillates with a period of 2.0 s. What is its displacement (1) 0.5 s and (2) 1.3 s after being released?

We know that:

$$x = A \cos(2\pi f)t$$

so in this case:

$$x = 0.10 \text{ m} \times \cos\left(2\pi \times \frac{1}{2.0}\text{ s}^{-1}\right)t$$

(1)
$$x = 0.10 \text{ m} \times \cos\left[\left(2\pi \times \tfrac{1}{2}\text{s}^{-1}\right) \times 0.5 \text{ s}\right]$$

$$= 0.10 \text{ m} \times \cos(\pi/2) \quad \text{(remember the angle is in radians!)}$$

$$= 0.10 \text{ m} \times 0$$

$$= 0$$

So the pendulum is at the centre of its motion – which is what we would expect, since $t = T/4$.

(2)
$$x = 0.10 \text{ m} \times \cos\left[\left(2\pi \times \frac{1}{2.0}\text{ s}^{-1}\right) \times 1.3 \text{ s}\right]$$

$$= 0.10 \text{ m} \times \cos(1.3\pi)$$

$$= -0.059 \text{ m}$$

The pendulum is 5.9 cm from the centre of its motion. The negative sign shows that it is on the opposite side of the swing to where it was released.

Displacement, velocity and acceleration in simple harmonic motion

Differential calculus

Wherever change happens, **calculus** is a powerful mathematical tool used to help understand it.

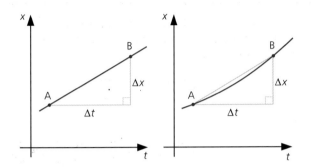

Figure 1.7.9 Distance–time graphs showing uniform speed and steadily increasing speed.

In figure 1.7.9, the line AB is a measure of the gradient of each graph. In the case of the first graph, the slope of AB is exactly equal to the slope of the graph, since the graph is a straight line between the two points. This graph represents constant speed – at any point between A and B, the instantaneous speed and the average speed between A and B are the same, $\Delta x/\Delta t$. (Remember that Δx means 'the difference between two values of x'.) But this is not the case with the second graph. Here the speed is increasing – there will only be one point between A and B where the instantaneous speed and the average speed are the same. In this case, to find the instantaneous speed at a

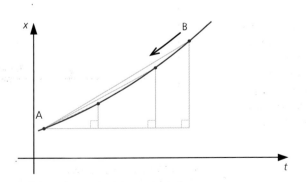

Figure 1.7.10 Reducing the size of Δt brings the slope of AB closer to the slope of the graph.

point (say point A), we need to find the rate of change of distance with time over the smallest time interval possible, so Δt needs to become *very* small.

Figure 1.7.10 shows that the closer we move point B towards point A, the nearer the slope of line AB will get to the slope of the graph. If we keep moving point B towards point A, eventually one point will be on top of the other. At this point, the slope of line AB will be exactly equal to the slope of the graph, so we can find the instantaneous speed. Using mathematical language:

$$\textbf{Slope of line} = \frac{dx}{dt} = \frac{\text{limit}}{\Delta t \to 0} \frac{\Delta x}{\Delta t}$$

In other words, as we move B closer and closer to A, Δt gets smaller and smaller ('the limit as Δt tends to zero'.) Eventually the slope of the line is the same as the slope of the graph, which we write as dx/dt.

The process of **differentiation** can be used to *calculate* the slope of a graph if the variable plotted on one axis is a known function of the variable plotted on the other axis. For example, consider the graph of $x = t^2$ shown in figure 1.7.11. Points A and B are a short distance apart, the slope of the line between them being $\Delta x/\Delta t$.

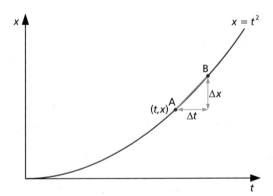

Figure 1.7.11

As we move from point A to point B, t changes to $(t + \Delta t)$ and x changes to $(x + \Delta x)$, so that point B has coordinates $((t + \Delta t), (x + \Delta x))$. It follows that:

$$x + \Delta x = (t + \Delta t)^2$$
$$= t^2 + 2t\Delta t + (\Delta t)^2$$

Now $x = t^2$, so:

$$t^2 + \Delta x = t^2 + 2t\Delta t + (\Delta t)^2$$

that is,

$$\Delta x = 2t\Delta t + (\Delta t)^2$$

and thus:

$$\frac{\Delta x}{\Delta t} = 2t + \Delta t$$

In the limit when $\Delta t \to 0$, $\Delta x/\Delta t$ becomes dx/dt and so:

$$\frac{dx}{dt} = 2t$$

In general, for the function $x = at^n$,

$$\frac{dx}{dt} = nat^{(n-1)}$$

For the trigonometrical functions $\sin x$ and $\cos x$, the following results apply:

x	dx/dt
$\sin(nt)$	$n \cos(nt)$
$\cos(nt)$	$-n \sin(nt)$

Since velocity is 'rate of change of displacement with time' and acceleration is 'rate of change of velocity with time', we can write

$$v = \lim_{\Delta t \to 0} \frac{\Delta x}{\Delta t} = \frac{dx}{dt}$$

and

$$a = \lim_{\Delta t \to 0} \frac{\Delta v}{\Delta t} = \frac{dv}{dt} = \frac{d}{dt}\left(\frac{dx}{dt}\right) = \frac{d^2x}{dt^2}$$

Velocity

Having constructed a model in which displacement varies cosinusoidally with time, it should be relatively straightforward to use the model to determine how velocity varies in this motion. Remember that

velocity = rate of change of displacement with time

and

acceleration = rate of change of velocity with time

This means that if we can see a pattern in the gradient of the displacement–time graph, as in figure 1.7.12, we will have some idea how velocity varies with time.

The shape and position of the second graph showing the gradient of the displacement–time graph suggests that while displacement varies as $\cos(2\pi f)t$, the slope of the graph (which is a measure of the *velocity* of the motion) varies as $-\sin(2\pi f)t$. So we can write:

$$v \propto -\sin(2\pi f)t$$

We know that the expression must be homogeneous, so the right-hand side of the equation must have the units of velocity, m s^{-1}. As it stands, the right-hand side is dimensionless – it is just a number. Since it would be useful to express v in terms of other quantities associated with the motion, we might start a search to find the constant of proportionality in this relationship by looking at the quantities already involved – A and $2\pi f$. At this point we may notice that the quantity $(2\pi f)A$ has the units of velocity. Could this be the constant? In fact, the constant is $-(2\pi f)A$, and:

$$v = -(2\pi f)A \sin(2\pi f)t$$

This means that the velocity has its maximum magnitude $(2\pi f)A$ when the object passes through the midpoint of the motion, and is zero at the two extremes of motion. Both of these seem reasonable in physical terms. The conclusive proof of the relationship shown in the box overleaf requires a little mathematics, but it is relatively easy to follow.

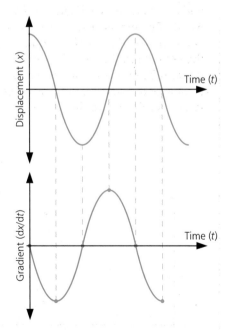

Figure 1.7.12 The magnitude of the displacement–time graph's slope is greatest where $x = 0$, and zero where $x = \pm A$. The slope is *negative* the first time the graph passes through the horizontal axis and *positive* the second time. This means that the slope of the graph varies as in the lower graph – which looks like a sine curve.

Proof of $v = -(2\pi f)A \sin(2\pi f)t$

This proof uses differential calculus, which provides us with the information that:

$$\frac{d}{dt}(\cos(2\pi f)t) = -(2\pi f)\sin(2\pi f)t$$

If:

$$x = A\cos(2\pi f)t \quad \text{and} \quad v = \frac{dx}{dt}$$

it follows that:

$$v = \frac{d}{dt}(A\cos(2\pi f)t) = -(2\pi f)A\sin(2\pi f)t$$

Alternative expression

Since $\omega = 2\pi/T$

$$= 2\pi f$$

we can also write this expression as

$$v = -A\omega \sin \omega t$$

Acceleration

The arguments used in investigating how acceleration varies in simple harmonic motion are essentially the same as those for velocity.

In this case, as figure 1.7.13 shows, the shape and position of the graph showing the gradient of the velocity–time graph suggests that while velocity varies as $-A(2\pi f)\sin(2\pi f)t$, the slope of the graph (which is a measure of the *acceleration* of the motion) varies as $-\cos(2\pi f)t$. Now we can write:

$$a \propto -(2\pi f)A\cos(2\pi f)T$$

Again, the expression must be homogeneous – multiplying the right-hand side by $2\pi f$ gives it the units of acceleration, and:

$$a = -(2\pi f)^2 A\cos(2\pi f)t$$

The proof of this relationship is given in the box on the opposite page.

Why 'simple harmonic' motion?

We can simplify the equation for acceleration enormously if we notice that the right-hand side involves the term $A\cos(2\pi f)t$, which we know is equal to x, the displacement. This means that we can write the equation for the acceleration as:

$$a = -(2\pi f)^2 x$$

This tells us that:
- the *acceleration* of the motion is proportional to the *displacement*
- the *direction* of the acceleration is *opposite* to the direction of the displacement
- the acceleration depends *only* on the period of the motion and the displacement.

Because the motion can be described by an equation that is straightforward, it is *simple*. The motion also has a displacement which varies sinusoidally, so it is *harmonic*. Hence the motion is called *simple harmonic motion*, or SHM.

SHM is defined in words as:

Motion in which the acceleration is directly proportional to the displacement from a fixed point and is always directed towards it.

Notice that in order for this motion to occur, the force which causes the motion must therefore be proportional to the displacement from the fixed point, and directed towards it. This fact is often important when it comes to solving problems involving SHM. Figure 1.7.14 illustrates the relationship between displacement, velocity and acceleration in SHM.

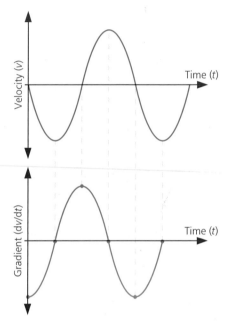

Figure 1.7.13 The magnitude of the velocity–time graph's slope is greatest where $v = 0$, and is zero where $v = \pm(2\pi f)A$. The slope is *positive* the first time the graph passes through the horizontal axis, and *negative* the second time. This means that the slope of the graph varies as the lower graph – which looks like a cosine curve.

Alternative expression

Once again, we can replace $2\pi f$ by ω, so

$$a = -A\omega^2 \cos \omega t$$

Since $x = A\cos \omega t$, it also follows that

$$a = -\omega^2 x$$

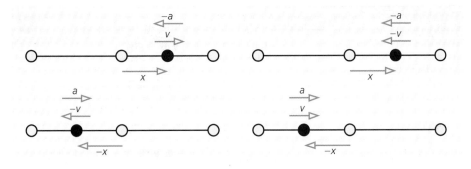

	$x = 0$ when $t = 0$	$x = A$ when $t = 0$
x	$A \sin (2\pi f)t$	$A \cos (2\pi f)t$
v	$A(2\pi f) \cos (2\pi f)t$	$-(2\pi f)A \sin (2\pi f)t$
a	$-(2\pi f)^2 A \sin (2\pi f)t = -(2\pi f)^2 x$	$-(2\pi f)^2 A \cos (2\pi f)t = -(2\pi f)^2 x$

When $x = 0$, $v = v_{max}$ ⎫ (See worked example on page 100 for the proof of these statements
When $x = A$, $a = a_{max}$ ⎭ about v_{max} and a_{max}.)

Figure 1.7.14 Displacement, velocity and acceleration are linked by a simple relationship in SHM.

Proof of $a = -(2\pi f)^2 A \cos (2\pi f)t$

The conclusive proof of this relationship uses the result that:

$$\frac{d}{dx}(\sin nx) = n \cos nx$$

If:

$$v = -(2\pi f)A \sin (2\pi f)t$$

and

$$a = \frac{dv}{dt}$$

it follows that:

$$a = \frac{d}{dt}(-(2\pi f)A \sin (2\pi f)t)$$

$$= -(2\pi f)^2 A \cos (2\pi f)t$$

Integral calculus

It may be useful to measure the area under a curve if the product of the quantities plotted on the two axes produces a physical quantity. For example, the area under a graph of force versus time may represent a change in momentum (see box 'Calculus and the impulse momentum equation', page 54), since $F\Delta t = \Delta(mv)$. However, the area under a graph such as a displacement versus time graph is not meaningful, since the quantity (diplacement × time) has no physical meaning.

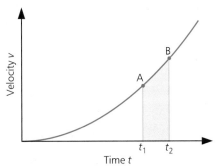

Figure 1.7.15

Figure 1.7.15 shows a velocity–time graph. The area shaded represents the displacement between points A

and B on the graph. We know that this area can be calculated as the sum of the areas of a number of strips, each of which has width Δt and height v. Allowing the widths of these strips to become very small, the area under the graph between t_1 and t_2 can be written as:

$$\text{Displacement } s = \int_{t_1}^{t_2} v \, dt$$

Where no relationship exists between v and t, there is little alternative to adding up the area of a finite number of strips, each of which must be calculated individually (computer programs exist which may help in doing this). If a relationship does exist, then **integral calculus** may be used to calculate an exact area under the graph. Integral calculus is effectively the inverse process of differentiation. In general:

$$\int_a^b f(x) \, dx = \left[F(x) \right]_a^b$$

where: $\frac{d}{dx}(F(x)) = f(x)$

The square brackets indicate that F(x) is to be evaluated at a and b, and the difference found.

In the graph shown in figure 1.7.15, $v = kt^2$, where k is a constant with the dimensions of acceleration. From this it follows that:

$$s = \int_{t_1}^{t_2} kt^2 \, dt = \left[\frac{kt^3}{3} \right]_{t_1}^{t_2} = \frac{kt_2^3}{3} - \frac{kt_1^3}{3}$$

The table lists the most commonly used results:

$y = f(x)$	$\int y \, dx = F(x)$
$y = x^n$	$\dfrac{x^{n+1}}{n+1}$ (*not true* for $n = -1$)
$y = x^{-1}$	$\log_e x$
$y = \sin(nx)$	$\dfrac{-\cos(nx)}{n}$
$y = \cos(nx)$	$\dfrac{\sin(nx)}{n}$

SHM defined

The mathematical definition of SHM is an example of a **differential equation**. Like other equations, differential equations have solutions – but these solutions are normally equations themselves.

The equation $a = -(2\pi f)^2 x$ can be written as:

$$\frac{d^2x}{dt^2} = -(2\pi f)^2 x \quad \text{(sometimes shortened to } \ddot{x} = -(2\pi f)^2 x\text{)}$$

Using integral calculus, the solution to this equation can be shown to be:

$$x = A \cos(2\pi f)t \quad \text{if } x = A \text{ when } t = 0$$

or:

$$x = A \sin(2\pi f)t \quad \text{if } x = 0 \text{ when } t = 0$$

which leads to the relationships defining velocity as:

$$v = -(2\pi f)A \sin(2\pi f)t \quad \text{if } x = A \text{ when } t = 0$$

or:

$$v = -(2\pi f)A \cos(2\pi f)t \quad \text{if } x = 0 \text{ when } t = 0$$

Notice that the motion depends on a restoring force and an inertial mass. All oscillating systems possess these two features. Although some oscillating systems may not be mechanical, it is still possible to see these two features at work.

In all of these equations we may replace $(2\pi f)$ with ω if desired.

Acceleration and velocity in SHM – worked example

A surfer bobbing up and down on the surface of waves moves with SHM of period 4.0 s and amplitude 1.5 m. What is the surfer's maximum (1) acceleration and (2) velocity, and where do these occur?

$$a = -(2\pi f)^2 x$$

$$T = 4.0 \text{ s, so } f = \tfrac{1}{4} \text{ s}^{-1}, \text{ and } a = -(2\pi \times \tfrac{1}{4} \text{ s}^{-1})^2 x$$

(1) Maximum acceleration occurs when x has its maximum value, that is, 1.5 m, so:

$$a_{max} = -(2\pi \times \tfrac{1}{4} \text{ s}^{-1})^2 \times 1.5 \text{ m}$$

$$= -3.7 \text{ m s}^{-2}$$

(the minus sign shows that acceleration is in the opposite direction to the displacement).

The surfer's maximum acceleration of 3.7 m s^{-2} occurs at maximum displacement, that is, at the crests and troughs of the waves.

(2) Maximum velocity – for SHM, we know that $x = A \cos(2\pi f)t$, assuming that time is measured in such a way that $x = A$ when $t = 0$. This means that the velocity of the surfer can be written as:

$$v = -(2\pi f)A \sin(2\pi f)t$$

This will have its maximum value of $+(2\pi f)A$ when $\sin(2\pi f)t = -1$, and its minimum value of $-(2\pi f)A$ when $\sin(2\pi f)t = +1$ ($\sin(2\pi f)t$ can have values between $+1$ and -1).

So:

$$v_{max} = (2\pi f)A$$
$$= (2\pi \times \tfrac{1}{4}\,s^{-1}) \times 1.5\,m$$
$$= +2.4\,m\,s^{-1}$$

The velocity has its maximum value when $\sin (2\pi f)t = -1$. Now when $\sin (2\pi f)t = -1$, $\cos (2\pi f)t = 0$, and as $x = A \cos (2\pi f)t$, the maximum velocity occurs when $x = 0$, that is, at the centre of the motion.

Examples of simple harmonic motion

(1) The simple pendulum

To show that a simple pendulum such as that in figure 1.7.16 executes SHM when it oscillates through a small angle, we must show that the restoring force acting on the bob is proportional to the bob's displacement from the centre of the motion (that is, the pendulum's resting position).

The forces acting on the bob are the gravitational attraction of the Earth W ($= mg$) and the tension in the string T. These may be resolved into components which act along the direction of the string and perpendicular to it (see figure 1.7.16). The component of W acting along the direction of the string is $W \cos \theta$. Since the length of the string is constant there is no acceleration in this direction, and so Newton's first law of motion applies. Taking forces acting upwards along the string as positive gives:

$$T + W \cos \theta = 0$$

Perpendicular to the string the only force acting is the component of W in this direction, which is $W \sin \theta$. This force produces an acceleration of the bob towards the equilibrium position O. If displacements (and hence velocities and accelerations) are taken as positive in a direction from left to right, then we may apply Newton's second law, which gives:

$$W \sin \theta = -ma \qquad \text{(the negative sign shows that the acceleration is towards O, and so is in the opposite direction to the displacement)}$$

Since $W = mg$, this becomes:

$$mg \sin \theta = -ma$$

or:

$$g \sin \theta = -a$$

Now if θ is small, $\sin \theta \approx \theta$. If θ is expressed in radians, we know that $\theta = x/l$, so we may write:

$$\frac{gx}{l} = -a$$

We can therefore write the equation of motion for the pendulum as:

$$a = -\frac{g}{l}\,x$$

Comparing this with: $\qquad a = -(2\pi f)^2 x$

$$(2\pi f)^2 = \frac{g}{l}$$

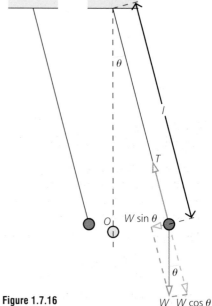

Figure 1.7.16

The simple pendulum – worked example

Calculate the length of a pendulum which has a period of 10.0 s, taking $g = 9.81\,m\,s^{-1}$.

Since $T = 2\pi\sqrt{\left(\dfrac{l}{g}\right)}$

$$l = \frac{T^2 g}{4\pi^2}$$

$$= \frac{(10.0\,s)^2 \times 9.81\,m\,s^{-2}}{4\pi^2}$$

$$= \frac{100\,s^2 \times 9.81\,m\,s^{-2}}{4\pi^2}$$

$$= 24.8\,m \text{ to 3 SF}$$

A pendulum with a period of 10.0 s will have a length of 24.8 m.

and so the *frequency* of the oscillation of the pendulum f is given by:

$$f = \frac{1}{2\pi}\sqrt{\left(\frac{g}{l}\right)}$$

and its period, T, is

$$T = \frac{1}{f} = 2\pi\sqrt{\left(\frac{l}{g}\right)}$$

Notice that the motion is not isochronous, that is, independent of the amplitude, since the relationship is only true for small amplitudes, when $\sin\theta \approx \theta$.

(2) Mass on a spring in a vertical plane

In the same way as the pendulum, to show that a mass on a spring such as in figure 1.7.17 moves with SHM, we must show that the restoring force on the spring is proportional to its displacement from the centre of motion.

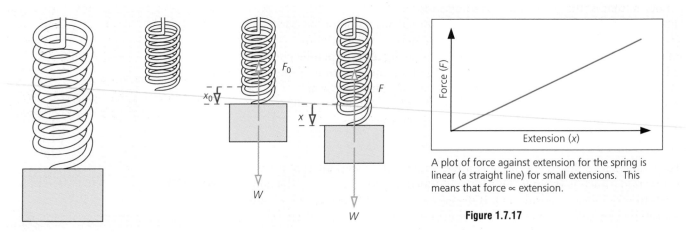

A plot of force against extension for the spring is linear (a straight line) for small extensions. This means that force ∝ extension.

Figure 1.7.17

Since the force exerted by a spring is proportional to its extension, we can write:

$$F \propto x \quad \text{or} \quad F = -kx$$

where k is a constant called the **spring constant**. F and x are vectors – the negative sign shows that they are acting in opposite directions. This law is known as Hooke's law, and is examined in more detail in section 2.2.

With the mass at rest, the spring stretches by a length x_0, so:

$$F_0 = -kx_0 = -W \quad \textbf{(taking forces and displacements in an upward direction as positive)}$$

With the mass pulled down a further distance x, the resultant upward force acting on the mass is $F + W$. Now $F = -k(x_0 + x)$, so applying Newton's second law gives us:

$$-k(x_0 + x) + W = ma$$

But $W = kx_0$, so:

$$-k(x_0 + x) + kx_0 = ma$$

from which:

$$-kx = ma \quad \text{or} \quad a = \frac{-k}{m}x$$

Comparing this with:
$$a = -(2\pi f)^2 x$$

$$(2\pi f)^2 = \frac{k}{m}$$

and so the *frequency* of the oscillation of the mass on the spring, f, is given by:

$$f = \frac{1}{2\pi} \sqrt{\left(\frac{k}{m}\right)}$$

and its period, T, is

$$T = \frac{1}{f} = 2\pi \sqrt{\left(\frac{m}{k}\right)}$$

This motion is isochronous under one condition – the spring must remain within the limit of proportionality (that is, $F \propto x$), and must be taut at all times.

Simple harmonic motion and circular motion

The fact that both circular motion and SHM contain a variable ω seems to indicate that there is some sort of connection between the two types of motion. Both motions are periodic, and the link between them, which is demonstrated in the box on page 104, is an interesting one.

The apparatus shown in figure 1.7.18 may be adjusted so that, as the turntable rotates and the mass on the spring oscillates, the shadow of the mass and the shadow of the ball on the turntable appear to move in exactly the same way. The ball itself moves in a circle, and its shadow moves with SHM. Similarity with the motion of a pendulum may be seen if a horizontal turntable is used.

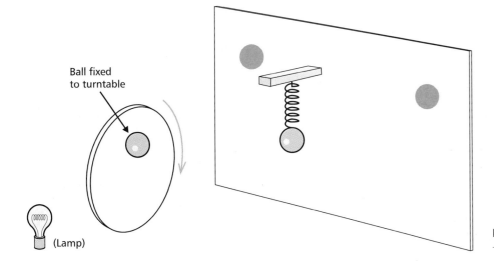

Ball fixed to turntable

(Lamp)

Figure 1.7.18 A mass on a spring oscillates with SHM – and the shadow of the ball on the turntable does so too.

Energy and oscillations

Energy in friction-free SHM

Consider a dynamics trolley tethered between two identical springs. In effect this is like fixing the trolley in the middle of a spring twice the length of either of the two springs, so the two springs together can effectively be regarded as one spring which obeys Hooke's law. If the trolley is pulled to one side of its equilibrium position as shown in figure 1.7.21 so that its displacement is x, the resultant force F exerted by the springs will then be $-kx$.

Demonstration of the link between circular motion and SHM

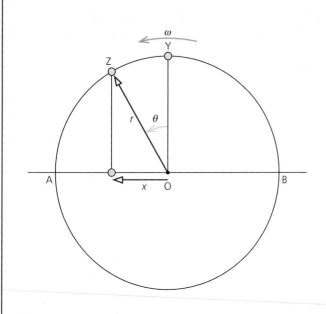

Figure 1.7.19

An object P moves in a circle of radius r with angular velocity ω about a point O (figure 1.7.19). If we project its motion onto a straight line AOB, we can show that this projected motion is simple harmonic.

Let P start from point Y at $t = 0$. The centripetal acceleration of P is a_P. At $t = t$, it will have reached point Z, and $\theta = \omega t$. At any point a_P will be directed towards O, and will be given by:

$$a_P = -\omega^2 r$$

(the negative sign showing that a is in the opposite direction to r).

The component of a_P along AOB is $a_P \sin \theta$, so:

$$a_P \sin \theta = -\omega^2 r \sin \theta$$

Now $r \sin \theta = x$, so it follows that if the projection of the motion of P onto line AOB has acceleration a when its displacement is x, then:

$$a = -\omega^2 x = -(2\pi f)^2 x$$

which is the equation for SHM.

To calculate the energy stored in a stretched spring, we need to calculate the work done on the spring in stretching it. The work done in extending the spring from an extension of 0 to an extension of x can be calculated quite easily – it is the energy transferred to it. Assuming that Hooke's law is obeyed, if we apply a force $F_{applied}$ to the spring which causes an extension x, then:

$$\textbf{Work done on spring (energy transferred to it)} = \frac{\textbf{average resultant force applied to spring}}{} \times \textbf{extension}$$

$$= \tfrac{1}{2} F_{applied} \, x$$

Now when the extension of the spring is x, $F_{applied}$ is given by:

$$F_{applied} = kx$$

(there is no negative sign here since $F_{applied}$ and x are in the same direction). So:

Figure 1.7.20 Oscillating objects (in this case the cone of the loudspeaker) have energy. In some cases, this energy can have quite dramatic effects!

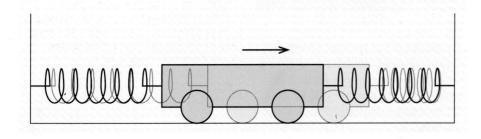

Figure 1.7.21

$$\text{Work done on spring} = \tfrac{1}{2}kx^2$$

and:

$$\text{Potential energy (at displacement } x\text{)} = E_p(x) = \tfrac{1}{2}kx^2$$

Now if frictional forces are neglected, this potential energy stored in the spring will all be converted into kinetic energy when the trolley is released and returns to its equilibrium position. At this point, $x = 0$, so $E_p = 0$. Applying the law of conservation of energy means that E_k at this point $= E_p(x)$. In general, this means that:

$$E_p + E_k = \text{constant} = E_p(\text{max})$$

The maximum potential energy of the system will be when the mass has $x = A$, so:

$$E_p(\text{max}) = \tfrac{1}{2}kA^2$$

So at any point at which the spring has extension x, the kinetic energy E_k will be given by:

$$E_k = E_p(\text{max}) - E_p(x)$$
$$= \tfrac{1}{2}kA^2 - \tfrac{1}{2}kx^2$$
$$= \tfrac{1}{2}k(A^2 - x^2)$$

Figure 1.7.22 illustrates this on a graph.

SHM and friction – damping

The systems we have examined so far have been assumed to be oscillating freely, without any friction acting. However, such free oscillations are only theoretical, since any real oscillating system is inevitably subject to frictional forces of many kinds, all of which act to decrease its energy and thus the amplitude·of the oscillations. In many cases this **damping** is quite deliberate. Figure 1.7.23 shows three types of damping.

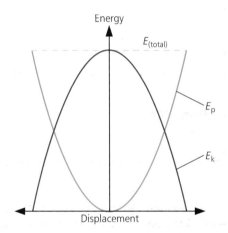

An alternative expression for velocity in SHM

Since $E_k = \tfrac{1}{2}k(A^2 - x^2)$
$\qquad = \tfrac{1}{2}mv^2$, we can write:

$$v^2 = \frac{k(A^2 - x^2)}{m}$$

or:

$$v = \pm \sqrt{\left(\frac{k(A^2 - x^2)}{m}\right)}$$

$$= \pm 2\pi f \sqrt{(A^2 - x^2)}$$

Figure 1.7.22 As the displacement of an object moving with SHM changes, its total energy remains constant, with E_k and E_p changing like this.

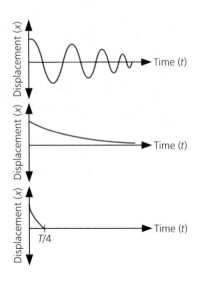

Light damping – the system oscillates about the equilibrium point with decreasing amplitude.

Heavy damping – the system takes a long time to return to its equilibrium point.

Critical damping – the system reaches equilibrium and comes to rest in the shortest time possible, about $T/4$.

Figure 1.7.23 Friction can be used to damp oscillations in three ways. Critical damping is especially common where it is necessary to make oscillations die away as quickly as possible, as in the up and down motion of a car or the rolling of a ship.

SHM and energy – resonance

The example of a wine glass being broken by a note of the right pitch being played or sung is not fiction – it really happens!

Any oscillating system has its own **natural frequency** of oscillation, for example, a child's swing. If energy is put into such a system at exactly the right time, the amplitude of the oscillations will increase. This is what you are doing when you push someone on a swing, assuming that you push in time with the swing's natural frequency. In the same way, the oscillations of a wine glass can be made to get larger and larger until it breaks, by singing or playing a note of the right pitch near it. Both of these pieces of behaviour are examples of **resonance**, a phenomenon that all oscillating systems can exhibit.

The phenomenon of resonance is of great importance in the worlds of science and of engineering, and we shall return to it later.

SUMMARY

- In **periodic motion**, an object repeats a pattern of movement over regular periods of time.
- An **oscillator** is an object that moves backwards and forwards in a periodic way. **Oscillation** is the motion of an oscillator.
- The **period** T of an oscillator is the time taken for one complete oscillation. The **frequency** f is the number of oscillations in a period of time. The **amplitude** A is the maximum displacement x of an oscillating object from its equilibrium position.
- **Isochronous motion** has a period independent of its amplitude.
- An oscillating object displays **simple harmonic motion** (SHM) if its displacement–time graph can be related to the graph of $\sin \theta$ or $\cos \theta$ against θ. In this case, the relationship between displacement and time is $x = A \sin (2\pi/T)t$ if the oscillation starts at its midpoint ($x = 0$ when $t = 0$). If the oscillation starts at an extreme ($x = A$ when $t = 0$), then $x = A \cos (2\pi/T)t$.
- The displacement of an object moving in a straight line with SHM may be written as $x = A \sin (2\pi f)t$ or $x = A \cos (2\pi f)t$.
- SHM is defined as motion in which acceleration is directly proportional to the displacement from a fixed point, and is always directed towards the fixed point.
- For a simple harmonic oscillator the potential energy at displacement x, $E_p = \frac{1}{2}kx^2$. The kinetic energy at displacement x, $E_k = \frac{1}{2}k(A^2 - x^2)$. From the law of conservation of energy, $E_p + E_k = E_p (\max) = \frac{1}{2}kA^2$.
- The motion of an object moving with constant angular velocity in a circle may be projected onto a straight line. This projection of the object moves with SHM along the straight line.
- Oscillating systems are subject to **damping**, resulting in loss of energy and successive decreases in amplitude, due to frictional forces. In some situations damping is a deliberate feature of the design of a system.
- An oscillating system has its own natural frequency of oscillation, and if its oscillations are reinforced at this frequency, **resonance** occurs resulting in oscillations of very large amplitude.

EXAMPLE

A pendulum clock gains 2 minutes a day. If the pendulum is 0.812 m long, by how much must its length be changed to make the clock run on time?

The pendulum must be *lengthened* to make the clock run on time, since:

$$T = 2\pi \sqrt{\left(\frac{l}{g}\right)}$$

increasing the length l of the pendulum will increase its period and make the clock run more slowly.

At present the clock gains 2 minutes per day, that is, it runs fast by a proportion:

$$\frac{2 \text{ minutes}}{24 \times 60 \text{ minutes}} = 1.3889 \times 10^{-3}$$

Let the present period of the clock be T_{old}, and the new (correct) period be T_{new}. T_{new} is thus given by:

$$T_{new} = T_{old} + 1.3889 \times 10^{-3}\, T_{old} = (1 + 1.3889 \times 10^{-3})\, T_{old}$$

$$\frac{T_{new}}{T_{old}} = \frac{2\pi \sqrt{\dfrac{l_{new}}{g}}}{2\pi \sqrt{\dfrac{l_{old}}{g}}} = \frac{\sqrt{l_{new}}}{\sqrt{l_{old}}} = (1 + 1.3889 \times 10^{-3})$$

Therefore:
That is,

$$\frac{l_{new}}{l_{old}} = (1 + 1.3889 \times 10^{-3})^2$$

so:

$$l_{new} = (1 + 1.3889 \times 10^{-3})^2 \times 0.812 \text{ m}$$
$$= 0.814\,26 \text{ m}$$

The pendulum must be lengthened by 2.26 mm.

QUESTIONS

(Assume $g = 10$ m s^{-2}.)

1 If the centre of mass of the girl and tyre in section 1.6 question 10 (page 88) is 5.5 m below the point where the rope is tied, how long will it take the swing to make one complete oscillation?

2 A simple pendulum is made from a bob of mass 0.030 kg suspended on a light string of length 1.2 m. Keeping the string taut, the bob is given a horizontal displacement of 0.1 m. Calculate:
   a the amplitude of the resulting oscillations
   b the period of the resulting oscillations
   c the maximum tension in the string and the point at which this occurs.

3 A parachutist descending under a parachute can be regarded as a simple pendulum. If the strings of a parachute are 8 m long, estimate the period of oscillation of a descending parachutist.

4 The piston of a car moves with motion which is approximately simple harmonic. If the amplitude of this oscillation is 8.0 cm and the maximum safe operating speed of the engine is 6600 rev min^{-1}, calculate the piston's maximum:
   a acceleration
   b speed.
   If the mass of the piston is 720 g, what is the maximum force acting on it due to its motion?

5 The midpoint of a violin string oscillates with an amplitude of 2.5 mm and frequency 440 Hz. Calculate:

   a the maximum speed of the string at this point
   b the maximum acceleration of the string at this point.
   A simple model suggests that the total energy of a string oscillating in this way can be found from the relationship:
   $$E = \tfrac{1}{2}(m/2)\, v^2$$
   where m is the mass of the string, 10 g, and v is its maximum velocity calculated in a above.
   c Using this relationship, calculate E.
   d Comment on this model.

6 According to an airline's records, on average 50% of an aircraft's passengers will suffer from airsickness if the airliner bounces up and down in a vertical plane for more than 5 minutes with a maximum acceleration of 0.25g and a frequency of about 0.3 Hz. Assuming that this motion is simple harmonic, what is the amplitude of this motion?

7 The extension of a spring increases by 2.0 cm when a force of 2.0 N acts on it.
   a Assuming that this extension has not permanently deformed the spring, what is its spring constant in N m^{-1}?
   b A second, identical spring is now attached to the end of the first spring and a force of 2 N applied to them (see figure 1.7.24(a)).
      i   What is the total extension of the two springs?
      ii What is the spring constant of the two springs connected together?
   c Four springs identical to the first spring are connected side by side and a force of 4 N is applied to them (see figure 1.7.24(b)).

i   What is the extension of each spring?
ii What is the spring constant of the four springs connected together?

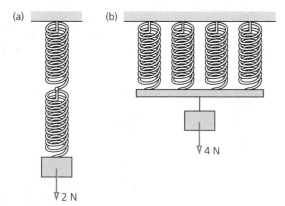

Figure 1.7.24

8 A mass of 0.12 kg is attached to a spring and moves backwards and forwards along the *x*-axis with displacement $-0.30 \text{ m} \le x \le +0.30 \text{ m}$. This motion is simple harmonic, with period 1.8 s.
  a What is the total energy of this motion?
  b When is the kinetic energy of the mass equal to zero?
  c When is the kinetic energy of the mass equal to its potential energy?

9 The body-mass measuring device in Skylab (see figure 1.2.10, page 25) comprised a seat mounted on a spring arrangement. This was calibrated before a flight using a mass of 66.91 kg in the chair, giving a period of oscillation of 2.088 s. During the flight an astronaut sat in the chair, producing a period of oscillation of 2.254 s. What was the mass of the astronaut?

10 A downward force of 250 N on the rear wing of a car of mass 725 kg displaces it downwards a distance of 25 mm. The shock absorbers on all the wheels of the car are identical. Calculate:
  a the spring constant of the spring in each shock absorber
  b the period of oscillation of the car as a whole when a driver of mass 75 kg sits in it.
  c What will happen when this car is driven at 17 m s^{-1} by this driver over a series of humps placed 15 m apart?

11 A fairground ride amusement consists of a walkway with rails which oscillates up and down with an amplitude of 0.5 m, the object being to walk along it. Assuming that the motion of the walkway is simple harmonic, what is the maximum frequency of oscillation of the walkway which ensures that a person on it is in contact with it at all times?

Developing Key Skills

Use a range of suitable reference sources to find out more about the physics of space travel and extra-terrestrial life. (This may include the physics of such exotic things as UFOs and television/film space travel, as well as space travel involving humans.) Adapt the information you find as necessary, and then present it for other students.

[Hint: You should begin this task by identifying a suitable *target question*. Examples might include:
● how could space vehicles cross vast distances in short periods of time?
● how likely is life elsewhere in our universe?
● what is a 'tractor beam' and how does it work?]

[Key Skills opportunities: C, A, IT]

1 An aircraft with a total mass of 1.2×10^4 kg is at rest at one end of a runway which is 2.2 km long. The aircraft accelerates along the runway with an acceleration of 2.5 m s^{-2} until it reaches its take-off speed of 75 m s^{-1}.

a Calculate
  i the time taken to reach take-off speed,
  ii the distance travelled in this time,
  iii the average increase in kinetic energy per second of the aircraft. **(4 marks)**

b Just as the aircraft reaches take-off speed, a warning light comes on in the cockpit. The maximum possible deceleration of the aircraft is 4.0 m s^{-2} and 2.5 s elapses before the pilot takes any action, during which time the aircraft continues at its take-off speed. Determine whether or not the aircraft can be brought to rest in the remaining length of runway. **(4 marks)**

(AQA 1998)

2 a Define *simple harmonic motion*. **(2 marks)**

b A light helical spring has a spring constant, k.
It hangs vertically and carries a mass, m, at its lower end.

By considering the forces acting on the mass when it is displaced in a vertical direction from its equilibrium position and released, show that the subsequent motion of the mass is simple harmonic.

Assume that Hooke's law is obeyed and that there is no damping. **(3 marks)**

c If $k = 30$ N m^{-1}, $m = 0.30$ kg and the initial displacement of the mass is 0.015 m, calculate
  i the period of the oscillation,
  ii the maximum kinetic energy of the mass,
  iii the maximum value of the tension in the spring during the motion,
  iv the minimum value of the tension in the spring during the motion. **(8 marks)**

d The spring, with the same mass attached, is taken to the Moon. State, with a reason, what would be the effect, if any, on the time period of the oscillations. **(2 marks)**

(AQA 1998)

3 a i Define (linear) *momentum*.
  ii State whether momentum is a scalar or a vector quantity. **(3 marks)**

b State the principle of conservation of (linear) momentum. **(2 marks)**

c In an inelastic collision, a piece of Plasticine of mass 0.20 kg falls and hits the ground with a vertical velocity of 8.0 m s^{-1}. It does not bounce but sticks to the ground.
  i Calculate the momentum of the Plasticine just before it hits the ground.
  ii State the transfers of momentum and of kinetic energy of the Plasticine which occur as a result of the collision **(3 marks)**

d Two strong magnets are held stationary with the north pole of one pushed up against the north pole of the other. On letting go, the magnets spring apart. Explain how the law of conservation of momentum applies in this case. **(2 marks)**

(OCR specimen)

4

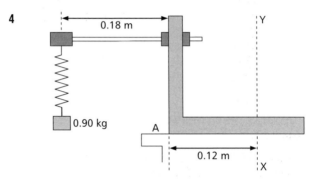

The mass of a retort stand and clamp is 1.6 kg and their combined centre of mass lies along the line XY. A spring which has a negligible mass is attached to the clamp and supports a mass of 0.90 kg, as shown in the diagram. The spring requires a force of 6.0 N to stretch it to 100 mm.

a Calculate the extension of the spring. **(2 marks)**

b Show that this arrangement will not tip (i.e. will not rotate about A) when the 0.90 kg mass is at rest in its equilibrium position. **(2 marks)**

c If the mass is lifted up and released, it will vibrate about the equilibrium position. Explain, without calculation, why the stand will tip if the amplitude exceeds a certain value. **(3 marks)**

(AQA specimen)

5 A lawnmower is placed on a test rig. The lawnmower motor can be run at any frequency from 6 Hz to 100 Hz. During one test, the amplitude of the vibration of the body of the lawnmower was measured over this frequency range. The diagram shows a sketch graph of the results.

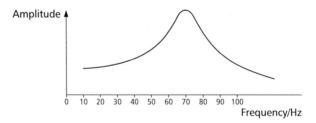

a Name the physical phenomenon which gives rise to the peak in the diagram. **(1 mark)**

b What condition is necessary for the amplitude of vibration, as shown in the diagram, to be a maximum? **(2 marks)**

c Suggest a suitable, safe range of operating frequencies for this lawnmower motor. **(1 mark)**

d On a copy of the diagram, draw the shape of the graph which would be obtained if the vibrations were more damped. **(2 marks)**

e Suggest one way in which, in practice, this increased damping may be achieved. **(1 mark)**

(OCR 1998)

6 A sky-diver jumps from an aircraft at altitude 4000 m and delays opening his parachute until he reaches altitude 1000 m.
In this question, consider only vertical velocity.

a During the first 3.0 s after leaving the aircraft, air resistance to his fall can be neglected. Calculate, for the first 3.0 s,
  i the vertical downward velocity (m s^{-1}) he will achieve,
  ii the vertical distance (m) he travels. **(4 marks)**

b Describing qualitatively how his velocity will change during the rest of the time he is falling, but before the parachute is opened. Explain why his velocity changes in the way you have described. **(5 marks)**

c When he opens his parachute at 1000 m, he is travelling downwards with a velocity of 60 m s^{-1}.
Draw two labelled sketch graphs on the same time-axis to show qualitatively the variation with time of
  i the parachutist's velocity as it is reduced to 5 m s^{-1} for landing,
  ii the force which the parachute exerts on the parachutist. **(6 marks)**

(OCR specimen)

7 In a particular executive toy, two balls A and B of equal mass are suspended on threads. When in their rest positions, the balls are just touching, as shown in (a).

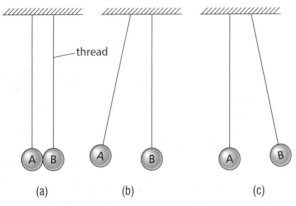

Ball A is pulled to one side (b) and then released. Ball A collides with ball B. As a result of the collision, ball A becomes stationary and ball B moves off (c).

a Given that ball A is stationary after impact, explain why the velocity of ball B immediately after impact is equal to the velocity of ball A just before impact. **(4 marks)**

b State, with a reason, whether the collision is elastic or inelastic. **(2 marks)**

c Suggest what will be observed when ball B returns to collide with ball A. **(2 marks)**

(OCR 1998)

8 a Describe, using a diagram, how driving wheels can generate a motive force. **(4 marks)**

b State three factors which affect the maximum motive force which can be exerted on a particular car. **(3 marks)**

c A car is using a constant motive force of 850 N when travelling at a constant speed of 35 m s^{-1} along a motorway. Calculate the motive power (in watts, W) which the engine is supplying. **(2 marks)**

d The car in **c** does work of 5.5×10^5 J against a stopping force before coming to rest.
  i Under normal conditions the stopping force (assumed constant) is 1200 N. Calculate the distance travelled (m) after the stopping force is applied under normal conditions.
  ii In icy conditions the stopping force is only 300 N. Calculate the new distance travelled (m) before stopping.
  iii Calculate the (assumed constant) force (in newtons, N) exerted on the car to stop it if, in an accident, it stops in a distance of 12 m. **(5 marks)**

e Making reference to your answers to **d**, describe how crumple zones help to reduce car accident injuries. **(4 marks)**

(OCR specimen)

9 A car built to attempt to break the World Land Speed record has a mass of 7.0×10^3 kg. It is propelled by jet engines which provide a resultant forward thrust of 180 kN.

a Calculate the time taken (in seconds) for the car to cover a distance of 1.0 km after starting from rest. Assume that the acceleration of the car is kept constant over this distance. **(2 marks)**

b i The rim of a wheel of the car is a circular strip of aluminium of average radius 0.60 m. No tyre is fitted to the rim, so the rim is in contact with the track.
  Calculate the magnitude of the force (in newtons, N) acting on an element of the rim of mass 1.0 kg when the car is travelling at its maximum steady speed of 350 m s^{-1}. **(2 marks)**

  ii Predict what might happen to a rubber tyre fitted to this rim. **(1 mark)**

(OCR 1998)

10

1 2 3 4 5 6 7 8 sensors

0.40 kg → 0.60 kg

In an experiment to investigate collisions on a level airtrack, eight optical sensors are positioned 0.10 m apart close to the track, as shown in the diagram. When a marker on a moving glider passes sensor number 1, an electronic timer is started. As the glider passes each sensor, the time taken for the glider to travel from sensor number 1 is recorded. A glider of mass 0.40 kg is given a push along the track. As it passes sensor number 5 it collides with, and sticks to, a stationary glider of mass 0.60 kg. The recorded times at each sensor are shown in the table.

sensor number	1	2	3	4	5	6	7	8
time/s	0	0.66	1.32	1.98	2.64	4.31	5.98	7.65

a Calculate the speed just before and just after the collision.
(2 marks)
b Show that momentum is conserved in the collision. **(2 marks)**
c Calculate the kinetic energy before the collision and the kinetic energy after the collision. Account for the difference. **(3 marks)**

(AQA specimen)

11 The diagram shows a pole-vaulter at rest at the start of the runway. His left hand is holding the pole at L; his right hand is pushing down at R to counterbalance the weight of the pole which acts at its centre of gravity G.

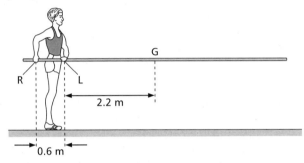

a Draw a free-body force diagram for the pole.
The pole weighs 26 N. Calculate the force which each of the pole-vaulter's hands exerts on the pole. **(6 marks)**
b During the vault, a modern pole bends dramatically. At the top of the vault the pole is vertical and the vaulter is instantaneously at rest.
  i Describe the energy changes which occur from the start of the run-up to the top of the vault.
  ii The graph shows the magnitude of the upward force *F*, which the pole exerts on the vaulter, plotted against *h*, the height of his centre of gravity above the ground.

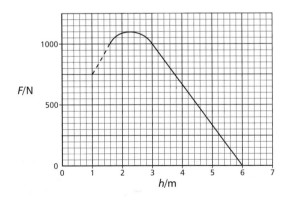

Calculate the work done by the push of the pole on the vaulter as his centre of gravity rises from 3.0 m to 6.0 m above the ground. **(6 marks)**

(Edexcel 1999 (part))

12 The diagram shows a free-body force diagram for an aircraft flying along a straight path and climbing at constant speed.

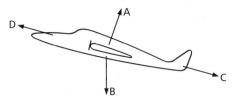

Name each of the four forces A, B, C and D and identify in each case what exerts the force. **(4 marks)**
State whether or not the resultant force is zero. Explain your answer. **(2 marks)**
(Total 6 marks)

(Edexcel 1999)

13 The diagram shows a working model of a fairground ride consisting of a vertical wheel on which are mounted four seats (and model passengers).

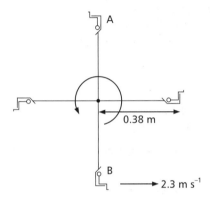

Each seat, always to be considered with its model passenger, has mass 1.02 kg and rotates in a circle of radius 0.38 m at a constant speed of 2.3 m s⁻¹.
a i Calculate the magnitude of the centripetal acceleration (m s⁻²) of a seat. (This acceleration has the same magnitude at all positions of the wheel.)
  ii Hence calculate the magnitude of the force (in newtons, N) needed to produce this acceleration. **(3 marks)**
b i Calculate the weight of a seat in newtons (N).
  ii Copy the diagram and add two arrows to show the weight of a seat at position A and at position B on the wheel. Label these arrows W. **(2 marks)**
c i Use your answers to **a ii** and **b** to calculate the values of the forces (in newtons, N) which the wheel exerts on a seat in the positions A and B.
  ii On your copy of the diagram, draw arrows to represent the forces in **i**. Label these arrows F_A and F_B. **(3 marks)**

(OCR 1998)

14 A cyclist travels down an inclined road without pedalling. The angle that the road makes with the horizontal is 6.8°, as shown in the diagram overleaf.

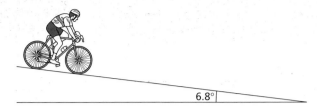

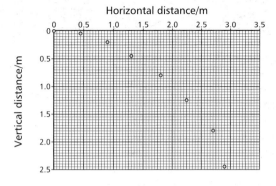

The cyclist and cycle have a combined weight of 760 N.

a Show that the component of the weight of the cyclist and cycle down the slope is 90 N. **(1 mark)**

b The variation with time t of the velocity v of the cyclist down the slope is illustrated in the graph.

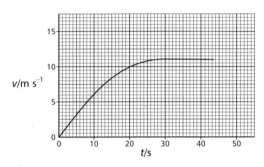

The cyclist reaches a constant velocity after 30 s.

  i Use the graph to determine
    1. the maximum velocity of the cyclist,
    2. the initial acceleration of the cyclist,
    3. the total distance travelled before reaching constant velocity. **(7 marks)**

  ii 1. Use your answer to **b i 2** to calculate the accelerating force acting on the cycle and cyclist at time $t = 0$.
    2. Hence determine the resistive force acting on the cycle and cyclist at time $t = 0$. **(2 marks)**

  iii State the magnitude of the total resistive force acting on the cycle and cyclist at time $t = 30$ s. **(1 mark)**

  iv Suggest why the total resistive force has changed between time $t = 0$ and time $t = 30$ s. **(2 marks)**

c The cycle is serviced in order to reduce friction and then the journey down the slope is repeated. State and explain what change, if any, will occur in the maximum velocity of the cycle down the slope. **(3 marks)**

d Having descended the slope, the cyclist travels along a horizontal straight section of road at a speed of 7.0 m s^{-1}. When the brakes are applied, the cyclist takes 3.5 s to come to rest.

  i Calculate the average force opposing motion during the time that the brakes are applied, assuming the cyclist is not pedalling.

  ii Comment on whether the brakes are efficient enough to bring the cycle to a halt when on the inclined road. **(4 marks)**

(OCR 1998)

15 A steel ball is projected horizontally from a catapult near the ceiling of a laboratory. Photographs of the position of the ball are taken at 0.10 s intervals. The photographs are superimposed and the result is illustrated in the graph.

The first photograph is taken at the instant when the ball is projected.

a **i** On a copy of the graph, draw
    1. the path of the ball,
    2. a tangent to the path at the position of the ball 0.40 s after being projected.

  ii Hence determine the angle (in degrees) of the path to the horizontal at the position of the ball 0.40 s after being projected. **(3 marks)**

b **i** Use your graph to show, by considering the horizontal motion of the ball, that air resistance is negligible.

  ii Hence calculate the horizontal velocity (m s^{-1}) of the ball. **(4 marks)**

c **i** From the graph, read off the vertical distance (m) through which the ball falls during the first 0.60 s of its motion.

  ii Use your answer to **i** to calculate
    1. the acceleration of free fall of the ball,
    2. the vertical speed (m s^{-1}) of the ball 0.60 s after projection. **(5 marks)**

(OCR 1998)

16 The graph shows the speed of a racing car during the first 2.6 seconds of a race as it accelerates from rest along a straight line.

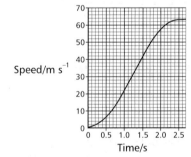

Use the graph to estimate
  i the displacement 1.5 s after the start,
  ii the acceleration at 2.0 s,
  iii the kinetic energy after 2.5 s given that the mass of the racing car is 420 kg. **(Total 6 marks)**

(Edexcel 1999)

FORCES & MOTION CONCEPT MAP

How to use the map

The map is a way of representing the structure of the knowledge contained in this section. It is designed to be used as you get towards the end of the section, when you should begin to see a pattern in the key concepts you have met. The map shows how one area of knowledge builds on another, so that more complex ideas develop as you go through the section.

As you study, try to think about how you learn best. Do you prefer to have understood one idea completely before going on to another? Or do you like to meet several related new ideas and then put these together rather like you might put together several pieces of a jigsaw at once?

The concept map will help you to see how ideas are related. You can use it to help you to put your knowledge and understanding in some sort of order so that you can organise your learning. You can also use it to organise your revision at the end of the section and before your examinations. Alternatively, try drawing up your own concept map as you revise.

Notes on the map

The key ideas in the section are contained in the green boxes. Solid lines with arrows between these boxes show how ideas in the section develop. Where parts of this section relate to other sections, dashed lines with arrows indicate this – the links are described in yellow boxes. Finally, some sections introduce and apply key mathematical skills – this is indicated by purple boxes, with double arrows indicating areas where the skill is applied.

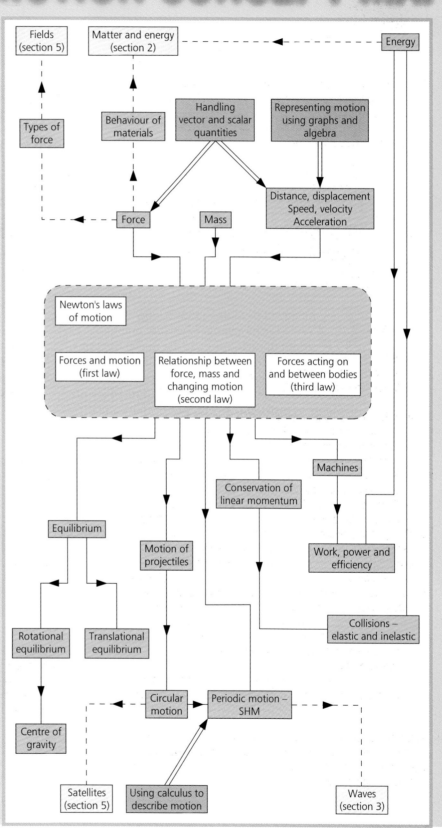

2 MATTER AND ENERGY

Introduction

Just as we see that everything around us is in motion, so we cannot fail to notice that material objects form the basis of our existence. The properties of matter and its behaviour make up an extremely important area of physics, whether we are talking about gases or what physicists call 'condensed matter' – that is, liquids and solids. Equally fundamental is the idea of energy, a powerful tool for understanding the behaviour of systems that we have already met in section 1.

One way of thinking about energy is as a 'reservoir for change', because energy stored in such things as the nuclei of atoms, or the air and petrol mixed in the cylinders of a car's engine, can cause things to happen. Since power = energy (work)/time, we can think of a store of energy as providing us with power that can be used over a given time – the greater the amount of stored energy we have, the larger the power and/or the time for which we can exert it.

Much of the rest of this book will concern, in one way or another, mass and energy. In this section we shall take a closer look at each of them.

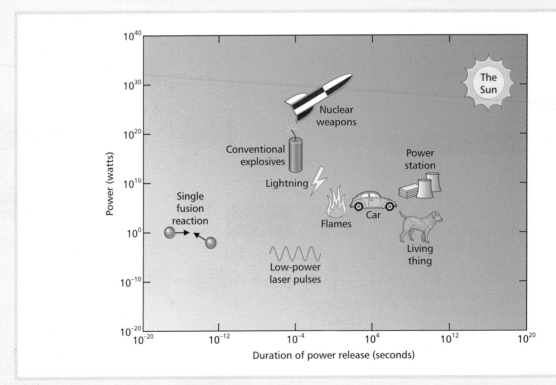

Figure 2.1 Power plotted against lifetime for a number of events. The further up and to the right you go, the more energy is involved.

FOCUS THE STRANGE STORY OF THE MISSING MATTER

Staring up into the night sky, we marvel at the beauty of the heavens. For astronomers exploring and attempting to understand them, there are often surprises in store in addition to the beauty. Not the least of these is the story of 'dark matter'.

The idea of 'missing matter' was first proposed in the 1930s by the astronomer Fritz Zwicky, and for some time it was thought that this matter would turn out to be lurking in the interiors of clusters of galaxies. Thanks to more than 50 years of careful observations, most astronomers now believe that as much as 90% of the Universe may consist of this missing matter, which cannot be seen because it does not radiate light. Astronomers currently prefer to use the term 'dark matter', since it is the light that is missing, not the matter.

So how can astronomers be so confident that the dark matter is out there if it cannot be seen? One part of the answer to this question lies in some clever observations, in which the *rotation curves* of spiral galaxies are measured.

By measuring the rotation of many spiral galaxies, astronomers have found that most of these galaxies have flat rotation curves as far out as they can be traced, even where no more stars are visible. These measurements suggest that the total mass of the matter in these galaxies must be more than 10 times greater than the matter in them which emits light.

So what is this dark matter? At the moment, astronomers are not really sure, although they have a number of candidates. It could possibly be ordinary matter, which would include very, very faint stars, black holes, cold gas or dust – all of which reflect or emit too little radiation for astronomers' instruments to pick up. Some astronomers suggest that it may be a class of dark objects called MACHOs (MAssive Compact Halo Objects) that sit invisibly in the halos surrounding galaxies. Another possibility is that the matter consists of exotic, unfamiliar particles that we have not yet worked out how to observe. Whatever the answer, the search for the missing matter looks likely to occupy astronomers for years to come.

Figure 2.1.1 There could be up to 10 times more matter in this picture than we can actually observe, possibly in the form of MACHOs, or in the form of Weakly Interacting Massive Particles, otherwise known as WIMPs.

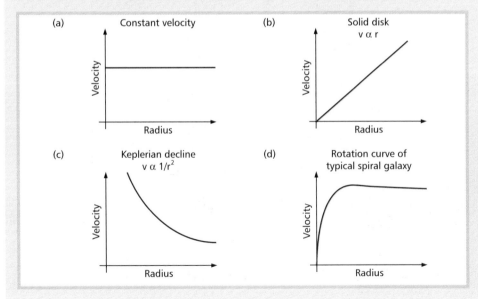

Figure 2.1.2 The rotation curves show the possible ways in which the velocity of a particular galaxy may vary with radius, that is the distance from its centre.
(a) The velocity is constant at all distances from the centre. This implies that the mass of the galaxy increases as the distance from the centre increases.
(b) The velocity is proportional to distance from the centre. This implies that the galaxy is behaving like a solid disc, in which the time to rotate about the centre is the same for all parts of the disc.
(c) The velocity is inversely proportional to the square of the distance. This is a situation that exists in our own solar system, in which the orbits of the planets obey a set of rules known as Kepler's laws. For this reason, a velocity which decreases with radius in this way is known as 'Keplerian decline'.
(d) This rotation curve is typical for a spiral galaxy. It shows that the galaxy rotates roughly as a solid disc in the centre, with approximately constant rotation in the outer edges. Very few galaxies show any evidence for Keplerian decline.

Describing matter

Although physics cannot give any answer to the question 'What exactly *is* matter?', it can help to describe and explain some of its properties. Figure 2.1.3 shows some of the models used to describe particles of matter.

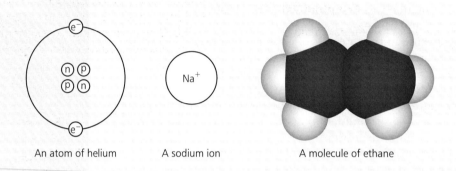

An atom of helium   A sodium ion   A molecule of ethane

Figure 2.1.3 The particles of matter in pictorial form – three types of *model*. In this section we shall be concerned with the way matter is made up of particles, although in most cases it will not be important exactly what these particles are. For most of the section the general term 'particle' will be used.

Phases of matter

Matter is generally thought of as coming in three forms – solid, liquid and gas. These three **phases** of matter form part of the physicist's model of matter, but to these must be added a fourth phase which exists only at enormously high temperatures. This phase is **plasma**. Even though plasma is not commonly found on Earth, it is probably the most important state of matter, as the stars, which contain much of the matter in the Universe, consist of plasma.

Figure 2.1.4 The four states of matter. Not every substance can exist in all states – for example, wood decomposes long before it reaches a temperature at which it would melt.

Measuring matter

Density

One of the differences between the phases of matter is their **densities**. This difference is particularly marked between the gas phase and the solid and liquid phases. Density is defined as mass per unit volume, and is calculated very simply:

$$\text{Density} = \frac{\text{mass}}{\text{volume}} \quad \text{or} \quad \rho = \frac{m}{V} \quad \text{(the Greek symbol } \rho, \text{'rho', is used to represent density)}$$

Like all relationships, this one is dimensionally homogeneous. Thus:

$$[\text{Density}] = \frac{[\text{mass}]}{[\text{volume}]} = \frac{M}{L^3} = M\,L^{-3}$$

The units of density in the SI system are $kg\,m^{-3}$.

The mole

The **mole** is the measure of the amount of substance. It is defined as the amount of substance containing as many entities (that is, atoms, molecules or ions) as there are atoms in 0.012 kg of carbon-12.

Experiments show that there are approximately 6.022×10^{23} atoms in 0.012 kg of carbon-12. Therefore a mole of oxygen molecules, for example, contains about 6.022×10^{23} molecules. It will contain *twice* this number of oxygen *atoms*, because each oxygen molecule consists of two atoms. The number of atoms in 0.012 kg of carbon-12 is usually given the symbol N_A, and is referred to as **the Avogadro constant**.

The kinetic theory of matter

As in any model, the model that physicists use to understand matter must do more than give a general description of the behaviour of matter. It must also have the power to *predict*. The development of the **kinetic theory of matter** is one of the great success stories of physics – the vast majority of people have heard of atoms and molecules. It is a theory which is simple to understand in principle, and which can provide an insight into the inner workings of the world around us.

Simple kinetic theory and the behaviour of matter

The kinetic theory of matter is based on the idea that all matter is made up of particles which are indivisible. This idea can be traced back nearly 2500 years to the Greek philosophers Leucippus and his pupil Demokritos, and it was the Ancient Greeks who gave us the words *atom* (from the Greek word meaning 'indivisible') and *kinetic* (from the Greek word meaning 'moving'). Although there is little direct evidence that matter can be modelled in this way, the fact that the kinetic theory works as a model provides powerful evidence for its being true. What follows in this section is an interpretation of the properties of matter, based on the kinetic theory.

Brownian motion

The dancing, zig-zag motion of smoke particles as they are bombarded by air molecules is known as **Brownian motion**. Figure 2.1.5 shows how Brownian motion can be demonstrated. This movement was first observed by the botanist Robert Brown in 1827, looking at pollen grains suspended in water. Nearly 80 years later, Einstein showed that this motion provided evidence for the existence of atoms.

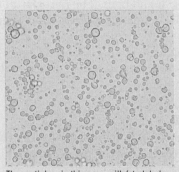

The particles, in this case milk fat globules, jostle around in a random way. Smoke particles appear as tiny bright specks.

Figure 2.1.5 Brownian motion

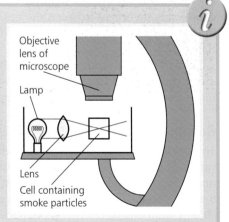

Objective lens of microscope

Lamp

Lens

Cell containing smoke particles

Kinetic theory and internal energy

As energy flows into a piece of matter its temperature may rise or it may change its state; in addition, the piece of matter usually increases in size very slightly. How can this behaviour be understood in terms of the kinetic theory?

As energy flows into the matter, the total amount of energy in it increases. In the language of physics, we say that its **internal energy** (U) increases. The internal energy is simply the total amount of energy – both kinetic and potential – possessed by all the individual particles in the matter. In visualising an increase in internal energy, we usually think of the kinetic energy of the molecules increasing as the matter is heated, with a mental picture of the particles moving more rapidly. If the piece of matter is a solid, as more and more energy is supplied to it and as its temperature increases, it will reach a point at which it melts (assuming that it does not undergo a chemical reaction before it reaches its melting point).

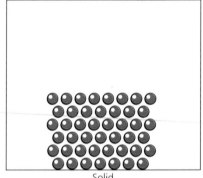

Figure 2.1.6

Solid to liquid to gas

The model for a solid is based on the idea that the particles which make up a solid are held together by forces, which keep the particles together with a definite shape. The forces can be visualised as being like tiny springs, so that any pair of particles is like two marbles joined by a spring, as shown in figure 2.1.6.

Some thought about this arrangement leads to three conclusions:

- The marbles and spring will behave as an *oscillator*, like those seen in section 1.7.
- The marbles will have an *equilibrium separation*, where the spring is neither pushing them apart nor pulling them together. At separations greater than this there will be a net attractive force between the marbles; at separations less than the equilibrium separation there will be a net repulsive force.
- As energy is fed into the system, the amplitude of the marbles' oscillations will increase.

At a simple level, this model helps to explain the properties of solids that we observe as a piece of solid matter is heated. Using these simple ideas, as the temperature of the solid increases, the particles vibrate more vigorously, taking up more room and so causing the solid to expand. Eventually, once enough energy has been supplied to raise the temperature of the solid to its melting point, the vibrations are vigorous enough to enable the particles to move a little more freely. Although there are still large forces acting between them, the particles are now able to move around to a limited extent.

The particles in the liquid move around relatively freely, although there is still sufficient force between them to keep them together in one place. Once the internal energy of the liquid is such that the particles are able to overcome completely the forces between them, the liquid boils. The particles in the gas that results move around completely independently of each other, except when they collide.

This model, shown in figure 2.1.7, appears at first sight to be quite satisfactory – but it has a number of oversimplifications. A more detailed interpretation for solids is given in figure 2.1.8.

Refining kinetic theory

To begin to refine the simple kinetic theory, it is helpful to consider the variation in attractive and repulsive forces between a pair of particles in a solid, imagining them starting a large distance apart and moving closer and closer together. Figure 2.1.8 shows the change in force between the particles and the change in potential energy as the particles move closer together.

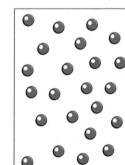

Solid

Liquid

Gas

Figure 2.1.7 This simple interpretation of the particulate nature of matter works, but only up to a point.

Although this description considers the forces between a pair of particles in a solid, it can equally well be applied to a collection of particles – in fact it forms the basis of a more sophisticated model of the kinetic theory, which we shall move on to consider in section 2.2.

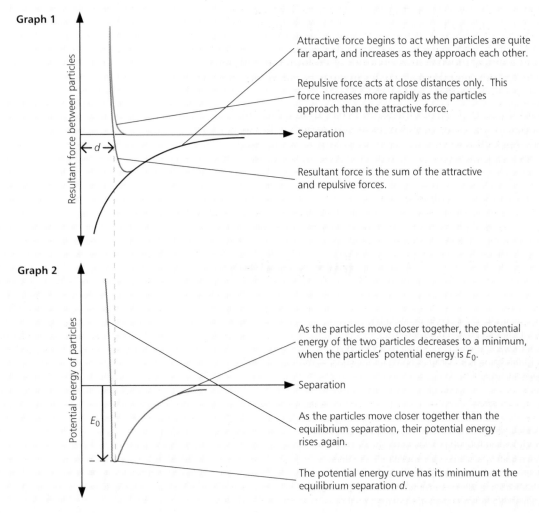

Graph 1

Attractive force begins to act when particles are quite far apart, and increases as they approach each other.

Repulsive force acts at close distances only. This force increases more rapidly as the particles approach than the attractive force.

Separation

Resultant force is the sum of the attractive and repulsive forces.

Graph 2

As the particles move closer together, the potential energy of the two particles decreases to a minimum, when the particles' potential energy is E_0.

Separation

As the particles move closer together than the equilibrium separation, their potential energy rises again.

The potential energy curve has its minimum at the equilibrium separation d.

Figure 2.1.8 Graph 1: The force between two particles in a solid has a repulsive and an attractive element. These two elements exactly cancel out at d, the equilibrium separation. At separations less than d the repulsive element is greater than the attractive element, and so the resultant force acts to push the particles apart. The reverse is true for separations greater than d. Graph 2: The potential energy of a pair of particles has its minimum value $(-E_0)$ when the particles are at their equilibrium separation.

SUMMARY

- The four **phases** of matter are solid, liquid, gas and plasma. Plasma only exists at extremely high temperatures.
- Two important measures of matter are its **density** ($\rho = m/V$) and the **mole**, which is 6.02×10^{23} entities of a substance. The number 6.02×10^{23} is the **Avogadro constant** N_A and represents the number of atoms in 0.12 kg of carbon-12.
- The **kinetic theory of matter** describes and predicts the behaviour of matter, and is based on the idea that matter is made up of particles.
- The **internal energy** of a system is the sum of the kinetic energy and potential energy possessed by all the particles in that system. An increase in internal energy may be visualised simply as the particles moving more rapidly.

- A solid can be modelled as a collection of particles held together by forces which behave like tiny springs. The particles and springs behave as oscillators, with an **equilibrium separation** – at separations less than the equilibrium separation the particles repel each other, and at separations greater than the equilibrium separation they attract each other. An increase in internal energy of the solid increases the amplitude of the oscillations of its particles.

- The particles in a liquid move with very limited freedom, but still have considerable forces between them. Particles in a gas move independently of each other except when they collide.

- A refinement of the kinetic theory for solids is based on a model considering a pair of particles with repulsive and attractive forces acting between them. These forces balance each other at the equilibrium separation d. The potential energy of the pair of particles has its minimum value E_0 at separation d.

QUESTIONS

1 Calculate:
   a   the number of atoms in 12.5 g of sodium (Na)
   b   the number of atoms in 16 g of helium (He)
   c   the number of water molecules in 54 g of water (H_2O)
   d   the mass of the same number of copper atoms as there are water molecules in **c**.
   Atomic masses: H = 1   He = 4   O = 16
   Na = 23   Cu = 63.5

2 A friend, sceptical about the existence of atoms and molecules, suggests that Brownian motion provides no evidence for the existence of these tiny particles – the movement of smoke particles can equally well be explained in terms of the movement of the air as a whole surrounding them. How would you argue against this interpretation of the experimental observations?

3 One model of a gas is a collection of particles moving about freely making perfectly elastic collisions with each other and with the walls of the container. Can this model adequately explain the pressure exerted by the Earth's atmosphere? Justify your answer.

4 Why is it possible to compress a gas, but almost impossible to compress a liquid or a solid?

5 Figure 2.1.9 shows a graph of potential energy versus separation for a pair of atoms. (The scale on each axis is in arbitrary units.)
   a   What is the equilibrium separation of the two atoms?
   b   For values of $r > 20$ length units, E is related to r by the relationship:
        $E = cr^n$, where c is a constant.
        Plot a graph to find the value of n.

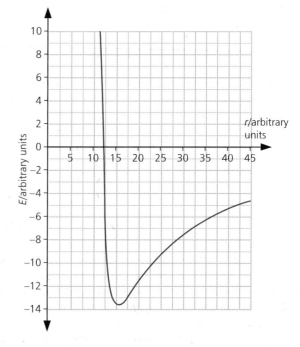

Figure 2.1.9

2.2 Solids, liquids and gases

Having looked at the basis of the kinetic theory of matter, we shall go on to apply the theory in turn to solids and then to fluids (liquids and gases). As already described in section 2.1, the model for a solid visualises the particles as pairs held together by forces that behave like little springs, so we shall consider this model in more detail. The model for liquids is not so clear cut, as we shall see, but effective kinetic theory can be developed to describe and predict the behaviour of gases under certain circumstances.

The physical properties of solids

The model for a solid described above suggests a study of the behaviour of a solid when subjected to a deformation. We shall apply this to the extension of a spring (Hooke's law) and the behaviour of a solid under tensile forces (the Young modulus and stress–strain behaviour). We shall also look at the effect of heating a solid in terms of the refined kinetic theory, and then classify solids according to their behaviours under certain conditions.

Deformation (1) – Hooke's law

We saw in section 1.7 how a knowledge of the relationship between stretching a spring and the force it exerted could be useful. This relationship was first discovered by Robert Hooke in 1676 and it is now generally known as **Hooke's law**. Hooke's law states that the force exerted by a spring is proportional to its extension. This is usually written:

$$F = -kx$$

The negative sign shows that the force exerted by the spring is in the opposite direction to the extension, as figure 2.2.1 shows. By using the force exerted *by* the spring rather than the force exerted *on* the spring, we ensure that we are always focusing on two properties concerned with the spring itself, rather than one property of the spring (its extension) and a property of something else (the size of the load used to extend the spring).

Simple investigations show that this law applies only up to a certain limit, beyond which the extension increases more rapidly than expected, and the spring remains permanently deformed when the load is removed. The limit at which this happens is termed the **proportionality limit**. If the spring is extended a little way beyond the proportionality limit, a point called the **elastic limit** is reached. For extensions up to the elastic limit the spring shows reversible behaviour – it returns to its original length on unloading. The constant of proportionality k is known as the **spring constant** – the larger the value of k, the stiffer the spring. Figure 2.2.4 illustrates the behaviour of springs with differing spring constants.

Although we do not usually make use of Hooke's law when considering the stiffness of a particular material, solids do show very similar behaviour to springs. This provides evidence for our model of solids featuring attractive and repulsive forces between the particles which behave a little like springs.

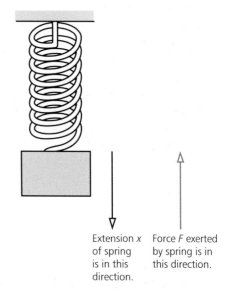

Extension x of spring is in this direction.

Force F exerted by spring is in this direction.

Figure 2.2.1

Hooke and Newton – bitter enemies

Robert Hooke was one of the main figures involved in plans for rebuilding London after the Great Fire of 1666. He was later to become president of the Royal Society, established in 1660 to promote scientific discussion.

Hooke and Newton often disagreed violently. Not the least of these disagreements was over Hooke's claim that Newton had stolen some of his ideas and published them in his *Principia*. This was just one of many disputes in which Newton became embroiled, during a life which included a spell in charge of the Royal Mint, and much energy devoted to alchemy and religion. (Newton believed in the existence of a 'hidden truth' that God had given to people in ancient time but which had subsequently been lost. He was convinced that traces of this truth could still be found if one knew where to look – and that alchemy was the key to enlightenment.)

'Crooked and of low stature', Hooke grew more deformed as he got older, with one eye 'full and popping'. On Hooke's death in 1703, Newton is reputed to have ordered all portraits of him destroyed. Newton is famously quoted as saying 'If I have seen further than other men, it is because I have stood on the shoulders of giants.' Was this intended as a reference to Aristotle and Galileo – or a putdown aimed at the unfortunate Hooke?

Figure 2.2.2 Robert Hooke (1635–1703). This is how we might imagine Hooke to have looked, given that there are no existing portraits of him.

Figure 2.2.3 Isaac Newton (1642–1727). A portrait painted to celebrate the 300th anniversary of the publication of his *Principia*.

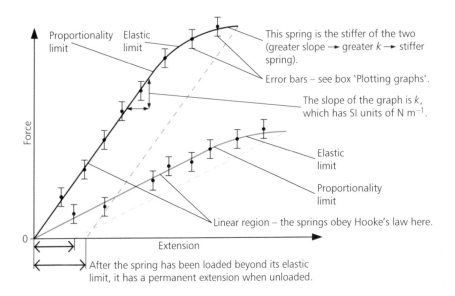

Figure 2.2.4 Graphs of force versus extension for two different springs.

Energy and Hooke's law

The energy involved in stretching a spring is not difficult to calculate, given that Hooke's law is obeyed. For a given extension x, the force exerted by the spring is $-F$. The energy stored in the stretched spring is equal to the work done on it as it is stretched, and we saw in section 1.7 that this is given by:

$$\text{Work done on spring} = \tfrac{1}{2}kx^2$$

Plotting graphs

Axes

In plotting a graph we represent the way in which one variable changes with respect to another variable. This is done by changing one variable (the **independent variable**) whilst keeping all other conditions constant, and making observations of the other variable in which we are interested (the **dependent variable**). When these variables are plotted on a graph, the convention is to plot the independent variable on the x-axis, and the dependent variable on the y-axis. In the case of the force–extension graph for Hooke's law, the dependent variable is the force exerted by the spring, which is measured for different extensions – hence this variable is plotted on the y-axis.

Errors

Any investigation will involve uncertainty in measurements. These uncertainties arise in different ways (see box 'Measuring the Young modulus – and treating experimental uncertainty', page 125). In plotting variables on a graph it is good practice to have some estimate of the likely uncertainty in the measurement of the dependent variable, and to show this as a vertical error bar. This can then be used in drawing a line through the points.

Lines

A line drawn through the points on a graph may be straight or curved, and it may pass through the origin or through some point on the y-axis. Before drawing a line through the points of a graph it is usually possible to have an intelligent idea about the likely shape and intercept of the line, particularly whether it should pass through the origin or not. Using the error bars, a line through the points can then be drawn, from which gradients and intercepts can be calculated as appropriate.

Non-linear stretching and potential energy

In calculating the work done in stretching a spring, we are in effect calculating the area under the force–extension graph, as figure 2.2.5 shows.

If the force–extension graph is not a straight line, the technique of dividing the area under the line into strips and calculating the area of each strip must be used to calculate the work done in stretching the spring.

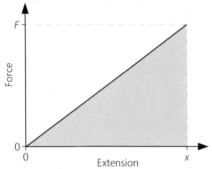

The shaded area is $\frac{1}{2}Fx$, and represents the work done in stretching this spring from zero extension to an extension of x.

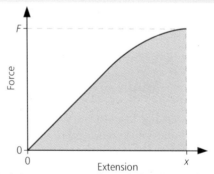

The shaded area represents the work done in stretching this spring from zero extension to an extension of x. The energy stored in the spring which is available to do useful work is less than the work done on the spring – why?

Figure 2.2.5

Hooke's law and a metal wire

In stretching a spring we are applying a **tensile** force (a force which puts something in **tension**, that is, tends to pull it apart). A simple investigation shows that a metal wire behaves in a similar way to a spring when a tensile force is applied, initially obeying Hooke's law. This may be explained with reference to the shape of the graph showing the force acting between two particles, figure 2.2.6. As the particles separate from the equilibrium position the graph is linear, and so the force between the particles increases in proportion to their separation. If we assume that as a force is applied, all the particles in a solid increase their separation in the same way, this proportionality between force and particle separation explains why Hooke's law applies to the metal wire.

Deformation (2) – stress, strain and the Young modulus

Situations involving a tensile force being applied to a material are common, especially in engineering. What might an engineer wish to know about a material's behaviour under tensile forces?

The amount of extension for a given force would be a useful start, and it could be helpful to know something about the force required to actually pull the material apart – its **tensile strength**. Both of these will require us to know something about the size of the sample of material used, especially its *area of cross-section*, since this will obviously have a great effect on its stretching behaviour and its strength. In a similar way, information about the *length* of the sample used is necessary to make sense of the amount of stretch for a given force.

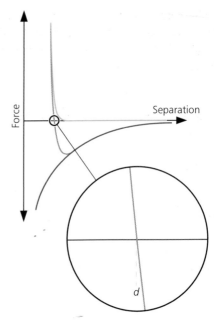

Figure 2.2.6

Tensile stress and tensile strain

These problems can be overcome by defining two new quantities such that information about length and cross-sectional area can be included in the data relating to the samples:

- If we consider *tensile force per unit area* rather than tensile force alone, this takes into account the sample's area of cross-section.
- If we consider *extension per unit length* rather than extension alone, this takes into account the length of the sample.

Tensile force per unit area is called **tensile stress**:

$$\text{Tensile stress} = \frac{\text{tensile force}}{\text{area of cross-section}}$$

The SI units of tensile stress are N m^{-2}, the same as those for pressure (so tensile stress is sometimes given in pascals).

The **tensile strength** of a material is the tensile stress at which the material breaks.

Extension per unit length is called **tensile strain**:

$$\text{Tensile strain} = \frac{\text{extension}}{\text{original length}}$$

Tensile strain has no dimensions, as it is the ratio of two lengths.

Samples of all materials are found to obey Hooke's law for sufficiently small tensile strains. Under these circumstances, the ratio of tensile stress:tensile strain is constant. This quantity is called the **Young modulus** E:

$$E = \frac{\text{tensile stress}}{\text{tensile strain}} = \frac{F/A}{x/l}$$

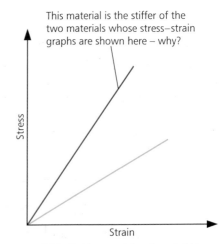

This material is the stiffer of the two materials whose stress–strain graphs are shown here – why?

Figure 2.2.7 The Young modulus of a material is a measure of how *stiff* it is – which is a reflection of how the forces between particles in the material vary as the distance between them changes.

The Young modulus has the same units as tensile stress. Table 2.2.1 shows some values of the Young modulus for different materials.

Figure 2.2.7 shows graphs of stress versus strain for materials with different Young moduli.

Material	Young modulus/Pa
Mild steel	2×10^{11}
Aluminium	7×10^{10}
Softwood (parallel to grain)	1.6×10^{10}
Brick	7×10^9
Concrete	4×10^{10}

Table 2.2.1 The Young modulus of a material is one piece of information used by engineers in selecting materials for particular uses.

Measuring the Young modulus – and treating experimental uncertainty

To measure the Young modulus all that is necessary in principle is to measure the extension of a sample for a given force and then to calculate the tensile stress and tensile strain, from which E can be calculated. In practice such a method is unlikely to lead to very reliable results.

To find E, a graphical method is usually used. Since:

$$E = \frac{\text{tensile stress}}{\text{tensile strain}}$$

it follows that a graph of tensile stress plotted against tensile strain will have slope E.

In order to plot the graph a number of measurements will need to be made, and to make these measurements an instrument must be used. The reading that this instrument gives will be influenced by the skill that the experimenter has in using it, and by the instrument's own limitations. This means that any measured quantity has some **uncertainty**.

As an example of this, the length of a piece of wire might be stated as 126 mm ± 2 mm. This tells us that there is an **absolute uncertainty** of 2 mm in the figure – the person who made the measurement is confident that the length of the wire lies between 124 mm and 128 mm, and that 126 mm is the best figure for it. The uncertainty could also have been stated as a **fractional uncertainty** (2/126 = 1/63) or as a **percentage uncertainty** (1.6%). Note that sometimes the word **error** is used to describe an uncertainty – it is important to realise that this does not mean a *mistake*, since all measurements involve uncertainty, no matter how accurate the equipment or skilled the experimenter.

Table 2.2.2 and the notes that follow show some measurements made in order to find E, and suggest possible percentage uncertainties for an investigation using simple equipment.

The largest uncertainty in any measurement of E comes in the measurement of extension. Accurate methods for measuring E thus concentrate on measuring x with as great a precision as possible.

Rules for calculating uncertainties

To calculate total uncertainties in relationships some simple rules can be applied:

- For quantities which are added or subtracted, *add* their *absolute* uncertainties.
- For quantities which are multiplied or divided, *add* their *percentage* uncertainties.
- For quantities which are raised to a power (x^2), *multiply* the *percentage* uncertainty by the power.
- Where expressions involve complex relationships or trigonometrical functions, it is best to calculate the final quantity twice, using the absolute uncertainties in the readings taken.

	Force F/N	Diameter of wire/m	Cross-sectional area A/m^2	Original length l of wire/m	Extension x of wire/m	Tensile stress = F/A	Tensile strain = x/l
Possible uncertainty in measurement	± 2% (if using slotted masses) (Note 1)	±2 % (using micrometer) (Note 2)	± 4% (depends on radius^2) (Note 3)	± 1.5% (using metre rule) (Note 4)	± 10% (Note 5)	± 6% (Note 6)	± 11.5% (Note 7)

Table 2.2.2 Measurements for finding E, together with possible uncertainties

Notes

(1) Slotted masses may have very variable uncertainties in their mass. If carefully selected, they are unlikely to have an uncertainty of more than ±2%. The mass used will need to be converted to weight using an appropriate value of g – the approximation of g to 10 N kg^{-1} itself leads to an uncertainty of more than +1%.

(2) A micrometer should be capable of measuring a wire 1 mm in diameter to within ±0.02 mm if used carefully. This is an uncertainty of ±2%, which will also be the uncertainty of the radius $(d/2)$.

(3) The cross-sectional area of the wire A is proportional to the square of its radius r ($A = \pi r^2$). Knowing the absolute uncertainty in r we can calculate a maximum value and a minimum value for A. In this case the value of r is 0.5 mm ± 0.01 mm, so:

$$A_{max} = \pi \times (0.5\ mm + 0.01\ mm)^2 = 0.82\ mm^2$$

and:

$$A_{min} = \pi \times (0.5\ mm - 0.01\ mm)^2 = 0.75\ mm^2$$

This is often a useful way of working for relationships which are rather complicated or which involve functions like sin or cos.

For simple relationships like this it is usually easier to use percentage uncertainties, noting that when two quantities are multiplied together (or one is divided by the other) the total uncertainty is the *sum* of the two percentage uncertainties. In this case this gives an uncertainty of ±4% in the cross-sectional area of the wire (percentage uncertainty in r + percentage uncertainty in r = 2% + 2%), that is, 0.79 mm^2 ± 4%, which corresponds with the calculations above. Some general guidelines on combining uncertainties are given in the text on the left.

(4) If a piece of wire 2 m long is used, its length l can be measured to within around 3 mm using a metre rule – an uncertainty of ±1.5%.

(5) The extension of the wire x depends on many factors such as its length, its cross-sectional area and the material it is made of. If extensions of the order of 5 mm are measured to within 0.5 mm, the uncertainty is ±10%.

(6) This is the sum of the uncertainties for F and A.

(7) This is the sum of the uncertainties for x and l.

The overall uncertainty in E is likely to be ±6% + ±11.5%, that is, ±17.5%.

The Young modulus – worked example

A lift is designed to hold a maximum of 12 people. The lift cage has a mass of 500 kg, and the distance from the top floor of the building to the ground floor is 50 m.

(1) What minimum cross-sectional area should the cable have in order to just support the lift and people in it? Why would the cable have to be thicker than this in practice?

(2) Estimate how much the steel lift cable will stretch if 10 people get into the lift at the ground floor, assuming that the lift cable has four times the area of cross-section calculated in (1).
(Young modulus of steel $= 2 \times 10^{11}$ N m^{-2}, tensile strength of steel $= 4 \times 10^8$ N m^{-2}.)

(1) Assume that the mass of an average person = 70 kg.

Tensile strength = tensile stress at breaking point = F/A

Load on cable = [(12 × 70 kg) + 500 kg] × 10 N kg^{-1}

= 13 400 N

Tensile strength $= 4 \times 10^8$ N m$^{-2} = \dfrac{13\ 400\ N}{area}$

Rearranging:

$$\textbf{Area} = \frac{\textbf{13 400 N}}{\textbf{4} \times \textbf{10}^8 \textbf{ N m}^{-2}} = \textbf{3.35} \times \textbf{10}^{-5} \textbf{ m}^2$$

Minimum area of cross-section of cable is 0.34 cm^2.
The cable would have to be thicker than this in practice because the tension in it will increase as it accelerates the lift upwards.

(2) Again, assume that the mass of an average person = 70 kg.

Load on cable = [(10 × 70 kg) + 500 kg] × 10 N kg^{-1}

= 12 000 N

$$\textbf{\textit{E}} = \frac{\textbf{tensile stress}}{\textbf{tensile strain}} = \frac{\textbf{\textit{F}/\textit{A}}}{\textbf{\textit{x}/\textit{l}}}$$

so:

$$\textbf{2} \times \textbf{10}^{11} \textbf{ N m}^{-2} = \frac{\textbf{12 000 N/1.36} \times \textbf{10}^{-4} \textbf{ m}^2}{\textbf{\textit{x}/50 m}}$$

Rearranging:

$$\textbf{\textit{x}} = \frac{\textbf{12 000 N/1.36} \times \textbf{10}^{-4} \textbf{ m}^2}{\textbf{2} \times \textbf{10}^{11} \textbf{ N m}^{-2}\textbf{/50 m}}$$

$$= \textbf{2.2} \times \textbf{10}^{-2} \textbf{ m}$$

The lift cable stretches by about 2 cm.

Deformation (3) – stress–strain behaviour

The behaviour of materials which are subject to stress is often represented by means of **stress–strain curves**. For a metal, a typical stress–strain curve looks like that shown in figure 2.2.8.

Classes of solids

Classifying materials

So far we have looked at the ability of a material to resist a tensile force, which is called its *stiffness*, and the tensile stress at which a material fails – its *tensile strength*. Both of these terms consider only situations in which the sample of material is under tension (that is, being pulled apart), without thinking about any other situation. Figure 2.2.9 shows some other types of force that might act on a solid.

Figure 2.2.8

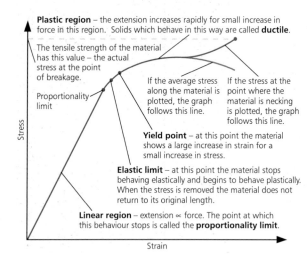

Plastic region – the extension increases rapidly for small increase in force in this region. Solids which behave in this way are called **ductile**.

The tensile strength of the material has this value – the actual stress at the point of breakage.

Proportionality limit

If the average stress along the material is plotted, the graph follows this line.

If the stress at the point where the material is necking is plotted, the graph follows this line.

Yield point – at this point the material shows a large increase in strain for a small increase in stress.

Elastic limit – at this point the material stops behaving elastically and begins to behave plastically. When the stress is removed the material does not return to its original length.

Linear region – extension ∝ force. The point at which this behaviour stops is called the **proportionality limit**.

Stress

Strain

As the stress increases, the sample begins to narrow at one point – this is called 'necking'. The stress is larger at this point than at other points along the sample (because stress ∝ 1/area), so that once this has occurred, the sample will begin to fail at this point.

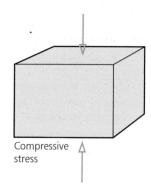

Compressive stress

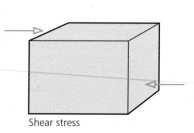

Shear stress

Some materials have very low tensile strength, but are strong when they are subjected to **compressive stress** – brick and concrete are two common examples of such materials. The strength of a material under **shear stress** is related to some extent to its tensile strength. In general, the *strength* of a material refers to its ability to withstand stress, whether tensile, compressive or shear.

Ductile materials are those which show plastic deformation (see figure 2.2.8) – metals usually behave like this. Materials which are not ductile are called **brittle**. It is important to understand that brittle does not mean weak – although glass is a brittle material, its tensile strength can be as great as that of aluminium. Some ceramics (materials generally made of clay) actually have a greater tensile strength than most metals!

Tough materials are strong (will resist large stresses), and also show plastic deformation before breaking. Tough materials are therefore not brittle, by definition. Figure 2.2.10 shows the stress–strain curves for some classes of materials with different properties.

Figure 2.2.9 In practical situations, materials need to be able to resist these sorts of deformations as well as tensile deformations.

Figure 2.2.10

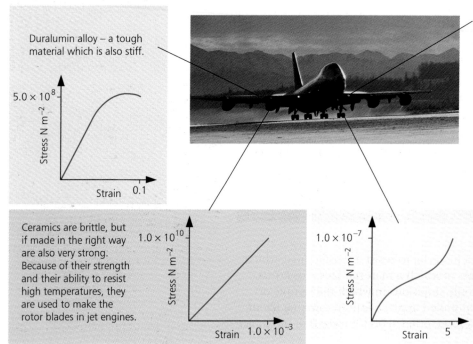

Duralumin alloy – a tough material which is also stiff.

5.0×10^8

Stress N m^{-2}

Strain   0.1

Copper is ductile – it has a large region in which it shows plastic behaviour. This, coupled with its high electrical conductivity, makes it ideal for drawing into wires for use in electrical circuits.

2.0×10^8

Stress N m^{-2}

Strain   0.2

Ceramics are brittle, but if made in the right way are also very strong. Because of their strength and their ability to resist high temperatures, they are used to make the rotor blades in jet engines.

1.0×10^{10}

Stress N m^{-2}

Strain 1.0×10^{-3}

1.0×10^{-7}

Stress N m^{-2}

Strain   5

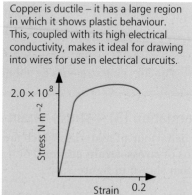

Rubber is initially reluctant to stretch, but then extends easily until it reaches a point where it becomes hard to stretch again. Its highly elastic behaviour makes it ideal for use in tyres and shock absorbers. Rubber is able to dissipate energy through a process called **hysteresis**. This is explained in section 2.5, page 187.

Metals, non-metals, polymers and glasses

There are other ways of classifying materials, besides using their mechanical properties. Chemists, for example, often make use of the metal/non-metal classification when describing a material, based on electrical and thermal properties. Whatever way of classifying is used, there are always exceptions to the rule. Metals usually exhibit ductile behaviour – but cast iron does not. Non-metals are usually brittle – but most plastics are not. In some cases, simple classification is impossible. Silicon and germanium behave like both metals and non-metals, especially in regard to their electrical properties, which lie between metallic and non-metallic behaviour.

In biological terms, probably the most important group of materials is the **polymers**. Polymeric materials contain chains of great length, made up of regularly repeating subunits called **monomers**. In proteins, the monomer subunits are amino acids, which are used to build up molecules of great complexity. Polymers are important too in the chemistry of artificial materials. Many modern materials used for a wide range of purposes are synthetic polymers made from oil. By suitable manipulation of the structure of the polymer, the properties of the material may be engineered to suit the application in which it is to be used.

Thermosetting polymers undergo a permanent change in their structure when they are heated in the process of shaping them. This means that they do not soften when they are subsequently heated, although they may decompose if heated strongly enough. **Thermoplastic** polymers are those polymers which soften on heating, becoming flexible and finally, when the temperature is high enough, melting. This behaviour is also shown by the **glasses**. At high temperatures the particles in a glass are free to move around, although they do not have sufficient energy to escape from one another completely – in other words, the material is a liquid. As the liquid cools, the random arrangement of moving particles becomes static, and the liquid solidifies without the long-range order that is usually associated with solids. Strictly speaking, such materials are not solids but liquids, figure 2.2.11.

The crystalline state

Whilst the force–separation and potential energy–separation curves we saw in figure 2.1.8 (page 119) may be used to help interpret and explain the behaviour of solids, a fuller explanation requires some understanding of the way in which the particles in a solid are arranged. The science of **crystallography** is concerned with this arrangement of particles.

Crystalline solids

A solid is said to be **crystalline** when its particles show a regular arrangement, with well-defined patterns being visible. The investigation of such structures is normally carried out using X-rays. Metals are usually **polycrystalline**, composed of a large number of small crystals (or **grains**), visible in figure 2.2.12.

Non-metals, for example sugar and salt, may also have structures which are crystalline. Even though on first thoughts a regular arrangement of the long molecules in a polymeric substance may seem unlikely, polymers may in fact be crystalline too, as figure 2.2.13 shows.

Amorphous solids

In contrast to the regularity apparent in crystalline structures, the structure of glasses contains little order. These materials are sometimes referred to as **amorphous** solids, which is simply a way of stressing the fact that they have little regularity in their internal arrangement of particles (the word 'amorphous' means 'without form').

Figure 2.2.11 Glass is a 'solid liquid' – its particles are fixed in position, as it is a solid, but have an irregular arrangement as in a liquid. Here glass is being blow-moulded into bottles.

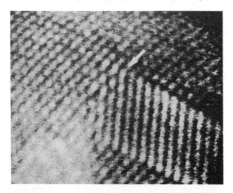

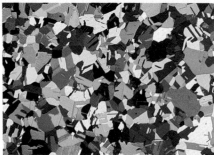

Figure 2.2.12 The high resolution electron micrograph shows the regular arrangement of gold atoms in the crystal lattice of metallic gold. On a larger scale, the grain boundaries between crystals can quite clearly be seen in the photograph of an etched piece of copper. (The surface film of oxide has been removed from this piece of metal using acid, and the surface then polished to reveal the crystals.)

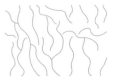

Highly branched structure leads to low-density material and non-crystalline structure.

Little branching means that chains pack closely together, and molecules may be regularly arranged, leading to a high density and crystalline areas.

Figure 2.2.13 Low-density poly(ethene) and high-density poly(ethene) are made in different ways, but they have the same chemical formula. The two types of poly(ethene) have very different properties.

Low-density poly(ethene)

High-density poly(ethene)

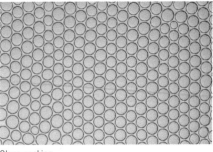

Tube connected to gas tap
Fine tube

Petri dish containing soap solution

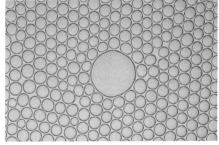

Close packing

Modelling crystalline structures

By blowing small bubbles on the surface of a soap solution to produce a 'bubble raft', the crystalline structure of materials can be modelled as shown in figure 2.2.14. In large areas of the bubble raft any one bubble is surrounded by a regular hexagon of six other bubbles. This is called a 'close-packed' arrangement, and represents the most efficient use of space in terms of filling it with particles. Slightly compressing or stretching the raft leads to bubbles being squashed together or pulled apart slightly, a process that can be thought of as modelling elastic deformations in a material, where the particles resume their original positions when the deforming force is removed. Greater deformation leads to a permanent change in the position of the bubbles, which provides a way of visualising plastic deformation. In some areas of the raft, a regular arrangement of bubbles may be disrupted slightly by a larger or smaller bubble; in others, areas of bubbles meet at different angles forming an analogy to grain boundaries in polycrystalline materials. Compressing or stretching the bubbles in one of these areas demonstrates how a fault in a part of the structure of a material may weaken it, and lead to permanent deformation and fracturing when a force is applied.

Disruption by a large bubble

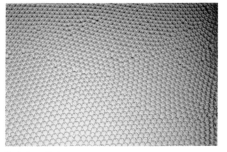

Grain boundaries

Figure 2.2.14 A bubble raft model of crystalline structures.

Composite materials

A very important class of materials is the **composite materials**. These materials consist of one type of material combined with another in order to obtain a material which combines the strengths of the two chosen materials without their weaknesses.

One of the best known composite materials is reinforced concrete. This is made by pouring liquid concrete over a network of steel rods. Concrete has great compressive strength but little tensile strength, while steel has good tensile strength. This combination produces a building material which is inexpensive, but which has much better ability to withstand tensile forces than concrete alone.

Biological systems also make use of composite materials. Wood (a composite of cellulose fibres joined together by lignin) is a natural composite construction material. Bone, figure 2.2.15, is another example of a natural composite, consisting of living cells in a matrix of collagen fibres and calcium salts. Such a composite has enormous compressive strength, with the ability to withstand shear deformation too. At the same time, bone is light – particularly important for flying animals.

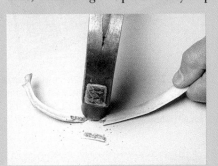
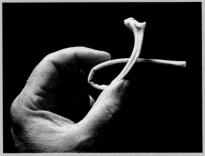

Figure 2.2.15 The combined properties of collagen and calcium salts make bone an extremely strong material weight for weight. Removal of the collagen fibres (left) leaves a material which is very brittle. On the other hand, removal of the calcium salts (right) leaves a material with little rigidity.

Fluids

The word **fluid** means flowing or capable of flowing. The term is therefore applied to liquids and gases, whose particles are capable of moving and so allow the liquid or gas to flow.

The tendency of fluids to resist flowing is called their **viscosity**, as figure 2.2.16 illustrates. Viscosity has enormous importance in areas of design such as the internal combustion engine (in relation to the flow of lubricating oil and cooling water through the engine) and aircraft (considering the flow of air around an aeroplane's wings and body).

Kinetic theory and fluids

In looking at the behaviour of fluids we shall consider particularly the link between the behaviour of particles of matter, and the overall behaviour of matter on a macroscopic scale. Although it is possible to develop effective kinetic theory models of solids and gases, the situation with liquids is not so clear cut. This stems largely from the fact that liquids have short-range order among their particles, which are packed almost as closely together as the particles in a solid, yet their particles are in motion, which means that overall they are nearly as mobile as the particles in a gas. Liquids are almost impossible to compress (like solids) but are capable of flowing (like gases), and such behaviour makes them very difficult to model.

The physical properties of fluids

Pressure

All fluids exert **pressure**, as of course do solids. The definition of pressure is:

$$\text{Pressure} = \frac{\text{perpendicular force}}{\text{area}} \qquad p = \frac{F}{A}$$

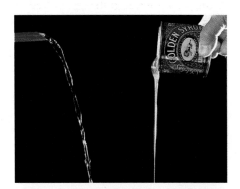

Figure 2.2.16 Not all fluids flow easily – water and treacle are both fluids, but their tendency to flow is very different. Air flows more easily than either.

To find the pressure exerted by a force that is not acting perpendicularly over a given area, the component of the force acting perpendicularly to the area must be found as a first step in the calculation (see box below).

The definition of pressure involves a vector (force), although pressure itself is not a vector quantity as it is defined as always being at right angles to the surface over which it acts.

The SI unit of pressure is the **pascal** (Pa), where $1\ Pa = 1\ N\ m^{-2}$.

Figure 2.2.17 1 Pa is a very small pressure – about the same as the weight of an apple at the Earth's surface acting over the area of an open newspaper. For this reason, kilopascals are often used: 1 kPa = 1000 Pa.

Finding pressure – worked example

Find the pressure exerted by a force of 260 N acting at an angle of 30° to an area of 2 m², as shown in figure 2.2.18.

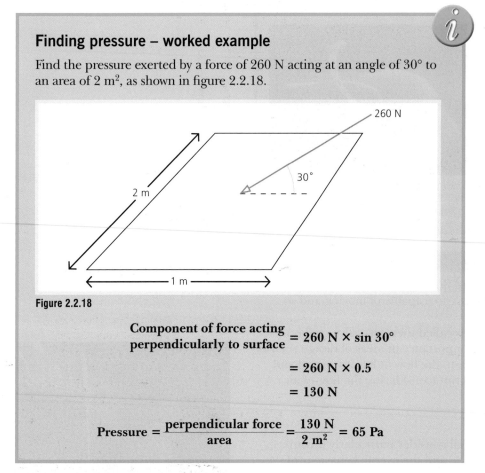

Figure 2.2.18

$$\text{Component of force acting perpendicularly to surface} = 260\ N \times \sin 30°$$

$$= 260\ N \times 0.5$$

$$= 130\ N$$

$$\text{Pressure} = \frac{\text{perpendicular force}}{\text{area}} = \frac{130\ N}{2\ m^2} = 65\ Pa$$

Observation of fluids leads to two conclusions about pressure within them:

1 Pressure applied to a fluid at rest is transmitted equally to all parts of the fluid and to the walls of the container it is in (this is **Pascal's law**).

2 The pressure below the surface of a fluid increases as the depth increases.

We shall go on to look at each of these observations in turn.

(1) Hydraulics

Pascal's law forms the basis for devices which make use of **hydraulics**, for example car braking systems and hydraulic jacks and presses. In essence, the idea behind these devices is that a small force is exerted over a small area, applying a pressure to a liquid, usually oil. The pressure is transmitted through the liquid to a large piston, which causes a large force to be exerted on it. In a completely different area of application, animals such as worms and sea anemones make use of the transmission of pressure within fluids in order to move around.

Hydraulics – worked example

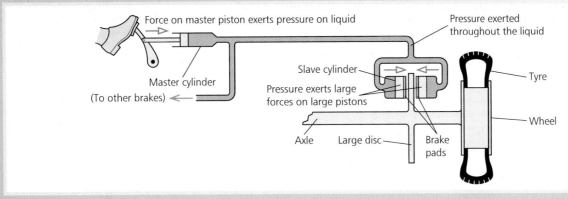

Figure 2.2.19

Figure 2.2.19 shows a car braking system. If the diameter of the piston in the master cylinder is 2 cm and that in each slave cylinder is 8 cm, what force is exerted on each brake pad when a force of 100 N is exerted on the piston in the master cylinder?

$$\textbf{Pressure exerted} \atop \textbf{on fluid} = \frac{\textbf{force on piston in master cylinder}}{\textbf{area of piston in master cylinder}}$$

$$= \frac{\textbf{100 N}}{\pi \times (\textbf{1} \times \textbf{10}^{-2} \textbf{ m})^2}$$

$$= \textbf{3.2} \times \textbf{10}^5 \textbf{ Pa}$$

This pressure is transmitted through the fluid and so is also exerted on the piston in each slave cylinder, so:

$$\textbf{3.2} \times \textbf{10}^5 \textbf{ Pa} = \frac{\textbf{force exerted by fluid on piston in slave cylinder}}{\textbf{area of piston in slave cylinder}}$$

$$= \frac{F}{\pi \times (\textbf{4} \times \textbf{10}^{-2} \textbf{ m})^2}$$

$$= \frac{F}{\textbf{5.0} \times \textbf{10}^{-3} \textbf{ m}^2}$$

so:

$$F = \textbf{3.2} \times \textbf{10}^5 \textbf{ Pa} \times \textbf{5.0} \times \textbf{10}^{-3} \textbf{ m}^2$$

$$= \textbf{1600 N}$$

The force of 100 N at the brake pedal becomes a force of 1600 N at each brake pad. (This really should not surprise us – the diameter of the slave cylinder piston is four times that of the master cylinder piston, so its area is $4^2 = 16$ times greater. The pressure in the fluid thus acts over an area that is 16 times greater, and so the force is 16 times greater too.)

(2) Pressure and depth

The observation that pressure increases with depth below the surface of a fluid is reasonably straightforward to understand in terms of the material properties of a fluid. In figure 2.2.20:

Volume of fluid in cylinder = height × cross-sectional area $= hA$

Mass of fluid in cylinder = volume × density $= hA\rho$

Weight of fluid in cylinder = mass × gravitational field strength $= hA\rho g$

So:

$$\textbf{Pressure exerted on base} = \frac{\textbf{weight}}{\textbf{area}} = \frac{hA\rho g}{A} = h\rho g$$

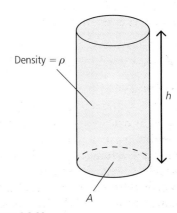

Figure 2.2.20

This relationship suggests that the pressure exerted at a point inside a fluid is proportional to the depth of the point below its surface. This is a reasonable deduction to make in the case of liquids – being incompressible, the density of a liquid can be taken as constant no matter what the pressure, so a liquid's density will remain the same at all depths within it. This is *not* a reasonable assumption for gases however – being compressible, their density *does* change with pressure. Use of the relationship $p = h\rho g$ with gases can therefore only be used in situations where it may reasonably be assumed that the density of the gas is constant over the difference in depth h. Figure 2.2.21 illustrates this point.

Upthrust

A famous legend has the Greek philosopher Archimedes running naked through the streets of Syracuse shouting 'Eureka!' ('I've found it!'). Supposedly, whilst getting into his bath, Archimedes was puzzling over the problem of telling a genuine gold crown from a fake one. On observing the overflow of water, he realised that each crown would displace its own volume of water and that it would experience an upwards force (or **upthrust**) as a result. Since the two crowns had equal masses (otherwise they could be distinguished by weighing them), the crown made from inferior metal would experience a greater upthrust than the genuine one because of its lower density. The key to distinguishing between the two crowns thus lay in weighing each crown while it was immersed in water.

Archimedes' discovery is now generally known as **Archimedes' principle**:

> **Any body wholly or partly immersed in a fluid experiences an upthrust equal to the weight of fluid displaced.**

Any floating object has an upthrust acting on it equal and opposite to its weight, while an object that sinks will have an upthrust on it that is *less* than its weight.

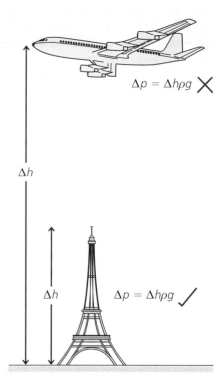

Figure 2.2.21 Over the difference in height involved in climbing the Eiffel Tower, it is probably reasonable to assume that the density of air is approximately constant. In principle it is therefore possible to calculate the height of the tower by measuring the air pressure at the top of the tower and at the base, and then using $\Delta p = h\rho g$ to calculate the height, although the accuracy of this method would probably not be very great (why?). This would *not* be a reasonable assumption in the case of an aircraft flying at a height of several thousand metres, however. (Although an aircraft's altimeter measures the height of the aircraft using atmospheric pressure, it is calibrated to take into account the change in the air's density with increasing height.)

In the diagram: $\Delta p = \Delta h\rho g$ ✗ (aircraft), $\Delta p = \Delta h\rho g$ ✓ (Eiffel Tower), with Δh labelled.

Figure 2.2.22 The fact that all these objects can float in a fluid (air or water) suggests that there is an upthrust acting on them. The shape of an object clearly has an effect on the amount of fluid displaced – a ship is designed so that it displaces its own weight in water while the majority of the ship remains above the water's surface.

Archimedes' principle justified

It is possible to explain Archimedes' principle by using the relationship between pressure and depth.

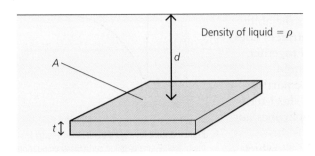

Density of liquid = ρ

Figure 2.2.23

Consider a uniform object as in figure 2.2.23 with cross-sectional area A and thickness t a distance d below the surface of a liquid with a density ρ.

Pressure on top face of object $= d\rho g$

So force downwards on top of object $= d\rho g A$

Pressure on bottom face of object $= (d + t)\rho g$

So upward force on bottom face of object $= (d + t)\rho g A$

And resultant upward force on object $= (d + t)\rho g A$
$$- d\rho g A$$
$$= t\rho g A$$

The volume of the object is tA, so this tells us that the object experiences an upthrust equal to the weight of liquid displaced, as $tA\rho$ is the mass of liquid displaced, and $tA\rho g$ its weight.

Calculations involving upthrust – worked example

A diver salvaging gold bullion from a shipwreck finds a gold bar which measures 30 cm × 10 cm × 10 cm. If the density of gold is 18 880 kg m⁻³, and the density of sea water is 1100 kg m⁻³, what force will be needed to lift the gold bar (1) on land, (2) on the sea bed? (g = 9.8 N kg⁻¹.) State any assumptions you make.

(1) **Volume of bar = 0.3 m × 0.1 m × 0.1 m = 0.003 m³**

So mass of bar = density × volume

$$= 18\ 880 \text{ kg m}^{-3} \times 0.003 \text{ m}^3$$

$$= 56.64 \text{ kg}$$

Weight of bar = mass × gravitational field strength

$$= 56.64 \text{ kg} \times 9.8 \text{ N kg}^{-1}$$

$$= 555 \text{ N}$$

This will be the force required to lift the bar on land.

(2) **Volume of water displaced by the bar $= 0.003$ m³**

So mass of water displaced by the bar = density × volume

$$= 1200 \text{ kg m}^{-3} \times 0.003 \text{ m}^3$$

$$= 3.6 \text{ kg}$$

Weight of water displaced by the bar = mass × gravitational field strength

$$= 3.6 \text{ kg} \times 9.8 \text{ N kg}^{-1}$$

$$= 35 \text{ N}$$

This is the upthrust exerted by the water on the bar, according to Archimedes' principle. Therefore the force needed to lift the bar on the sea bed is:

$$F = 555 \text{ N} - 35 \text{ N}$$

$$= 520 \text{ N}$$

The calculation in (1) neglects the upthrust of the air on the gold bar, since the density of air is only about 1.3 kg m⁻³, which means the upthrust on the bar will be 0.003 m³ × 1.3 kg m⁻³ × 9.8 N kg⁻¹, that is, about 0.04 N, which is very small compared with 555 N.

A particle model for liquids

Liquids are difficult to model well, as their properties lie between those of a gas and a solid, as mentioned earlier. Since solids do not expand appreciably when they melt, it seems reasonable to conclude that the separation of particles in a liquid is similar to that in a solid. However, the particles in a liquid must be freer and more easily able to move than those in a solid, since it has the ability to flow. On the other hand, the upper surface of a liquid (its **free surface**) does not need to be restrained by a container in order to keep the liquid together, which implies that there must be forces keeping the particles in a liquid together. This balance of freedom to move versus forces keeping the particles together leads to a model of a liquid in which there is considerable short-term and short-range structure, although in the long term any one particle does not remain in contact with the same particles for any length of time. It is this 'neither one thing nor the other' behaviour, illustrated in figure 2.2.24, which makes a liquid much more difficult to model successfully than a solid or (as we shall see shortly) a gas.

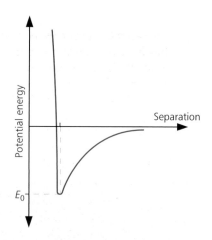

Figure 2.2.24 In a solid the internal energy $U \ll E_0$, the potential energy of the particles at equilibrium separation (see page 119). The particles therefore cannot overcome the attractive forces between themselves, and are fixed in position. In a gas, $U \gg E_0$ – the particles are easily able to overcome the forces between themselves, and are completely free to move. In a liquid, $U \approx E_0$ – at any given moment some particles may have sufficient energy to overcome the attractive forces, but many will not, so there is a pattern of restricted movement.

The liquid surface

Free surface energy

The attractive forces within the body of a liquid mean that it is necessary to do work on a particle in order to move it from the body of the liquid to the layer of molecules at the surface. Since this is so, the particles in the surface layer of a liquid must possess more energy than those in the body of the liquid. The surface of a liquid is thus said to have **free surface energy**.

Another way of putting this would be to say that if a particle in the body of the liquid has n_1 nearest neighbours and one in the surface layer has n_2 nearest neighbours (obviously $n_1 > n_2$), the energy required to move a particle from the body of the liquid to the surface will be $(n_1 - n_2)E_0$, since E_0 is the energy required to separate a particle from *one* of its nearest neighbours.

One consequence of this is that liquids tend to occupy volumes in which the surface area:volume ratio is at a minimum. Hence liquid droplets tend to be spherical in shape, since this minimises the surface area for a given volume, and so makes the surface area and hence the free surface energy a minimum.

Surface tension

Another consequence of the free surface energy is that the surface of a liquid exhibits **surface tension**, as illustrated in figure 2.2.25. The argument to establish this can be summarised as follows:
(1) The particles in the surface layer and the body of the liquid are constantly moving and changing places.
(2) Over time, as many particles must enter the surface layer from the body of the liquid as enter the body of the liquid from the surface layer (neglecting particles leaving the liquid altogether to go into the vapour phase – a fair assumption if the liquid is far from its boiling point).

(3) It is easier for particles to leave the surface layer than to enter it, as they have free surface energy.

(4) To maintain the balance in numbers of particles entering and leaving the surface layer, there must be fewer particles per unit volume in the surface layer than in the body of the liquid.

(5) The particles in the surface layer must therefore be further apart than the particles in the body of the liquid, so that there is a greater attractive force between the particles in the surface layer than between the particles in the body of the liquid.

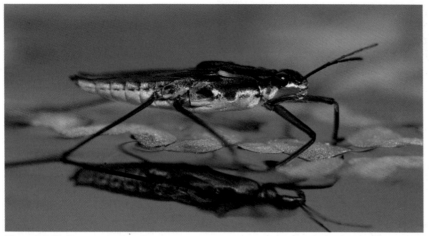

Figure 2.2.25 The attractive force between water molecules causes the surface of the water to behave as if it has a 'skin', a phenomenon which some insects are able to exploit to their advantage.

Water

Water is an unusual liquid, as figure 2.2.26 overleaf shows.

The physical and chemical properties of water arise from the interactions between its molecules. Unusually strong intermolecular forces (called **hydrogen bonds**) are caused by the electrical structure of the water molecule, and give rise to water's exceptionally high boiling point. An open structure of water molecules in six-membered rings is formed as water freezes, producing a solid which is less dense than its liquid. Like any other liquid, water has a short-term structure which would be revealed if we could take a 'snapshot' of the arrangement of the molecules instantaneously – over a time period of no longer than 10^{-9} s. Such a snapshot would show the existence of regions of molecules with an ice-type structure, surrounded by free molecules. With an exposure 100 times longer than this, the molecules would appear blurred as the free molecules and those in the ice-type structures rapidly changed places.

Gases

The gas laws

The interdependence of the pressure, temperature and volume of a gas were investigated in the seventeenth and eighteenth centuries, when the relationships known as **Boyle's law**, **Charles' law** and the **pressure law** were established. These relationships, together with the laws of mechanics, form the basis of the kinetic theory of gases.

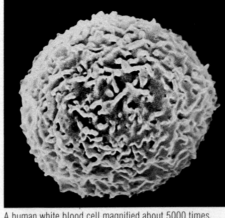

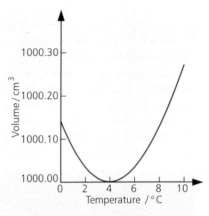

If water solidified in the same way as as other substances, pond life would be impossible, since ice would form at the bottom of a pond instead of at the surface.

A human white blood cell magnified about 5000 times. The structure of the water molecule and its electrical properties mean that water molecules can surround other particles which have an electrical charge, however small, and so dissolve them. Such behaviour has enabled the development of life.

The volume of 1 kg of water at different temperatures around the freezing point.

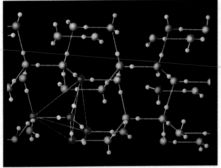

Six-membered rings in ice.

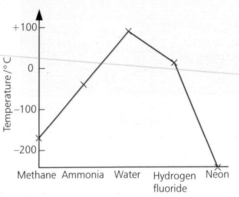

The boiling point of water is unusually high.

Figure 2.2.26 Water covers three-fifths of the Earth's surface, and is a substance we encounter every day. Yet for all our familiarity with it, water is one of the most remarkable substances. Its solid form floats in the liquid. Water is a liquid at room temperature and pressure, whereas substances with particles of a similar mass are gases. It is capable of dissolving a tremendous range of substances, making it the ideal medium for life, both inside and outside cells.

Boyle's law states that:

> **For a constant amount of gas, the pressure is inversely proportional to the volume if the temperature remains constant.**

or:

$$p \propto \frac{1}{V} \text{ for constant } T$$

Charles' law states that:

> **For a constant amount of gas, the volume is proportional to the absolute temperature if the pressure remains constant.**

or:

$$V \propto T \text{ for constant } p$$

The **pressure law** states that:

> **For a constant amount of gas, the pressure is proportional to the absolute temperature if the volume remains constant.**

or:

$$p \propto T \text{ for constant } V$$

The term 'absolute temperature' is explained in section 2.3.

Investigating the gas laws

In the seventeenth century, Robert Boyle investigated the relationship between the pressure and the temperature of a fixed mass of gas, and found that:

$$pV = \text{constant}$$

if the temperature of the gas was kept constant. A plot of p against V results in a curve called an **isotherm**, shown in figure 2.2.27. A straight line graph results if p is plotted against $1/V$, since $p \propto 1/V$.

The investigation of the variation of the volume of a gas with its temperature shows that there is a simple relationship between these two quantities, as the graph in figure 2.2.27 shows. The plot of volume versus temperature intercepts the x-axis at –273 °C, which suggests that if a gas did not eventually liquefy as it was cooled, it would occupy zero volume at this temperature, and we could write $V \propto T$, where T is the **absolute temperature** measured in **kelvins** (K), obtained by adding 273 to the Celsius temperature. The ideas behind temperature scales are explained in section 2.3. For the moment it is sufficient to note that the behaviour we have described applies only to **ideal gases**, and that **real gases** often behave somewhat differently.

Investigation of the variation of the pressure of a gas with its temperature shows a similar relationship to that found between volume and temperature.

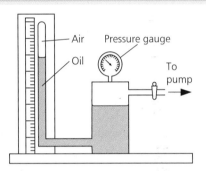

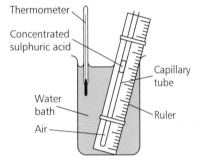

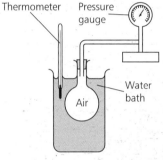

Boyle's law
Gas (usually air) is trapped in a glass tube by light oil. Pressure is exerted on the oil by a pump, which compresses the gas. Pressure is measured with a gauge and volume by the length of the air column.

Charles' law
Gas (usually air) is trapped in a capillary tube by a bead of concentrated sulphuric acid (this ensures that the air column is dry). The gas is heated in a water bath, and the volume measured by the length of the column.

Pressure law
Gas (usually air) is trapped in a flask and heated in a water bath, or an oil bath if temperatures above 100 °C are required. Pressure is measured with a pressure gauge.

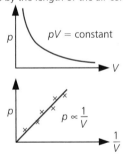

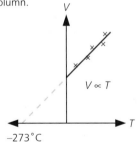

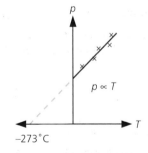

Figure 2.2.27 Investigating the gas laws

Combining the gas laws

The three gas laws may be summarised as follows:

$$pV = \text{constant (if } T \text{ is constant)}$$

$$p/T = \text{constant (if } V \text{ is constant)}$$

$$V/T = \text{constant (if } p \text{ is constant)}$$

Combining them gives:

$$\frac{pV}{T} = \text{constant}$$

The constant depends on the amount of gas involved. This is an amount of matter, which is measured in moles (see page 117). Investigation shows that for a given pressure and temperature, doubling the amount of a gas doubles its volume. The constant may therefore be written as nR, where n is the number of moles of gas. R is a constant known as the **molar gas constant**, which has the approximate value 8.3 J mol^{-1} K^{-1}.

We can now write down the equation of state for a gas:

$$\frac{pV}{T} = nR \quad \text{or} \quad pV = nRT$$

This equation describes the way a fixed amount of gas behaves as its pressure, volume and temperature change. Experimental evidence shows that this mathematical model for the behaviour of a gas is only satisfactory when the gas is at relatively low pressures and high temperatures, that is, when it is far from liquefaction. (The behaviour of **real** and **ideal** gases will be discussed later in this section.)

The gas laws – worked example

At the top of Mount Everest the temperature is around 250 K, with atmospheric pressure around 3.3×10^4 Pa. Using these two values, and taking the temperature at sea level as 300 K, the atmospheric pressure at sea level as 1.0×10^5 Pa and the density of air at sea level as 1.2 kg m^{-3}, how does the density of air at the top of Mount Everest compare to its density at sea level?

$$\text{Volume of 1 kg of air at } 300 \text{ K and } 1.0 \times 10^5 \text{ Pa} = \frac{\text{mass/density under these conditions}}{}$$

$$= 1 \text{ kg}/1.2 \text{ kg m}^{-3}$$

$$= 0.83 \text{ m}^3$$

Therefore, at sea level:

$$p_1 = 1.0 \times 10^5 \text{ Pa}$$

$$V_1 = 0.83 \text{ m}^3$$

$$T_1 = 300 \text{ K}$$

And at the top of Everest:

$$p_2 = 3.3 \times 10^4 \text{ Pa}$$

$$V_2 = ? \text{ (to be calculated for 1 kg of air)}$$

$$T_2 = 250 \text{ K}$$

Since pV/T = constant, we may write:

$$\frac{p_1 V_1}{T_1} = \frac{p_2 V_2}{T_2}$$

Substituting:

$$\frac{1.0 \times 10^5 \text{ Pa} \times 0.83 \text{ m}^3}{300 \text{ K}} = \frac{3.3 \times 10^4 \text{ Pa} \times V_2}{250 \text{ K}}$$

so:

$$V_2 = \frac{1.0 \times 10^5 \text{ Pa} \times 0.83 \text{ m}^3 \times 250 \text{ K}}{3.3 \times 10^4 \text{ Pa} \times 300 \text{ K}}$$

$$= 2.1 \text{ m}^3$$

This is the volume of 1 kg of air at the top of Mount Everest. Its density is 1 kg/2.1 m^3 = 0.48 kg m^{-3}.

The model for a gas

As far as gases are concerned, there are two particular areas of contribution to the kinetic theory, some 150 years apart.

A gas as a collection of particles

In the late seventeenth century, Robert Hooke attempted to explain the pressure exerted by a gas in terms of the particles of the gas making collisions with the walls of its container. He based this speculation on one which Robert Boyle had advanced following his own investigations. This was just before Newton's development of his laws of motion, and the combination of Hooke's work and Newton's laws laid the foundation for ideas about the quantitative behaviour of gases based on a model of them as a collection of particles. (This model was further reinforced in the early part of the nineteenth century by the work of the chemists John Dalton, Joseph Gay-Lussac and Amadeo Avogadro, although the existence of atoms was not generally accepted until the very end of the nineteenth century.)

Distribution of energy and the kinetic theory

In the mid-nineteenth century Ludwig Boltzmann and James Clerk Maxwell were working quite independently of each other in Vienna, Austria and Cambridge, England respectively. The two scientists developed a statistical treatment of the distribution of energy amongst a collection of particles. This led to a greater understanding of the way in which the macroscopic properties of matter may be related to the microscopic properties of the particles of which it is composed, and to the development of the kinetic theory through a branch of physics now called statistical mechanics, which is particularly important in modelling the way energy distributes itself among groups of atoms.

The pressure exerted by a gas

The link between the work of Newton and Hooke on the one hand, and Maxwell and Boltzmann on the other, can be shown in the development of a mathematical model to link the pressure of a gas with the mechanical properties of its particles.

Consider one particle colliding with the shaded wall and rebounding with a velocity equal and opposite to its initial velocity, that is, $-c_{x1}$, as shown in figure 2.2.28. This process causes a force to be exerted on the wall. Newton's third law tells us that the wall exerts an equal and opposite force on the particle. This force causes a change in the particle's momentum, $\Delta(mc)$:

$$\Delta(mc) = mc_{x1} - -mc_{x1} = 2mc_{x1}$$

The particle bounces backwards and forwards between the two walls, exerting a force on each. Since velocity = distance/time, the time between two successive collisions with the shaded wall will be given by:

$$\textbf{Time} = \frac{\textbf{distance}}{\textbf{velocity}} = \frac{2l}{c_{x1}}$$

This means that in each time interval of $2l/c_{x1}$, the particle makes *one* collision with the shaded wall of the box, in which the change of momentum is $2mc_{x1}$.

As force = change of momentum/time, we can say that the force causing this change of momentum is given by:

$$\textbf{Force} = \frac{\Delta(mc)}{\Delta t} = \frac{2mc_{x1}}{2l/c_{x1}} = \frac{mc_{x1}^2}{l}$$

This is the *average* force exerted on the wall by the particle over a series of impacts, as illustrated in figure 2.2.29.

Now since pressure = force/area, we can express the pressure p_1 exerted on the shaded wall by:

$$p_1 = \frac{(mc_{x1}^2/l)}{l^2} = \frac{mc_{x1}^2}{l^3}$$

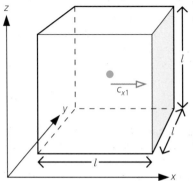

The sides of the box all have length l, so the area of each face is l^2 and the volume is l^3.

Figure 2.2.28 Our starting point for deriving a mathematical relationship between the motion of the particles of a gas and its pressure is a single particle moving parallel to one side of a cubic box. To begin, we *assume* that the particle makes perfectly elastic collisions with the walls of the container, so that it moves continuously along a line joining two opposite walls of the container, rebounding at each wall. (The velocity of the particle is written as c rather than v to avoid any possible confusion with V for volume. The initial velocity of the particle is written as c_{x1} – we shall add other particles later, with velocities c_{x2}, c_{x3}, etc.)

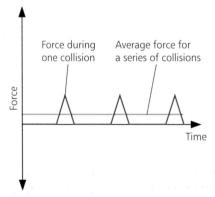

Figure 2.2.29 The area under a force–time graph represents the **impulse** (see page 54), so the area under the average force graph and that under the instantaneous force graph are the same.

Now imagine that there are N particles moving along the x-axis in the same way as the first particle we have been considering. Their velocities will be c_{x1}, c_{x2}, c_{x3}, ..., c_{xN} respectively. Each particle will exert a pressure on the shaded wall in the same way as the first particle. The total pressure p exerted by all N particles on the wall will be the sum of the individual pressures exerted by each particle:

$$p = \Sigma p_n = p_1 + p_2 + p_3 + ... + p_N$$

$$= \frac{mc_{x1}^2}{l^3} + \frac{mc_{x2}^2}{l^3} + \frac{mc_{x3}^2}{l^3} + ... + \frac{mc_{xN}^2}{l^3}$$

$$= \frac{m}{l^3}(c_{x1}^2 + c_{x2}^2 + c_{x3}^2 + ... + c_{xN}^2)$$

The mean of all the squares of the velocities (the **mean square velocity**) can be written as $\overline{c_x^2}$. This is given by the expression:

$$\overline{c_x^2} = \frac{(c_{x1}^2 + c_{x2}^2 + c_{x3}^2 + ... + c_{xN}^2)}{N}$$

Thus:

$$N\overline{c_x^2} = (c_{x1}^2 + c_{x2}^2 + c_{x3}^2 + ... + c_{xN}^2)$$

and the expression for the total pressure exerted on the shaded wall by all N particles becomes:

$$p = \frac{Nm\overline{c_x^2}}{l^3}$$

We must now consider the situation if we take into account the fact that we have a collection of particles moving with a range of speeds in random directions. Any one particle may have its velocity c resolved into three perpendicular components, as figure 2.2.30 shows.

We may resolve the mean square velocities in the same way, so that:

$$\overline{c^2} = \overline{c_x^2} + \overline{c_y^2} + \overline{c_z^2}$$

Since there is a large number of particles and they are all moving in random directions, it follows that *on average* the mean square velocities in the x, y and z directions are all equal, that is:

$$\overline{c_x^2} = \overline{c_y^2} = \overline{c_z^2}$$

Since we already know that:

$$\overline{c^2} = \overline{c_x^2} + \overline{c_y^2} + \overline{c_z^2}$$

it follows that:

$$\frac{\overline{c^2}}{3} = \overline{c_x^2} = \overline{c_y^2} = \overline{c_z^2}$$

The pressure exerted on the shaded face (and indeed, any of the other five faces, since we have just shown that the velocities of the particles are equal along all three axes) is now given by:

$$p = \frac{Nm\overline{c_x^2}}{l^3} = \tfrac{1}{3} \times \frac{Nm\overline{c^2}}{l^3} = \tfrac{1}{3} \times \frac{Nm\overline{c^2}}{V}$$

where V is the volume of the box.

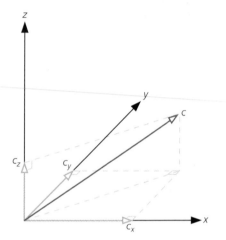

Figure 2.2.30 By applying Pythagoras' theorem we can resolve c into three perpendicular components, and $c^2 = c_x^2 + c_y^2 + c_z^2$.

But Nm is the total mass of the particles in the box, so the quantity Nm/V is the density of the gas, ρ. The pressure of the gas can thus be written as:

$$p = \tfrac{1}{3}\rho\,\overline{c^2}$$

Figure 2.2.31 summarises the derivation of this expression, and the assumptions made at each stage.

Model of a gas as a collection of particles (work of Boyle, Hooke and Dalton, plus experimental evidence of Brownian motion interpreted by Einstein)

Pressure exerted by gas due to collisions of particles with walls of container

Consistent with the observations that:
(1) the pressure of a gas increases with increasing temperature, and
(2) the idea that increasing the temperature of a gas involves raising its internal energy by allowing energy to flow into it *assuming* that the increased internal energy of the gas is actually contained in the increased kinetic energy of its particles

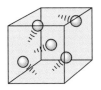

Pressure exerted on walls by a collection of particles is equal to the *sum* of the pressures exerted on the walls by each individual particle.

Assumes that in the collection of particles the interaction between particles – except when they are colliding – is negligible. This is another assumption which is convenient, since it simplifies the construction of the model, but which requires some justification later in terms of what the model produces. We are also assuming that the volume of the particles themselves is negligible compared with the volume occupied by the gas as a whole. The volume change when a liquid becomes a gas can justify this second assumption, as 1 cm³ of a liquid may produce over 1000 cm³ of a gas at atmospheric pressure, so the particles in the gas must be considerably further apart than in the liquid.

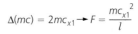

$$\Delta(mc) = 2mc_{x1} \rightarrow F = \frac{mc_{x1}^2}{l}$$

Assumes that:
(1) Collisions between particle and walls are perfectly elastic (no loss of kinetic energy in collisions), and
(2) Newtonian mechanics (i.e. Newton's laws of motion) can be applied.
If (1) is untrue, the particle would lose energy during collisions, its velocity would decrease and so the pressure exerted on the walls would decrease, unless energy constantly flowed into the gas. This is contrary to experimental observations, so (1) seems reasonable.
Assumption (2) is difficult to justify. Without this assumption it would be difficult to make any progress in constructing the model. The best that can be done is to say that a model constructed with this assumption built in seems to produce results which relate well to experimental evidence.

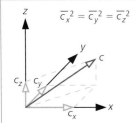

$$\overline{c_x^2} = \overline{c_y^2} = \overline{c_z^2}$$

The average distribution of velocities over time is the same in all directions.

This assumption can be justified on the grounds that a gas exerts the same pressure on each part of its container.

Figure 2.2.31 The macroscopic behaviour of a gas understood in terms of its microscopic properties. This link between the work of Hooke and Newton and that of Maxwell and Boltzmann involves a number of steps in which assumptions are made.

Molecular speeds

We now have a relationship between the speed of the molecules in a gas and its density – in other words, a relationship between its microscopic and macroscopic properties. If we take the density of some typical gases at room temperature, we can use this relationship to obtain a figure for the speed of their molecules.

Air at room temperature and pressure

ρ_{air} (at 25 °C) = 1.18 kg m^{-3}, $p = 1.01 \times 10^5$ Pa

$$p = \tfrac{1}{3}\rho\overline{c^2}$$

$$1.01 \times 10^5 \text{ Pa} = \tfrac{1}{3} \times 1.18 \text{ kg m}^{-3} \times \overline{c^2}$$

$$\overline{c^2} = \frac{3 \times 1.01 \times 10^5 \text{ Pa}}{1.18 \text{ kg m}^{-3}}$$

$$\sqrt{\overline{c^2}} = \sqrt{(2.57 \times 10^5 \text{ m}^2 \text{ s}^{-2})}$$

$$= 507 \text{ m s}^{-1}$$

Chlorine at room temperature and pressure

$\rho_{chlorine}$ (at 25 °C) = 3.17 kg m^{-3}, $p = 1.01 \times 10^5$ Pa

$$p = \tfrac{1}{3}\rho\overline{c^2}$$

$$1.01 \times 10^5 \text{ Pa} = \tfrac{1}{3} \times 3.17 \text{ kg m}^{-3} \times \overline{c^2}$$

$$\overline{c^2} = \frac{3 \times 1.01 \times 10^5 \text{ Pa}}{3.17 \text{ kg m}^{-3}}$$

$$\sqrt{\overline{c^2}} = \sqrt{(9.56 \times 10^4 \text{ m}^2 \text{ s}^{-2})}$$

$$= 309 \text{ m s}^{-1}$$

The speeds here are the square root of the mean of the squares of the speeds of the molecules – the **root-mean-square** (r.m.s.) speeds. This is *not* the same as the mean speed of the molecules. These speeds are of the order of the speed of sound in gases. It is unlikely that the speed of a sound wave passing through a gas could be faster than the speed at which the molecules of the gas itself could travel, so this initial check on the model seems fairly reasonable.

Ideal and real gases

These models of gases compare with experimental results quite well. In one way this is unsurprising, since the models are both based quite firmly on experimental observations. Even the first model, of the gas as a collection of particles, is based on the known behaviour of gases. In another way it is surprising, since we have apparently described the behaviour of a large collection of particles in very simple terms.

The models describe the behaviour of **ideal** gases. Such gases have negligible forces between their particles, which take up negligible volume. Their volume and pressure decrease linearly as the temperature decreases, until both reach zero at the absolute zero of temperature. Clearly such gases cannot exist! **Real** gases do have attractive forces between their particles, since it is possible to liquefy them. Similarly, the particles of real gases do occupy a significant volume, since they liquefy to form almost incompressible liquids.

But under the right circumstances, real gases *can* approximate to the behaviour of an ideal gas. In order for this to be so, a gas must be well away from the conditions at which it would liquefy. This means ensuring that $U \gg E_0$ (see figure 2.2.24, page 136) and that the size of the particles of the gas is negligible compared with the distance between them. This can be done by making sure that the temperature of the gas is well above its **critical temperature**, which is the temperature at which it may be liquefied by pressure alone. The gas must also be at a pressure well below its **critical pressure**, which is the pressure at which it becomes a liquid when at its critical temperature.

One piece of circumstantial evidence which suggests that the model for a real gas can be quite a simple one, like that we have produced, is that under similar conditions of temperature and pressure (far from the critical point of the gas), one mole of any gas occupies the same volume – around 22.4 dm³ (2.24×10^{-2} m³) at 273 K and 101.35 kPa.

The behaviour of gases – comparing two models

We now have two equations that describe the behaviour of a gas, one in terms of the behaviour as seen in scientific investigations, the other based on a mechanical model of the particles in the gas. What conclusions can we draw?

$$pV = nRT \qquad \text{(equation 1)}$$

$$p = \tfrac{1}{3}\rho\,\overline{c^2} = \tfrac{1}{3} \times \frac{Nm}{V} \times \overline{c^2} \qquad \text{(equation 2)}$$

$\overline{E_k}$, the mean kinetic energy of the gas particles, is $\tfrac{1}{2}m\overline{c^2}$, so equation (2) can be written as:

$$p = \tfrac{2}{3} \times \frac{N}{V} \times \tfrac{1}{2}m\overline{c^2} \quad \text{or} \quad pV = \tfrac{2}{3} \times N \times \tfrac{1}{2}m\overline{c^2} = \tfrac{2}{3} \times N \times \overline{E_k}$$

Comparing this with equation (1) we get:

$$nRT = \tfrac{2}{3} \times N \times E_k \quad \text{or} \quad E_k = \tfrac{3}{2} \times \frac{n}{N} \times RT$$

We know that:

$$n = \text{number of moles of gas}$$

and:

$$N = \text{number of particles in the gas}$$

From the definition of the mole (page 117), it follows that:

$$N = n \times N_A$$

so:

$$\frac{n}{N} = \frac{1}{N_A}$$

This means that we can now write:

$$\overline{E_k} = \tfrac{3}{2} \times \frac{R}{N_A} \times T = \tfrac{3}{2}kT \text{ where } k = \frac{R}{N_A}$$

The constant k is called the **Boltzmann constant** – it is effectively the gas constant for one particle of a gas, compared with R which is the gas constant for one mole of a gas. The value of k is 1.38×10^{-23} J K^{-1}.

Since:

$$E_k = \tfrac{3}{2}kT$$

it follows that we can also write an expression for U, the internal energy of the gas (which is simply the sum of all the individual molecules' kinetic energies):

$$U = \tfrac{3}{2}RT$$

that is, the internal energy of a gas is proportional to its temperature.

Like many tales, the story of the kinetic theory has its triumphs and its tragedies – and nowhere are these more closely entwined than in the life of Ludwig Eduard Boltzmann.

Born in Vienna in 1844, Boltzmann is one of the key figures in the development of the kinetic theory of matter. Entering the University of Vienna at the age of 19 as a student of mathematics and physics, Boltzmann obtained the Chair of Mathematical Physics at the University of Graz six years later. A long and distinguished career followed, with appointments at universities in Austria and Germany. The early years of Boltzmann's career were particularly productive, and he became widely known. By all accounts he was an outstanding teacher, including in his lectures things that were then quite unheard of in physics, such as multidimensional and curved space. A student wrote:

Tritt der gewöhnliche Mensch auf den Wurm, so wird er sich krümmen; Ludwig Boltzmann tritt auf; Siehe, es krümmt sich der Raum!

(When a normal human being treads on a worm, it will curl up; when Ludwig Boltzmann treads the stage: Look, space curls up!)

He was also an extremely tender-hearted man who felt deeply responsible for the welfare of his students, and who would worry endlessly when one of his students failed an examination.

Later years of Boltzmann's life brought increasing administrative work and ill-health, and he fretted at his scientific colleagues' scepticism towards his revolutionary ideas, for the atomic theory of matter was far from universally accepted in the 1890s. In particular, Boltzmann found the open hostility of his colleague Ernst Mach (a well-known and respected professor at the University of Vienna who vehemently denied the possibility of the existence of atoms) very hard to bear. After years of declining mental and physical health, Boltzmann took a short holiday in the village of Duino, on the Adriatic coast, in September 1906. It was here that he committed suicide by hanging himself from the crossbar of a window frame. His body was discovered by his 14-year-old daughter.

Figure 2.2.32 Ludwig Boltzmann at the age of 24.

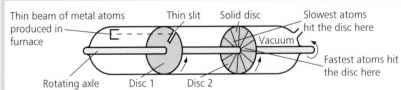

Metal atoms pass through the slit in disc 1 and travel along until they strike disc 2, to which they stick. The time taken for an atom to travel between disc 1 and disc 2 depends on its speed. The relative distribution of velocities can be found by analysing the number of metal atoms which have struck the disc at different points, which can be done by cutting the disc into sectors (like slices of a cake) and weighing them.

Figure 2.2.33 Boltzmann's work laid many of the foundations of the physics of matter that were to come in the first part of the twentieth century. Seventy years after his death, Zartmann and Ko showed that experimental measurements of the distribution of velocities among the molecules of a gas agreed closely with Boltzmann's predictions.

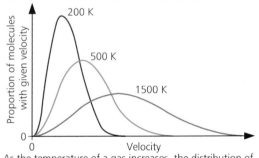

As the temperature of a gas increases, the distribution of molecular speeds within it changes. At higher temperatures the average speed of the molecules increases (the internal energy of the gas is greater), although the proportion of molecules with the most probable speed decreases.

SUMMARY

- **Hooke's law** says that the force F exerted by a spring is proportional to its extension x, $F = -kx$. The work done on a spring within its proportionality limit is equal to the energy stored in the spring, work $= \frac{1}{2}kx^2$.

- Applying the model of the kinetic theory for solids, the force–separation curve for a pair of particles is a straight line in the area of the equilibrium separation d.

- **Tensile stress** is tensile force per unit area, and the **tensile strength** of a material is the tensile stress at which it breaks. **Tensile strain** is the extension per unit length. For a material that obeys Hooke's law, the ratio of tensile stress:tensile strain is constant and is the **Young modulus** for the material, $E = (F/A)/(x/l)$.

- **Stress–strain curves** represent the behaviour of materials when subjected to stress. The extension is proportional to the force, up to the **proportionality limit**. The **elastic limit** represents the point beyond which the sample will not return to its original length when unloaded. In the **plastic region** the extension increases rapidly for a small increase in force.

- Materials may be subjected to **tensile stress**, **compressive stress** and **shear stress**. Brick and concrete have low tensile strength but are strong under compressive stress. Most metals are ductile (they show plastic deformation) while some materials such as ceramics may be **brittle**. **Tough** materials are not brittle and can resist large stresses.

- **Polymers** contain very long chain molecules made up of repeating subunits called **monomers**. **Thermoplastic** polymers soften on heating and melt, while **thermosetting** polymers do not.

- **Crystalline** solids have particles which are arranged regularly. Metals are usually **polycrystalline**, containing large numbers of small crystals or **grains**. **Amorphous** solids are those which are not crystalline – their particles show no long range order.

- When a force F is applied perpendicularly over an area A, the pressure p exerted is given by $p = F/A$.

- Liquids and gases are **fluids**. The tendency of fluids to resist flow is their **viscosity**.

- **Pascal's law** states that pressure applied to a fluid at rest is transmitted equally throughout the fluid. This is applied in the technology of **hydraulics**.

- The pressure p below the surface of a fluid increases as the depth h increases, $p = h\rho g$ where ρ is the density of the fluid and g the gravitational field strength. This can only be applied to gases where the density is constant, i.e. where h is small.

- **Archimedes' principle** states that any object wholly or partially immersed in a fluid has an **upthrust** acting on it equal to the weight of the fluid displaced.

- The behaviour of a liquid is difficult to model at particle level as there are considerable short-range forces but these are short term and the particles therefore move in relation to each other over a longer period of time.

- **Boyle's law** states that for a fixed mass of gas, the pressure is inversely proportional to the volume at constant temperature, $p \propto 1/V$ for constant T.

- **Charles' law** states that for a constant mass of gas, the volume is proportional to absolute temperature if the pressure remains constant, $V \propto T$ for constant p.

- The **pressure law** states that for a fixed mass of gas, the pressure is proportional to the absolute temperature if the volume remains constant, $p \propto T$ for constant V.

- Combining the gas laws results in the **equation of state** for a gas, $pV = nRT$ where R is the **molar gas constant**.

- The pressure p exerted by a gas on the walls of its container is given by $p = \frac{1}{3}\rho \overline{c^2}$ where ρ is the density of the gas and $\overline{c^2}$ the mean square velocity of its particles.

- An **ideal gas** has zero forces between its particles which take up zero volume. A **real gas** can approximate to ideal behaviour if the temperature is well above its **critical temperature** (the temperature at or below which it may be liquefied by pressure alone) and the pressure is well above its **critical pressure** (the pressure at which it liquefies at its critical temperature).

- The kinetic energy of a particle in an ideal gas of temperature T is given by $\overline{E_k} = \frac{3}{2}kT$, where k is the **Boltzmann constant**. $k = R/N_A$, the gas constant for one particle of gas. The internal energy U of the gas as a whole is $U = \frac{3}{2}RT$.

EXAMPLES

1 *A heavy uniform beam 6 m long and weighing 6.0×10^4 N is to be suspended at one end by a steel rope 5.0 m long and 0.5 cm in diameter and at the other end by a nylon rope 5.0 m long and 5.0 cm in diameter. The ropes are fastened together above the beam as shown in figure 2.2.34(a). Will the beam be horizontal when suspended? If not, which end of the beam will be lower? (Take E for nylon as 3.6×10^9 Pa and for steel as 1.9×10^{11} Pa.)*

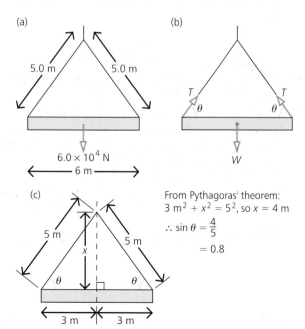

Figure 2.2.34

Figure 2.2.34(b) shows the forces acting on the beam. To begin, assume that any angle the beam makes with the horizontal is small so that the angles between each rope and the beam are effectively equal and the tension in the two ropes is equal too. For equilibrium we can write:

$$T \sin \theta + T \sin \theta = W$$

that is,

$$T = W/(2 \sin \theta)$$

where $\sin \theta = 0.8$ (see figure 2.2.34(c)). We know that:

$$E = \frac{\text{tensile stress}}{\text{tensile strain}} = \frac{F/A}{\Delta l/l}$$

so to find Δl we can write:

$$\Delta l = \frac{F}{A} \times \frac{l}{E}$$

Let the extension of the nylon rope be Δl_{nylon} and that of the steel rope be Δl_{steel}.
Since $F = W/(2 \sin \theta)$, it then follows that:

$$\Delta l_{nylon} = \frac{6.0 \times 10^4 \text{ N}/2 \times 0.8}{\pi \times (2.5 \times 10^{-2} \text{ m})^2} \times \frac{5.0 \text{ m}}{3.6 \times 10^9 \text{ Pa}}$$
$$= 2.7 \times 10^{-2} \text{ m}$$

Similarly, for the steel rope:

$$\Delta l_{steel} = \frac{6.0 \times 10^4 \text{ N}/2 \times 0.8}{\pi \times (0.25 \times 10^{-2} \text{ m})^2} \times \frac{5.0 \text{ m}}{1.9 \times 10^{11} \text{ Pa}}$$
$$= 5.0 \times 10^{-2} \text{ m}$$

Thus the nylon rope stretches by 27 mm while the steel rope stretches by 50 mm – so the end of the beam fastened to the steel rope will be lower.

2 *If the density of nitrogen at STP is 1.251 kg m⁻³, calculate the r.m.s. speed of nitrogen molecules at 127°C. (Take STP as 273 K and 101.35 kPa.)*

We know that:

$$p = \tfrac{1}{3}\rho \overline{c^2}$$

where p is the pressure exerted by the gas, ρ is its density and $\overline{c^2}$ is the mean square speed of the particles in the gas. Thus for nitrogen at STP we can write:

$$1.0135 \times 10^5 \text{ Pa} = \tfrac{1}{3} \times 1.251 \text{ kg m}^{-3} \times \overline{c^2}$$

so:

$$\sqrt{\overline{c^2}} = \sqrt{\left(\frac{1.0135 \times 10^5 \text{ Pa}}{\tfrac{1}{3} \times 1.251 \text{ kg m}^{-3}} \right)}$$
$$= 493 \text{ m s}^{-1}$$

The kinetic energy of a molecule of an ideal gas is given by:

$$E_k = \tfrac{3}{2}kT$$

That is, the molecule's kinetic energy is proportional to T, the absolute temperature. The r.m.s. speed of the particles is thus proportional to $\sqrt{T}$, so:

$$\frac{\text{r.m.s. speed at 400 K}}{\text{r.m.s. speed at 273 K}} = \frac{\sqrt{400}}{\sqrt{273}}$$

that is,

$$\text{r.m.s speed at 400 K} = \frac{\sqrt{400}}{\sqrt{273}} \times 493 \text{ m s}^{-1}$$
$$= 597 \text{ m s}^{-1}$$

QUESTIONS

(Assume $g = 10$ m s⁻², $N_A = 6.02 \times 10^{23}$.)

1 A spring is extended 0.25 m by a force of 30 N. What is the spring constant of the spring?

2 A rubber band is 5.3 cm long when unloaded. It stretches to a length of 8.9 cm when subjected to a load of 1.5 N, and to a length of 13.5 cm when subjected to a load of 3.0 N. Does it obey Hooke's law over this range? Justify your answer.

3 A steel wire 3.6 m long and 0.6 mm in diameter carries a mass of 7.0 kg. By how much does the wire stretch in excess of its original length?
(Take E for steel as 1.9×10^{11} N m⁻².)

4 The strings of a squash racquet are strung to a tension of 75 N. If the racquet could be strung with 6.10 m of nylon 1.5 mm in diameter under no tension, how much nylon is actually used to string the racquet? (Take E for nylon as 3.6×10^9 N m⁻².)

5 In fitting a metal rim to a wooden cart wheel, the rim is made slightly too small to fit over the wheel. It is then heated strongly until it can be slipped over the wheel, when it is cooled and contracts, holding the wheel together. A wheel of diameter 1.80 m is fitted with a steel rim with an original diameter of 1.79 m. If the cross-sectional area of the steel of the rim is 0.25 cm², what is the tension in the rim when it is fitted to the wheel, after it has been cooled?
(Take E for steel as 1.9×10^{11} N m⁻², and assume that the wheel does not contract as the rim is cooled.)

6 A rope 15 m long consists of 6.0 m of nylon with a diameter of 1.5 cm attached to 9.0 m of steel wire with a diameter of 1.0 cm. By how much will this rope stretch if subjected to a load of 5000 N? (Take E for nylon as 3.6×10^9 N m⁻² and E for steel as 1.9×10^{11} N m⁻².)

7 A friend without much knowledge of physics jokingly suggests that rather than use radio waves it would be much better to use copper wire to transmit signals between a satellite in orbit and the ground. Apart from the obvious practical problems, explain to your friend the mechanical problems with this idea in terms of the strength of copper. (The tensile strength of copper is 2.4×10^8 N m⁻², and its density is 8920 kg m⁻³.)

8 Explain why solids expand on heating, using a potential energy versus separation curve in your explanation.

9 Describe the properties of the following materials using the words *tough*, *ductile*, *brittle*, *weak*, *elastic*, *stiff* and *strong* as appropriate:
a copper   **b** glass   **c** steel
d rubber   **e** concrete   **f** jelly
g digestive biscuit   **h** chocolate   **i** toffee.

10 How does a *tough* material differ from a *brittle* one? Sketch a stress–strain graph to explain your answer.

11 Explain how a plastic may have a crystalline structure.

12 The deepest part of the ocean is thought to be the Marianas Trench in the Pacific Ocean, with a depth of 1.1×10^4 m. What pressure does the water exert at this depth?
(Take the density of sea water as 1025 kg m⁻³.)

13 Estimate the length of a giraffe's neck. What minimum pressure must the giraffe's heart exert in order to pump blood to its brain?
(Take the density of the giraffe's blood as 1000 kg m⁻³.)

14 Without using mathematics, explain the following in terms of simple kinetic theory:

   a A gas fills any container into which it is put and exerts a pressure on the walls of the container.

   b The pressure of a gas rises if it is heated in a vessel of fixed volume.

   c The pressure in an oxygen cylinder falls as oxygen is withdrawn from it, whereas the pressure in a chlorine cylinder remains constant until almost all of the chlorine has been withdrawn. (The critical temperature of chlorine is 146 °C, while that of oxygen is −118 °C.)

15 Airliners have pressurised cabins to enable passengers to be comfortable at altitudes of 10 000 m or so. The air pressure at this altitude outside the aeroplane is 28 kPa. If the pressure in the cabin is maintained at 100 kPa, what is the resultant force acting on a door of area 2 m² in the side of the airliner?

16 A beaker of water is standing on a balance. If you dip your finger into the water, what happens to the reading on the balance?

17 A hot-air balloon has a volume of 2000 m³ and carries a load of 500 kg (basket, gas cylinders and burner plus two passengers). If the pressure of the air inside and outside the balloon is the same (because the base of the balloon is open) and the density of the air outside the balloon is 1.2 kg m⁻³, what is the minimum temperature of the air in the balloon for it to get off the ground if the outside air temperature is 20 °C?

18 The volume of a helium atom is around 10^{-30} m³. What fraction of any volume of helium gas at STP is free space? (STP is 273 K and 101.35 kPa. Under these conditions 1 mol of an ideal gas occupies 2.24×10^{-2} m³.)

19 The stated pressure for the air in a car tyre is 26 lb in⁻² above atmospheric pressure. The air in the tyre is at 20 °C. What is the pressure in the tyre after a long journey, when the temperature of the air in it has risen by 5 °C?

20 Estimate the average kinetic energy of an air molecule at room temperature. (Take $k = 1.38 \times 10^{-23}$ J K⁻¹.)

21 Calculate the r.m.s. speed of the particles in the following gases at STP:

   a chlorine (density = 3.17 kg m⁻³)

   b nitrogen (density = 1.25 kg m⁻³)

   c helium (density = 0.179 kg m⁻³).

   (Take STP as 273 K and 101.35 kPa.)

22 Using a model of a gas as a collection of particles, derive an expression for the pressure exerted by a gas on the walls of its container in terms of its density and the speed of the particles. State clearly any assumptions you make.

23 a Calculate the r.m.s. speed of the particles in a sample of helium gas at STP.

   b If the total translational kinetic energy of the molecules in the helium is 2×10^{-6} J, what is the temperature in another vessel containing twice the mass of helium in which the total translational kinetic energy is 4×10^{-5} J? (The density of helium at STP is 0.1785 kg m⁻³. Take STP as 273 K and 101.35 kPa.)

24 Estimate the number of impacts that air molecules make with the palm of your hand each second, assuming that air consists entirely of nitrogen.

Developing Key Skills

The focus on page 3 took a brief look at the physics of bungee jumping, and introduced the idea of building a simple model in order to predict how far the jumper would fall before the bungee brings them to rest.

Having reached this point in the book, you now have enough physics tools at your disposal to build such a model. Here are some hints to help you.

- Write down a simple relationship between the height of the bungee jumper above the ground and their gravitational potential energy.
- Write down a relationship between the work done on a spring and its extension.
- Now use these relationships to write down a relationship between the energy that must be transferred from the jumper to the bungee in order to bring the jumper to rest.

Use your model to perform some sample calculations. You will need to make assumptions as you apply your model, and for some of the values you use in your calculations – be sure to state these clearly.

When you are satisfied with your model, use it to write a straightforward technical guide for the operator of a bungee jumping 'ride' at a fairground. The guide should be short (no more than one side of A4 paper) and written in such a way that it is easy to understand for someone with little or no knowledge of physics. It should enable the ride operator to set up the bungee jump safely to ensure that there is no danger of anyone using it hitting the ground.

[Key Skills opportunities: C, A, IT]

2.3 Energy, temperature and change of state

So far we have seen that the development of a theory to understand the behaviour of matter is closely associated with an understanding of the way in which matter and energy interact. The physicist's understanding of matter and energy is based on a model of matter made up of particles (the **kinetic theory**), with matter having a certain **internal energy** which is the sum of the energies possessed by the individual particles of which the matter is composed. The internal energy of matter increases as temperature increases, so that the changes of state (melting and boiling) which occur as the temperature of a substance increases may be understood by thinking of how the energy possessed by the particles may enable them to overcome the attractive forces between them.

Before considering any further the way in which the ideas of heat, energy and temperature are related, it is useful to examine the development of these ideas over the last few hundred years.

A brief history of heat

Invisible motion versus invisible fluid

In the same way as the nature of matter had been discussed since the time of the Ancient Greeks, the nature of heat caused much speculation. Aristotle believed that hotness and dryness, as opposed to coldness and dampness, were two of the 'active properties' which defined an element. Later philosophers and scientists were agreed on the importance of heat and its relationship to matter, but disagreed about its nature.

By the late eighteenth century, two opposing theories had been proposed to account for the behaviour of matter and heat. In the seventeenth century, René Descartes and Robert Hooke had described heat as the 'ceaseless motion of particles', thus advancing an explanation that was only finally accepted at the end of the nineteenth century. At the beginning of the eighteenth century, the idea that heat was a fluid came to prominence, chiefly through the work of the Dutch scientist Hermann Boerhaave. This fluid later became known as **caloric**, and the theory as the caloric theory of heat.

As the eighteenth century drew to a close, the steam engine became very important as a means of providing the movement needed in factories, and later in transport too. It became vital to have some understanding of heat and its effect on matter, and many scientists and engineers began to study the problem. One of these was the American Benjamin Thompson (1753–1814), who travelled widely in Europe, becoming a Count of the Holy Roman Empire and War Minister of Bavaria. He is now generally known as Count Rumford.

Rumford noticed that when cannons were being made by boring out a block of metal, the metal got very hot. The explanation of the time for this was that the boring squeezed caloric out of the metal as it was bored out of the barrel. Rumford tried boring a cannon with a blunt borer, surrounding both the borer and the end of the cannon with a water-filled box as shown in figure 2.3.2. His account of these experiments was described in a paper entitled 'Enquiry concerning the source of heat which is excited by friction', in which Rumford concluded that heat should be considered as a form of motion.

Figure 2.3.1 Count Rumford (Benjamin Thompson) (1753–1814).

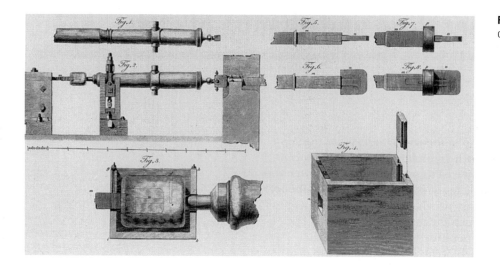

Figure 2.3.2 Rumford's apparatus for investigating the conversion of work into heat.

Heat, work and energy

Rumford's work was taken further by James Prescott Joule, working in Manchester, England in the mid-nineteenth century. Joule showed that it was possible to increase the temperature of a substance by doing work in exactly the same way that the temperature of the substance could be increased by heating it. He used a raised weight to do work in three different ways – to churn water in a cylinder, to force water to flow through narrow tubes and to compress air in a cylinder. In each case he measured the temperature changes occurring, and in each case he found that the ratio of the work done to the temperature rise was the same, allowing for experimental uncertainties. Repetition of this work by other physicists produced the same result.

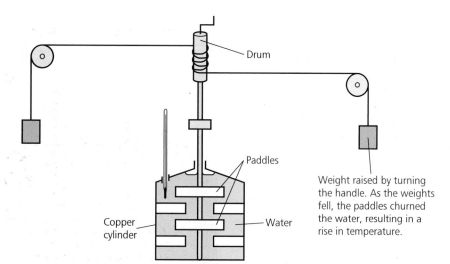

Drum

Paddles

Weight raised by turning the handle. As the weights fell, the paddles churned the water, resulting in a rise in temperature.

Copper cylinder

Water

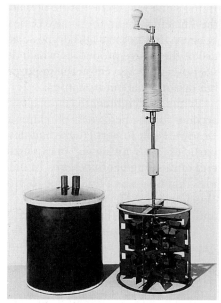

Figure 2.3.3 Joule's apparatus for exploring the conversion of work into heat.

This work provided the evidence that was needed to show that energy could be transferred to a body so that its internal energy was raised, which resulted in an increase in its temperature. Joule called this idea that mechanical work could give rise to a temperature change the **mechanical equivalent of heat.**

At the same time as Joule, other scientists and engineers were also working to understand heat and energy, with a view to making the steam engine more efficient. This work led to the new science of **thermodynamics** – to which we shall return in sections 2.4 and 2.5.

Heating and temperature changes

Our modern understanding of heat which is derived from the work of Joule and others is based around the concept of energy. Nowadays, the term 'thermal energy' is often used instead of 'heat energy', although we should strictly use the latter when talking about energy transferred by means of a temperature difference. The link between temperature and thermal energy is important, since temperature is the way we tend to think about thermal energy in our everyday lives. The definition of exactly what temperature *is* presents us with considerable difficulties, as sections 2.4–5 will show. In this respect, temperature and time are very similar – they are both reasonably straightforward to measure, but their essence lies much deeper than our familiarity with them would suggest.

The effect of temperature on a solid

As a general rule, solids expand when they are heated. Using a simple interpretation of kinetic theory like that in section 2.1, this expansion may be put down to the increasing movement of the particles in the solid – which is partly correct.

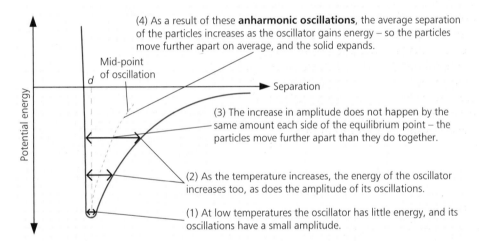

(4) As a result of these **anharmonic oscillations**, the average separation of the particles increases as the oscillator gains energy – so the particles move further apart on average, and the solid expands.

(3) The increase in amplitude does not happen by the same amount each side of the equilibrium point – the particles move further apart than they do together.

(2) As the temperature increases, the energy of the oscillator increases too, as does the amplitude of its oscillations.

(1) At low temperatures the oscillator has little energy, and its oscillations have a small amplitude.

Figure 2.3.4 The effect of temperature on the oscillation of a pair of particles.

A further explanation is possible using the graph of potential energy versus separation for each pair of particles, figure 2.3.4. Remember that each pair of particles can be thought of as an oscillator. As the energy of the oscillator increases, so does the amplitude of its oscillations.

Measuring temperature

In principle it is quite easy to measure temperature using a material which has an easily measurable property that changes with temperature (for example, volume or electrical resistance) and devise an instrument that makes use of this. This instrument then needs to be brought into contact with the object which is to have its temperature measured so that the temperatures of the two become equal.

The practical situation is a little more complicated, as figure 2.3.5 shows.

The mercury-in-glass thermometer

A mercury column in a glass tube provides one way of measuring temperature. The changing volume of mercury in a glass bulb is seen and measured by the mercury moving up a narrow bore. Such an instrument provides the basis of a temperature scale called the 'mercury-in-glass temperature scale'. In order to ensure that this scale can be reproduced in different places (for example, so that

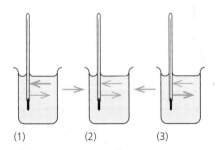

Figure 2.3.5 A thermometer must reach the same temperature as the object it is measuring. If a thermometer is put into a liquid with a temperature higher than the temperature of the thermometer, heat will flow into the thermometer from the liquid (diagram 1). If the thermometer is hotter than the liquid, heat will flow in the opposite direction (diagram 3). Once the thermometer and the liquid reach the same temperature (diagram 2), the rate at which heat flows from the thermometer to the liquid is the same as the rate at which heat flows from the liquid to the thermometer – we say that the thermometer and the liquid are in **thermal equilibrium**.

a physicist in Japan can describe experimental results to a colleague in Moscow), the scale must have fixed reference points. These are chosen as the 'ice point' and the 'steam point' of water under conditions which are specified.

A mercury-in-glass thermometer may be made and calibrated at the two fixed points described above by placing it in melting ice and marking the position of the end of the mercury thread when it reaches a steady length, and repeating this for the steam point. The interval between the two marks may be divided into 100 equal divisions, which produces temperatures on the mercury-in-glass scale measured in **degrees centigrade**. The term 'centigrade' does not describe a scale of temperature – it is merely a way of dividing up the distance between the ice and steam points. Temperatures are now usually referred to in degrees **Celsius** rather than in degrees centigrade. The difference between these two terms is explained in the box on page 155.

A temperature θ on the mercury-in-glass scale is then defined as:

$$\theta = \frac{l_\theta - l_0}{l_{100} - l_0} \times 100\,°C$$

where l_θ is the length of the mercury thread at temperature $\theta\,°C$, and l_0 and l_{100} its lengths at $0\,°C$ and $100\,°C$ respectively.

Any two thermometers set up in this way, using any properties that change with temperature, will certainly agree at the two fixed points (by definition). Any two *identical* mercury-in-glass thermometers (made of exactly the same glass, with exactly uniform bores, etc.) will agree at the two fixed points, and also at the points in between. However, a mercury-in-glass thermometer will not necessarily agree with another type of thermometer between the fixed points. This is because the two properties chosen will not necessarily change in exactly the same way with temperature, so a mercury-in-glass thermometer will not agree exactly with a platinum resistance thermometer at, say, 50 °C.

The constant volume gas thermometer

Thermometers which give more accurate readings at all points on their scales use the properties of gases to measure temperatures. They are called **constant volume gas thermometers**, shown in figure 2.3.6.

The ideal gas equation $pV = nRT$ provides us with one way of defining temperature. As the gas in the thermometer is kept at a constant volume, and as the mass of the gas is fixed too, it follows that the pressure exerted by the gas is proportional to its temperature. If the gas is under conditions far from its critical point (well above the temperature at which it can be liquefied by pressure alone, and at low pressures too) then it behaves almost ideally, and the relationship between the temperature and the pressure of the gas is linear, as shown in figure 2.3.7. Since any gas will behave almost ideally under these conditions, it follows that any gas may be used in the thermometer to measure temperature.

The absolute scale of temperature

The relationship between the pressure and temperature of an ideal gas, and the existence of an absolute zero of temperature, mean that it is possible to define a temperature scale which has as its fixed points absolute zero and the ice point. This was the basis of the **absolute scale of temperature**, proposed by Lord Kelvin in 1848. Since the ice point is difficult to establish in practice, a temperature very near it was chosen – the **triple point** of water. This is the one and only temperature at which water can exist in all three phases at once in equilibrium. The unit of temperature on this scale is called the **kelvin** (K). One kelvin was defined as 1/273.16 of the temperature of the triple point of water compared with absolute zero, a figure which makes its size the same as that of

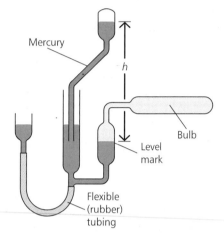

Figure 2.3.6 The constant volume gas thermometer. A gas is trapped in the bulb. As the temperature of the gas changes, its volume is kept constant by raising or lowering the tube to keep the mercury at a constant level. The pressure of the gas in the bulb is then p = atmospheric pressure (measured with a barometer) + $h\rho g$.

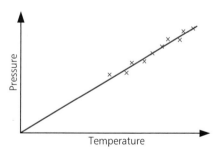

Figure 2.3.7 The change in pressure of an ideal gas kept in a constant volume as its temperature changes leads to a scale of temperature defined by measuring the pressure of a gas. This temperature scale is called the **ideal gas scale** – using this scale, a doubling in the pressure of the gas represents a doubling of its temperature. Notice that the pressure exerted by the gas falls to zero as its temperature decreases.

the Celsius scale. Since the triple point of water is 0.01 °C, it follows that there is a simple relationship betweeen temperature on the absolute scale and temperature on the Celsius scale:

$$T_{absolute} = T_{Celsius} + 273.15$$

What's in a name – centigrade or Celsius?

The difference between the Celsius scale of temperature and a scale in degrees centigrade is not important in everyday terms, but is relevant to the definitions of heat, temperature and energy. Kelvin's proposal for a new temperature scale was important not because of the simplicity of the relationship between the pressure and temperature of an ideal gas, but because it said something more fundamental about the nature of heat, temperature and energy.

The idea of internal energy suggests that in raising the temperature of a particular object by n degrees we *always* increase its internal energy by the same amount by transferring the same amount of energy to it. Given this, it is then necessary to find a way of measuring temperature which is based on some physical property which varies linearly with the transfer of energy. (In other words, if an energy transfer of E results in a measured temperature rise of θ, an energy transfer of $2E$ will result in a measured temperature rise of 2θ.) The ideal gas scale of temperature, based on the use of the constant volume gas thermometer, achieves this, although in practice the scale still depends on the properties of a specific substance, the gas in the

thermometer, whose behaviour can only ever *approach* that of an ideal gas.

In order to define temperature solely in terms of the flow of energy into and out of a system, a complete definition of temperature uses the efficiency of heat engines (see section 2.4) as its basis. The **absolute thermodynamic scale of temperature** is based on this and has as its unit the kelvin (K) which is defined, as already described, as 1/273.16 of the temperature of the triple point of water.

The **Celsius scale** of temperature was derived from the absolute thermodynamic scale because a practical scale was needed that had the same fixed points as the thermodynamic scale. It was defined as follows:

$$T_{absolute} = T_{Celsius} + 273.15$$

The Celsius scale and the mercury-in-glass centigrade scale thus coincide for all practical purposes, although the Celsius scale is based on thermodynamic temperature, while the centigrade scale has the ice point and steam point as its two fixed points. Figure 2.3.8 illustrates the three temperature scales.

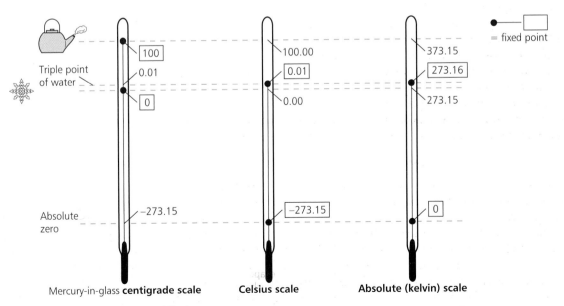

Figure 2.3.8 How the three scales of temperature are defined.

Liquid nitrogen boils at 77 K. It was first made in 1877, by using the fact that a gas cools as it expands. It was another 30 years before liquid helium (boiling point 4.2 K) was made, since when scientists have managed to reach temperatures of fractions of a kelvin. Cooling things to temperatures close to absolute zero is not easy, and subtle techniques have to be employed in order to creep ever closer to it. Figure 2.3.9 explains two of the methods used.

But why do physicists want to reach lower and lower temperatures? In answer to this question, one physicist points out that each time the lowest temperature reached falls by a factor of 10, some new phenomenon is found, making the range of temperatures between 0.001 K and 0.01 K as interesting as 100 K to 1000 K. As we reach lower and lower temperatures, materials start to behave in very strange ways. **Superconductivity** is one of these – the discovery that some metals (but not copper, the common conductor found in the electrical wiring of our homes) lose their electrical resistance at low temperatures. Another strange effect close to absolute zero is **superfluidity**. If liquid helium is cooled to a temperature lower than 2.2 K, its viscosity drops to zero and the atoms in the liquid can flow past one another without any opposition – the helium is said to be a superfluid (figure 2.3.10). An important principle of quantum physics called the 'uncertainty principle' tells us that, no matter how much we cool something, its particles cannot have zero kinetic energy; instead, the particles are always left with a small amount of energy, called the 'zero point energy'. Close to absolute zero, helium atoms still have sufficient zero point energy to overcome the interactions between them – and it is this that is the cause of liquid helium's superfluidity.

Figure 2.3.10 A drop of superfluid liquid helium on a caesium metal surface tilted at 10°. The droplet does not slide down the surface but remains stationary, despite its zero viscosity. This behaviour is due to the interactions between the helium atoms and the atoms of the surface on which the drop is placed. On surfaces other than caesium, helium spreads out and flows easily, even through microscopic holes.

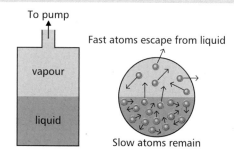

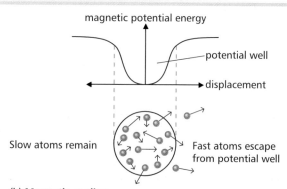

(a) **Cooling by evaporation**
As the more energetic molecules escape from the surface of a liquid the molecules remaining behind have a lower average kinetic energy. This means that the temperature of the liquid becomes lower. This is the principle behind the body's mechanism for cooling (see page 160 in this section). By evaporating liquid helium at very low pressure, temperatures down to about 0.7 K can be reached.

(b) **Magnetic cooling**
Certain atoms behave like tiny bar magnets, due to the configuration of their electrons. By creating a magnetic field with a strength that varies across space, physicists can trap these atoms in a 'potential well'. Since the atoms have a range of kinetic energies, the more energetic atoms may escape from the well. This lowers the average kinetic energy of the atoms left behind, producing a cooling effect similar to evaporative cooling. Temperatures as low as 2×10^{-8} K have been reached using this technique.

Figure 2.3.9 Two methods of cooling to low temperatures.

The International Practical Temperature Scale

Because of the difficulty in working over a wide range of temperatures, the **International Practical Temperature Scale** was proposed in 1968. Known as IPTS-68, the scale defines a number of additional fixed points at temperatures far away from the triple point of water. These may be used for calibration purposes when working at or near these temperatures. Some of the fixed points in the International Temperature Scale ITS–90, a revised version of IPTS-68, are given in table 2.3.1.

Practical thermometers

The constant volume gas thermometer provides an accurate and fairly easily reproduced way of measuring temperatures which can be simply related to the thermodynamic scale of temperature. However, such thermometers are large and slow to use, since it takes a long time for them to reach thermal equilibrium with whatever they are measuring. For this reason, although constant volume gas thermometers are used as **standards**, against which other thermometers may be calibrated, they are not often used to measure temperature directly. Instead, a variety of practical thermometers are used. The choice of thermometer for a particular measurement depends on many factors, including the following.

- Temperature range. The thermometer must be physically capable of recording temperatures in the range required. Mercury thermometers, for example, cannot be used below –39 °C, the freezing point of mercury.
- Size. Apart from physical limitations, a large thermometer will take longer to reach thermal equilibrium with whatever it is measuring, and may even affect the temperature of it in the process. (Think about what is likely to happen if the bulb of a mercury-in-glass thermometer is put in a thimbleful of very hot water.)
- Accuracy. This is partly affected by the first two factors (a short mercury-in-glass thermometer will have smaller distances representing each degree than a longer one for the same temperature range), but also depends on the choice of temperature dependent property.

Table 2.3.2 and figure 2.3.11 overleaf show some of the different types of thermometers in use.

Fixed point	Temperature/K
Triple point of hydrogen	13.81
Triple point of oxygen	54.361
Melting point of oxygen	90.188
(Triple point of water	273.16)
Freezing point of tin	505.1181
Freezing point of gold	1337.58

Table 2.3.1

The effect of heating

Heat capacity

It is common experience that different objects require different amounts of heat to change their temperatures by similar amounts. The **heat capacity** C of an object is the amount of heat required to raise its temperature by a given amount. The SI unit of heat capacity is thus $J\,K^{-1}$.

Whilst heat capacity is useful to know in certain circumstances, it applies only to a single object. **Specific heat capacity** c gives the heat capacity per unit mass of substance, and is obviously more generally useful. Its SI unit is $J\,kg^{-1}\,K^{-1}$. If we represent the amount of heat transferred as ΔQ, mass as m and temperature rise as ΔT, then heat capacity and specific heat capacity are defined as follows:

$$C = \frac{\Delta Q}{\Delta T} \qquad c = \frac{\Delta Q}{m\Delta T}$$

Specific heat capacity relates to a *substance*, while heat capacity relates to an *object*.

	Thermometer	Thermometric property and temperature range	Advantage(s)	Disadvantage(s)
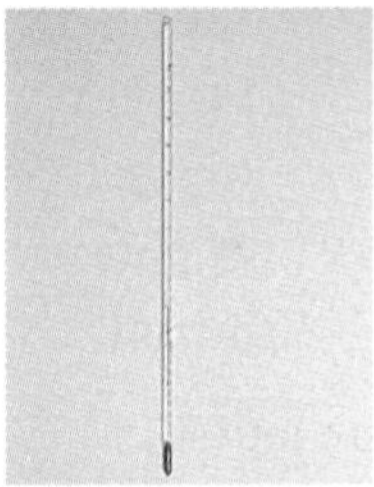	Liquid-in-glass	Change of volume of liquid – usually mercury or ethanol. Mercury: −10°C to 350°C Ethanol: −100°C to 50°C	Cheap and simple.	Accuracy depends on length and range. Not suitable for measuring temperature of very small objects.
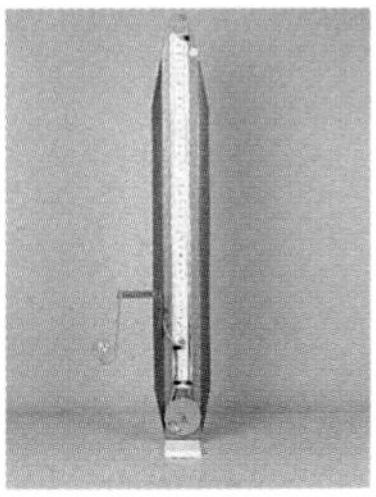	Constant volume gas	Change of pressure of gas at constant volume. If helium is used, temperatures of a few kelvins can be measured. The upper limit of the temperatures for which gas thermometers are used is around 500 K.	Possible to get same results with different instruments.	Large and bulky. Not suitable for measuring temperature of small objects.
	Platinum resistance	Change of resistance of platinum wire. Used over a wide range of temperatures from around 15 K to over 900 K.	Almost as accurate as but easier to use than gas thermometers.	Not as large as gas thermometers but still not suitable for measuring the temperatures of small objects.
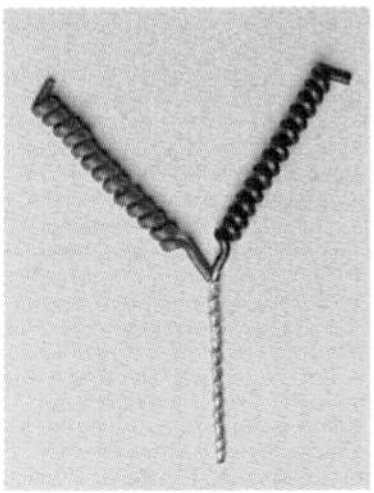	Thermocouple	E.m.f. produced when junction between two metals is warmed. Range depends on metals used.	E.m.f. produced is small, so difficult to get accurate measurement of temperature without very sensitive electrical equipment.	Can measure temperature of very small objects as well as rapidly changing temperatures.
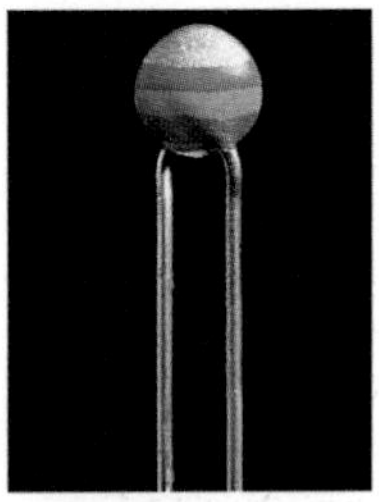	Thermistor	Changing resistance of a semiconductor.	Can provide a way of measuring temperature if electrical signal required (e.g. if computers used to monitor a process).	Not capable of great accuracy. Differences between individual thermistors means that calibration is required.
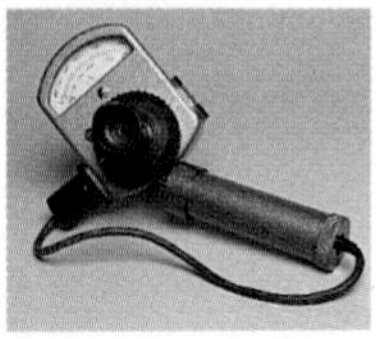	Optical pyrometer	Filament of lamp is viewed against radiation emitted by very hot object. Current through filament is adjusted so that it is the same colour as the object – it is then at the same temperature as the object. Used above about 1000 K.	Simple to use. Can be used at high temperatures where no other method would be possible.	Needs calibration before use.

Figure 2.3.11   **Table 2.3.2**

Heat capacity – worked example

A saucepan with a heat capacity of 800 J K^{-1} contains 3 kg of water at 25 °C. How much thermal energy is required to raise the temperature of the saucepan and water to 75 °C? (Specific heat capacity of water = 4200 J kg^{-1} K^{-1}.)

Temperature rise = 75 °C – 25 °C = 50 °C = 50 K

$$\Delta Q = C\Delta T$$

Thermal energy required to raise saucepan through 50 K = $C \times$ 50 K

= 800 J K^{-1} × 50 K

= 40 000 J

$$\Delta Q = mc\Delta T$$

Thermal energy required to raise water through 50 K = mc × 50 K

= 3 kg × 4200 J kg^{-1} K^{-1} × 50 K

= 630 000 J

Thermal energy required to heat saucepan and water through 50 K = 630 000 J + 40 000 J

= 670 000 J

2

For gases, **molar heat capacity** is often used. This gives the thermal energy required to increase the temperature of one mole of the gas by a given amount. The SI unit is J K^{-1}mol^{-1}. The heat capacity of a gas must be given under certain specified conditions, explained in section 2.5.

Thermal energy and change of state – latent heat

Figure 2.3.12 shows that when a substance is heated and changes state, its temperature remains constant whilst the change of state occurs, provided that thermal energy is supplied at a rate which allows the two phases (solid and liquid or liquid and gas) to remain in thermal equilibrium. The thermal energy that needs to be supplied to cause this change in state is called **latent** (hidden) **heat** L.

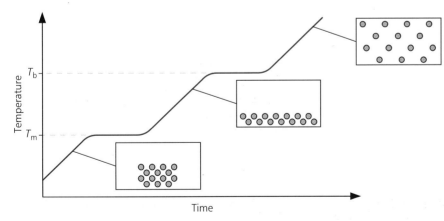

Figure 2.3.12 The kinetic theory interprets the temperature changes shows as follows: thermal energy supplied during the change of state is used to 'prise' the particles of the substance further apart, giving the particles sufficient energy to overcome the forces of attraction between them (completely in the case of liquid to gas, only partly in the case of solid to liquid). This heat is called **latent heat** – latent means 'hidden'.

A substance's **specific latent heat** l is defined as the thermal energy required to change the state of a certain mass of that substance without any temperature change. The SI unit of specific latent heat is J kg^{-1}.

$$l = \frac{\Delta Q}{m}$$

Materials generally have two latent heats, one for melting (or **fusion**), l_f, and one for boiling (or **vaporisation**), l_v. (The external atmospheric pressure at which latent heat is measured must be specified, since it affects the amount of energy required to change the state of a substance.) In most cases, $l_v > l_f$ because of the large volume change which occurs on vaporisation of a liquid. Because of the latent heat of vaporisation, evaporation causes cooling, as illustrated in figure 2.3.13.

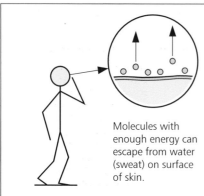

Molecules with enough energy can escape from water (sweat) on surface of skin.

As the most energetic molecules escape from the water, the less energetic ones are left behind. This means that the internal energy of the water is then lower, so its temperature is lower – the runner cools down.

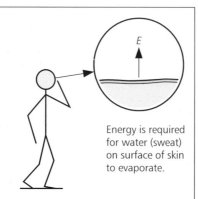

Energy is required for water (sweat) on surface of skin to evaporate.

The energy needed for the water to evaporate comes from the rest of the water. This means that as the water evaporates it cools – the runner cools down.

Figure 2.3.13 Two explanations for why sweating cools you down. Although these explanations appear different at first sight, they both explain the cooling that occurs when liquids evaporate in terms of the reduction in internal energy per unit mass of the liquid which remains behind.

Latent heat – worked example

The lid is left off a kettle so that its automatic cut-out does not work. The kettle supplies energy to the water in it at a rate of 3 kW. If there is 1 kg of water in the kettle, how long after the water reaches 100 °C will the kettle boil dry, ignoring heat losses to the surroundings? (Specific latent heat of water = 2.3×10^6 J kg^{-1}.)

$$\Delta Q = ml$$

Energy required to vaporise 1 kg of water
$$= 1 \text{ kg} \times 2.3 \times 10^6 \text{ J kg}^{-1}$$
$$= 2.3 \times 10^6 \text{ J}$$

Time taken to supply this energy
$$= \frac{2.3 \times 10^6 \text{ J}}{3000 \text{ W}}$$
$$= 767 \text{ s}$$

The kettle will boil dry in a little less than 13 minutes.

Measuring specific heat capacity and specific latent heat

The measurement of both specific heat capacity and specific latent heat relies on an accurate measurement of the amount of heat supplied, and so electrical methods of heating are usually used as shown in figure 2.3.14. In both cases it is important to be able to minimise heat losses, or at least to be able to measure them, and many methods of doing this have been devised. The two methods shown here demonstrate the principles of measuring these two important quantities.

Measuring the specific heat capacity of a solid

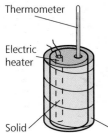

The solid for which the specific heat capacity is being measured is well insulated to reduce heat losses. It is heated by an electrical heater. The energy supplied can be measured directly by a joulemeter in the circuit, or by measurements of the current through the heater, the potential difference across it and the length of time it is switched on.

Thermometer
Electric heater
Solid
Lagging

Measuring the latent heat of vaporisation of a liquid

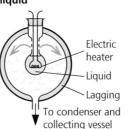

A liquid is heated and boiled by an electric heater. The time taken to boil away a known mass of liquid is measured, and the specific latent heat is calculated from this quantity and the amount of energy supplied.

Electric heater
Liquid
Lagging
To condenser and collecting vessel

By carrying out the experiment supplying energy to the liquid at two different rates, the latent heat of vaporisation can be found and thermal energy losses to the surroundings eliminated.

Measuring the specific heat capacity of a fluid by a continuous flow method

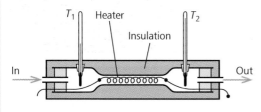

T_1 Heater Insulation T_2
In Out

A fluid (liquid or gas) flows through a tube, in which there is an electric heating element. The rise in temperature of the fluid is measured ($T_2 - T_1$), as is the rate of flow of fluid mass through the tube (m). By using two different flow rates and adjusting the power to the heater to give the same temperature rise, the specific heat capacity of the fluid can be found, and heat losses to the surroundings eliminated.

Eliminating the effect of heat energy lost to the surroundings

Continuous flow method for specific heat capacity of a fluid
Electrical energy supplied in time t = energy transferred to fluid + energy lost to surroundings
so:
$$IVt = mc(T_2 - T_1) + E$$
(I = heater current, V = p.d. across heater terminals, t = time for mass of fluid m to flow)
For a different flow rate m_2 in time t_2, I and V are adjusted to make ($T_2 - T_1$) the same as before. Now:
$$I_2V_2T_2 = m_2c(T_2 - T_1) + E$$
The energy E transferred to the surroundings is the same in each case, since the initial and final temperature of the fluid is unchanged. Subtracting the second equation from the first gives:
$$IVt - I_2V_2t_2 = mc(T_2 - T_1) - m_2c(T_2 - T_1)$$
The only quantity unknown in this equation is c, which can therefore be calculated.

Measurement of latent heat of vaporisation
Electrical energy supplied in time t = energy transferred to liquid + energy lost to surroundings
so:
$$IVt = mL_v + E$$
(I = heater current, V = p.d. across heater terminals, t = time for mass of fluid m to flow)
I and V are adjusted to give a different rate of vaporisation, m_2 in time t_2. Now:
$$I_2V_2t_2 = m_2L_v + E$$
The energy E transferred to the surroundings is the same in each case, since the temperature of the liquid is unchanged – it remains at boiling point. Subtracting the second equation from the first gives:
$$IVt - I_2V_2t_2 = mL_v - m_2L_v$$
The only quantity unknown in this equation is L_v, which can therefore be calculated.

Figure 2.3.14 The principles of measuring specific heat capacity and specific latent heat.

Methods of transfer

Figure 2.3.15 illustrates how heat energy can be transferred by conduction, convection and radiation.

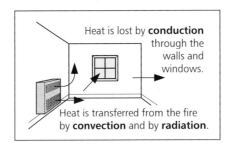

Heat is lost by **conduction** through the walls and windows.

Heat is transferred from the fire by **convection** and by **radiation**.

Conduction

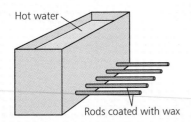

Hot water

Rods coated with wax

Comparing thermal conductivities. The wax melts at different rates depending on the thermal conductivity of the material of the rod. Metals are generally better conductors of heat than non-metals.

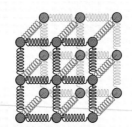

The model of a solid as a collection of particles held together by bonds which behave rather like springs can be used to explain how thermal conduction occurs.

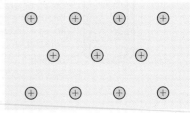

By imagining that the atoms in a metal are held together by a mobile 'sea' of electrons, the high thermal conductivity of metals can be explained.

Convection

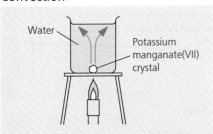

Water

Potassium manganate(VII) crystal

Convection currents occur when a fluid is heated, expands and so becomes less dense. It then experiences an upthrust from the surrounding denser fluid, and rises, being replaced from underneath by denser fluid.

Radiation

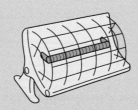

Objects radiate energy in the form of electromagnetic radiation, even at low temperatures. As the temperature of something increases, so does the range in frequencies of the radiation it emits – so an electric fire radiates a great deal in the orange and red part of the visible spectrum, while a star radiates at frequencies right up into the ultraviolet and beyond, thus appearing white.

A thermal imaging camera can be used to detect the infrared radiation from a person obscured by smoke in a burning building.

The photograph shows a 'heat print' left by a woman's body seen one minute after she stood up.

Conduction

Conduction is the mechanism by which heat energy is transferred through solid materials. Under the right circumstances, conduction may be an important mechanism for heat transfer in fluids too, but this is not usually the case.

A 'thought experiment' indicates that there are a number of factors which are likely to affect the flow of heat energy through a block of solid material like that in figure 2.3.16.

Figure 2.3.15 The principles of conduction, convection and radiation.

It seems reasonable to assume as a starting point that increasing the area of cross-section of the solid through which the heat energy flows is likely to increase the rate of flow – after all, we should expect more heat energy to be lost through the wall of a house than through the wall of one room in it. Similarly, we might reasonably expect the rate of flow to decrease as the thickness of the material increases. Such speculation is confirmed by experiment. Provided that a **steady state** has been reached (in which the temperature at any point has reached a steady value which does not change with time), then the rate of flow of heat energy $\Delta Q/\Delta t$ is given by:

$$\frac{\Delta Q}{\Delta t} \propto A \frac{\Delta T}{\Delta x}$$

Besides the physical dimensions of the matter through which the heat energy is travelling, experience and experiment both tell us that the rate at which heat energy travels through a material depends in some way on the material itself (see box 'Measuring thermal conductivity' on page 165). The **thermal conductivity** λ of the material through which the heat energy is travelling is the constant of proportionality in this relationship, so:

$$\frac{\Delta Q}{\Delta t} = -\lambda A \frac{\Delta T}{\Delta x}$$

The quantity $\Delta T/\Delta x$ is called the **temperature gradient** across the solid – it is this which causes the heat energy to flow. Since $\Delta T/\Delta x$ is negative and $\Delta Q/\Delta t$ is positive (see figure 2.3.16), the relationship includes a negative sign so that the sign of each side is the same.

Table 2.3.3 gives the thermal conductivities of some materials.

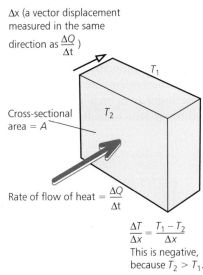

Δx (a vector displacement measured in the same direction as $\frac{\Delta Q}{\Delta t}$)

Cross-sectional area = A

Rate of flow of heat = $\frac{\Delta Q}{\Delta t}$

$\frac{\Delta T}{\Delta x} = \frac{T_1 - T_2}{\Delta x}$
This is negative, because $T_2 > T_1$.

Figure 2.3.16

> ### The units of thermal conductivity
>
> $$\frac{\Delta Q}{\Delta t} = -\lambda A \frac{\Delta T}{\Delta x}$$
>
> **Units of left-hand side = (energy/time) = J s^{-1}**
>
> **Units of right-hand side = (λ) × area × temperature/distance**
>
> $$= (\lambda) \times \text{m}^2 \times \text{K m}^{-1}$$
>
> $$= (\lambda) \times \text{m} \times \text{K}$$
>
> Putting units of left-hand side equal to units of right-hand side gives:
>
> $$\text{J s}^{-1} = (\lambda) \times \text{m} \times \text{K}$$
>
> so: $$(\lambda) = \text{J s}^{-1} \times \text{m}^{-1} \times \text{K}^{-1}$$
>
> $$= \text{W m}^{-1}\,\text{K}^{-1}$$
>
> The SI units of thermal conductivity are watts per metre per kelvin.

Material	Thermal conductivity/ W m^{-1} K^{-1}
Copper	385
Aluminium	238
Steel	60
Concrete	1.5
Brick	1.0
Glass	0.8
Poly(ethene) – high density	0.5
Wood	0.1–0.4

Table 2.3.3

A model for conduction

The main phenomenon that a model for conduction of heat energy needs to explain is the difference in conductivity between metals and non-metals.

The model for non-metallic solids consists of an arrangement of particles with forces between the particles which can be considered to have similar behaviour to springs, as shown in figure 2.3.18 (and described in section 2.1,

A comparison of different flow phenomena

The flow of heat through a solid material by conduction, the flow of liquid through a pipe and the flow of electric current through a wire are all governed by similar relationships. In each case the flow depends on cross-sectional area, on a 'pressure difference' of some sort, and on the distance through which the flow occurs.

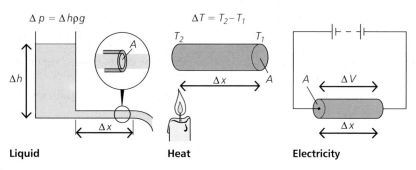

Figure 2.3.17

	Liquid	**Heat**	**Electricity**
Flow rate	$\Delta Q/\Delta t$	$\Delta Q/\Delta t$	$\Delta Q/\Delta t$
Cross-sectional area	A	A	A
'Pressure difference'	Δp	ΔT	ΔV
Distance through which flow occurs	Δx	Δx	Δx
Relationship	$\dfrac{\Delta Q}{\Delta t} \propto \dfrac{A\Delta p}{\Delta x}$	$\dfrac{\Delta Q}{\Delta t} \propto \dfrac{A\Delta T}{\Delta x}$	$\dfrac{\Delta Q}{\Delta t} \propto \dfrac{A\Delta V}{\Delta x}$
Constant of proportionality	depends on the area of the pipe and the viscosity of the liquid	λ thermal conductivity	σ electrical conductivity

Table 2.3.4

Table 2.3.4 and figure 2.3.17 show how it is possible to draw an analogy between a liquid flowing through a pipe and thermal and electrical conduction. Note that, although this model makes it possible to calculate thermal and electrical flow rates, it does not provide evidence for heat or electricity as a fluid. This should always be borne in mind when constructing models to help understand physical phenomena.

page 118). As energy is given to particles in one region, the amplitude of their oscillations increases. This increase in oscillations is transmitted to neighbouring particles, and the energy spreads through the solid. Because the process involves the amplitude of oscillations building up through exchange of energy with nearby particles, the spread of energy is slow, and so the conductivity of most non-metallic solids is low.

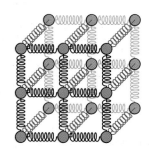

Figure 2.3.18 The model for a non-metallic solid

The model for a metal is based on a lattice which is broadly similar to the lattice present in non-metallic solids. The difference in conductivity is accounted for by the presence of free electrons which are able to move through the lattice. These electrons are responsible for keeping the positive metal ions together in the lattice. The electrons are free to move, although they do collide with each other and with the metal ions in the lattice. If one region of the solid is at a higher temperature than the rest, the ions in that part of the lattice will be vibrating with a larger amplitude than those in the rest of lattice, as was the case with the model for non-metals. In this case however, it is highly likely that free electrons will collide with one of the ions in the lattice and gain energy in doing so. The electron will move off through the lattice and collide with other electrons or other ions, transferring the energy in the process. Thus the energy from one region of the lattice may be rapidly transferred to another region, and high thermal conductivity results, as shown by figure 2.3.19.

A free electron colliding with a rapidly oscillating ion in the lattice here ...

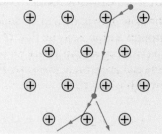

... will move away rapidly and collide with electrons and/or ions in another region of the lattice, thus transferring thermal energy very rapidly through the lattice.

Figure 2.3.19 The model for thermal conduction in a metal.

2

Measuring thermal conductivity

There are two different problems to be faced when measuring thermal conductivity, shown in figure 2.3.20. Both methods involve supplying heat to one part of the conductor and measuring the rate at which it flows into a **heat sink** at the other end of it. For a poor conductor, the main problem is getting sufficient heat flow, so a thin disc of the material is used. For a good conductor the main problem is making the temperature difference large enough to be measurable, so here a long bar of the material is used.

Method for a poor conductor (Lee's disc)

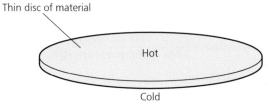

Thin disc of material

Hot

Cold

The disc is thin to ensure sufficient heat flows through it to be measurable. No lagging is needed, since little heat is lost through the sides of the disc in comparison with its face.

Method for a good conductor (Searle's bar)

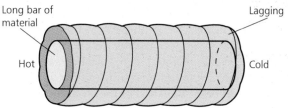

Long bar of material

Lagging

Hot

Cold

The bar is long to ensure that sufficient temperature difference exists between its ends in order to be accurately measured. The bar is lagged, since a large quantity of heat would otherwise be lost through the sides of it.

Experimental details

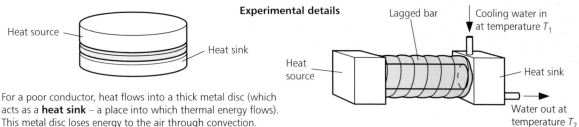

For a poor conductor, heat flows into a thick metal disc (which acts as a **heat sink** – a place into which thermal energy flows). This metal disc loses energy to the air through convection. Calculation of the heat flow involves a separate experiment in which the disc is heated and allowed to cool – the rate of loss of heat is calculated from the rate at which it cools and its heat capacity.

In the case of a good conductor, flowing water is used as the heat sink – the rate of water flow and its temperature rise can be used to calculate the rate at which heat is flowing through the bar.

Figure 2.3.20

Thermal conductivity – worked example

Estimate the rate at which heat energy flows through a window with an area of 1 m² if the room is kept at 20 °C and the outside temperature is 0 °C. The glass in the window is 5 mm thick, and its thermal conductivity is 0.8 W m⁻¹ K⁻¹.

$$\frac{\Delta Q}{\Delta t} = -\lambda A \frac{\Delta T}{\Delta x}$$

$$\textbf{Temperature gradient} = \frac{(20\,°C - 0\,°C)}{5 \times 10^{-3} \text{ m}} = 4000 \text{ K m}^{-1}$$

$$\textbf{So energy flow} = \Delta Q/\Delta T = \frac{-0.8 \text{ W m}^{-1} \text{ K}^{-1} \times}{1 \text{ m}^2 \times 4000 \text{ K m}^{-1}}$$

$$= -3200 \text{ W}$$

So the window has a heat flow of 3.2 kW through it.

Is this reasonable? Common sense suggests not, since this is the equivalent of three single-bar electric fires!

The reason for the strange result is that we have assumed that the outer surface of the glass is at the same temperature as the outside air, and the inner surface is at the same temperature as the air in the room. This cannot be true, since under these conditions heat energy would not enter the glass from the air in the room, neither would it leave the glass to enter the air outside, as in neither case is there a temperature difference to cause the heat energy to flow. In the real-life situation, there will always be a thin layer of air next to the glass which has a temperature different from that of the air around it,

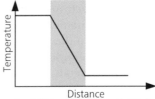

Temperature gradient if surfaces of glass have same temperature as the air around them. Large gradient gives large heat flow.

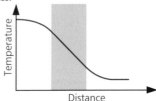

Temperature gradient if there is a layer of still air at the surface of the glass. The gradient is much smaller now, so the rate of heat flow is less.

Figure 2.3.21

and as a result the temperature gradient across the glass will be less, as figure 2.3.21 shows.

U-values

Architects and heating engineers use **U-values** to calculate the flow of heat energy through building materials. The U-value is quoted for a given thickness of a particular material, and is based on actual measurements made using that material. The U-value is defined as:

$$\textbf{U-value} = \frac{\textbf{rate of energy flow}}{\textbf{area} \times \textbf{temperature difference}}$$

It has the units W m⁻² K⁻¹.

An application of thermal conductivities is in double glazing, illustrated in figure 2.3.22.

The two sheets of glass are close enough to prevent convection occurring in the air between them.

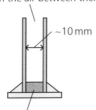

~10 mm

Good double glazing incorporates a 'thermal break' in the frames, to prevent heat loss through them. This also prevents moisture from the air in the room condensing on the frames in cold weather.

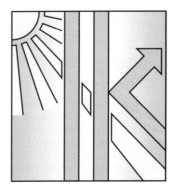

'Low E' glasses have been specially developed to reduce energy loss by radiation transmitted through the glass.

Figure 2.3.22 Preventing energy losses through windows has exercised the ingenuity of scientists and engineers for many years. Double glazing is very effective, since the thermal conductivity of air is around 0.025 W m⁻¹ K⁻¹ – around 30 times less than glass – so even a thin layer of air is very effective. The use of special glasses can also reduce the heat lost by radiation through windows.

SUMMARY

- When a solid is heated, the amplitude of the oscillations of its particles increases. These oscillations are **anharmonic** (the particles move further apart from the equilibrium separation than they do together). As a result, the average separation of the particles increases, and the solid expands.

- Temperature changes can be measured using a mercury-in-glass thermometer which may be calibrated at two reference points, the **ice** and **steam points** of water. A **centigrade** scale has 100 divisions between these two points.

- The **constant volume gas thermometer** uses the ideal gas equation $pV = nRT$ to measure temperature. Temperatures measured using such thermometers give a good approximation to the **absolute scale of temperature**, measured in **kelvins**. The **Celsius** scale is derived from the absolute temperature scale such that $T_{absolute} = T_{Celsius} + 273.15$. The Celsius scale and the centigrade scale coincide for practical purposes.

- The **International Temperature Scale ITS-90** gives fixed points for reference over a range of temperatures.

- Constant volume gas thermometers are usually used as standards against which to calibrate other more practical thermometers such as liquid-in-glass thermometers, platinum resistance thermometers and thermocouples.

- The **heat capacity** C of an object is the amount of thermal energy which must be supplied to an object to produce unit rise in temperature, $C = \Delta Q/\Delta T$ where ΔQ is the thermal energy transferred and ΔT the change in temperature. **Specific heat capacity** c is the amount of thermal energy which must be supplied to unit mass of a substance to produce unit rise in temperature, $c = \Delta Q/m\Delta T$. The **molar heat capacity** of a substance is the heat capacity per mole of that substance.

- **Latent heat** L is the thermal energy which must be supplied to bring about a change of state at constant temperature. **Specific latent heat** l is the latent heat per kilogram of a substance, $l = \Delta Q/m$. The **latent heat of fusion** l_f is generally lower than the **latent heat of vaporisation** l_v because of the large volume change on vaporisation.

- Heat energy may be transferred by **conduction**, **convection** and **radiation**. In conduction, the **rate of flow of heat energy** is given by $\Delta Q/\Delta t = -\lambda A \Delta T/\Delta x$ where λ is the **thermal conductivity** of the material, A its cross-sectional area and $\Delta T/\Delta x$ the **temperature gradient** across the solid.

EXAMPLE

Figure 2.3.23 shows a cross-section through two windows, one single glazed (a) and the other double glazed (b). Dimensions and temperatures are given on the diagrams. Compare the rate of flow of heat energy through the two windows.

The calculation of the rate of flow of heat energy through the single-glazed window is straightforward. We know that:

$$\frac{\Delta Q}{\Delta t} = -\lambda A \frac{\Delta T}{\Delta x}$$

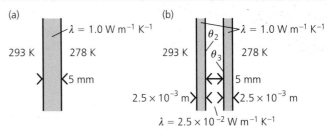

Figure 2.3.23

where $\Delta Q/\Delta t$ is the rate of flow of heat energy, $\Delta T/\Delta x$ is the temperature gradient across the material, A is the cross-sectional area and λ is the thermal conductivity of the material. We can rearrange this:

$$\frac{\Delta Q}{\Delta t}\frac{1}{A} = \frac{\lambda \Delta T}{\Delta x}$$

The left-hand side of this equation is the rate at which heat energy flows through unit area – call this q_s for the single-glazed window and q_d for the double-glazed window. To find q_s:

$$q_s = 1.0 \text{ W m}^{-1}\text{ K}^{-1} \times \frac{293 \text{ K} - 278 \text{ K}}{5.0 \times 10^{-3} \text{ m}}$$
$$= 3.0 \times 10^3 \text{ W m}^{-2}$$

The rate of flow of heat energy through the single-glazed window is 3 kW m^{-2}.

To find q_d we need to obtain three expressions, one for each layer through which the heat energy flows. Note the temperatures θ_2 and θ_3 in figure 2.3.23(b), showing the temperature on the inner surfaces of the glass sheets. Assume that the rate of flow of heat energy through each of the three layers is the same – a reasonable assumption once the temperature at all points through the layers has settled down and is not changing with time.
For the inner glass:

$$q_d = 1.0 \text{ W m}^{-1}\text{ K}^{-1} \times \frac{293 \text{ K} - \theta_2}{2.5 \times 10^{-3} \text{ m}}$$

so:

$$(293 \text{ K} - \theta_2) = 2.5 \times 10^{-3} \text{ W}^{-1}\text{ m}^2\text{ K} \times q_d \quad \text{(equation 1)}$$

For the air layer:

$$q_d = 2.5 \times 10^{-2} \text{ W m}^{-1}\text{ K}^{-1} \times \frac{\theta_2 - \theta_3}{5.0 \times 10^{-3} \text{ m}}$$

so:

$$\theta_2 - \theta_3 = 0.2 \text{ W}^{-1}\text{ m}^2\text{ K} \times q_d \quad \text{(equation 2)}$$

For the outer glass:

$$q_d = 1.0 \text{ W m}^{-1}\text{ K}^{-1} \times \frac{\theta_3 - 278 \text{ K}}{2.5 \times 10^{-3} \text{ m}}$$

so:

$$(\theta_3 - 278 \text{ K}) = 2.5 \times 10^{-3} \text{ W}^{-1}\text{ m}^2\text{ K} \times q_d \quad \text{(equation 3)}$$

Adding equations 1, 2 and 3 gives:

$$(293 \text{ K} - \theta_2) + (\theta_2 - \theta_3) + (\theta_3 - 278 \text{ K}) =$$
$$(2.5 \times 10^{-3} + 0.2 + 2.5 \times 10^{-3}) \text{ W}^{-1}\text{ m}^2\text{ K} \times q_d$$

which simplifies to:

$$(293 \text{ K} - 278 \text{ K}) = 15 \text{ K} = 0.205 \text{ W}^{-1}\text{ m}^2\text{ K} \times q_d$$

giving:

$$q_d = \frac{15 \text{ K}}{0.205 \text{ W}^{-1}\text{ m}^2\text{ K}}$$
$$= 73.2 \text{ W m}^{-2}$$

The ratio of the rate of flow of heat energy per unit area for the two windows is:

$$\frac{q_s}{q_d} = \frac{3000 \text{ W m}^{-2}}{73.2 \text{ W m}^{-2}} = 41$$

Heat energy is lost through the single-glazed window 41 times faster than through the double-glazed window.

QUESTIONS

1 What type of thermometer would you use to measure the temperature of:
  a a liquid at its freezing point, thought to be around −15 °C
  b the exposed surface of a domestic hot water cylinder
  c the air outside a car travelling along a motorway
  d a small sample of liquid (about 1 cm^3) taken from a reaction vessel?
  Give reasons in each case.

2 a How is temperature on a centigrade scale defined?
  b A particular thermocouple produces an e.m.f. of 3.9 mV at the ice point, 7.8 mV at the steam point and 4.5 mV at some unknown temperature. Calculate the unknown temperature on the centigrade scale of the thermocouple.

3 If a refrigerator is left switched on with its door open, what happens to the temperature of the room it is in?

4 a How much energy is required to raise the temperature of 1 kg of water from 10 °C to boiling point (100 °C)?
  b How quickly could this be done using a 2.5 kW electric kettle?
  (Take the specific heat capacity of water as $4.2 \times 10^3 \text{ J kg}^{-1}\text{ K}^{-1}$.)

5 A piece of hot iron is quenched by dropping it into 5.0 kg of water. If the mass of the iron is 2.0 kg and the water increases in temperature from 20 °C to 42 °C, what was the temperature of the iron before it was dropped in the water? (Take the specific heat capacity of water as $4.2 \times 10^3 \text{ J kg}^{-1}\text{ K}^{-1}$, and the specific heat capacity of iron as 450 J kg^{-1} K^{-1}.)

6 An engine is cooled by passing water through the engine block. Water flows through the block at a rate of 1.5 kg s^{-1}, warming by 14 °C as it does so. If useful work is obtained from the engine at a rate of 135 kW, what is its efficiency? (Take the specific heat capacity of water as $4.2 \times 10^3 \text{ J kg}^{-1}\text{ K}^{-1}$.)

7 One type of 'storage heater' makes use of blocks of concrete which are heated overnight using cheap electricity. The blocks then heat the room in which the heater is placed, cooling down slowly as they do so. A particular room is heated for 12 hours each day using a 2 kW electric fire. If this heater is to be replaced by a storage heater, calculate the volume of concrete that the storage heater must contain if the maximum temperature the concrete can be heated to is 90 °C and the transfer of heat energy effectively stops once the concrete has cooled to 30 °C. Comment on the feasibility of this plan. (Take the specific heat capacity of concrete as 850 J kg^{-1} K^{-1} and its density as 2700 kg m^{-3}.)

8 What is the shortest time for which a 2.5 kW kettle containing 1.5 kg of boiling water can be left without boiling dry? (Take the specific latent heat of vaporisation of water as 2.26×10^6 J kg^{-1}.)

9 While jogging at a steady rate, energy must be removed from the body by conduction, convection and radiation at a rate of about 850 W in order to keep it at a steady temperature. If 50% of this energy is removed through the evaporation of sweat, how much sweat is produced per hour by a jogger? (Take the specific latent heat of vaporisation of sweat as 2.26×10^6 J kg^{-1}.)

10 The ice on a frozen driveway to a factory is melted using a jet of steam produced by a boiler. If 1800 kg of ice at 0 °C is turned into water at 2 °C, what is the smallest mass of steam that this requires? Assume that the steam is initially at 100 °C and ends up as water at 2 °C.
(Take the specific latent heat of fusion of ice as 3.34×10^5 J kg^{-1}, the specific latent heat of vaporisation of water as 2.26×10^6 J kg^{-1} and the specific heat capacity of water as 4.2×10^3 J kg^{-1}.)

11 A shallow pond is covered with ice 6.0 cm thick. If the air temperature is −10 °C and the water below the ice has a temperature of 0 °C, calculate:
  a the rate at which heat energy flows through the ice per unit area
  b the rate at which the thickness of the ice increases.
  c What difference would it make if the ice was covered with a layer of compacted snow 5 cm thick?
(Take the thermal conductivity of ice as 1.25 W m^{-1} K^{-1}, the specific latent heat of fusion of ice as 3.34×10^4 J kg^{-1}, the density of water as 1000 kg m^{-3} and the thermal conductivity of compacted snow as 0.21 W m^{-1} K^{-1}.)

12 An expanded polystyrene box is used to transport medical supplies at a temperature of −79 °C, cooled by solid carbon dioxide ('dry ice'). The box measures 40 cm × 40 cm × 40 cm internally, and it has walls 5 cm thick. Using the internal measurements of the box, calculate:

  a the rate at which heat energy flows out of the box if the external temperature is 20 °C
  b how long a piece of dry ice with a mass of 10 g would keep the inside of the box at −79 °C.
(Take the thermal conductivity of expanded polystyrene as 8.36×10^{-4} W m^{-1} K^{-1} and the latent heat of vaporisation of dry ice as 5.77×10^6 J kg^{-1}. Solid carbon dioxide undergoes direct vaporisation (sublimation) from solid to gas at atmospheric pressure.)

13 Estimate the rate at which heat energy is lost from a hand in a woollen glove on a very cold day when the air temperature is −5 °C. Assume that the glove traps a layer of still air 3 mm thick, and that the skin of the hand is at 34 °C.
(Take the thermal conductivity of air as 2.4×10^{-2} W m^{-1} K^{-1}.)

14 You have just poured yourself a cup of coffee and are poised to add the milk. The doorbell rings. Will your cup of coffee with milk be hotter if you add the milk before you answer the door or when you come back from answering it? Justify your answer.

Developing Key Skills

You have been asked to write and present a short television programme (no more than five minutes long) to explain to viewers with no science background why scientists use measurements like metres and kilograms rather than feet and pounds. The editor commissioning this programme is very keen that you also explain to viewers why the weather forecast gives temperatures in degrees Celsius rather than any other units.

Produce a script for the programme, together with any visual aids (charts, graphs, etc.) that you need, and present it to an audience with limited science background knowledge.

[Key Skills opportunities: C, A, IT]

The interaction of energy and matter governs all our lives. We take for granted our ability to flick a switch and fill a room with light, or to get in a car and in minutes travel distances that would have taken our ancestors hours if not days. Energy and matter interact on other scales too – from the remnants of the explosion of a star, hundreds of light years in diameter, to the nucleus of the atom, one billionth of a millimetre in diameter, the way in which energy and matter behave affects the entire Universe.

The importance of this behaviour has not always been recognised. The understanding of this area of physics grew out of the Industrial Revolution and the rise of the steam engine as a means of power. The nineteenth century saw the growth and development of industry in Great Britain, and a similar growth in the understanding of the world around us. As we shall see, the steam engine and the atom between them gave rise to a branch of physics which is a powerful tool for interpreting what we see around us, from the scale of atoms to a scale which encompasses the entire Universe, its birth and its death. This branch of physics is called **thermodynamics**.

Thermodynamics

The development of thermodynamics

The science of thermodynamics covers the study of thermal energy and mechanical energy, or work. The importance of this area of science became established in the early part of the nineteenth century, as the power of the steam engine began to be harnessed.

Carnot and heat as caloric

The person who first realised the need to understand how to build better steam engines was a Frenchman, Sadi Carnot. In his work entitled 'Réflexions sur la puissance motrice du feu' ('Reflections on the motive power of heat') published in 1824, Carnot set out his understanding of the way a steam engine worked. His understanding was based on the idea of **caloric** – heat as an invisible, massless fluid. A steam engine, according to Carnot, worked rather

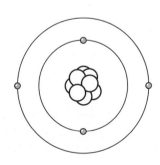

Figure 2.4.1 The behaviour of energy and matter is probably the most fundamental interaction in the Universe. We take it for granted, yet everything we do depends on it.

like a water mill, heat running 'downhill' from the boiler to the condenser and driving the shafts of the engine in the process.

Even though Carnot's work was based on a misconception, he established a principle (which scientists and engineers after him called **Carnot's principle**) which is still valid today:

> **The motive power of heat is independent of the agents set to work to realise it; its quantity is fixed solely by the temperatures of the bodies between which ... the transfer of heat is effected.**

Although the meaning of this may not be clear on first reading, the result of Carnot's principle is that any heat engine (which includes not only the steam engines of Carnot's day but also our modern internal combustion engine as well as the boilers and turbines found in power stations) has a maximum efficiency. This maximum efficiency depends *only* on the temperature of the source of heat energy and on the temperature of what Carnot called the cooling circuit. This has enormous implications for the design and use of heat engines – we shall see what these are in section 2.5.

Joule and the conversion of work into heat

Joule's experiments described in section 2.3, page 152, were carried out some 20 years after Carnot published the results of his deliberations on the steam engine. The painstaking work carried out by Joule in the workshops of his father's brewery showed beyond question that work could be converted *quantitatively* into heat. As we have seen, the result of Joule's work was to provide the evidence that was needed to foster the development of the kinetic

Figure 2.4.2 Sadi Carnot was born in Paris in 1796. His idea of caloric as the motive power driving a steam engine was based firmly on the water mill as a model. He thought of the total amount of caloric being unchanged as it ran through the steam engine, rather as the amount of water stays constant as it runs through a water wheel.

theory of matter, and to bring about a far greater understanding of the relationship between heat energy and temperature. But it did more than this. Joule had showed that Carnot's work was based on a premise that was clearly false – the notion that heat was a substance like water, which could run 'downhill' and do work in the process.

Kelvin, Clausius and the second law of thermodynamics

Joule met another eminent scientist, William Thomson, at the 1847 meeting of the British Association for the Advancement of Science. (Having begun to attend Glasgow University at the age of 10, and been appointed Professor of Natural Philosophy there at 22, Thomson was later to become Lord Kelvin, lending his name to the scale of temperature he proposed.) Kelvin believed that Joule's work could be reconciled with Carnot's if it were possible to develop *two* laws about the behaviour of heat and mechanical energy rather than just one. He set out his thoughts on this in his paper 'On the dynamical theory of heat', published in 1851.

Kelvin's work was taken further by the German physicist Rudolf Gottlieb. As was popular at the time, Gottlieb adopted the classical name of Clausius, by which he is nowadays usually known. Like Thomson, Clausius also believed that it was possible for both Joule *and* Carnot to be right if there were two fundamental laws underlying the behaviour of energy. Quite independently, Thomson and Clausius produced two versions of a law which we now know as the **second law of thermodynamics**, and to which we shall come very shortly.

The conversion of energy

Clausius and Kelvin saw that it was not the quantity of *heat* that remained unchanged in the operation of a steam engine, but the quantity of *energy*. They also saw that the way in which that energy was distributed changed as a result of the steam engine's operation, and changed in a way that is irreversible. This insight into the behaviour of energy tells us an astonishing amount about the behaviour of the world, and is particularly valuable when we come to think about supplying our energy needs for heating, lighting and transport.

Heat and the behaviour of particles of matter

In addition to his formulation of the second law, Clausius also speculated that it was possible to explain the behaviour of heat by explaining the behaviour of

---

Naming the laws of thermodynamics

There are four laws of thermodynamics, explained in turn in this section. The **second law** was formulated first, by Clausius and Thomson. Although these two scientists expressed themselves in slightly different ways, fundamentally they both produced the same law, which concerns the odd behaviour of thermal energy – for example, why hot objects cool but cool objects do not spontaneously become hot, and why a rolling ball comes to rest but a stationary ball does not begin to roll of its own accord.

The **first law** came after the second law, and is based on the work of Joule. This is the law that gives us the statement 'Energy is conserved', although the first law

tells us more than this (see box 'More than just energy conservation' on page 175). Both Clausius and Kelvin were responsible for developing and untangling the first and second laws from the work of Joule and Carnot.

The **zeroth law** was developed in the 1930s as something of an afterthought, and is important when dealing with the theoretical basis of temperature. It is called the zeroth law since it comes logically before the first and second laws, whose names were well established when the zeroth law was formulated.

The **third law** deals with the behaviour of matter and energy at low temperatures.

the particles of which matter was composed. This work was taken up by Boltzmann, who perceived that explaining the behaviour of the particles of matter would lead not only to a better understanding of the behaviour of matter and energy, but also further towards an understanding of the workings of nature itself. His achievements in bringing about such greater understanding are all the more remarkable when one considers that the existence of atoms was in serious dispute at the time of this work.

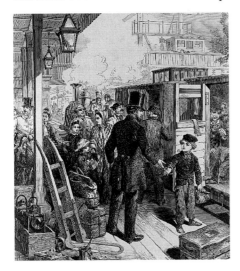

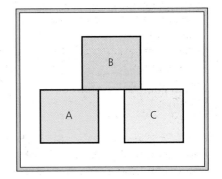

Figure 2.4.3 The nineteenth century saw the industrial revolution, the refining of the steam engine and the birth of the science of thermodynamics. The twentieth century saw the further development of thermodynamics, though physics went on to address the nature of the Universe through other theories. The quantum theory and the theories of relativity came to the fore in the early part of the century, and chaos theory and the search for a grand unified theory of matter in the latter part.

The laws of thermodynamics

The zeroth law

The zeroth law of thermodynamics states that:

> **Two bodies which are in thermal equilibrium with a third body must be in thermal equilibrium with each other.**

Although the zeroth law was the third of the laws of thermodynamics to be formulated, it is one which underpins all the others, since it concerns the idea of temperature. Like time and mass, temperature is something of which we all have experience. And like mass and time, temperature is very difficult to define. Because of this, mass, time and temperature are said by physicists to be **fundamental quantities**, which cannot be defined in terms of any other quantity. So what exactly do we mean by temperature?

Imagine three identical metal blocks, A, B and C. A has been outside in the summer sun for some time, B has been in a cool room, while C has been in a refrigerator. What will happen if we put A, B and C in contact together inside an insulating container, as shown in figure 2.4.4?

A and B are in good thermal contact, so we know that there will be a net flow of energy from A to B, since A is hotter than B. For the same reason, there will be a net flow of energy from B to C. Given time, A, B and C will come into **thermal equilibrium** – that is to say, there will be no net heat energy flow between A and B or between B and C. This is the zeroth law of thermodynamics. Our experience of the behaviour of matter and energy tells us that when this is the case, A, B and C are at the same **temperature**; that is, the temperature of an object is a statement about whether it is in thermal equilibrium with other objects.

The importance of the zeroth law is in the measurement of temperature. If A is a constant volume gas thermometer, and B is a platinum resistance thermometer, A may be used to calibrate B. If B is then taken away from A, and

Figure 2.4.4

is brought into contact with C, this effectively brings C into thermal equilibrium with A; in other words, it is as if the temperature of C is being measured directly with A, as figure 2.4.5 illustrates.

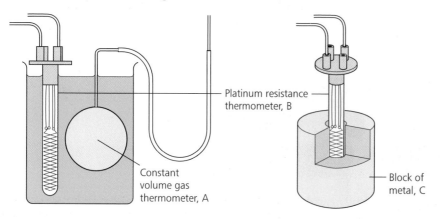

Figure 2.4.5 The constant volume gas thermometer A indicates a temperature θ when the platinum resistance thermometer B is in thermal equilibrium with it, and B indicates a temperature of $\theta + \Delta\theta$. When B is in thermal equilibrium with the block of metal C, B indicates a temperature of $\theta + \Delta\theta$. A, B and C are therefore all in thermal equilibrium at a temperature of θ on the constant volume gas thermometer scale.

The zeroth law gives at least some way of defining temperature – it is the property which determines whether a system is in thermal equilibrium with other systems.

The first law

The **first law of thermodynamics** states that:

> **The change in internal energy of a system is equal to the sum of energy entering the system through heating and energy entering the system through work done on it.**

The work of Joule in the last century gave rise to the idea that energy as a quantity is conserved whenever any process takes place, replacing the idea of caloric as an unvarying quantity. This work is expressed most often in terms of the 'law of conservation of energy', which is in fact a simplification of the first law of thermodynamics.

Joule's work on the mechanical equivalent of heat revealed that a transfer of an amount of energy ΔE to a system, whether through mechanical, electrical or other means, could give rise to an increase in the internal energy ΔU of a system by an exactly equivalent amount, in other words:

$$\Delta E = \Delta U$$

In Joule's studies, ΔE was measured as a quantity of work, which may be represented by ΔW, in which case:

$$\Delta W = \Delta U$$

Instead of doing work, an alternative way to increase the internal energy of a system is to heat it (that is, to transfer energy to it by means of a temperature gradient). The temperature of the system may be increased by allowing an amount of energy ΔQ to enter the system. If the increase in temperature of the system is the same as the increase brought about by using mechanical work, its internal energy must have increased by the same amount. This means that we can write:

$$\Delta Q = \Delta U$$

The language of thermodynamics

In thermodynamics the behaviour of a **system** is studied in relation to its **surroundings**. Between them the system and surroundings make up the **Universe**, although the surroundings may in fact only represent a small part of the Universe, such as a room or a thermostatically controlled water bath.

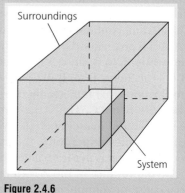

Figure 2.4.6

Changes and heat energy flows

A change which involves no heat energy flow into or out of a system is called an **adiabatic** process. An example of a process which is very nearly adiabatic is the very rapid compression of a gas which occurs when the plunger of a bicycle pump is pushed in while the hole at the end of the pump is blocked up, as shown in figure 2.4.7.

Changes which involve *no* temperature change are called **isothermal**. In these changes heat energy is allowed to flow into or out of the system. This means that in practice such changes must take place infinitely slowly (or 'quasistatically'), so that heat energy can flow into or out of the system down a tiny temperature gradient. In the example of the bicycle pump, we could make the change very nearly isothermal by using a pump with metal walls (to conduct heat in or out

quickly), and by carrying out the compression extremely slowly.

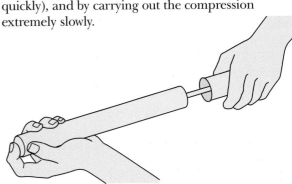

Figure 2.4.7 As the plunger of the pump is pushed in, the air in it is compressed. The mechanical work done in compressing the gas increases the internal energy of the air in the pump, and its temperature rises. If this is done rapidly there is little chance for the thermal energy to escape through the walls of the pump while the gas is being compressed, and the process is very nearly adiabatic.

Many changes do not happen *entirely* through transfer of energy by heating or *entirely* through transfer of energy by work – particularly in the case of heat engines, when a mixture of these two methods of transfer occurs. This means that the change in internal energy ΔU that results is due to a combination of work and heating, and so:

$$\Delta U = \Delta Q + \Delta W$$

This is the first law of thermodynamics, stated in words on page 174.

Signs and symbols in the first law

Although the symbols ΔU, ΔQ and ΔW are recognised widely as referring to internal energy change, heat energy transfer and work done respectively, there are different conventions for the way in which the last two are applied, as shown in figure 2.4.8.

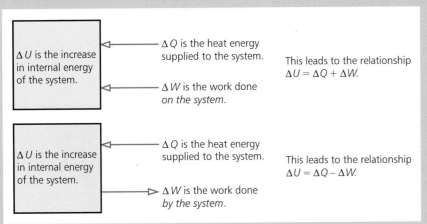

Figure 2.4.8 The first law can be found written in both these forms. In order to understand which convention is being used, look carefully at how the energy changes and work done are described. When solving any problem, stick to the same convention throughout!

More than just energy conservation

While the first law does tell us that 'Energy is conserved', there is slightly more to it than this.

If a system (say a gas contained in a box) is described in terms of the masses, velocities and positions of all its particles, then the conservation of energy comes about by straightforward consideration of the mechanics of the system, as we saw in our study of collisions in section 1. The first law tells us that we do not need to have detail at a *microscopic* level in order to formulate a law of conservation of energy – simply describing the system in terms of *macroscopic* quantities (pressure, volume and so on for the gas *as a whole*) is sufficient.

A simple example of the first law

Some air in a bicycle pump is compressed so that its volume decreases and its internal energy increases. If 25 J of work are done by the person compressing the air, and if 20 J of thermal energy leave the gas through the walls of the pump, what is the increase in the internal energy of the air?

Let: ΔU = increase in internal energy of air

ΔQ = heat energy flowing *into* the air

and: ΔW = work done *on* the air

Then the first law can be written as:

$$\Delta U = \Delta Q + \Delta W$$

In this case: $\Delta W = 25$ J

and: $\Delta Q = -20$ J (the negative sign shows that energy *leaves* the air)

so: $\Delta U = -20$ J + 25 J

$$= +5 \text{ J}$$

The internal energy of the air in the pump *increases* by 5 J.

The second law

The similar difficulty in defining both time and temperature has already been highlighted. The **second law of thermodynamics** makes this similarity between the two quantities even more striking. It can be stated as:

> **No process is possible in which there is an overall decrease in the entropy of the Universe.**

This evidently requires some elaboration, which is given below.

Imagine making a short film, lasting three or four seconds, of the two processes pictured in figure 2.4.9. Now imagine the film running backwards. Which would look strange?

The film of the swinging pendulum would look the same whether run forwards or backwards, but the film of the ball bouncing would seem very unreal indeed! Both of these processes involve energy changes, changes in which the first law tells us the total amount of energy remains constant. The gravitational potential energy of the pendulum is transferred to kinetic energy and back to gravitational potential energy again – a 'two-way' process. Yet the energy transferred from the ball as it falls and hits the ground, producing thermal and sound energy as it does so, never gets transferred back to the ball again – the energy flow here seems to be a 'one way' process. And even apparently 'two-way' processes like a swinging pendulum eventually come to a stop. Why does energy behave in this way?

Before we answer this question, we need to look at two apparently unrelated questions:

1 Why does diffusion happen?

2 How is energy like the particles of a gas?

(1) Why does diffusion happen?

Imagine what happens when the cover slide between the gas jars shown in figure 2.4.10 is removed. Our experience tells us that, given long enough, we shall find the bromine vapour spread evenly throughout the two gas jars – we should not expect to find all of it in one jar. In order to convince ourselves of why this is so, it is best to look at a much simpler situation, where many fewer particles are involved. We can imagine starting off with only five bromine particles in the left-hand jar, rather than the 10^{22} or so there would be in the jar in the photograph, and figure 2.4.11 shows the result.

Figure 2.4.9

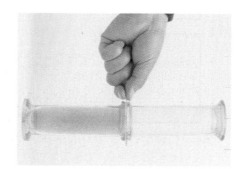

Figure 2.4.10

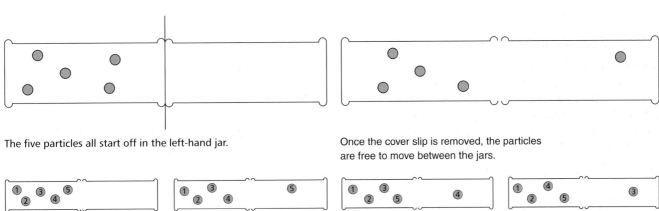

The five particles all start off in the left-hand jar.

Once the cover slip is removed, the particles are free to move between the jars.

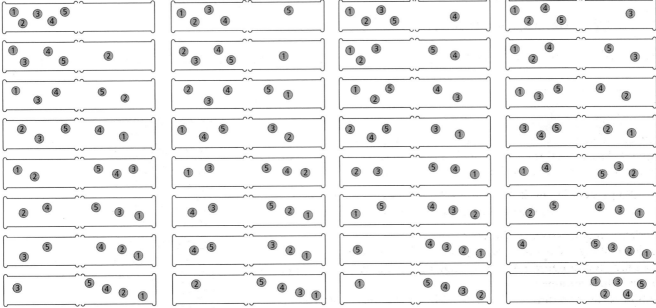

If we increase the number of particles in the gas jars to 50, W becomes 2^{50}, or about 10^{15}. And for a real situation with something like 10^{22} particles, W has an enormous value – about $2^{10^{22}}$. Only two of these arrangements have all the particles in one jar, whereas the majority of them have the particles spread more or less evenly between the jars.

To have some idea of what this means, imagine that it were possible to make a note of the position of all the particles in the two jars once every second. Only *once* in every $2^{10^{22}}$ seconds would we be likely to see all the particles in the left-hand jar. The age of the Earth is thought to be something like 10^{17} seconds – so we should have a very long wait indeed, and we are quite justified in saying that gases *always* spread out.

Figure 2.4.11 Each particle has two possible ways of being arranged – in the left-hand jar or in the right-hand jar. If we represent the number of possible arrangements for particle 1 as W_1, for particle 2 as W_2 and so on, then the total number of ways W that the five particles can be arranged between the two jars is given by:
$$W = W_1 \times W_2 \times W_3 \times W_4 \times W_5$$
$$= 2 \times 2 \times 2 \times 2 \times 2 = 2^5 = 32$$
Since only one of these 32 ways results in all the particles being in the left-hand jar, it would be surprising if this arrangement were to happen very often.

Chaos and entropy

In the model of the distribution of bromine particles, W represents the number of possible arrangements of particles that exist. Combining values of W is done by multiplying them together, which results in extremely large numbers when there are many particles involved. For practical purposes it is useful to have a property of a system which measures the number of possible arrangements, and expresses this as a number which is not too difficult to handle. The property that is defined in order to do this is **entropy**. The entropy S of a system is defined by the relationship:

$$S = k \log_e W$$

The entropy of a system is a measure of the **disorder** or **chaos** in it – the larger the entropy, the more disorder. So the changes that occur when a gas is allowed to diffuse into a larger volume represent an increase in entropy, since the number of ways of arranging the particles (that is, the disorder) increases.

The constant of proportionality k in the relationship is the Boltzmann constant, the gas constant for an individual particle met on page 145 (the reasons for this are beyond the scope of this book). Entropy has the same units as the Boltzmann constant of J K^{-1} in the SI system.

Why the even distribution?

The argument we have just seen explains why it is that we never see all the bromine particles in one of the gas jars – not that it *cannot* happen, but that it is *extremely unlikely* to happen. What it does *not* explain is why there is always (once a steady state has been reached) an even distribution of particles between the two gas jars.

A simple way of answering this is to say that as there are only *two* ways of making all the N particles appear in one gas jar or the other out of 2^N ways of arranging them, we do not see either of these arrangements – that is, there are few ways of making this arrangement happen, so it happens only infrequently. Conversely, there are many ways of distributing the particles more or less evenly between the two gas jars, so this arrangement is found frequently.

The graphs in figure 2.4.12 show that as the number of particles N increases, the likelihood of finding a given departure from $N/2$ particles in each gas jar decreases too. By the time N has reached the number

of particles in the gas jars, the likelihood of a departure from a distribution of $N/2$ in each gas jar by even a tiny amount is so small as to be negligible.

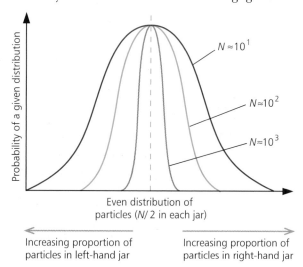

Figure 2.4.12

Figure 2.4.13 Unlikely as it may seem, the same idea is needed to explain why photosynthesis occurs, how photocopiers work and why energy behaves as it does!

Although the laws of thermodynamics seem to forbid us to make something that can take heat energy from an object and transfer that energy to an object that is warmer, the existence of refrigerators shows that this is quite possible, as energy is transferred from the inside of the fridge (at, say, 3 °C) to the warmth of the kitchen (at, say, 20 °C). The technology that makes this possible is called the 'heat pump', and it does not contravene the laws of thermodynamics at all.

The heat pump used in a refrigerator or air conditioner makes use of a liquid which has a boiling point near room temperature when at high pressure, but a boiling point below 0 °C when at atmospheric pressure. For many years the liquids used in refrigerators were substances called chlorofluorocarbons, but concern over the effect of these compounds on the layer of ozone in the Earth's atmosphere has meant their replacement with less harmful substances in recent years.

Figure 2.4.15 A refrigerator appears to contravene the second law by moving heat energy from a cold place to a warmer one, causing a *decrease* in entropy. However, it does this only because elsewhere in the Universe a lump of coal, a stream of water or the nucleus of an atom is involved in a process which *increases* the entropy of the Universe by a greater amount.

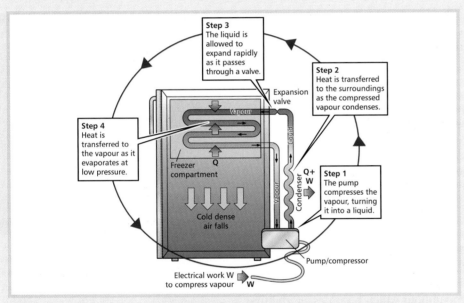

Step 3 The liquid is allowed to expand rapidly as it passes through a valve.

Step 2 Heat is transferred to the surroundings as the compressed vapour condenses.

Step 4 Heat is transferred to the vapour as it evaporates at low pressure.

Step 1 The pump compresses the vapour, turning it into a liquid.

Expansion valve

Vapour

Freezer compartment

Q

Cold dense air falls

Condenser

Q+ W

Pump/compressor

Electrical work W to compress vapour

W

Figure 2.4.14 The four steps in the refrigeration cycle are common to all heat pumps. If you carefully feel the thin pipes at the back of a refrigerator that is running, you will find that they are hot – it is the temperature difference between these tubes and the air surrounding them that allows the heat to be transferred.

A heat pump can also be used to provide heating for homes and offices, by extracting energy from the cold surroundings outside and pumping this into the warm interior of the buildings. This process is exactly equivalent to the function performed by a refrigerator – in both cases, the heat pump transfers energy from a cold place to a warmer one. At first sight this seems to contravene the second law, since the energy Q lost from the cold place reduces its entropy by more than the increase in entropy brought about by Q flowing into the warmer place. However, the second law is safe! In order to make the heat pump function, an amount of work W has to be done on the refrigerant. It is the dumping of this work as heat into the warm place that tips the balance and makes the overall process one in which there is an *increase* in entropy.

(2) How is energy like the particles of a gas?

Investigations about the way atoms behave when they interact with energy sources lead physicists to believe that atoms do not deal in energy in 'any old amounts' but only in set quantities. Section 6 explains in more detail the nature of the experiments that suggest this, but for now it is sufficient to say that atoms can increase or decrease the energy they have only in set amounts called **quanta** (singular **quantum**). Figure 2.4.16 illustrates the importance of quanta when dealing with small quantities of energy.

Figure 2.4.16 The smallest unit of money becomes unimportant when you are dealing in very large sums, but it is very important when the sum of money is small. Energy is like this – when we deal in large amounts, the fact that it comes in quanta can be ignored. But when we deal with very small amounts, as we do when thinking about individual atoms, the energy quantum becomes very important indeed.

Putting together the idea of particles distributing themselves between gas jars with energy coming in quanta gives us a way of explaining the behaviour of energy in the examples of the pendulum and the bouncing ball on page 176, and will lead us to the second law.

A simple model for the behaviour of energy

The world around us is a complicated place, and the Universe even more so, but it is possible to model what is happening in them by virtue of the fact that there are some simple processes going on in both of them. A very simple model universe is shown in figure 2.4.17. In it, the universe consists of 2500 atoms, each of which may have either one quantum of energy or none. An atom which has one quantum we shall call *on*, and one with no quanta we shall call *off*. The universe we are modelling contains two regions, A with 100 atoms and B with 2400 atoms, and 40 quanta, all of which are to be found in region A when we start our observations.

Figure 2.4.17 The situation at the 'birth' of our universe. Region A in the bottom left-hand corner of the screen has many atoms which are *on* (white dots), while region B has none. This corresponds to a great deal of energy stored in A, and none in B.

What will happen if we allow this universe to evolve? By the mechanism of thermal conduction we saw in section 2.3, as the atoms in region A oscillate they transfer energy from one to another. This results in an atom which is *on* passing its quantum of energy on to its neighbour which becomes *on*, the first atom becoming *off* as this happens. This process continues at the boundary of regions A and B, so that energy flows from A into B and throughout B. As this happens, the total amount of energy in A decreases, and that in B increases. Figure 2.4.18 on page 181 shows this process.

Is there an 'end result' to this evolution? On the scale that we have been observing, that is, to an observer looking at individual atoms, the answer is no – the quanta are constantly shuffling between atoms. But to a more distant observer who is only looking at the distribution of energy between regions A and B the answer is yes – eventually there comes a point where the distribution of energy between A and B does not change, and a steady state is reached. The second observer is us in our everyday lives, looking at our simple universe in the way we normally look at the universe in which we live. This observer sees only the pattern of energy distribution, not the constant shuffling of quanta which deeper observation perceives.

 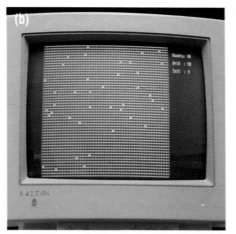 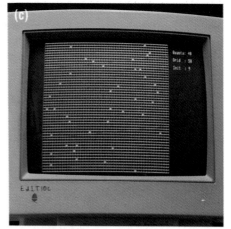

Figure 2.4.18 Our universe (a) shortly after its birth, (b) and (c) once a steady state has been reached. In (b) and (c) note that although the *arrangement* of quanta is different, there is a similar *distribution* of quanta between regions A and B in each case.

Our simple model provides us with a way of understanding the way thermal energy behaves. Energy localised in region A spreads out and finds its way throughout the universe, just as the particles of bromine spread out through the two gas jars. Just as the laws of probability govern the behaviour of particles of matter, so they govern the behaviour of quanta of energy, making the concentration of energy from a 'spread out' distribution into a 'localised' distribution unlikely in a system as small and simple as ours, and effectively impossible in a universe as large and complex as the real one.

The concept of temperature

Notice that the simple model provides a concept of temperature too. Once a steady state is reached and there is no net flow of energy between A and B, a state of thermal equilibrium exists between the two regions. Our understanding of temperature so far means that for this to happen A and B must both be at the same temperature. The implication of this is that temperature is a measure of the 'concentration' of energy in a region – although B has more quanta than A at thermal equilibrium, they both have the same concentration, and it is the concentration of quanta which governs their movement, just like the particles of bromine. Figure 2.4.19 illustrates this point.

Entropy and energy

In the same way as a spreading out of particles represented an increase in entropy, the spreading out of thermal energy represents an overall increase of entropy too. Although quanta leaving region A reduce its entropy, because there are now fewer ways of arranging the smaller number of quanta in A, the quanta entering B more than compensate by raising the entropy of B, since there are many more ways of arranging the quanta in A and B than there were in A alone. In this way, the overall entropy increases.

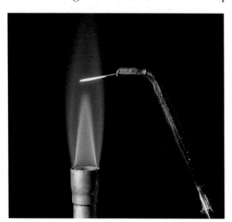 

Figure 2.4.19 Although the basin of water contains more quanta, the concentration of quanta in it is much lower than the concentration in the red-hot pin. Putting your hand in the basin won't hurt you, because the rate at which quanta move between the water and your skin is quite slow. The red-hot pin is a different matter, however!

The evolution of the second law of thermodynamics

This discovery about the behaviour of energy in our simple universe is similar to the one made by Clausius. The difference is that while we have approached the behaviour of energy from a viewpoint of particles and quanta, Clausius approached it from the work of Carnot and Joule, examining the workings of heat and energy whilst considering the steam engine. Clausius stated this behaviour in his form of the second law (there is another form of the law stated by Kelvin – we shall come to this shortly):

The spontaneous transfer of energy from a cooler body to a hotter body is not possible.

But what about Kelvin's statement? Kelvin had also studied the work of Carnot and Joule, and came to similar conclusions to Clausius. Clausius and Kelvin both stated the second law using different words. Their statements tell us slightly different things about the behaviour of matter and energy, although the essential sense of the two forms is the same. Kelvin considered the energy flows in the steam engine (from the boiler or **heat source** to the condenser or **heat sink**) and concluded:

The complete conversion of energy from a heat source into work is not possible.

Just as Clausius's interpretation of the behaviour of energy can be arrived at from examination of particles and quanta, so can Kelvin's, as shown in figure 2.4.21.

Figure 2.4.20 Clausius (Rudolph Gottlieb), 1822–88. 'Die Energie der Welt ist Konstant. Die Entropie der Welt strebt einem maximum zu.' ('The energy of the world is constant. The entropy of the world tends to increase.') This is another way of saying that energy cannot flow spontaneously from a cool body to a hot one.

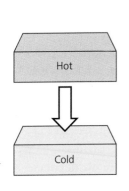

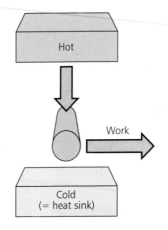

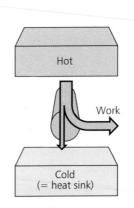

When a hot object comes into contact with a cooler one, there is a net flow of energy from the hot body to the cooler one simply because there are more ways of arranging the quanta when this happens.

If energy is removed from a heat source (i.e. a hot body), the entropy of the body decreases. If all this energy is then converted into work, the overall change in entropy is a decrease, which contravenes the second law.

If a small amount of energy is allowed to flow into the heat sink, the rise in entropy of the heat sink can offset the drop in entropy of the heat source – so the second law is satisfied.

Figure 2.4.21 In order to convert heat into work, we must sacrifice some heat to a heat sink, so that the entropy of the Universe does not decrease.

It is almost impossible to imagine that energy could flow into a ball from the table on which it is resting and cause it to fly up in the air – Clausius's statement can convince us of that. But what if the ball were placed on the hotplate of a cooker? It is easy to imagine that the 5 J or so of energy required to raise the ball could then flow into it. The energy that flows into the ball under these circumstances is represented by the random motion of the particles in the ball. But for the ball to fly upwards, the particles need to have motion in the same direction – upwards! This is highly unlikely to happen, and so the ball on the hotplate may get warmer, but will not fly up in the air. This is the result of Kelvin's statement of the second law.

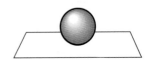

Figure 2.4.22 Experience tells us that a ball does not begin to bounce spontaneously. The second law explains why.

The third law

The **third law of thermodynamics** may not be a law in the same sense as the other laws we have seen. Stated simply it says that:

Absolute zero cannot be reached in a finite number of steps.

This seems to be a necessary condition if we consider that to cool a body we require a cooler body into which heat can flow, although there are other ways of cooling which rely on energy absorption by physical changes, as we saw on page 179.

SUMMARY

- **Thermodynamics** studies the interconversion of thermal energy (heat) and mechanical energy (work), and has its origins in the development of the steam engine.

- The **zeroth law of thermodynamics** states that two bodies which are in thermal equilibrium with a third body must be in thermal equilibrium with one another. This has important implications in the measurement of temperature.

- The **first law of thermodynamics** states that the change in internal energy of a system is equal to the sum of energy entering the system through heating and energy entering the system through work done on it, $\Delta U = \Delta Q + \Delta W$.

- The **second law of thermodynamics** states that no process is possible in which there is an overall decrease in the entropy of the Universe.

- **Entropy** S is a measure of the distribution of matter and energy in a system, $S = k \log_e W$, where W is the number of possible arrangements and k the Boltzmann constant. An increase in entropy represents an increase in chaos or disorder in a system.

- Energy can only enter or leave a system in set amounts called **quanta**.

- The quantisation of energy is usually only observable at the scale of atoms and molecules. As quanta of thermal energy in a system disperse, the entropy of the system increases and it becomes extremely unlikely that the thermal energy will concentrate itself in a small part of the system again.

- The **third law of thermodynamics** states that absolute zero cannot be reached in a finite number of steps.

QUESTIONS

1 A volume of gas is trapped in a cylinder at atmospheric pressure. If the gas is compressed quickly (adiabatically) its temperature and pressure increase and it can do work. If the gas is allowed to cool again it can still do work – where does the energy to enable it to do work come from?

2 A lump of lead with a mass of 0.50 kg is dropped from a height of 20 m onto a hard surface. It does not rebound, but remains there at rest. What are:

a ΔQ

b ΔW

c ΔU

for this process?

d What is the temperature change in the lead immediately after the impact?

(Take the specific heat capacity of lead as 128 J kg^{-1} K^{-1}, and assume $g = 10$ m s^{-2}.)

3 A refrigerator works by cooling a fluid, allowing it to expand rapidly from its liquid state to its gaseous state (effectively the reverse of the process considered in question **1**). Using the first law of thermodynamics, explain how a refrigerator is able to extract energy from food inside it.

4 A refrigerator is an example of a **heat pump**, capable of transferring energy from a cold place to a warmer one. Heat pumps are also used to cool buildings in summer (transferring energy from the cool interior of the building to the hot outside) and to warm them in winter (transferring energy from the cold outside to the warmer interior of the building). Do heat pumps contravene the first and second laws of thermodynamics? Explain your answer.

5 Is it reasonable to expect a cold cup of tea to warm up spontaneously? Explain your answer.

6 Tidying an untidy room reduces its entropy. Does this process contravene the second law of thermodynamics?

Developing Key Skills

The following passage is taken from Sadi Carnot's original work about the steam engine (page 170), published in 1824. (A few of the spellings have since become obsolete.) Use this passage to help you to write a short section of an encyclopedia biography of Carnot, in English, entitled 'Why Carnot believed an understanding of the steam engine was important for society'.

Réflexions sur la Puissance Motrice du Feu

Personne n'ignore que la chaleur peut être la cause du mouvement, qu'elle possède même une grande puissance motrice: les machines à vapeur, aujourd'hui si répandues, en sont une preuve parlante à tous les yeux. C'est à la chaleur que doivent être attribués les grands mouvemens qui frappent nos regards sur la terre; c'est à elle que sont dues les agitations de l'atmosphère, l'ascension des nuages, la chute des pluies et des autres météores, les courans d'eau qui sillonnent la surface du globe et dont l'homme est parvenu à employer pour son usage une faible partie; enfin les tremblemens de terre, les éruptions volcaniques, reconnaissent aussi pour cause la chaleur.

C'est dans cet immense réservoir que nous pouvons puiser la force mouvante nécessaire à nos besoins; la nature, en nous offrant de toutes parts le combustible, nous a donné la faculté de faire naître en tous temps et en tous lieux la chaleur et la puissance motrice qui en est la suite. Développer cette puissance, l'approprier à notre usage, tel est l'objet des machines à feu.

L'étude de ces machines est du plus haut intérêt, leur importance est immense, leur emploi s'accroît tous les jours. Elles paraissent destinées à produire une grande révolution dans le monde civilisé. Déjà la machine à feu exploite nos mines, fait mouvoir nos navires, creuse nos ports et nos rivières, forge le fer, façonne les bois, écrase les grains, files et ourdit nos étoffes, transporte les plus pesans fardeaux, etc. Elle semble devoir un jour servir de moteur universel et obtenir la préférence sur la force des animaux, les chutes d'eau et les courans d'air. Elle a, sur la premier de ces moteurs, l'avantage de l'économie: sur les deux autres, l'avantage inappréciable de pouvoir s'employer en tous temps et en tous lieux, et de ne jamais souffrir d'interruption dans son travail.

Si quelque jour les perfectionnements de la machine à feu s'étendent assez loin pour la rendre peu coûteuse en établissement et en combustible, elle réunira toutes les qualités désirables, et fera prendre aux arts industriels un essor dont il serait difficile de prévoir toute l'étendue.

Non seulement, en effet, un moteur puissant et commode, que l'on peut se procurer ou transporter partout, se substitue aux moteurs déjà en usage; mais il fait prendre aux arts où on l'applique une extension rapide, il peut même créer des arts entièrement nouveaux.

[Key Skills opportunities: C, IT]

2.5 Applications of thermodynamics

Sections 2.1–4 have shown how the models of matter and energy developed by physicists lead to a greater understanding of their behaviour. In this section we shall be concerned with some of the practical aspects of this interaction.

Applying the first law – working and heating

The first law of thermodynamics can be summarised as:

$$\Delta U = \Delta Q + \Delta W$$

We shall now apply this first to solids and then to gases, and finally look again at heat engines.

Solids – energy changes and deformation

We saw in section 2.2 that the behaviour of materials under tension could be understood in the context of the behaviour of their particles, and by using simple mechanics to study the forces acting. Having looked at the laws of thermodynamics, we can now return to this topic and take matters just a little further.

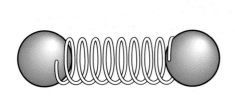
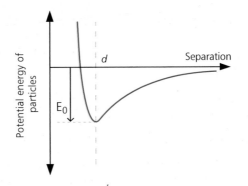
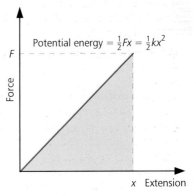

Figure 2.5.1

Figure 2.5.1 reminds us that the model of a solid consists of particles with forces between them which behave under certain circumstances like springs. It also reminds us that it is possible to derive a simple relationship between energy stored under tension and extension for something like a piece of wire, by using Hooke's law. Although this is useful, for the engineer or materials scientist it is often more useful to have some idea of the strain energy of a solid under tension based on its Young modulus. This is relatively straightforward to obtain.

By definition the Young modulus E is given by:

$$E = \frac{\textbf{tensile stress}}{\textbf{tensile strain}} = \frac{F/A}{x/l}$$

We also know (see figure 2.5.1) that when the proportionality limit is not exceeded, the strain energy stored in a solid under tension is given by:

$$\textbf{Strain energy} = \tfrac{1}{2}Fx$$

This can be rewritten as:

$$\text{Strain energy} = \tfrac{1}{2} \times \frac{F}{A} \times \frac{x}{l} \times Al$$

Using the definitions of tensile stress and tensile strain, this becomes:

$$\text{Strain energy} = \tfrac{1}{2} \times \text{stress} \times \text{strain} \times \text{volume}$$

or:

$$\text{Strain energy per unit volume} = \tfrac{1}{2} \times \text{stress} \times \text{strain}$$

Strain energy – worked example

The steel mooring cable of a ship has a length of 10 m and a cross-sectional area of 10^{-3} m², and is under a tension of 10^5 N. The Young modulus of steel is 2×10^{11} Pa. What is the strain energy stored in the cable?

In this example it will be convenient to have a relationship between strain energy per unit volume and Young modulus. From the definition of the Young modulus we can write that:

$$\text{Strain} = \frac{\text{stress}}{E}$$

so:

$$\frac{\text{Strain energy}}{\text{per unit volume}} = \tfrac{1}{2} \times \frac{\text{stress}^2}{E} = \tfrac{1}{2} \frac{(F/A)^2}{E}$$

Substituting values into this:

$$\frac{\text{Strain energy}}{\text{per unit volume}} = \tfrac{1}{2} \times \frac{(10^5 \text{ N}/10^{-3} \text{ m}^2)^2}{2 \times 10^{11} \text{ N m}^{-2}}$$

$$= \tfrac{1}{2} \times \frac{10^{16} \text{ N}^2 \text{ m}^{-4}}{2 \times 10^{11} \text{ N m}^{-2}}$$

$$= 2.5 \times 10^4 \text{ J m}^{-3}$$

Since the volume of the cable is 10^{-3} m² $\times$ 10 m $= 10^{-2}$ m³, the total strain energy stored in it is given by:

$$\text{Strain energy} = 2.5 \times 10^4 \text{ J m}^{-3} \times 10^{-2} \text{ m}^3$$

$$= 250 \text{ J}$$

This is about the same amount of energy as the kinetic energy of a 1 kg mass travelling at 22 m s^{-1} (about 50 miles per hour) – not inconsiderable!

The first law and plastic and elastic deformation

Where does the strain energy in an object under tension come from? Since work is done in stretching the object, the force that stretches it does the work which causes energy to be stored in the stretched object. (Remember that the forces between particles in a solid behave like tiny springs – the energy is stored in these 'springs', to be released when the external force causing the deformation is removed.) The first law of thermodynamics tells us that we may recover all of the energy put in by the force causing the deformation, but only if the deformation is elastic. Why is this?

In deforming a solid past its elastic limit, some of the work done is used to cause a rearrangement in the particles of the solid, with planes of particles moving over one another (see section 2.2, page 130). This work actually increases the internal energy of the solid (a material undergoing plastic deformation becomes slightly warmer), and the second law shows that this energy is not returnable, since it is lost to the surroundings as heat.

For elastic deformation there is no change in internal energy, and so all the work done is stored as elastic energy in the solid, and is returned when the deformation is removed. Where plastic deformation occurs however, the internal energy of the solid increases. This means that not all of the work done in stretching the solid is stored as strain energy – some is used to increase the internal energy of the solid (to make it warmer), and it is this energy which cannot be recovered on removing the deformation.

Rubber shows a marked deformation of this sort. For a piece of rubber the stress–strain graph for loading and unloading looks like that shown in figure 2.5.2.

When a rubber band is stretched, Hooke's law is not obeyed for the majority of the deformation, as figure 2.5.2 shows. Line OAB shows the stretching of the band as it is loaded, while BCO shows the situation as the rubber is unloaded. The graph clearly shows that the strain for a particular stress is greater for loading than unloading. This effect is called **hysteresis** (which means 'lagging behind'), and occurs to a much smaller extent with metals as well as rubber.

The work done on the rubber when it is stretched is represented by the area under line OAB. The energy released as the rubber is unloaded is represented by the area under line BCO. The difference in these two areas is the shaded area in figure 2.5.2. This area represents the increase in internal energy of the rubber. As a result of this, rubber that is continually loaded and unloaded gets hot – question 3 on page 195 explores this effect further.

Gases – work done in changes of volume

The first law can be used to examine the energy changes that happen when a gas expands and does work. Consider the situation shown in figure 2.5.3.

If the gas in the cylinder exerts a force F on the piston, the force does work as the gas expands. As part of this thought experiment, we can arrange for three conditions to be met:

1 negligible friction between the piston and the walls of the cylinder
2 the force moves the piston at a steady rate so that the external force exerted on the piston is equal to the force exerted by the pressure p of the gas in the cylinder
3 the change in volume ΔV is very small, so that the pressure exerted by the gas is effectively constant.

Under these circumstances, the gas will do work ΔW against the force holding the piston. This work can be calculated as:

$\Delta W = F\Delta x$ (**F and Δx are both in the same direction, so both are positive**)

Now the force that the gas exerts on the piston is given by:

$F = pA$ (**A = area of face of piston, p = pressure of gas**)

Combining these two equations gives us:

$$\Delta W = pA\,\Delta x$$

As $A\Delta x$ is the change in volume ΔV of the gas, this means that:

$$\Delta W = p\Delta V$$

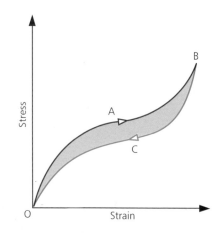

Figure 2.5.2 Stress–strain graph for rubber showing hysteresis.

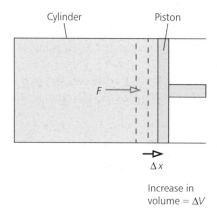

Figure 2.5.3 A gas in a cylinder being compressed by a piston.

Larger changes in volume

For larger changes in volume we cannot assume that p remains constant. A graph of p against V is shown in figure 2.5.4. $\Delta W = p\Delta V$, so the work done is the area under the graph. In order to calculate the work done on the gas, we can use the 'sum of the strips' method that we have used before. However, in this case, there is a mathematical relationship between p and V, so mathematical tools can be used instead of counting the squares on the strips.

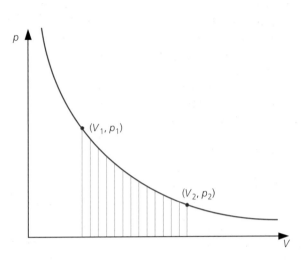

Figure 2.5.4 Work done in going from (V_1, p_1) to (V_2, p_2) is sum of the area of the strips, each of which has area $p\Delta V$.

For a small increase in volume ΔV, p can be regarded as constant, so $\Delta W = p\Delta V$ for this small change.

For an ideal gas, $pV = nRT$, so $p = nRT/V$.
The volume of the gas changes from V_1 to V_2, so:

$$\Delta W = \int_{V_1}^{V_2} p \, \mathrm{d}V = \int_{V_1}^{V_2} nRT \frac{1}{V} \, \mathrm{d}V = nRT \log_e \frac{V_2}{V_1}$$

Note that this assumes that the temperature remains constant during the compression of the gas (that is, this is an isothermal process). If this is not so, then the expression becomes more complex.

Work and internal energy

Figure 2.5.5 shows how the work done on the piston by the gas results in a decrease in internal energy of the gas.

The first law enables us to calculate the change in internal energy of the gas. If we write the first law in the form:

$$\Delta U = \Delta Q + \Delta W$$

ΔW will be negative, since work is done *by* the system. So we may write that:

$$\Delta U = \Delta Q - \Delta W$$

For this change we know that $\Delta W = p\Delta V$, so:

$$\Delta U = \Delta Q - p\Delta V$$

If ΔQ is zero, the internal energy of the gas decreases by $p\Delta V$.

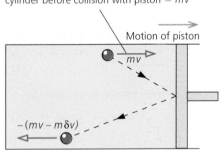

Component of momentum along axis of cylinder before collision with piston = mv

Motion of piston

mv

$-(mv - m\delta v)$

Component of momentum along axis of cylinder after collision with piston $= -(mv - m\delta v)$

Figure 2.5.5 As a gas expands it does work and its internal energy decreases. This can be explained on the basis of the kinetic theory. As molecules collide with the piston moving out of the cylinder, they produce an impulse on the piston. As a result they rebound from the piston with less momentum than they had before hitting the piston. This decreased momentum means that the internal energy of the gas decreases as the piston moves out of the cylinder.

Converting heat energy into work – heat engines and the first law

Sections 2.3 and 2.4 have referred to heat engines, in the context of the definition of thermodynamic temperature and in the context of the limits of efficiency of such devices. We shall therefore conclude this section by looking at heat engines and the importance of thermodynamics in their design.

As we saw in section 2.4, a heat engine is essentially something which takes energy from a heat source and converts some of that energy into work. The second law requires that in doing this we cannot turn all of the energy from the heat source into work, only some of it – we shall return to the implications of this shortly. In the last century the main heat engine of importance was the steam engine. The twentieth century saw the rise of the internal combustion engine, but the steam engine lives on in its modified form as the steam turbine used in power stations, whether powered by a lump of coal, a barrel of oil or an exploding atom.

To understand the way a heat engine works requires an understanding of the properties of gases as well as some knowledge of the behaviour of thermal energy and work. The essence of any heat engine is a series of changes of pressure and volume in a **working agent**, as shown in figure 2.5.6. In the case of the steam engine, this working agent is steam, while in the case of the internal combustion engine it is a mixture of hydrocarbon fuel and air. The engine provides a means of drawing energy from the heat source. In the case of the steam engine this is the boiler, while in the internal combustion engine – as its name implies – the heat source is inside the cylinder, provided by the rapid burning of the hydrocarbon fuel/air mixture.

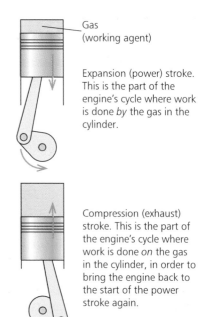

Gas
(working agent)

Expansion (power) stroke. This is the part of the engine's cycle where work is done *by* the gas in the cylinder.

Compression (exhaust) stroke. This is the part of the engine's cycle where work is done *on* the gas in the cylinder, in order to bring the engine back to the start of the power stroke again.

Figure 2.5.6 Any heat engine works by alternately compressing a gas (the working agent) and allowing it to expand again, taking energy from a heat source as it does so. The first law tells us that a heat engine can produce only as much work as there is energy in the heat source. The second law tells us that a **heat sink** is needed as well as a heat source.

The second law – what energy crisis?

The consequences of Clausius

Section 2.4 showed how the 'spreading out' of energy is a natural consequence of the quantisation of energy and the laws of statistics. The Clausius statement of the second law reflects this, however you like to put it:

The entropy of the world always tends to increase

or:

The spontaneous transfer of energy from a cooler body to a hotter body is not possible.

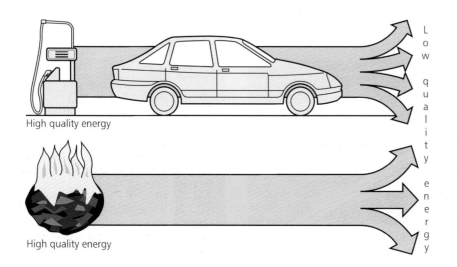

High quality energy

High quality energy

Low quality energy

Figure 2.5.7 Although the first law tells us that the total quantity of energy in any process is constant, the second law tells us that as soon as any physical process involves the transfer of energy to thermal energy that energy begins to disperse. Once dispersed the energy cannot then be used to do as much as it could before.

FOCUS ALTERNATIVE ENERGY SOURCES

We live surrounded by complex machines, taking for granted our ability to accomplish everyday tasks using energy in a way that would astonish a time-traveller from the nineteenth century. For some of us at least, this increasing mechanisation has produced a life that is free from the physical restrictions that shackled our ancestors. But the price of this transformation is the consumption of large amounts of energy, usually in the form of fossil fuels.

Of course, it is not strictly correct to talk in terms of an *energy crisis*, as the conservation of energy ensures that the energy we use today will not disappear, merely become more spread out or dissipated. Instead, we should think of the crisis as one of *entropy*. As we consume our precious stocks of fuels that are low in entropy, the exchange that nature demands for our use of fossil fuels is the increase in entropy as the quanta spread out.

Eventually the world will need to find sources of energy other than fossil fuels, and it is here that the so-called alternative sources of energy come in. The devices built to harvest energy from wind, sun and waves are many and varied, and often ingenious too. Another thing alternative energy devices have in common is their large size and modest power output, at least compared to current technologies. This is a direct result of the constraints imposed on us by the second law – for our devices designed to capture energy from our surroundings have the uphill task of harvesting the precious quanta from high-entropy sources, with their low energy density.

The dissipation of energy into a high-entropy state is something predicted by the second law, and is called by physicists the 'heat death of the Universe', for once energy is spread out uniformly there will be no way of effecting change, and all processes in the Universe must cease. Perhaps we are not heading directly for the heat death of the Earth, as the input of solar radiation means that we shall have an energy source on which to depend for some time to come. But unless alternative energy sources become a good deal more productive than they are at the moment, humankind could be facing a very different future indeed.

Figure 2.5.8 The development of machines has freed us from the need to labour hard just to make a living.

Figure 2.5.9 Two possible sources of alternative energy, built to harvest energy from sunlight and from the movement of air over the Earth's surface.

The important lesson from the second law as far as Clausius is concerned is that energy flows in such a way that it always tends to disperse. Thus, although a hot cup of tea may cool down, a cool cup of tea will never spontaneously warm up – even though the first law says that this is quite possible. So the *quantity* of energy involved in any process remains unchanged, but the *quality* of it *diminishes*. This means that fuels and systems at high temperatures represent **high quality energy**. This becomes **low quality energy** as it is used for heating our homes and factories and driving our cars and buses, as illustrated in figure 2.5.7.

This, then, is the problem facing our world – we do not have an energy crisis, but an *entropy* crisis. The quantity of energy is the same as ever it was, but as we burn our fossil fuels the quanta in them become dispersed, and the entropy of the Universe increases. 'Alternative energy' provides an answer of sorts, but even here the second law is at work. As we try to harness the quanta in low quality energy sources like the Sun and the wind, enormous networks of 'harvesting machines' in the form of wind farms or solar energy farms are required in order to capture the dispersed quanta. Compared with supplying the energy demands of an energy-hungry society in this way, looking for a needle in a haystack is a positively easy task.

The consequences of Kelvin

As energy flows from a hot body into its surroundings, Clausius realised that this represented an increase in the entropy of the Universe. The Kelvin statement of the second law:

> **The complete conversion of energy from a heat source
> into work is not possible**

considers that the increase of the entropy of the Universe results from (a) a *decrease* in the entropy of the hot body as quanta flow out of it and (b) an *increase* in the entropy of the cooler surroundings which more than compensates for the reduction in entropy of the hot body.

This appreciation of the entropy changes involved in thermal energy flows results inevitably in the realisation that, as the removal of energy from a heat source (the boiler of a steam engine or the burning fuel/air mixture in an internal combustion engine) results in a reduction of entropy, *the conversion of heat completely into work is not possible* in a cyclical process. (A cyclical process is the sort of process used in a heat engine, in which the working agent is alternately compressed and then allowed to expand and do work.) Fortunately, the second law comes to our rescue. By allowing some of the energy removed from the heat source to flow into a **heat sink** (at a lower temperature than the source), the reduction in entropy of the heat source can be compensated for by the increase in entropy of the heat sink.

A few quanta flowing into or out of the heat source do not change the entropy much.

The same number of quanta flowing into or out of the heat sink change the entropy by a large amount, since there are far fewer quanta in it.

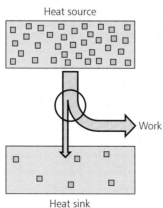

Figure 2.5.10 A way of representing what happens in a heat engine.

Heat Death

It was Clausius himself who pointed out one of the inevitable consequences of work and increasing entropy. We can regard the Universe as a system which energy can neither enter nor leave – in other words, a system in which the total amount of energy is constant. (Physicists call this kind of system a *closed system*.) As we have just seen, when work is done some energy is inevitably wasted as it becomes dissipated in the form of heat. As more and more work is done, more and more energy is dissipated in this way, increasing the entropy of the Universe. According to this model, all of the energy in the Universe will eventually be spread uniformly throughout the Universe, which will be at a constant temperature as a result. In this state of equilibrium, further work will be impossible since there can be no further increase in entropy – a situation known as 'the heat death of the Universe'. The American novelist and poet John Updike (b.1932) protests about the inevitability of this conclusion in his 'Ode to Entropy':

Some day – can it be believed? –
in the year 10^{70} or so,
single electrons and positrons will orbit
one another to form atoms bonded
across regions of space
greater than the present observable universe.
'Heat death' will prevail.
The stars long since will have burnt their hydrogen
and turned to iron.
Even the black holes will have decayed.
Entropy!
thou seal on extinction,
thou curse on Creation.
All change distributes energy,
spills what cannot be gathered again.
Each meal, each smile,
each foot-race to the well by Jack and Jill
scatters treasure, lets fall
gold straws once woven from the resurgent dust.

The night sky blazes with Byzantine waste.
The bird's throbbling is expenditure,
and the tide's soughing,
and the tungsten filament illumining my hand.

A ramp has been built into probability
the universe cannot re-ascend.
For our small span,
the sun has fuel, the moon lifts the lulling sea,
the highway shudders with stolen hydrocarbons.
How measure these inequalities
so massive and luminous
in which one's self is secreted
like a jewel mislaid in mountains of garbage?
Or like that bright infant Prince William,
with his whorled nostrils and blank blue eyes,
to whom empire and all its estates are already assigned.
Does its final diffusion
deny a miracle?
Those future voids are scrims of the mind,
pedagogic as blackboards.

Did you know
that four-fifths of the body's intake goes merely
to maintain our temperature of 98.6°?
Or that Karl Barth, addressing prisoners, said
the prayer for stronger faith is the one prayer
that has never been denied?
Death exists nowhere in nature, not
in the minds of birds or the consciousness of flowers,
not even in the numb brain of the wildebeest calf
gone under to the grinning crocodile, nowhere
in the mesh of woods or the tons of sea, only
in our forebodings, our formulae.
There is still enough energy in one overlooked star
to power all the heavens madmen have ever proposed.

Source: John Updike, *Facing Nature: Poems*, London, André Deutsch, 1986.

Efficiency

The second law acts like the first law in that it is one of nature's energy accounting systems. In contrast to the first law, however, the second law does not tell us the balance of our energy account, but rather tells us how much tax we have to pay. But the law is one-way. If we wish to convert thermal energy into work in a cyclical process (that is, to make use of a high quality energy source), we must dump some of it into a cold part of the Universe, paying our energy tax to nature. If we wish to squander some or all of our hard-won work into thermal energy again, we are free to do so without paying tax.

The exact amount of energy tax payable is simple. The second law tells us that the limit to the efficiency of any heat engine is governed by the temperatures of its heat source and its heat sink:

$$\text{Efficiency} = \left(1 - \left(\frac{T_{\text{heat sink}}}{T_{\text{heat source}}}\right)\right) \times 100\%$$

So the key to making an engine as efficient as possible is to make the temperature ratio as large as possible.

The efficiencies of some real heat engines

A modern power station uses steam at around 800 K as a heat source, with the heat sink at a temperature of about 373 K (the temperature at which steam condenses at atmospheric pressure). The limit to the efficiency of the power station is thus:

$$\text{Efficiency} = \left(1 - \frac{T_{\text{heat sink}}}{T_{\text{heat source}}}\right) \times 100\%$$

$$= \left(1 - \frac{373}{800}\right) \times 100\%$$

$$= (1 - 0.47) \times 100\%$$

$$= 53\%$$

An internal combustion engine has a heat source (the burning fuel in the cylinder) which briefly reaches temperatures of around 3300 K. The exhaust gases leave the cylinder at about 1400 K, so in this case the efficiency could be:

$$\text{Efficiency} = \left(1 - \frac{140.0}{3300}\right) \times 100\%$$

$$= (1 - 0.42) \times 100\%$$

$$= 58\%$$

In both these cases the actual efficiency is less than the theoretical maximum efficiency calculated from the second law – around 40% in the case of the power station, and 25% in the case of the internal combustion engine.

The importance of this application of the second law is that there is a limit to the efficiency of any heat engine, imposed not by the limits of the design, but by the temperatures of the heat source and heat sink it uses. No matter how well designed the power station or car engine, as long as the operating temperatures are fixed, the limits to efficiency we have just calculated apply. We could of course raise the temperature of the heat source, or lower the temperature of the heat sink, but this would bring other problems, not least those of the properties of materials at extremes of temperature.

Figure 2.5.11 The sacrifice of some of the energy in fuels being released into the surroundings is the price we pay for being able to make fuels work for us.

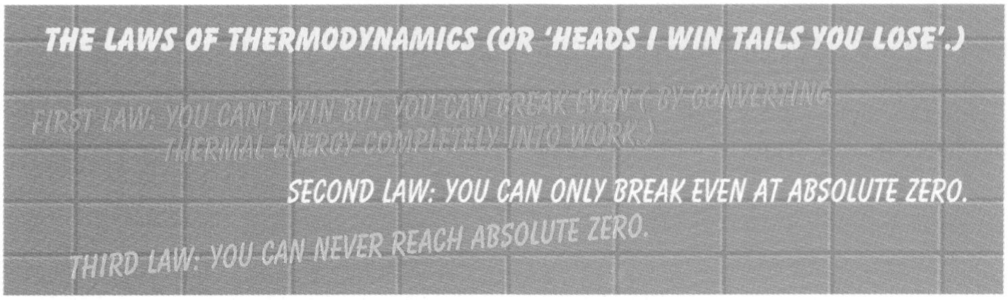

Figure 2.5.12

THE LAWS OF THERMODYNAMICS (OR 'HEADS I WIN TAILS YOU LOSE'.)

FIRST LAW: YOU CAN'T WIN BUT YOU CAN BREAK EVEN (BY CONVERTING THERMAL ENERGY COMPLETELY INTO WORK.)

SECOND LAW: YOU CAN ONLY BREAK EVEN AT ABSOLUTE ZERO.

THIRD LAW: YOU CAN NEVER REACH ABSOLUTE ZERO.

SUMMARY

- For a solid under tension, **strain energy per unit volume** $= \frac{1}{2} \times$ stress $\times$ strain $= \frac{1}{2} \times F/A \times x/l$. Application of the first law to a solid under strain says that all the energy supplied by the force causing the deformation can be recovered if the deformation is **elastic**. For a **plastic** deformation, the particles in the solid are rearranged, causing an increase in internal energy which cannot be recovered.

- The non-reversible behaviour shown by a solid when deformed past its elastic limit is known as **hysteresis**.

- The **molar heat capacity** c for a gas is usually quoted either under conditions of **constant pressure**, c_p, or under conditions of **constant volume**, c_v.

- $c_p - c_v = R$.

- In a heat engine, a **working agent** undergoes a series of compressions and expansions. The first law of thermodynamics says that a heat engine can only produce as much work as there is energy in the heat source.

- The second law of thermodynamics requires that in a heat engine an amount of energy must be transferred directly from the heat source to a **heat sink** in order that there is no decrease in entropy as heat is converted to work.

- The maximum theoretical efficiency of a heat engine is given by efficiency $= (1 - T_{\text{heat sink}}/T_{\text{heat source}}) \times 100\%$.

EXAMPLE

1.0×10^{-3} m³ of air at 20 °C and 101.35 kPa is heated at constant pressure until its volume doubles. Calculate:
a the final temperature of the gas
b the work done by the gas as it expands.

a Assume that the air behaves ideally – a fair assumption since under these conditions both oxygen and nitrogen are far from their critical points. The equation of state of an ideal gas is $pV = nRT$, which leads to the expression:

$$\frac{p_1 V_1}{T_1} = \frac{p_2 V_2}{T_2} \quad \text{for changes in } p, V \text{ and/or } T \text{ of a fixed amount of gas}$$

In this instance $p_1 = p_2$, so:

$$\frac{1.0 \times 10^{-3} \text{ m}^3}{293 \text{ K}} = \frac{2.0 \times 10^3 \text{ m}^3}{T_2}$$

which gives:

$$T_2 = \frac{2.0 \times 10^{-3} \text{ m}^3}{1.0 \times 10^{-3} \text{ m}^3} \times 293 \text{ K}$$
$$= 586 \text{ K}$$

The final temperature of the gas is 586 K.

b As the gas expands it does work ΔW given by:

$$\Delta W = p\Delta V$$
$$= 1.0135 \times 10^5 \text{ Pa} \times 1.0 \times 10^{-3} \text{ m}^3$$
$$= 101 \text{ J to 3 SF}$$

The work done by the gas in expanding is 101 J.

QUESTIONS

1 A copper wire 2.1 m long and 1.5 mm in diameter is subjected to a load of 200 N. What is the strain energy stored in the wire? (Take E for copper as 1.1×10^{11} N m^{-2}.)

2 Steel rods are sometimes used to keep old buildings together when two opposite walls have begun to bow outwards, as shown in figure 2.5.13. One such rod has a diameter of 2.5 cm and is 8.3 m long. When inserted into the building it is fastened in such a way that it exerts a force of 1.5×10^4 N on each wall.
   a What is the tension in the rod?
   b What is the strain energy stored in the rod?
   (Take E for steel as 1.9×10^{11} N m^{-2}.)

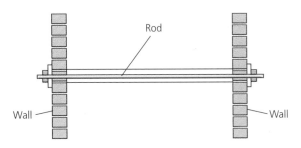

Figure 2.5.13

3 Take a rubber band – one that is about 0.5 cm wide and 15 cm long will be very suitable. Hold the rubber band between thumb and first finger of each hand so that there is about 3 cm of it between each hand. Now stretch the band quickly and hold it against your top lip or your cheek. What do you feel? Hold the band steady for a few seconds and allow it to contract to its relaxed length again. Hold it against your cheek again – now what do you feel?
   Explain your observations in terms of the first law of thermodynamics and a suitable stress–strain graph.
   The rubber used to make car tyres must be able to undergo many cycles of stretching and compressing like the cycle to which you have just subjected the rubber band (it must be **resilient**). Why?

4 A person walking vigorously inhales about 0.75 kg of air each hour. This inhaled air is warmed and humidified (its water vapour content raised) by the body. It is then exhaled at 37 °C and 100% humidity (that is, the air cannot hold any more water vapour at this temperature). A polar explorer walking across the ice at the North Pole inhales air at −30 °C and 0% humidity. Calculate the rate at which energy is transferred from the explorer's body via the lungs.

(Take the molar mass of air as 0.029 kg, the specific heat capacity for air as 29 J mol^{-1} K^{-1} and the specific latent heat of vaporisation of water as 2.26×10^6 J kg^{-1}. 1 kg of air at 37 °C and 100% humidity contains 0.041 kg of water vapour.)

5 In an attempt to produce a model which more closely follows the behaviour of real gases than the equation $pV = nRT$, the Dutch physicist Johannes Van der Waals produced a modified relationship, now called Van der Waals' equation:

$$\left(p + \frac{a}{V^2}\right)(V - b) = nRT$$

   where a and b are constants.
   a The second term on the left-hand side of the equation suggests that the particles of a real gas in a particular container move in a smaller volume than the particles of an ideal gas in the same container – why should this be?
   b The first term on the left-hand side of the equation suggests that the pressure exerted by a real gas is less than that exerted by an ideal gas – why?
   c What are the units of the constant a?

6 Nuclear reactions can result in temperatures as high as 10^{10} K (see section 6.3).
   a Write down an expression for the maximum efficiency of a heat engine working between this temperature and a heat sink at 300 K.
   b Is it likely that a power station using nuclear processes could achieve such an efficiency? Justify your answer.

7 Figure 2.5.14 shows a perpetual motion machine. Explain why the first law of thermodynamics predicts the failure of this machine. (Such a perpetual motion machine is sometimes called a 'perpetual motion machine of the first kind'.)

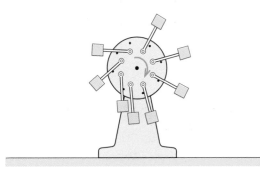

Figure 2.5.14

8 Figure 2.5.15 shows another perpetual motion machine which uses the chemical energy in sea water to produce electricity via a simple battery. This electricity is then used to drive an electric motor powering the ship. Explain why the second law of thermodynamics predicts the failure of this machine. (Such a perpetual motion machine is sometimes called a 'perpetual motion machine of the second kind'.)

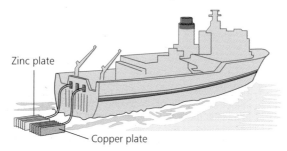

Zinc plate

Copper plate

Figure 2.5.15

9 Entropy is a measure of the disorder in a system. The concept of **negentropy** has been suggested – negentropy is a measure of the order in a system. Do you agree with the statement 'In our lives we do not so much consume energy as consume negentropy'? Give your reasons.

Developing Key Skills

Some 13-year-old students are working on a project about energy conservation in their geography and English lessons. Their English teacher wishes to use the poem 'Ode to Entropy' (page 192) with them, and has asked you to produce a short worksheet that will explain to pupils the scientific ideas that they need in order to appreciate the poem.

Produce a suitable worksheet. If possible, ask some younger students to read it to see if they understand the ideas you are aiming to communicate to them.

[Key Skills opportunities: C, IT]

1 a i State what is meant by *thermal equilibrium*.

ii Explain thermal equilibrium by reference to the behaviour of the molecules when a sample of hot gas is mixed with a sample of cooler gas and thermal equilibrium is reached.

(3 marks)

b A sealed container holds a mixture of nitrogen molecules and helium molecules at a temperature of 290 K. The total pressure exerted by the gas on the container is 120 kPa.

molar mass of helium $= 4.00 \times 10^{-3}$ kg mol^{-1}

molar gas constant R $= 8.31$ J K^{-1} mol^{-1}

the Avogadro constant N_A $= 6.02 \times 10^{23}$ mol^{-1}

i Calculate the root mean square speed of the helium molecules.

ii Calculate the average kinetic energy of a nitrogen molecule.

iii If there are twice as many helium molecules as nitrogen molecules in the container, calculate the pressure exerted on the container by the helium molecules. **(6 marks)**

(AQA 1999)

2 A small house uses a tank containing 1.2 m^3 water as a thermal store. During the night its temperature rises to 98 °C. During the day, its temperature drops as the water is pumped round the house radiators to keep the house warm.

The density of water is 1000 kg m^{-3} and its specific heat capacity is 4200 J kg^{-1} K^{-1}. Calculate the energy given out by the water on a day when its temperature drops from 98 °C to 65 °C. **(3 marks)**

The six radiators in the house give out an average power of 1.5 kW each. For how long can they all operate at this power before the water temperature drops to 65 °C? **(3 marks)**

Explain why this heating system operates more effectively early in the morning than towards the evening. **(2 marks)**

(Total 8 marks)

(Edexcel 1999)

3 Explain the difference between finite and renewable energy resources. Give one example of each. **(2 marks)**

Describe one method for harnessing solar power. **(3 marks)**

A medium sized coal power station has an output of about 2000 MW. The average value of the power delivered from the Sun to the area around the power station is 220 W m^{-2}. Calculate the working area required for a solar power station with a power output equal to that of the coal station if the efficiency of the solar power station is 15%. **(2 marks)**

Use your answer to explain why solar power stations are unlikely to be the major solution to mankind's demand for energy. **(1 mark)**

(Total 8 marks)

(Edexcel 1999)

4 The diagram shows a home refrigerator. The contents of the refrigerator are at a constant temperature of 5 °C and the outside surface of the refrigerator is at a constant temperature of 20 °C. The outside dimensions of the refrigerator are shown on the diagram. Calculate the outside surface area of the refrigerator.

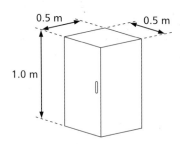

The walls are 5.2 cm thick and have an average thermal conductivity of 0.018 W m^{-1} K^{-1}. Estimate the rate of flow of heat through the walls. **(3 marks)**

Explain how it is possible for the contents of the refrigerator to be at a constant temperature even though energy is continuously flowing in from outside. **(3 marks)**

The equation $\Delta U = \Delta Q + \Delta W$ is applied to the *contents* of the refrigerator.

State the value of ΔU and explain how you arrive at this value.

(2 marks)

ΔQ has two components. What are they? **(2 marks)**

Explain why ΔW is zero. **(1 mark)**

(Total 11 marks)

(Edexcel 1999)

5 Most countries have building regulations which contain instructions about limiting heat transfer. In countries which are cold in the winter, these instructions are designed to reduce the amount of heating required. In tropical countries, the same principles can be used to reduce the need for air conditioning. The instructions apply to domestic and public buildings and are enforced in order to reduce the amount of energy required to keep buildings at a comfortable temperature. This has the effect of reducing the amount of fossil fuel which needs to be burnt and, hence, of reducing the emission of greenhouse gases into the atmosphere.

In order to calculate heat gains or losses, a thermal transmittance coefficient or U-value is measured for each type of building material. The U-value is the rate of heat transfer, in watts, through one square metre of a structure when the air temperatures on each side of the structure differ by 1 kelvin. The following U-values will be needed in answering this question.

U-value for bricks 100 mm thick $= 8.2$ W m^{-2} K^{-1}

U-value for thermal insulation 50 mm thick $= 1.4$ W m^{-2} K^{-1}

Answer the following questions using the information given.

a What is stated in the passage as an advantage of enforcing regulations which limit heat transfer to and from buildings?

(1 mark)

b Explain why it is that the same physical theory can be applied to a situation where a house is to be kept warm in cold weather and to one where a house is to be kept cool in hot weather. **(3 marks)**

c Using the definition given in the passage, write down an equation relating the rate R of heat transfer to the difference in temperature ΔT between the two surfaces of the material, the surface area A of the material and the U-value U of the material. **(1 mark)**

d Calculate the rate of heat transfer flow (in watts, W) through a brick wall 100 mm thick and of dimensions 3.0 m x 5.0 m when the temperature on the inside is 20 °C and on the outside is 0 °C. **(2 marks)**

e A composite wall is constructed from two 100 mm brick walls separated from one another by 50 mm of thermal insulation, as shown in the diagram.

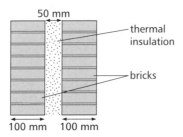

In order to calculate the rate of heat transfer through such a wall, a composite U-value, U_c, has to be used. U_c is given in terms of the U-values of the individual materials by the equation

$$\frac{1}{U_c} = \frac{1}{U_1} + \frac{1}{U_2} + \ldots$$

Use the equation to find
i U_c for the composite wall shown in the diagram,
ii the rate of heat transfer (in watts, W) through a wall of dimensions 3.0 m x 5.0 m when the temperature on the inside is 20 °C and on the outside is 0 °C. **(5 marks)**

f On a copy of the axes below, sketch a graph to show how the rate of heat transfer through a wall, such as that shown in the previous diagram, varies with the thickness of the insulation. Label the vertical axis with suitable values. **(4 marks)**

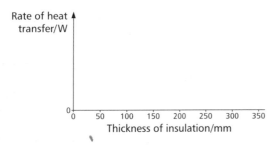

g Suggest a factor which will also affect heat losses from a room, in addition to loss by conduction which has already been considered. Indicate how the effect of this factor may be minimised. **(2 marks)**

(OCR 1998)

6 a By considering differences in structure, state how the density change which takes place when a solid changes to a liquid compares with the density change when a liquid changes to a gas. **(3 marks)**

b State one similarity and one difference between evaporation and boiling. **(2 marks)**

c What is meant by the *internal energy* of a system? **(2 marks)**

d Use the first law of thermodynamics to calculate the difference (in joules, J) between the internal energy of 1.00 kg of water at 100 °C and 1.00 kg of steam at 100 °C at a pressure of 1.01 x 10^5 Pa. [A mass of 1.00 kg of steam at this pressure and temperature occupies 1.67 m³ and the specific latent heat of vaporisation of water is 2.26 x 10^6 J kg⁻¹.] **(4 marks)**

(OCR 1998)

7 a The pressure p of an ideal gas is related to its volume V and thermodynamic temperature T by the ideal gas equation. State the ideal gas equation, explaining any other symbols used. **(2 marks)**

b i The equation $pV = \frac{1}{3}Nm\langle c^2 \rangle$ relates the product of pressure and volume of a gas to the mean-square-speed $\langle c^2 \rangle$ of its molecules. Identify the symbols N and m in the above equation.

ii By comparing this equation with that in **i**, deduce the relation between the average translational kinetic energy of a molecule and the temperature of the gas. **(5 marks)**

c Using your result in **b ii**, explain what is meant by the absolute zero of temperature. **(1 mark)**

(OCR specimen)

8 a Define *specific latent heat of vaporisation*. **(2 marks)**

b A mass of 1.5 kg of ice at its melting point of 273 K is supplied continuously with thermal energy.
The specific latent heat of fusion of ice is 3.3 x 10^5 J kg⁻¹.
The specific heat capacity of water is 4.2 x 10^3 J kg⁻¹ K⁻¹.
The specific latent heat of vaporisation of water is 2.3 x 10^6 J kg⁻¹.
Calculate the energy required to convert all of the ice to steam at 373 K. **(3 marks)**

(OCR specimen)

9 a State two similarities and two differences between evaporation and boiling. **(4 marks)**

b The specific heat capacity of water is 4.19 x 10^3 J kg⁻¹ K⁻¹ and the specific latent heat of vaporisation of water is 2.26 × 10^6 J kg⁻¹. Calculate the energy (in joules, J) required to boil dry a saucepan initially containing 1.50 kg of water at 20 °C. Neglect heat losses and the energy used in heating the saucepan. **(4 marks)**

c Energy is supplied to the water in the saucepan in **b** at a rate of 1800 W. Calculate the minimum time (in seconds) from when the water is at 20 °C that it will take for all the water to be boiled away. **(2 marks)**

(OCR 1998)

10 Write down the ideal gas equation. **(1 mark)**
Use your equation to express the unit for the universal gas constant in SI *base* units. **(3 marks)**
Sketch a graph that shows the relationship between pressure and absolute temperature for a fixed mass of ideal gas at constant volume. **(2 marks)**
State the assumption which would enable gas pressure measurements to be used to define a practical scale of temperature. **(1 mark)**

(Total 7 marks)

(Edexcel 1999)

11 a Describe the molecular structure of a metal, a polymer and a glass. **(9 marks)**

b Describe an experiment to determine the Young modulus of the material of a wire. **(8 marks)**

c The value of the Young modulus for a particular mild steel is 2.10×10^{11} Pa. A wire made of this steel has an area of cross-section of 1.08×10^{-6} m^2 and a length of 3.75 m. Calculate the tension which must be applied to the wire to make it stretch by 1.00×10^{-3} m. Assume that Hooke's law applies to this extension.

(4 marks)

(OCR 1998)

12 A metal wire of unextended length l and cross-sectional area A is supported at one end from a fixed point and a mass of weight W is attached to its free end, as shown in the following diagram.

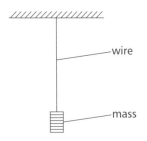

The wire is found to extend by a length e when the weight is attached.

a i Derive expressions, in terms of l, A, W and e for
  1. the spring constant k of the wire,
  2. the Young modulus E of the material of the wire.

ii Using your answers in **i**, show that k is related to E by the expression $kl = EA$.

iii Calculate the spring constant for a wire of length 1.5 m, of diameter 1.2 mm, and made of metal having a Young modulus of 1.1×10^{11} Pa. **(7 marks)**

b A car is being designed in order to break the world land speed record. One proposal for the wheels is to use metal discs but, at high speeds, the wheels may break up. Each wheel disc, made of metal of density ρ, has radius r and is rotated at angular speed ω about an axis through its centre, as shown in the following diagram.

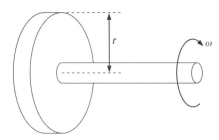

The disc breaks up when the ultimate tensile stress σ of the metal is given by $\sigma = \rho r^2 \omega^2$.

i Explain what is meant by *ultimate tensile stress*. **(2 marks)**

ii Use base units to check the homogeneity of the equation. **(3 marks)**

iii Calculate, for a disc of radius 60 cm, constructed from steel of density 7900 kg m^{-3} and having an ultimate tensile stress of 5.5×10^8 Pa, the maximum possible values of
  1. the angular speed of the disc,
  2. the linear speed of the car. **(4 marks)**

iv Suggest, showing your reasoning, whether discs made of an alloy of density 6900 kg m^{-3} and ultimate tensile stress 3.5×10^8 Pa would be a better alternative to steel discs. **(4 marks)**

(OCR 1998)

13 Write an essay on the topic of work, energy and power.

a Give an explanation of the terms *work*, *energy* and *power*, a statement of the SI units for each and an explanation as to why the kilowatt hour (kWh) is used as an electrical unit for domestic purposes. **(5 marks)**

b Suggest, from the defining equation $W = Fs$, how power may be related to force and velocity, and hence suggest why power must be delivered continuously to the driving wheels of a car in order to maintain a constant velocity. **(6 marks)**

c Explain what is meant by kinetic energy and derive, from the equations of motion, an expression for the kinetic energy of a body. **(4 marks)**

d Explain what is meant by internal energy and hence discuss the energy changes that occur enabling some of the potential energy of a block of metal to be converted into internal energy when the block falls and hits the ground. **(6 marks)**

(OCR 1998)

14 The graph shows the behaviour of a material when subjected to stress.

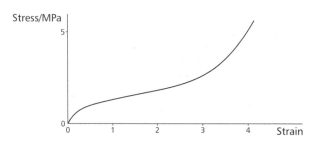

Give an example of a material which behaves in this way when put under stress.

Add to a copy of the graph a second line which shows the behaviour of a brittle material with a Young modulus of approximately 10 MPa. **(3 marks)**

Describe with the aid of diagrams the difference in structure between a crystalline solid and a polymeric one. **(4 marks)**

(Total 7 marks)

(Edexcel 1999)

15 a The figure shows the graph of pressure, p, against the reciprocal of the volume, $\frac{1}{V}$, for one mole of an ideal gas as the pressure is varied.

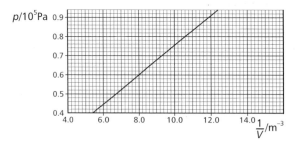

i What is the physical significance of the slope of this graph?
(**1 mark**)

ii Use the graph to show that the pressure and volume changes of the gas take place under isothermal conditions. (**3 marks**)

b An ideal gas expands isothermally. State the first law of thermodynamics and explain how it applies to this expansion.
(**3 marks**)

(OCR 1998)

16 The diagram represents a side view of a solar panel. Water is heated by the Sun and passes through the device without being pumped. The chamber has a large surface area facing the Sun.

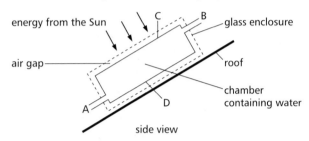

side view

a In which direction does the water heated by the Sun flow through the chamber? Explain your answer. (**1 mark**)

b The surfaces C and D are painted in order to increase the efficiency of the solar panel. State the colour of the paint which should be used on each surface and explain why. (**3 marks**)

c How does the glass enclosure increase the efficiency of the solar panel? (**1 mark**)

d In a series of experiments it was found that the efficiency of the solar panel was affected by the width of the air gap between the panel and the glass enclosure.

i Suggest why the efficiency of the solar panel is low when the air gap is too narrow.

ii Suggest why the efficiency of the solar panel is also low when the air gap is too wide. (**2 marks**)

(AQA 1999)

17 a Describe the processes involved in
i thermal conduction,
ii thermal convection. (**3 marks**)

b

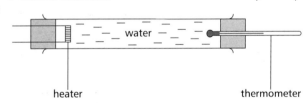

heater   thermometer

A long glass tube containing cold water is fitted with a heater at one end and a thermometer at the other, as shown in the diagram. During the period immediately after the heater has been switched on, describe and explain how the thermometer reading would change if the tube were
i horizontal,
ii vertical, with the thermometer above the heater,
iii vertical, with the thermometer below the heater. (**5 marks**)

(AQA 1999)

18 a Explain what is meant by *the triple point temperature of water* and how the triple point temperature of water is used in defining the SI unit of temperature. (**3 marks**)

b Show how the absolute zero of temperature can be defined in terms of the properties of:
i an ideal gas; (**1 mark**)
ii ideal gas molecules. (**2 marks**)

(OCR 1998)

19 a Describe the processes that occur when thermal energy is distributed through:
i a liquid by convection; (**4 marks**)
ii a non-metallic solid by conduction. (**3 marks**)

b The following symbols represent the thermal properties of water:
l_v = specific latent heat of vaporization;
l_f = specific latent heat of fusion;
c = specific heat capacity.
A mass M of steam at 100 °C is used to melt a mass m of ice at 0 °C. The result is a mass $(M + m)$ of water at a temperature θ which is between 0 °C and 100 °C.
Using the principle that losses and gains of thermal energy are equal, write an equation that will relate θ, l_v, l_f, c, M and m. A solution for this equation for θ is **not** required. (**3 marks**)

(OCR 1998)

20 a Steel wire is a polycrystalline material with elastic properties. Explain the terms *polycrystalline* and *elastic*. (**2 marks**)

b A laboratory tensile test was carried out on a specimen of steel wire. The graph shows the relation obtained between the tension F and the extension e of the wire.

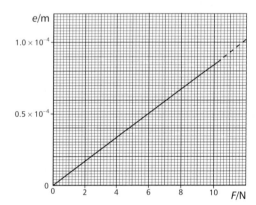

F and e are related by the expression $F = ke$.
i Express the unit of k in SI base units. (**1 mark**)
ii Deduce a relation between k and the Young modulus E of steel. Identify any further quantities introduced. (**2 marks**)

c The diameter and unextended length of the wire in **b** were 1.2 mm and 2.0 m respectively. Using these values, and data from the graph where appropriate, calculate:
i the cross-sectional area (m²) of the wire; (**2 marks**)
ii the Young modulus (Pa) of the wire material. (**2 marks**)

d An increasing tension was applied to the wire. The wire snapped as its extension exceeded 1.5 mm. Assuming that the values of k and the cross-sectional area remained constant, calculate the work done (in joules, J) in stretching the wire from its unextended state to its breaking point. (**3 marks**)

(OCR 1998)

MATTER & ENERGY CONCEPT MAP

How to use the map

The map is a way of representing the structure of the knowledge contained in this section. It is designed to be used as you get towards the end of the section, when you should begin to see a pattern in the key concepts you have met. The map shows how one area of knowledge builds on another, so that more complex ideas develop as you go through the section.

As you study, try to think about how you learn best. Do you prefer to have understood one idea completely before going on to another? Or do you like to meet several related new ideas and then put these together rather like you might put together several pieces of a jigsaw at once?

The concept map will help you to see how ideas are related. You can use it to help you to put your knowledge and understanding in some sort of order so that you can organise your learning. You can also use it to organise your revision at the end of the section and before your examinations. Alternatively, try drawing up your own concept map as you revise.

Notes on the map

The key ideas in the section are contained in the green boxes. Solid lines with arrows between these boxes show how ideas in the section develop. Where parts of this section relate to other sections, dashed lines with arrows indicate this – the links are described in yellow boxes.

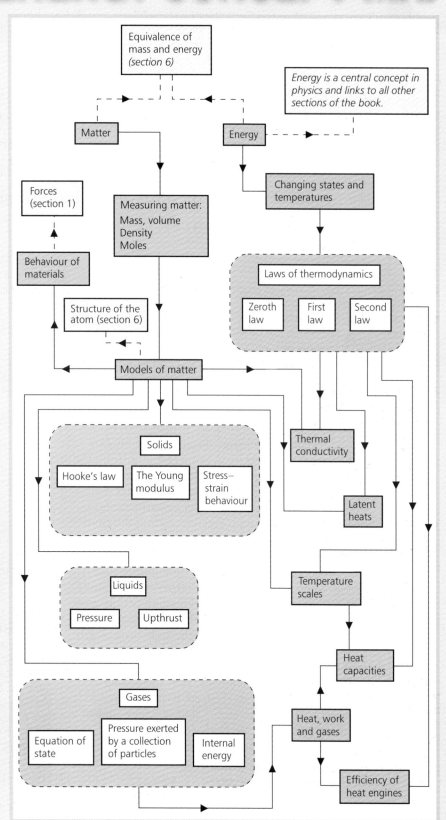

3 WAVES

Introduction

Why are waves important? In practical terms, waves find uses in many areas of human life, as you will find as you study the ideas in this section. For this reason alone, an understanding of waves is important. But to a physicist there are other reasons for studying them too, reasons which involve a better *understanding* of the world (and indeed the Universe) around us.

All waves are caused by disturbances, which result in some sort of oscillation. (If you have already studied Section 1.7, you will know how periodic oscillations can be understood using the principles of mechanics, together with some simple knowledge of energy.) These oscillations spread out (we say that they are **propagated**) as waves, and may travel large distances, resulting in disturbances being set up at points far away from the point where the original disturbance occurred. This means that waves are **carriers of energy**, and that they can produce a phenomenon a considerable distance from its cause. If you are reading this book by daylight, you can do so thanks to complex events involving charged particles at the surface of the Sun about 8 minutes ago. Thanks to these disturbances, a huge range and intensity of electromagnetic waves began their journey, blasting off in all directions into space at a dizzying speed of 300 000 kilometres per second. Some of these waves of the right wavelength have been reflected off this book and into your eye, enabling you to see what is on this page.

Our work in this section will start by looking at the properties of waves – reflection, refraction, diffraction and interference – that you have almost certainly met before. We shall examine these properties in greater depth, and then go on to look at light and sound. In the final part of the section we shall see how the properties of waves enable us to use them for a wide range of purposes – from probing the depths of space to sending e-mail.

Figure 3.1 Strong or subtle, waves form part of our world, and also play a part in the way we perceive it.

An earthquake is normally the result of the movement of rocks in the Earth's crust, caused as the stresses set up along a crack (or **fault**) in the crust are released, making rocks move past each other with great force. This disturbance sets up vibrations, which cause waves to travel through the Earth. The point at which the rocks move, creating the disturbance, is called the **focus** of the earthquake; the point on the surface directly above the focus is the **epicentre**.

The disturbance sets up a series of waves which spread out from the focus and travel through the body of the Earth. These waves are of two types. P (pressure) waves are longitudinal waves which can travel through the solid rock of the mantle and through the liquid of the Earth's core. In contrast, S (shear) waves are transverse and can travel only through solid material.

In addition to the P and S waves, other waves spread out from the epicentre of the earthquake and travel across the surface; it is these waves that cause the damage around the epicentre. There surface waves are also of two types. L (Love) waves are transverse, while R (Rayleigh) waves have both longitudinal and transverse character.

The energy carried by the waves of an earthquake may be as much as 10^{18} J. The Richter scale is used to express this energy as the **magnitude** of the earthquake.

When they occur out at sea, earthquakes can produce huge water waves called **tsunami** (tidal waves). These waves have wavelengths of 100 to 400 km, and travel at speeds of up to $750 \, \text{km h}^{-1}$. Their height in the open sea is only about a metre or so, but as they enter shallow water near land the waves slow down, the water piles up and the height of the waves may then reach several metres or more. Tsunamis of up to 70 m have been recorded.

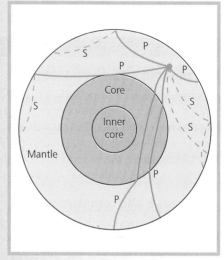

Figure 3.1.1 P and S waves travelling through the body of the Earth. Notice that these waves do not follow a straight path, due to the effect of materials of different densities on their speeds.

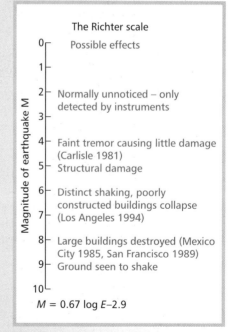

The Richter scale

Magnitude	Possible effects
0	
1	
2	Normally unnoticed – only detected by instruments
3	
4	Faint tremor causing little damage (Carlisle 1981)
5	Structural damage
6	Distinct shaking, poorly constructed buildings collapse (Los Angeles 1994)
7	
8	Large buildings destroyed (Mexico City 1985, San Francisco 1989)
9	Ground seen to shake
10	

$M = 0.67 \log E - 2.9$

Figure 3.1.2 The Richter scale relates the energy E of an earthquake to its magnitude M.

Figure 3.1.3 Tsunamis may do immense amounts of damage, and travel huge distances – it is not unknown for a tsunami to travel right across the Pacific Ocean. Between 479 BC and the present day nearly 300 instances of devastating tsunamis have been recorded.

Mechanical and electromagnetic

All waves consist of some sort of disturbance travelling through space. Some waves require a material substance (called a **medium**) through which to travel. Waves like this are called **mechanical waves**, for example water waves, sound waves and seismic waves which travel through the Earth's crust during earthquakes. **Electromagnetic waves** require no medium through which to travel. We shall examine both of these types of wave during the course of this section.

Transverse and longitudinal

Another obvious distinction is that between **transverse** and **longitudinal** waves. This classification is based on the way the waves travel.

In a transverse wave, the direction in which the disturbance takes place is at right angles to the direction in which the wave travels. (The direction of travel is referred to as the **direction of propagation** of the wave.) In a longitudinal wave, the disturbances take place in a direction parallel to the direction of propagation of the wave. Both types of wave can be demonstrated using a long steel spring called a 'slinky', as shown in figure 3.1.4.

Progressive and stationary

Waves that are produced on a slinky as in figure 3.1.4 travel from one end of it to the other – they are examples of **progressive** waves. It is also possible to

To make a transverse wave travel along the slinky, the end of the spring is moved to and fro at right angles to the length of the spring.

To make a longitudinal wave travel along the slinky, the end of the spring is moved to and fro parallel to the length of the spring.

In a transverse wave, the oscillations occur at right angles to the direction of travel of the wave.

In a longitudinal wave, the oscillations occur parallel to the direction of travel of the wave. As a result, a longitudinal wave consists of a series of **compressions** (C) and **rarefactions** (R).

Figure 3.1.4 The propagation of a transverse wave and a longitudinal wave along a slinky. In both cases the wave carries energy from left to right, away from the source of the waves.

produce waves on a slinky which do not travel along it – these are called **stationary** or **standing** waves. We shall return to these two types of waves at the end of this section.

Circular and plane

Seen from above, the waves which result from a stone being dropped into a pond appear as a series of circles, like the waves on the ripple tank in figure 3.1.5(a). Waves like this are called **circular waves**. Waves on the surface of the sea often appear as a series of parallel lines, like those on the ripple tank in figure 3.1.5(b). These are **plane waves**.

Continuous waves and wave trains

The waves on the surface of the sea seen from a ship in the middle of the ocean may seem to go on for ever, but of course they do not – they all reach land eventually. Physicists often want to refer to waves that *do* go on for ever, that is, that have an infinite length in the direction of propagation. Such waves are the products of physicists' imaginations, but are often used in situations where it is important to model what is happening in the middle of a wave rather than at the start or end of it. Waves that go on for ever are called **continuous waves**, while waves which do have a beginning and an end are called **wave trains**. Where we are considering a very short wave motion, the term **pulse** is used – a wave pulse does not contain repeated oscillations. These three types of wave are shown in figure 3.1.6.

A continuous wave

A wave train

A pulse

Figure 3.1.6 A continuous wave, a wave train and a pulse.

Representing waves

Wavefronts and rays

So far we have viewed waves 'side on', and drawn them as if looking at them in cross-section. Often we require different ways of representing waves, however.

If we consider a ripple spreading out on the surface of a pond after a pebble has been thrown into the water, a 'snapshot' of the ripple at some instant can be represented as a circle with its centre at the point where the pebble entered the water. The circle is called a **wavefront**, and passes through every point on the ripple which has the same phase – usually the crest. ('Phase' is explained on page 207.)

Straight lines may also be drawn from the point of the disturbance to show how the ripple spreads out in all directions. These lines pass through the wavefronts at 90°, as shown in figure 3.1.7, and are called **rays**.

The vital statistics of a wave

There are a number of essential measurements which are associated with any wave. If the wave is a progressive one, the **speed** at which it travels will be one of these. This is linked to two other measurements of the wave, its **wavelength**

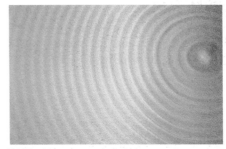

(a) Circular waves on a ripple tank

(b) Plane waves on a ripple tank

In diagrams representing waves, the lines represent the crests of the waves, and are referred to as **wavefronts**.

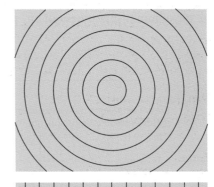

Figure 3.1.5 Plane waves can be thought of as a special case of circular waves – they are effectively circular waves which have their source a very long distance away.

and its **frequency**. The relationship between these three quantities is illustrated in figure 3.1.8. The two snapshots are taken a time T apart. In the second snapshot, the pulse has moved a distance of one wavelength λ, so the speed of the wave c is given by:

$$c = \frac{\lambda}{T}$$

Now T is the time taken for a point on the wave to move through one complete oscillation, that is, T is its **period**. From the work on oscillations in section 1.7 we know that this is related to the **frequency** of the oscillation f such that:

$$f = \frac{1}{T} \quad \text{or} \quad T = \frac{1}{f}$$

which means that we can write:

$$c = \frac{\lambda}{1/f} = f\lambda$$

Although this relationship has been derived using a transverse wave as an example, it also applies to longitudinal waves. Note that the frequency of a wave is by definition the same as the frequency of its source, since it is a measure of the rate at which oscillations are occurring in the wave, and these oscillations are directly caused by an oscillating source.

Another important measurement concerned with any wave is its **amplitude**, the maximum displacement of any point on the wave, illustrated in figure 3.1.9.

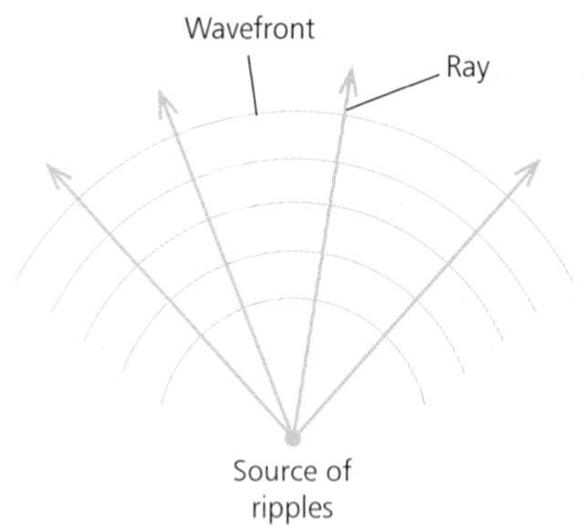

The amplitude of a transverse wave is the maximum displacement from the centre (equilibrium) position, *not* the distance between a peak and a trough.

The amplitude of a longitudinal wave is the maximum displacement of any point on the wave from the equilibrium position, just as in the transverse wave.

Between them, wavelength and amplitude would appear to give all the information needed to describe a wave in non-mathematical terms. This is not quite true, however. As anyone familiar with musical instruments knows, a note of the same pitch played on different instruments sounds quite different. This is in part due to the way in which the instrument vibrates to produce the note, and gives rise to the idea of the **quality** or **timbre** of a sound. We shall return to this on page 214, and to other aspects of the physics of sound waves in sections 3.3 and 3.4.

Making waves

The amplitude of driven oscillations

In considering waves in greater detail, we shall need to think about how they are produced. Section 1.7 examined systems oscillating freely and under damped conditions. We shall now look at systems which are oscillating in response to an input of energy from an external source. Such oscillations are called **driven** or **forced oscillations**.

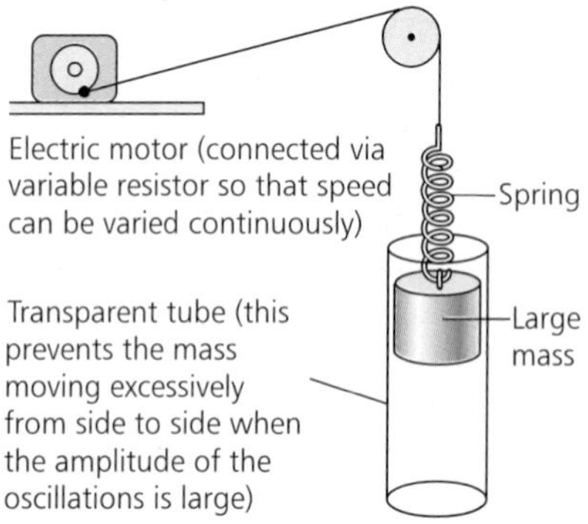

Figure 3.1.7 A ray is constructed at 90° to the wavefronts.

Figure 3.1.8 The drawings show two 'snapshots' of a wave *pulse* travelling through points A, B and C.

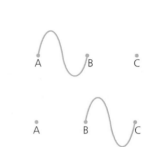

Figure 3.1.9 The amplitude of a wave is defined in the same way as the amplitude of an oscillation, given in section 1.7.

Figure 3.1.10 Any system in which driven oscillations occur has two elements. The first of these provides the energy to cause the oscillations (the **forcing** element), while the second tends to oppose them (the **inertia** element). In this case, the forcing element is provided by the motor and the inertia element by the mass on the end of the spring.

If a large mass on a spring is set up as shown in figure 3.1.10, the effect of driving it with oscillations of varying frequency can be investigated (note that although the *frequency* of the driving oscillations can be varied, their *amplitude* remains constant). If the speed of the motor is high, the top of the spring is moved up and down rapidly and the mass hardly moves at all (the amplitude of the *driven* oscillations is small). As the speed of the motor is reduced, the amplitude of the driven oscillations increases until it reaches a maximum. At this point the driving frequency is the same as the natural frequency of oscillation of the mass on the spring. As the driving frequency decreases further, the amplitude of the driven oscillations again decreases. Figure 3.1.11 illustrates this graphically.

In systems such as this we say that the system exhibits **resonance** at the frequency f_0. Any oscillating system can behave in this way. In particular, the interaction of waves and oscillating systems can frequently result in resonance.

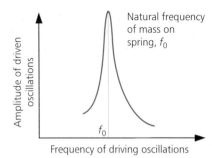

Figure 3.1.11 The variation of the amplitude of driven oscillations with the frequency of the driving oscillations. Note that this graph represents the behaviour of the system once it has settled down into a **steady state** – at any new driving frequency the mass initially oscillates with variable amplitude.

The effect of damping on resonance

In the example of the mass on the spring in figures 3.1.10 and 3.1.11, there is a limit to the amplitude of the oscillations that the mass makes, even when the driving frequency and the driven frequency are the same. This is partly because the length of the spring is a physical limit to the amplitude of the oscillations of the mass, but is also due to the fact that there is some damping of the oscillations, which absorbs energy. Figure 3.1.12 shows the effect of damping on the driven oscillations of a system. As the driving frequency approaches the natural frequency of the system, the amplitude of the oscillations increases rapidly if the system is only lightly damped. This increase is less and less marked as the damping of the system increases.

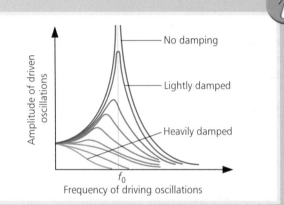

Figure 3.1.12 Light damping has little effect on the natural frequency of oscillation of a system, although it does affect the amplitude. Heavier damping not only reduces the amplitude of the driven oscillations, but also reduces the natural frequency. The mass on the spring in figure 3.1.10 could be damped more heavily by putting it into a liquid such as oil.

Driven oscillations and phase

Observation of the movement of the mass on the spring in figure 3.1.10 shows that when the driving frequency is the same as the natural frequency of oscillation of the mass on the spring, the oscillations of the mass lag a little behind the oscillation of the wire from which the spring is hung. This difference in displacement is called a **phase difference**. Figure 3.1.13 makes this clearer.

Oscillations which are in step with one another are said to be **in phase**, while those in which the oscillations are always in opposite directions are said to be **antiphase**. Antiphase oscillations (for example, when one pendulum always

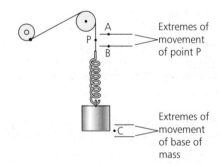

Figure 3.1.13 The movement of the mass lags behind the oscillation of the wire from which it hangs. When the wire has its maximum displacement the mass is at its equilibrium position and moving to 'catch up' with the wire, which means that there is one-quarter of a complete cycle between the oscillations.

When point P is at A, the base of the mass is at C and moving upwards.
When point P is at B, the base of the mass is at C and moving downwards.

swings from left to right while the other swings from right to left) are exactly half a cycle out of step. Since one cycle contains 2π radians, antiphase oscillations have a phase difference of $2\pi/2$ radians $= \pi$ radians. The oscillations in figure 3.1.13 are one-quarter of a cycle apart, so they have a phase difference of $2\pi/4$ radians $= \pi/2$ radians.

Describing phase differences further

We saw in section 1.7 that the shadow of a ball on a turntable oscillates with simple harmonic motion. Figure 3.1.14 shows a displacement–time graph for the shadows of two balls on a turntable with an angle $\pi/2$ between them.

The equation for the displacement of an object which is performing simple harmonic motion is:

$$x = A \sin 2\pi ft$$

In the case of two objects executing simple harmonic motion with different amplitudes and a phase difference between them, we can write:

$$x_1 = A_1 \sin 2\pi ft$$

and:

$$x_2 = A_2 \sin(2\pi ft + \phi)$$

ϕ is called the **phase angle**, and represents the phase difference between the two oscillations.

For the shadows of balls A and B, $A_1 = A_2$, and $\phi = -\pi/2$. This means that the equations describing the motion of the shadows may be written as:

$$x_A = A \sin 2\pi ft$$

and:

$$x_B = A \sin(2\pi ft - \pi/2) = -A \cos 2\pi ft$$

These two relationships are clearly represented by the graphs in figure 3.1.14.

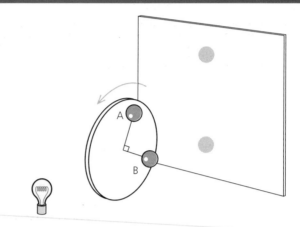

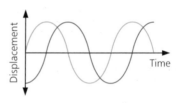

The blue line represents the motion of ball A's shadow, which is a sine curve.
The red line represents the motion of ball B's shadow, which is a cosine curve with $\cos 2\pi ft = -1$ when $t = 0$

Figure 3.1.14 The *circular* motion of balls A and B on the turntable has a phase difference of $\pi/2$ radians, since this is the angle between them. This is also the phase difference between the simple harmonic motions of their shadows on the screen. In both cases ball B lags ball A by $\pi/2$ radians. This is reflected in the displacement–time graphs for the simple harmonic motion of the shadows.

Applying the equations of SHM to waves

All waves are produced by oscillations of some sort. This may be as simple as a drop of rain falling onto the surface of a pond, causing a small volume of water to oscillate and a circular wave to be propagated outwards from it, it may be a hand oscillating and producing a wave along a slinky, or it may be the more complex process of an electron oscillating to produce the interlocking electric and magnetic fields which make up an electromagnetic wave.

Because waves and oscillations are linked in this way, the equations which describe the motion of an object oscillating with simple harmonic motion can be used to obtain equations which describe the behaviour of a wave. Provided that we only wish to describe the behaviour of the very simplest type of waves – those which vary sinusoidally – then the relationships are not too complex, and are given in figure 3.1.15.

Figure 3.1.15 The derivation of the equation for a progressive wave

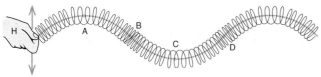

Transverse wave travels along slinky with velocity v ($v = f\lambda$).

Hand (H) oscillates from side to side with SHM, period = T, amplitude = A.

A snapshot of a transverse wave travelling along a slinky. Each point on the wave oscillates from side to side with the same amplitude A and frequency f. The frequency of oscillation and the period are related in the same way as they are in SHM, $f = 1/T$. The phase of the oscillations varies along the wave. Points which are a distance λ apart oscillate in phase, while those which are a distance $\lambda/2$ apart oscillate antiphase.

Longitudinal wave travels along slinky with velocity v ($v = f\lambda$).

Hand (H) oscillates back and forth with SHM, period = T, amplitude = A.

A snapshot of a longitudinal wave travelling along a slinky. Each point on the wave oscillates back and forth with the same amplitude A and frequency f. The frequency of oscillation and the period are related in the same way as they are in SHM, $f = 1/T$. The phase of the oscillations varies along the wave. Points which are a distance λ apart oscillate in phase, while those which are a distance $\lambda/2$ apart oscillate antiphase. Point B on the wave is at a point of **compression** – the points to the left of B are displaced to the *right* of their equilibrium position, while those to the right of B are displaced to the *left* of their equilibrium position. The reverse is true of point D, which is at a point of **rarefaction** – the points to the left of D are displaced to the *left* of their equilibrium position, while those to the right are displaced to the *right* of their equilibrium position.

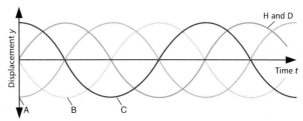

Displacement–time graphs for points A, B, C and D along each wave, and for H.
H and D are a distance of λ apart, so they are in phase.
A is one-quarter of a cycle *behind* H, a phase difference of $-\pi/2$ radians.
B is half a cycle behind H, a phase difference of $-\pi$ radians.
C is three-quarters of a cycle behind H, a phase difference of $-3\pi/2$ radians.

3

It will help to remember the shapes of the graphs of $\sin\theta$ and $\cos\theta$ against θ when thinking about the equations that describe the behaviour of the waves.

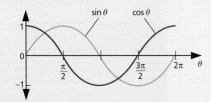

In each case H and D move in exactly the same way, as they are in phase. That is, as H moves up (in the transverse wave) or to the right (in the longitudinal wave) D moves with it. The displacement of H and D in each case is described by the same relationship, given alongside the graphs.

Transverse: $y = A \sin 2\pi f t$ Longitudinal: $x = A \sin 2\pi f t$

On each wave, A is one-quarter of a cycle behind H, so there is a phase difference of $-\pi/2$ radians. This means that the displacement of A in each case is described by these equations:

$$y = A \sin(2\pi f t - \pi/2)$$
$$= -A \cos 2\pi f t$$

$$x = A \sin(2\pi f t - \pi/2)$$
$$= -A \cos 2\pi f t$$

On each wave, B is half a cycle behind H, a phase difference of $-\pi$ radians.
On each wave, C is three-quarters of a cycle behind H, a phase difference of $-3\pi/2$ radians. The displacements of B and C on each wave are described by the equations:

B:　$y = A \sin(2\pi f t - \pi)$
　　$= -A \sin 2\pi f t$
C:　$y = A \sin(2\pi f t - 3\pi/2)$
　　$= A \cos 2\pi f t$

$x = A \sin(2\pi f t - \pi)$
$= -A \sin 2\pi f t$
$x = A \sin(2\pi f t - 3\pi/2)$
$= A \cos 2\pi f t$

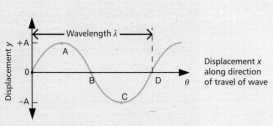

A 'snapshot' of the displacement of the points along the length of a transverse wave moving from left to right.

The 'snapshot' is of a **progressive wave** which is moving from left to right. All of the points on the wave have the same amplitude and period of oscillation, but the phase of the oscillations varies as the distance from the origin varies. For any point on the wave, $y = A \sin(2\pi x/\lambda)$. This equation enables us to find the displacement of any point anywhere along the wave in the 'snapshot'.
For a point on the wave whose displacement is varying sinusoidally with time we know that we can write:

$$y = A \sin(2\pi f t + \phi)$$

We also know that the phase lag of any point on the wave is $2\pi x/\lambda$. So:

$$\phi = -2\pi x/\lambda, \text{ and } y = A \sin(2\pi f t - 2\pi x/\lambda)$$

Since $2\pi f = 2\pi/T$, this becomes:

$$y = A \sin 2\pi \left(\frac{t}{T} - \frac{x}{\lambda} \right)$$

This is the equation for a progressive wave moving away from the origin along the x-axis in the positive direction.

Some properties of waves

The principle of superposition

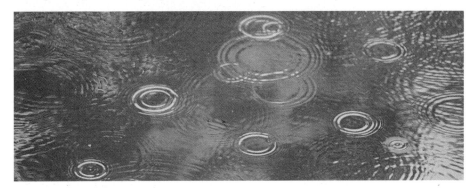

Figure 3.1.16 Waves can cross each other's paths without disturbing each other.

When two wave pulses are sent from opposite ends of a slinky spring, each pulse travels through the other and on to the end of the spring as if the other pulse were not there. If both pulses have the same phase, at the point where the two cross a large pulse can be seen for a brief instant, before the two pulses continue on their way. On the other hand, if the two pulses are antiphase the spring appears undisplaced while the two pulses cross. Figure 3.1.17 illustrates this.

This behaviour of waves can also be observed using water waves on a ripple tank, although it is not quite so easy to do. The behaviour is summarised as the **principle of superposition**, which states that:

> **Where two or more waves meet, the total displacement at any point is the sum of the displacements that each individual wave would cause at that point.**

(Since displacement is a vector quantity, in determining the total displacement it is important to remember to take into account whether each individual displacement is positive or negative.)

The principle of superposition applies to *all* waves, and we shall return to it in section 3.2 when considering diffraction and interference.

Polarisation

In contrast to superposition, which is something that all waves exhibit, the phenomenon of **polarisation** is something which only transverse waves show. Figure 3.1.18 shows some of the planes in which the oscillations in a transverse wave may occur. A wave in which the oscillations take place in a number of planes is called **unpolarised**, while a wave in which the oscillations occur in one plane only is said to be **plane polarised** in that direction.

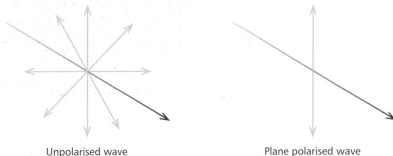

Unpolarised wave   Plane polarised wave

Figure 3.1.18 In an unpolarised wave, oscillations may occur in any plane at different times, while in a plane polarised wave they occur in only one plane.

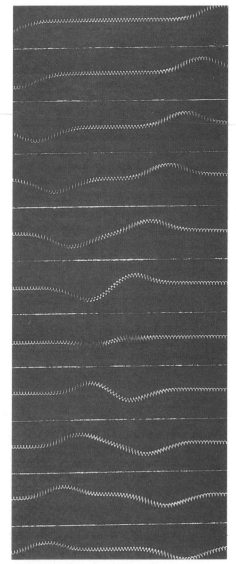

Figure 3.1.17 As two antiphase pulses cross, they produce zero displacement of the spring. In contrast, two pulses in phase would produce a large pulse which is the sum of their amplitudes.

Electromagnetic waves are transverse waves, and so may be polarised. This is used in a number of ways, for example as shown in figure 3.1.19.

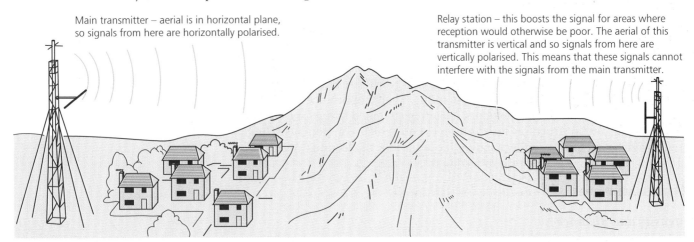

Main transmitter – aerial is in horizontal plane, so signals from here are horizontally polarised.

Relay station – this boosts the signal for areas where reception would otherwise be poor. The aerial of this transmitter is vertical and so signals from here are vertically polarised. This means that these signals cannot interfere with the signals from the main transmitter.

Figure 3.1.19 Polarisation may be used to prevent signals from different television transmitters at similar frequencies from interfering with each other.

Light from the Sun or from an electric filament lamp is unpolarised because the waves are emitted at random from the atoms of the object. Such light may be plane polarised by passing it through a polarising filter. Many crystals are capable of behaving in this way. In **polaroid**, long molecules of quinine iodosulphate are lined up so that only light waves oscillating in one particular plane can pass through. In this way, two pieces of polaroid which have the molecules aligned at 90° to each other will not allow any light through. Figure 3.1.20 illustrates the use of polaroid.

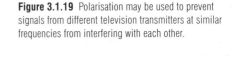

Polarising filter cuts out horizontally polarised light

Light which is reflected from the surface of the water is mainly horizontally polarised.

Unpolarised light from the Sun

Light reflected from object below the surface of the water is mainly vertically polarised, and so passes through the polarising filter.

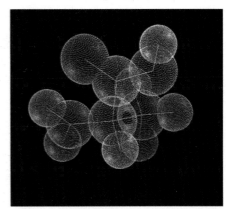

Figure 3.1.21 The molecules of life react to plane polarised light – all but the simplest biological molecules exhibit **optical activity**, the ability to cause the plane of oscillation of light to change as it travels through their solutions. This is a model of a molecule of alanine, the simplest optically active amino acid, which rotates the plane of polarised light.

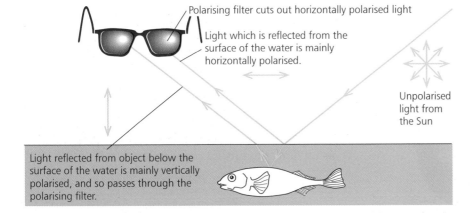

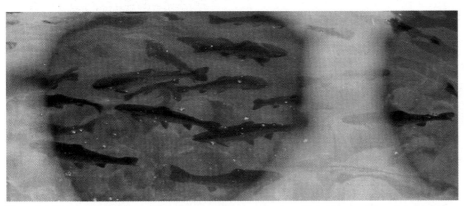

Figure 3.1.20 Polaroid sunglasses reduce glare from the water surface by cutting out horizontally polarised light.

Progressive and stationary waves

The classification of waves into progressive and stationary waves mentioned briefly on page 204 emphasises different applications of ideas about waves under different circumstances. Progressive waves are important because of their properties of 'action at a distance' – in other words, their properties as energy carriers. (Think of the way a pebble thrown into the water causes a water wave to spread out over the surface of a pond, carrying energy with it.) Stationary waves appear at first sight to be a contradiction in terms. Their importance lies in oscillations which occur in many systems, including stretched strings and in columns of air, and in structures such as bridges and vehicle components. They also provide a vital tool for understanding the behaviour of electrons and other subatomic particles, as we shall see in section 6.

Progressive waves

Intensity and distance

A wave spreading out from a point source, like a circular wave spreading out from a stone dropped into a pond, carries energy with it which is spread over a larger and larger area as the wave spreads out. It is often useful to know something about the **intensity** of a wave under these circumstances. When a wave spreads out through space, intensity is defined as the energy carried by the wave passing normally through unit area in unit time. In the SI system this means that the units of intensity are $J\ m^{-2}\ s^{-1}$ or $W\ m^{-2}$ (as $1\ W = 1\ J\ s^{-1}$).

There is an important relationship between the intensity of a wave and the distance from its source, which is known as the **inverse square law**:

$$\text{Intensity} \propto 1/(\text{distance})^2$$

The inverse square law

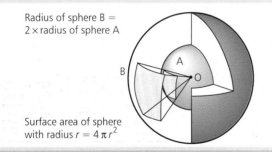

Radius of sphere B = 2 × radius of sphere A

Surface area of sphere with radius $r = 4\pi r^2$

Figure 3.1.22

A light bulb at point O in figure 3.1.22 has a power output of P (that is, it produces light energy at a rate of $P\ J\ s^{-1}$). The light waves from O spread out in all directions through the two spheres A and B, both of which have their centres at O. As this happens, the energy carried by the light becomes spread over a larger and larger area. If the radius of sphere A is r, this means that the intensity of the light when it has travelled a distance r from point O will be given by:

$$\text{Intensity} = P/4\pi r^2$$

in other words:

$$\text{intensity} \propto 1/d^2$$

where d is the distance from the source.

When the light passes through sphere B it has travelled through twice the distance, that is, $2r$, and its intensity has further reduced by a factor of $2^2 = 4$:

$$\text{Intensity} = P/4\pi (2r)^2 = P/16\pi r^2$$

Worked example

A lamp has a light output of 10 W. What will be the intensity of the light from the lamp at a distance of 2 km?

As the light spreads out the energy becomes distributed over the surface of a sphere. Therefore at a distance of 2 km, the 10 W of light energy will be spread over the area of a sphere with a radius of 2 km. So:

$$\text{Intensity at 2 km} = \frac{10\ W}{4\pi \times (2 \times 10^3\ m)^2} = \frac{10\ W}{5 \times 10^7\ m^2}$$

$$= 2 \times 10^{-7}\ W\ m^{-2}$$

Amplitude and intensity

Since a wave consists of oscillations, our knowledge of simple harmonic motion leads us to expect that there must also be a relationship between the amplitude of a wave (which of course is the same as the amplitude of the oscillations in the wave) and the energy it carries. We saw in section 1.7 that for an object oscillating with SHM, its energy depends on the square of the oscillation's amplitude. This relationship also applies to waves, where the intensity of a wave is a measure of the energy it is carrying. Thus:

$$\text{Intensity} \propto (\text{amplitude})^2$$

Stationary waves

Stationary waves are also known as **standing waves**. The words 'stationary' and 'standing' in this context refer to the fact that the wave is not progressive, and that the positions of the peaks and troughs in it are not moving. This is most easily visualised as a string on, say, a guitar. When the string is plucked it vibrates. Parts of the string vibrate to and fro, while other parts do not move. At its simplest, the string vibrates in a single loop, with a stationary point at either end and a point of maximum oscillation in the middle, as figure 3.1.24 shows.

Figure 3.1.23 A surfer will tell you that the energy associated with waves depends on the square of their amplitude. 6 m waves have $6^2 = 36$ times more energy associated with them than 1 m waves – which makes for much more difficult (and exciting) surfing!

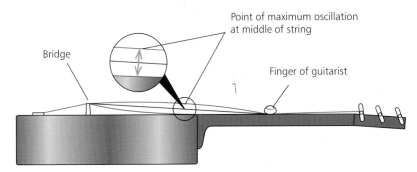

Figure 3.1.24 This illustrates the simplest way in which a string may vibrate, called its **fundamental** mode. The points of no oscillation are called **nodes**, while the point of maximum oscillation is an **antinode**.

Stationary waves on a stretched string

Transverse stationary waves may be investigated using a length of rubber cord in the apparatus shown in figure 3.1.25.

As the frequency of vibration of the cord is gradually increased, resonance is observed. At certain, very definite frequencies, the cord vibrates in sections as the small diagrams show. A stroboscope enables the motion of the cord to be seen either frozen or slowed down, when the up and down motion of the cord along its length can clearly be seen. This investigation can also be done by making waves along a slinky spring using your hand as the source of vibrations. The fact that stationary waves can only be set up at certain frequencies is quickly and easily established using this method.

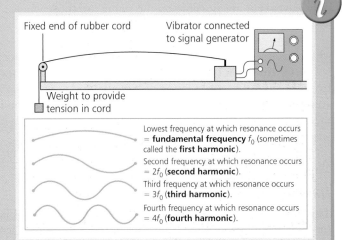

Figure 3.1.25 Varying the frequency of the supply to the vibrator enables a series of transverse stationary waves to be produced on the rubber cord. The particular frequency associated with a given mode of vibration of the cord is sometimes referred to as the **eigenfrequency** of that mode of vibration.

Setting up a stationary wave

The shape of the vibrating guitar string is due to the formation of a stationary wave on it. At the instant the string is plucked a progressive transverse wave travels along it from left to right. This wave is reflected back from the end of the string, and the result is a stationary wave. Although it is not easy to visualise, the principle of superposition can be used to explain how two progressive waves travelling in opposite directions can produce a stationary wave, as figure 3.1.27 shows.

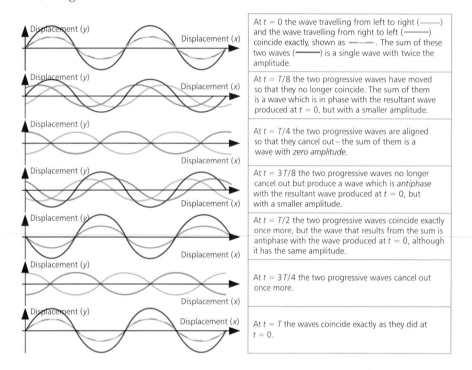

	At $t = 0$ the wave travelling from left to right (——) and the wave travelling from right to left (——) coincide exactly, shown as ——. The sum of these two waves (——) is a single wave with twice the amplitude.
	At $t = T/8$ the two progressive waves have moved so that they no longer coincide. The sum of them is a wave which is in phase with the resultant wave produced at $t = 0$, but with a smaller amplitude.
	At $t = T/4$ the two progressive waves are aligned so that they cancel out – the sum of them is a wave with *zero amplitude*.
	At $t = 3T/8$ the two progressive waves no longer cancel out but produce a wave which is *antiphase* with the resultant wave produced at $t = 0$, but with a smaller amplitude.
	At $t = T/2$ the two progressive waves coincide exactly once more, but the wave that results from the sum is antiphase with the wave produced at $t = 0$, although it has the same amplitude.
	At $t = 3T/4$ the two progressive waves cancel out once more.
	At $t = T$ the waves coincide exactly as they did at $t = 0$.

Figure 3.1.27 Two progressive waves moving in opposite directions produce a stationary wave.

For a string stretched between two fixed points like the guitar string in figure 3.1.24, the amplitude of the vibration of the string must be zero at each end, since it is fixed at these points. Given this restriction, it can be shown that the only waves that are possible on the string are those where:

$$\lambda = 2l/n$$

where l is the length of the string and n is a whole number: 1, 2, 3, etc.

This means that nodes will occur on the string at a distance of 0, $\lambda/2$, λ, $3\lambda/2$ from the end of it, and that neighbouring nodes are separated by a distance of $\lambda/2$, as are neighbouring antinodes. It also means that the fundamental mode of vibration of a string is an oscillation with a wavelength *twice* the length of the string, that is, $\lambda = 2l$. These points are shown in figure 3.1.28.

The box 'Reflections and stationary waves' on page 221 gives more detail about how the wave is reflected at the ends of the string.

Harmonics and overtones

The importance of this consideration of stationary waves is that many systems (not just stretched strings) have a set of natural frequencies of vibration. The set of vibrations associated with a particular system (whether it be a string or an air column in a musical instrument, a tall skyscraper or the wing of a jet airliner) is called its **harmonics** or **eigenfrequencies**, and the second and higher harmonics are sometimes (especially in the case of musical instruments) referred to as **overtones**.

Electrons and waves

Waves crop up in the most unexpected places. As we shall see in Section 6, the behaviour of electrons in many circumstances is best understood if we consider it in terms of waves rather than particles. For example, an electron in an atom can be modelled as a standing wave on a string.

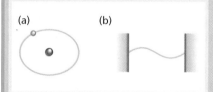

(a)   (b)

Figure 3.1.26 The behaviour of the electron in the hydrogen atom can be understood in terms of a standing wave on a string.

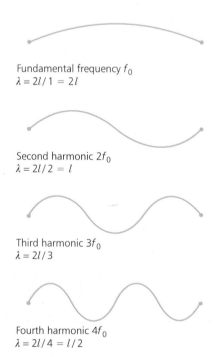

Fundamental frequency f_0
$\lambda = 2l/1 = 2l$

Second harmonic $2f_0$
$\lambda = 2l/2 = l$

Third harmonic $3f_0$
$\lambda = 2l/3$

Fourth harmonic $4f_0$
$\lambda = 2l/4 = l/2$

Figure 3.1.28 The first four modes of vibration of a stretched string. Notice that the distance between adjacent nodes or antinodes is always $\lambda/2$, and that there is always a node at each end of the string.

Figure 3.1.29 Different instruments produce different sounds, due to the combination of different overtones and changes in loudness at the start and end of the note.

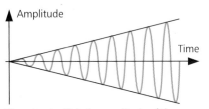

Amplitude

Time

The rate at which the amplitude of the vibrations increases at the start of a note is sometimes called the **attack**.

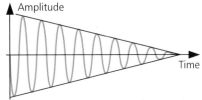

Amplitude

Time

The term **decay** is sometimes used to describe the rate at which the amplitude of the vibrations dies away.

The note played on a piano is the result of the vibration of a string set in motion by being hit with a soft felt hammer. The way in which any string vibrates is governed by the way it is set in motion (basically *where* and *how* it is hit). This is also true for any other instrument – the French horn, for example, has a vibrating air column instead of a string. The fundamental mode of vibration has the largest amplitude of any mode, and determines the **pitch** of the note produced. It is the combination of the fundamental mode of vibration coupled with the particular overtones for an instrument which determines the **quality** or **timbre** of a note, and which results in the difference in sound between two different instruments playing a steady note of the same pitch. The way the loudness of the note changes also enables us to hear the differences between the notes produced by different musical instruments (figure 3.1.29).

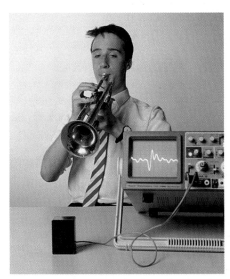

Figure 3.1.30 The complex vibrations produced by the fundamental and overtones of the singer's vocal cords and the air column in the trumpet can be seen clearly on the oscilloscope screen. These complex waveforms have been produced by the combination of a series of standing waves.

Investigating stationary waves using sound waves and microwaves

Both sound waves and microwaves can be used to investigate stationary waves, as figure 3.1.31 shows. Microwaves are electromagnetic waves with a wavelength of around 3 cm – see section 3.3.

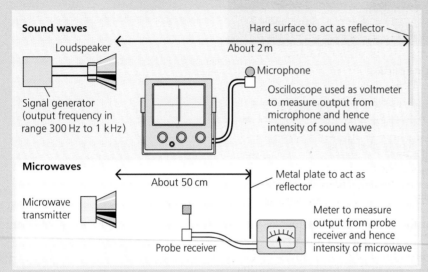

Figure 3.1.31 Investigating the production of stationary waves using sound waves and microwaves.

Moving the detector (the microphone in the case of sound waves, the probe receiver in the case of microwaves) along the line between the wave source and the reflector enables alternating points of high and low signal strength to be found. These are the antinodes and nodes of the stationary wave. The distance between successive nodes or antinodes can be measured, and corresponds to half the wavelength λ. If the frequency f of the source is known or can be measured, this information can be used to calculate the speed c of propagation of the two progressive waves which produce the stationary wave, from the relationship $c = f\lambda$.

SUMMARY

- Waves are oscillations that are **propagated** (spread out) from a source, carrying energy.

- **Mechanical waves** need a medium through which to travel, while **electromagnetic waves** do not and can therefore travel through a vacuum.

- In **transverse waves**, the direction of oscillation is at right angles to the direction of propagation, while in **longitudinal waves** the direction of oscillation is parallel to the direction of propagation. Longitudinal waves consist of a series of **compressions** and **rarefactions**.

- Waves may be represented by drawing **wavefronts** or **rays**. A wavefront represents the parts of a wave which are in phase, while a ray is drawn at right angles to the wavefronts.

- The **wavelength** λ of a wave is the distance from a point on the wave to the next point on the wave in phase with it. The **amplitude** A of a wave is the maximum displacement of the wave from the equilibrium position. The **period** T of a wave is the time taken for one oscillation, and the **frequency** f is the number of oscillations per second, $f = 1/T$.

- The speed c of a wave is related to its wavelength and frequency by $c = f\lambda$.

- **Driven oscillations** are caused by an input of energy from an external **driving oscillator**. The frequency of the driven oscillations is the same as the frequency of the driving oscillations. **Resonance** occurs when the frequency of the driving oscillations matches the natural frequency of the driven oscillator and oscillations of large amplitude are set up.

- Oscillations which are exactly in step with each other are said to be **in phase**, while those which are exactly out of step are said to be **antiphase**. Antiphase oscillations have a phase difference of π radians.

- The **principle of superposition** states that where two or more waves meet, the total displacement at any point is the sum of the displacement of each wave at that point. Hence two waves each with displacement A at a point produce a resultant wave with displacement $2A$ at that point, while two waves with displacements $+A$ and $-A$ produce a resultant wave with zero displacement.

- **Polarisation** may be exhibited by transverse waves. If the oscillations take place in a number of planes, the wave is **unpolarised**. If the oscillations are only in one plane, the wave is **polarised**. An unpolarised wave may be polarised by passing it through a material that allows through oscillations in only one plane.

- The **intensity** of a progressive wave is the energy carried by it when passing through a given area in a given time. For a wave travelling in three-dimensional space, intensity and distance travelled are related by the inverse square law, intensity $\propto 1/(\text{distance})^2$.

- The intensity of a wave is proportional to the square of its amplitude.

- Stationary waves consist of **nodes** or points of zero displacement and **antinodes** or points of maximum displacement. A stretched string fixed at one end and vibrating with its **fundamental mode** has a node at each end and an antinode in the centre.

- A stationary wave can be visualised as two progressive waves moving in opposite directions. Stationary waves are possible on a string of length l only where the wavelength $\lambda = 2l/n$, where n is a whole number 1, 2, 3, etc. For f_0, $\lambda = 2l$.

EXAMPLE

A church organ consists of open-ended pipes of different lengths, ranging from 2.4 m to 30 mm. Calculate the range of fundamental frequencies produced by the pipes.

The fundamental mode of vibration of a stretched string is with a single antinode in the centre of the string and a node at each end (figure 3.1.32(a)). In contrast, the fundamental mode of vibration of the air in an open-ended organ pipe has an antinode at each (open) end of the pipe where the air is free to vibrate with large amplitudes. By definition, this mode has $\lambda = 2l$, where l is the length of the pipe, figure 3.1.32(b).

Therefore in this case, we have wavelengths ranging from a value of $\lambda_1 = 2 \times 2.4$ m $= 4.8$ m, to $\lambda_2 = 2 \times 0.03$ m $= 0.06$ m, giving corresponding frequencies of f_1 and f_2:

$$f_1 = c/\lambda_1$$
$$= 340 \text{ m s}^{-1}/4.8 \text{ m}$$
$$= 71 \text{ Hz}$$

$$f_2 = c/\lambda_2$$
$$= 340 \text{ m s}^{-1}/0.06 \text{ m}$$
$$= 5670 \text{ Hz}$$

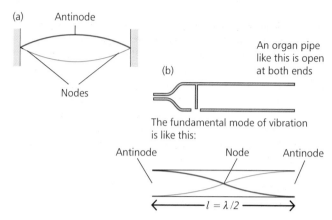

Figure 3.1.32

QUESTIONS

1 If you are given a metal rod and a hammer, how must you hit the rod to produce:
  a a transverse wave
  b a longitudinal wave?

2 While playing with a 'slinky' spring on the floor, a child wiggles the end of the spring from side to side, sending a transverse wave along it. The amplitude of the wave decreases as the wave travels along the spring. Sketch graphs to show:
  a how the displacement of the spring varies along its length at a given time
  b how the displacement of the spring varies with time at a given point.
  c How do the terms *wavelength*, *frequency* and *amplitude* apply to the features of these graphs?

3 Some time after a large ship has passed, the waves of its wash strike the shore at a rate of 15 per minute. The waves are 10 m apart. What is their speed?

4 The human ear is sensitive to sounds between about 20 Hz and 20 000 Hz. Taking the speed of sound as 340 m s⁻¹, calculate the corresponding range of wavelengths.

5 Copy and complete table 3.1.1.

Radio station	Wavelength/m	Frequency/Hz
BBC Radio Solent		9.99×10^5
Viking Radio	3.10	
West Sound		9.75×10^7
BBC Radio Cornwall	4.76×10^2	

Table 3.1.1

6 Figure 3.1.33 shows a wave travelling in the positive x direction, away from the origin. Details of the measurements of the wave are shown in the diagram.

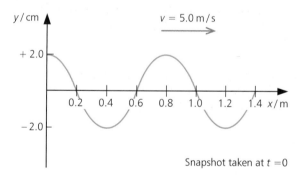

Figure 3.1.33

  a What is the wave's period?
  b What is the mathematical relationship that describes this wave in terms of x and t?
  c Copy the diagram and add to it a line to show a wave exactly $\pi/2$ radians *behind* the first wave.

7 Waves on the open sea caused by a steady wind of velocity v_1 have a height of 3.4 m and a period of 11 s, while those caused by a steady wind of velocity v_2 have a height of 6.1 m and a period of 15 s. What is the ratio of the powers carried by these two different waves?

QUESTIONS

8 A particular room has no windows, and the walls of the room are painted a dull black to minimise the reflection of light from them. A single light bulb is placed in the room as the only source of illumination. A photocell is used to record the light level at varying distances from the lamp. (When it is illuminated, the photocell causes a current to flow in a circuit in which it is connected – over a modest range of light levels the magnitude of the current is proportional to the illumination.) Table 3.1.2 shows the current produced by the photocell at different distances from the lamp.

Distance/m	1.0	2.0	2.5	3.0	4.5	6.0
Photocell reading/mA	200	52	31	22	10	5.5

Table 3.1.2

Plot a suitable graph to show that the intensity of the light radiating from the lamp obeys an inverse square law.

9 Plane waves are produced on the water in a ripple tank by means of a horizontal bar of wood which oscillates up and down. The waves travel 29.4 cm in 1.4 s, and there is a distance of 3.0 cm between their crests. Calculate
   a the velocity of the waves,
   b the frequency of the vibrations of the piece of wood.

10 The timbre of the note produced by a stringed instrument like a guitar can be affected by plucking the string in different places along its length. Using words and diagrams, define the word *timbre*, and explain how plucking the string differently affects the note.

11 The G string of a violin has a fundamental frequency of 196 Hz. What are the frequencies of the second, third and fourth harmonics of this string?

12 A set of open-ended church organ pipes is required to produce notes with fundamental frequencies in the range 32 Hz to 4096 Hz. Taking the velocity of sound in air as 340 m s^{-1}, calculate the required length of
   a the longest pipe,
   b the shortest pipe.

13 Many people enjoy singing in the shower or the bath because their voice is reflected from the hard walls and resonates (produces standing waves). If a shower cubicle measures 1 m × 1 m × 2.5 m, calculate the four lowest resonant frequencies of the standing waves produced by a singer in the cubicle. Can you suggest why a man's voice is enhanced by singing in the shower more than a woman's voice?

Developing Key Skills

A group of young school students is about to start studying earthquakes. Write and produce a simple Web page for them that will introduce them to the ideas of waves travelling through the Earth and that gives a simple (non-mathematical) explanation of how the magnitude of earthquakes is measured. Your page should include some links to other Web sites where the students can find further information to help them in their studies.

[Key Skills opportunities: C, IT]

3.2 Properties of waves in motion

The understanding of waves and their application requires a study of their properties and behaviour. We saw in section 3.1 that it is possible to understand the behaviour of waves based upon the idea that the parts of a wave are in oscillation, and that the tools used to understand the behaviour of an object in oscillation can be used to understand the behaviour of a wave. This section now concerns the properties of waves, and applies to all wave motion. The examples used in explaining the properties often involve transverse waves since it is easier to model the properties using such waves, but the properties are shown in just the same way by longitudinal waves. For example, sound waves exhibit refraction and diffraction in just the same way as light waves, although since the wavelength of sound waves is much longer than that of light waves, the sizes of the objects which cause these effects are very different. We shall meet evidence that both light and sound can be considered to travel as wave motions in section 3.3.

Waves as models

Physicists use waves as models, to help them to understand why some things behave as they do. We have seen in section 3.1 that stationary waves are valuable when we are trying to understand the behaviour of oscillating systems. We shall now go on to concentrate on how waves can help us to understand the phenomena of reflection, refraction, diffraction and interference. We shall return to the subject of waves and models in section 3.3, when we consider the way in which light behaves and the explanations advanced for its behaviour.

The Dutch scientist Christiaan Huygens, a contemporary of Newton, used a model to explain the behaviour of waves. He explained the spreading out of a wave from a point source (like the ripple on a pond) by considering each wavefront as a new set of disturbances, as shown in figure 3.2.1.

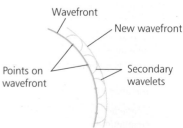

The first wavefront is considered as a set of points which act as centres of disturbance. There is an infinite number of such points on the wavefront, but obviously only a finite number of them may be drawn. Each point gives rise to a new 'mini wavefront' or **secondary wavelet,** which has the same speed (and hence wavelength) as the original wavefront. The new wavefront is the line which is tangential to the secondary wavelets.

Figure 3.2.1 The idea of a wavefront as a set of disturbances producing a new wavefront is called **Huygens' construction**. Huygens' construction is an explanation for the way in which a circular wave spreads out, eventually leading to a plane wave as the radius of the circular wave becomes very large. This model of wave behaviour is useful in explaining other properties of waves.

Reflection

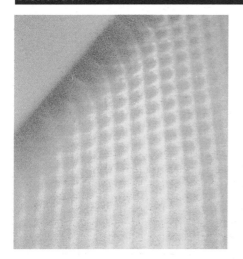 

Figure 3.2.2 In the case of water waves we see the reflections of the wavefronts, while we see the rays in the case of light.

Reflection is the word used to describe what happens when a wave arrives at a barrier and alters direction, as shown in figure 3.2.2. Experiment indicates that there is a simple relationship between the angles made with the barrier by the incident and reflected waves. Figure 3.2.3 shows this.

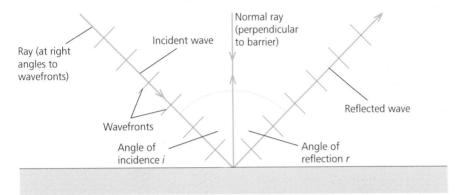

Ray (at right angles to wavefronts)

Incident wave

Normal ray (perpendicular to barrier)

Reflected wave

Wavefronts

Angle of incidence *i*

Angle of reflection *r*

Figure 3.2.3 The experimental result that angle of incidence = angle of reflection is known as the **law of reflection**. Notice that angles are measured between the rays and the **normal ray**, which is perpendicular to the surface of the barrier. Whilst this may appear an unnecessary complication, it is important to use this convention, since the normal ray provides the only way of measuring angles where the surface is not flat.

Reflections and stationary waves

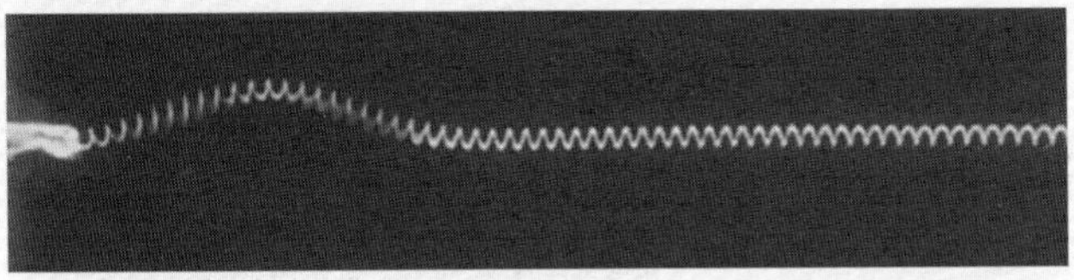

Just prior to reflection

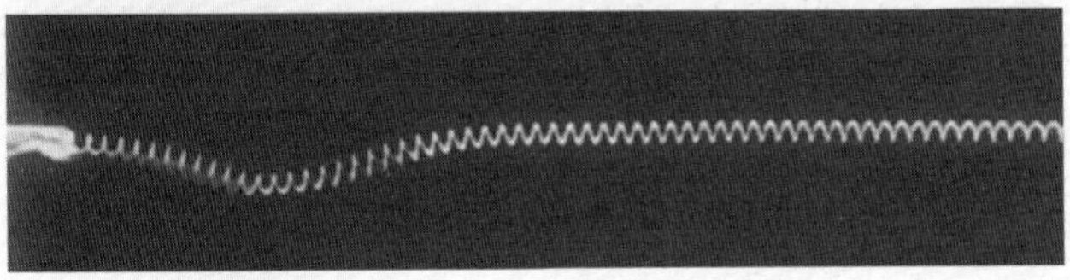

Just after reflection

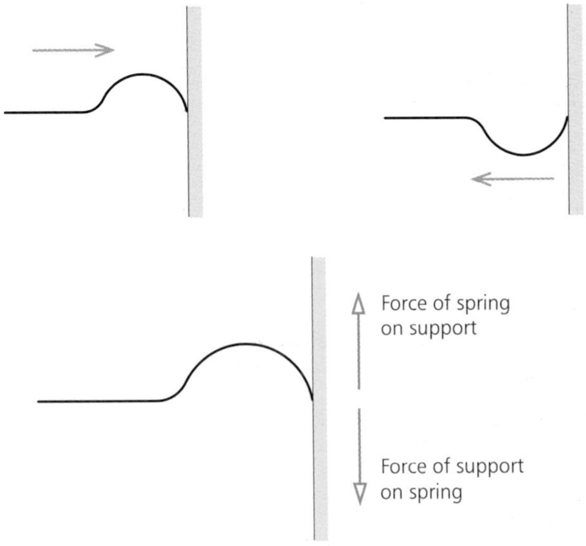

The formation of a stationary wave on a string as described in section 3.1 relies on the reflection of a progressive wave at the ends of the string. It is also dependent on the fact that such a reflection gives rise to a phase change of π radians, as illustrated in figure 3.2.4.

This phase change on reflection occurs *only* when a 'hard' reflection occurs, where the spring is connected to a massive solid object. Where the spring is joined to a light object (another, lighter spring for example) reflection also occurs at the boundary between them, but with no phase change.

◀ **Figure 3.2.4** As the pulse reaches the end of the spring the spring exerts a force on the support. The support exerts a force equal in size but opposite in direction on the spring, and so the pulse is reflected with a phase change of π radians.

Force of spring on support

Force of support on spring

Air

Glass

Glass

Air

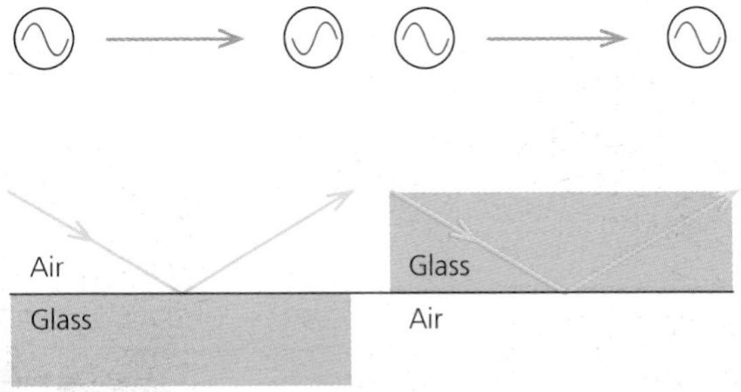

Figure 3.2.5 Other waves behave in the same way as waves on a slinky spring. For example, light waves are reflected with a phase change of π radians when travelling from a less dense medium to a more dense medium, but with no phase change at a more dense-to-less dense boundary. In general, if a wave is reflected at a boundary the reflected wave will suffer a phase change of π radians if $\lambda_1 > \lambda_2$, where λ_1 is the wavelength of the wave in the first medium and λ_2 is the wavelength of the wave in the second medium.

Refraction

Refraction may occur when a wave, for example light, travels from one medium into another – say from air into glass – and its direction of travel is changed, as shown in figure 3.2.6. As we shall see in section 3.3, there are two ways of explaining this phenomenon which both depend on a change in velocity. As in the case of reflection, experiment shows that there is a straightforward relationship between the angle made by the incident ray with the normal ray and the angle made by the refracted ray with the normal ray. This relationship is called **Snell's law**, which rays:

$$\sin i / \sin r = \text{constant}$$

See worked example 3 on page 236.

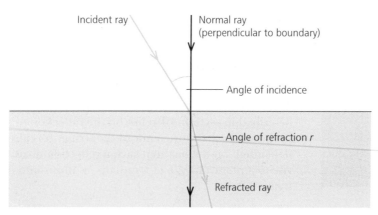

Figure 3.2.7 The constant in Snell's law is called the **refractive index** n for the medium.

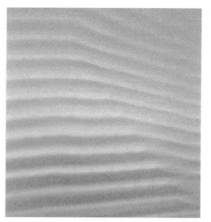

Figure 3.2.6 As for reflection, water waves and light rays provide two different ways of viewing refraction. Note the faint reflection of the incident ray from the face of the glass block at the bottom of the photograph.

Strictly speaking, the refractive index for a wave travelling from one medium (medium 1) into another medium (medium 2) should be written as $_1n_2$. This can be shown (see box opposite) to equal the ratio of the speed of the wave in medium 1 to the speed of the wave in medium 2. For rays entering medium 1 from medium 2 the ratio is reversed, and so in full:

$$_1n_2 = \frac{1}{_2n_1} = \frac{\sin\theta_1}{\sin\theta_2} = \frac{c_1}{c_2}$$

where:
θ_1 is the angle between the ray and the normal in medium 1,
θ_2 is the angle between the ray and the normal in medium 2,
c_1 is the speed of the wave in medium 1,
c_2 is the speed of the wave in medium 2.

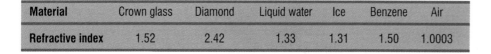

Material	Crown glass	Diamond	Liquid water	Ice	Benzene	Air
Refractive index	1.52	2.42	1.33	1.31	1.50	1.0003

Table 3.2.1 Values for the refractive index of various substances. Since refractive index varies with wavelength for many media, the values are quoted for a wavelength of 5.89×10^{-7} m.

Huygens' construction and refraction

In figure 3.2.8, AB = BC and A'B' = B'C'.

Speed of wave in medium 1 = c_1

Speed of wave in medium 2 = c_2

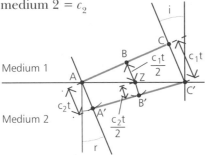

Figure 3.2.8

(λ_1 is the wavelength of the wave in medium 1, and λ_2 the wavelength in medium 2. Note that the *frequency* of the wave is the frequency of its source, therefore this remains unchanged whichever medium the wave is moving in.)

CC' = $c_1 t$, so AA' = $c_2 t$.

BZ = $c_1 t/2$ (because B is halfway between A and C), so ZB' = $c_2 t/2$.

i = angle CAC', and r = angle AC'A'.

The wavefront ABC is just arriving at the boundary.

In the time that the wavefront travels from point C to point C', a distance of $c_1 t$, the wavefront will travel from point A to point A', a distance of $c_2 t$. This means that A acts as a source of secondary wavelets with radius $c_2 t$. Similarly, point Z acts as a source of secondary wavelets with radius $c_2 t/2$.

The new wavefront is the line which joins the secondary wavelet centred on A to that centred on Z and which passes through point C' – this is line A'B'C'.

Now: $$\sin i = \sin \text{CAC}' = \frac{c_1 t}{\text{AC}'}$$

and: $$\sin r = \sin \text{ACA}' = \frac{c_2 t}{\text{AC}'}$$

so: $$\frac{\sin i}{\sin r} = \frac{c_1 t/\text{AC}'}{c_2 t/\text{AC}'} = \frac{c_1 t}{c_2 t} = \frac{c_1}{c_2} = \frac{f\lambda_1}{f\lambda_2} = \frac{\lambda_1}{\lambda_2}$$

Since c_1 and c_2 are the wave speeds in media 1 and 2 respectively, and these are constant, this relationship confirms Snell's law.

Real and apparent depth

Snell's law enables us to explain very convincingly why the depth of water in a swimming pool is always greater than it appears to be.

In figure 3.2.9, imagine that point O is on the bottom of the pool. Light from point O travels upwards and is refracted away from the normal as it leaves the water. Because it is refracted, a person looking at this light ray sees it as coming from a point O', above O. In this way the depth of the pool appears to be PO' rather than PO.

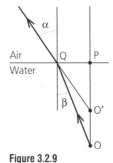

Figure 3.2.9

Using Snell's law:

$$_{\text{air}}n_{\text{water}} = \frac{\sin \alpha}{\sin \beta} = \frac{\sin \text{QO'P}}{\sin \text{QOP}}$$

$$= \frac{\text{QP}/\text{QO}'}{\text{QP}/\text{QO}}$$

$$= \frac{\text{QO}}{\text{QO}'}$$

When the object is viewed directly from above, QO ≈ PO and QO' ≈ PO', so

$$_{\text{air}}n_{\text{water}} = \frac{\text{PO}}{\text{PO}'} = \frac{\text{real depth}}{\text{apparent depth}}$$

The depth of a swimming pool

A swimming pool is filled with water to a depth of 1.8 m. How deep does it appear to be to someone standing on the side of the pool and looking straight down into it? (The refractive index of water is 1.5.)

Using the relationship $_{air}n_{water} = \dfrac{\text{real depth}}{\text{apparent depth}}$ we can write

$$1.5 = \frac{1.8\,\text{m}}{x}$$

where x is the apparent depth of the pool.

Rearranging:

$$x = \frac{1.8\,\text{m}}{1.5}$$

$$= 1.2\,\text{m}$$

The pool appears to be 1.2 m deep.

Total internal reflection

As a wave travels from a less dense medium and enters a medium that is more dense, it slows down and is refracted so that it makes a smaller angle with the normal ray, as we saw in figure 3.2.7. The reverse is true for a wave leaving a denser medium, when it is refracted away from the normal ray. (Some is also reflected from the boundary, as figure 3.2.10 shows.) At a certain angle of incidence to the boundary θ_c, called the **critical angle**, the ray leaves the glass at almost 90° to the normal.

Any increase in angle then causes the ray to be totally reflected inside the glass. This is called **total internal reflection**. Total internal reflection obeys the laws of reflection.

If the direction of the rays in figure 3.2.10 is reversed, the incident ray is in air and the refracted ray is in glass. This means that $i = 90°$ (to a good approximation) and $r = \theta_c$.

Applying Snell's law:

$$n = \frac{\sin i}{\sin r} = \frac{\sin 90°}{\sin \theta_c}$$

Since $\sin 90° = 1$:

$$\sin \theta_c = \frac{1}{n}$$

The critical angle for container glass (used to make bottles and jars) is 41°, although it varies considerably with the composition of the glass. It also depends on the wavelength of the light.

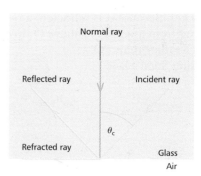

Figure 3.2.10 Total internal reflection.

Diffraction and interference

This section concludes by describing diffraction and interference, two more properties of waves in general. In the laboratory these properties are most commonly investigated using light, and the examples given here therefore mainly involve light.

Diffraction

The term **diffraction** is used to describe the interaction between waves and solid objects. When a wave passes through a gap or round an object it may be deviated from its path. The degree of this diffraction that occurs depends on the relationship between the size of the gap or the object and the wavelength of the wave – when the two are close together in size, diffraction occurs, as figure 3.2.11 illustrates.

   We shall examine the diffraction of light in detail shortly, but before doing so it is necessary to examine another general property of waves – **interference**.

Interference

The principle of superposition which we met in section 3.1, and which we saw explain the behaviour of waves crossing each other, also provides an explanation for interference: see figure 3.2.12. Interference effects using light were first demonstrated at the beginning of the nineteenth century by Thomas Young. Although these experiments provided strong evidence for the wave nature of light, physicists did not accept that light had wave-like properties until much later on.

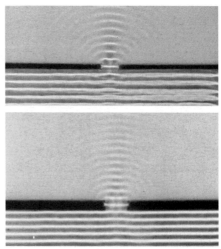

Figure 3.2.11 Diffraction occurs only when the wavelength of the wave and the size of the object or gap are close together. Light waves are not appreciably diffracted by a person, hence the crisp shadow formed on a sunny day. They *are* appreciably diffracted by the point of a pin, however. The same applies to waves passing through a gap, as the pictures of the waves on the ripple tank show. This also explains why you can *hear* a car coming round a corner before you can *see* it.

Figure 3.2.12 Two circular waves (produced by dippers) on a ripple tank overlap to produce a distinctive pattern, where waves reinforce each other in some regions and cancel each other out in others. This phenomenon is called **interference**.

Two-source interference patterns

Young's experiment used two narrow slits to produce an interference pattern from light. Figure 3.2.13 shows how the experiment can be repeated, and shows a similar arrangement for observing the interference of sound waves.

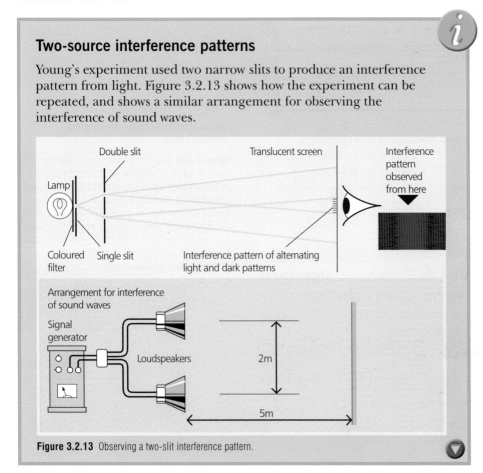

Figure 3.2.13 Observing a two-slit interference pattern.

Similar results can be obtained using sound, which is of course a longitudinal wave. In this case two loudspeakers driven by a single signal generator can be used, ensuring that the two sources are in phase (that is, the cones of both loudspeakers move forwards and backwards together). For a sound with a pitch of 1000 Hz, the two loudspeakers should be placed about 2 m apart. An observer walking along line AB will hear the intensity of the sound rise and fall, as constructive and destructive interference alternate.

Explaining interference

The production of an interference pattern by two parallel slits can be explained by thinking about the phase of the waves arriving at the screen. Figure 3.2.14 exaggerates the distance between the two slits in order to make the situation clearer, and explains how the pattern of light and dark bands (often referred to as **fringes**) arises. A light band will be a region of **constructive interference**, as waves superimpose in phase, so the *difference* in distance travelled to the screen by waves from A and B must be a whole number of wavelengths $n\lambda$. A dark band will be a region of **destructive interference**, as waves superimpose antiphase, so the difference in distance travelled by the waves will be a number of half wavelengths ($n\lambda/2$).

Waves meet in phase– **constructive interference**

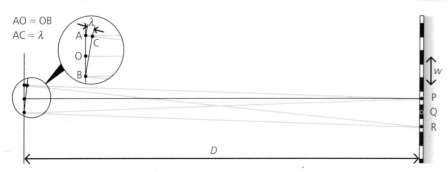

Waves meet antiphase– **destructive interference**

Figure 3.2.14 Light waves leave slits A and B in phase. Since AP = BP, the waves must arrive at P in phase, so **constructive interference** occurs here and a bright area is seen. The distance AR is exactly one wavelength more than the distance BR, so the waves also arrive at R in phase, leading to a bright area here also. The distance AQ is exactly half a wavelength more than the distance BQ, so the waves arrive at Q antiphase, resulting in a dark area.

Some reasonably straightforward trigonometry enables us to derive a relationship between D the distance from the slits to the screen, w the distance between successive light or dark fringes, s the slit separation and λ the wavelength of the light used. Referring again to figure 3.2.14, we know that:

$$\text{AR} - \text{BR} = \lambda$$

If angle ABC = θ, then:

$$\sin\theta = \text{AC/AB} = \lambda/s \qquad \textbf{(equation 1)}$$

But the diagram also shows that $\sin\theta = \text{PR/OR}$. Since θ is very small (remember that this diagram exaggerates the position – in practice PR is about 2 mm while OP is about 1 m) OR $\approx$ OP, so we can write:

$$\sin\theta \approx \text{PR/OP}$$

Since PR = w and OP = D, we can use the expression $\sin\theta = \lambda/s$ given above and write:

$$\frac{\lambda}{s} = \frac{w}{D} \quad \text{or} \quad \lambda = \frac{ws}{D}$$

Phase difference and path difference

The difference between the distance travelled by one ray and another is called the **path difference**, Δx. This path difference causes a **phase difference** for the two rays. These two are related by the equation

$$\text{phase difference} = \frac{2\pi\Delta x}{\lambda}$$

where λ is the wavelength of the light. The phase difference is in radians (2π radians $= 360°$).

Interference – worked example

Light with an unknown wavelength passes through two narrow slits 0.3 mm apart and forms an interference pattern on a screen 2.0 m away from the slits. If the distance between the fringes in the interference pattern is 3 mm, what is the wavelength of the light?

We know that the wavelength λ, the fringe separation w, the slit separation s and the distance D from the slits to the screen are related by the equation:

$$\lambda = \frac{ws}{D}$$

so we may substitute the values known into the relationship:

$$\lambda = \frac{3 \times 10^{-3}\text{ m} \times 0.3 \times 10^{-3}\text{ m}}{2.0\text{ m}} = \frac{0.9 \times 10^{-6}\text{ m}^2}{2.0\text{ m}}$$

$$= 4.5 \times 10^{-7}\text{ m}$$

The wavelength of the light is 4.5×10^{-7} m, at the violet end of the spectrum. (Wavelengths of light are often expressed in nm (nanometres). 1 nm $= 10^{-9}$ m, so this light has a wavelength of 450 nm.)

More about interference patterns

(1) Why the filter as well as the double slit?

Figure 3.2.13 shows a filter between the light source and the double slit. This is necessary to ensure that the light used in the experiment is **monochromatic** or of one wavelength only (although in fact filters usually allow through a range of wavelengths rather than a single wavelength). Without the filter the fringes are blurred and consist of a range of colours:

$$\lambda = \frac{ws}{D} \quad \text{or} \quad w = \frac{\lambda D}{s}$$

Thus if there is a range of wavelengths, there will be a range of fringe separations too. A filter is not necessary if a monochromatic source is used. A sodium lamp is effectively monochromatic, since the intensity of the light emitted by it at a wavelength of 5.89×10^{-7} m is many times that emitted at other wavelengths. Many lasers also produce monochromatic light.

(2) Why the single slit as well as the double slit?

Even if a monochromatic source is used, the light emitted from it contains many imperfections. The source emits light due to the loss of energy by excited electrons within the atoms of the source (see section 6.5). Different parts of the source therefore emit light at slightly different times and with different phases. Although this **incoherence** happens so rapidly that it is invisible to our eyes, it makes interference between light from two different parts of a source impossible to observe. The single slit in front of the source therefore ensures that the light reaches both slits in phase, so that the slits act as sources of waves rather like the dippers used to produce two simultaneous circular waves in the ripple tank in figure 3.2.12. Interference could not be observed if the dippers did not have a constant phase relationship. (The use of laser light overcomes these problems, since laser light is **coherent** – there is a constant phase relationship between all parts of the source.)

Interference patterns – diffraction at a single slit

The production of fringes seen in Young's experiment (figure 3.2.13) depends on diffraction to produce circular waves from each of the slits. These circular waves then overlap to produce an interference pattern, just as circular waves from two dippers in the ripple tank shown in figure 3.2.12 overlap and interfere. If diffraction at the slits did not occur, all that would be seen on the screen would be two light areas where light had travelled through the slits and hit the screen without being deviated in any way. This diffraction of the light by each slit may have an important effect on the appearance of the fringes, as we shall now see.

Investigating diffraction at a single slit

The apparatus shown in figure 3.2.15 may be used to investigate the diffraction of light at a single slit.

Using a piece of white card or paper enables marks to be made to record the spacing of the bands in the diffraction pattern. Note that this investigation relies on the properties of laser light, and will not work without modification if an ordinary light source is used. (If a laser is not available a bright lamp with a linear filament may be viewed through the slits. It will also be necessary to work in a darkened room.) The properties of laser light are described in section 3.3.

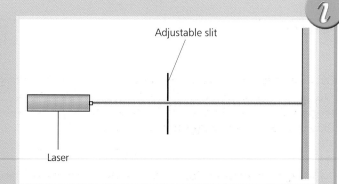

Figure 3.2.15 The light from the laser is diffracted by the slit, which should be placed about 1 m from the screen. The width of the slit is slowly reduced, starting at about 2 mm, until a diffraction pattern is seen on the screen. *Never* view laser light directly – the diffraction pattern should be viewed by scattering the light from an opaque screen (a piece of thick white paper or card is adequate for this).

Using apparatus like that described in figure 3.2.15, the diffraction of monochromatic light produces a diffraction pattern like that shown in figure 3.2.16.

The central region of the diffraction pattern shows a bright area. On either side of this there is a dark band, with successive light and dark bands following it as we move away from the centre of the pattern. The width of the central light band is twice that of the other light bands. The light bands get progressively less intense as the distance from the centre of the pattern increases.

Just as for refraction and reflection, the behaviour of light as it passes through a narrow slit like this can be explained using Huygens' construction. Figure 3.2.17 shows how this is done.

Note that we assume that waves reaching the slit are plane waves travelling in a direction perpendicular to the slit. As the wave passes through the slit, each point on the wave may be considered to act as the source of a new, circular wavefront, as we saw earlier. This means that a plane wavefront with the same width as the slit will travel away from the slit in the same direction as the original wave was travelling. Now consider a direction which makes an angle θ with the original direction of travel in such a way that there is a path difference of one wavelength between the wavelet from A and that from B (see figure 3.2.17). Point C is midway between points A and B. The wavelet from point C is therefore exactly antiphase with the wavelet from point A, and so the two wavelets can cancel out. For every secondary wavelet formed at a point along AC, there can always be found another secondary wavelet from a point along

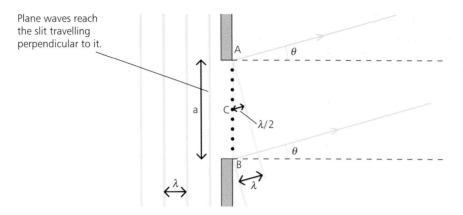

Plane waves reach the slit travelling perpendicular to it.

Figure 3.2.17

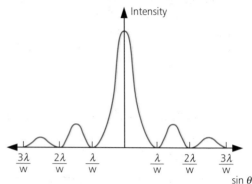

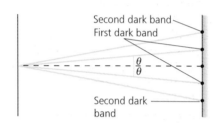

Second dark band
First dark band
Second dark band

Figure 3.2.16 The production of an interference pattern by diffraction at a single slit is sometimes referred to as **Fraunhofer diffraction.**

BC with which the wavelet can cancel. In this way all the light coming from AC cancels out all the light coming from BC, no light energy flows at angle θ to the original direction of travel, and a dark band appears on the screen in this direction. From the diagram it can be seen that:

$$\sin \theta = \lambda/a$$

Since the conditions for light from the two halves of the slit cancelling each other will also exist when the path difference is 2λ, 3λ, and so on, it follows that in general the minima of intensity occur at angles given by:

$$\sin \theta = n\lambda/a, \text{ where } n = 1, 2, 3 \ldots$$

At points between these angles not all the light is cancelled and so light bands appear. The intensity of these bands decreases as θ increases since more and more secondary wavelets are available to be paired with others out of phase as the angle gets bigger. (Note that this analysis is strictly only true if the waves reaching the screen are still plane waves – this will only be so if the distance from the slit to the screen is very large compared to the width of the slit.)

For small angles, $\sin \theta \approx \theta$ if θ is in radians, and so we can write $\theta = n\lambda/a$. If light of wavelength 6×10^{-7} m passes through a slit 3×10^{-4} m wide, the angle between the centre of the pattern and the first minimum will be given by:

$$\theta = \frac{6 \times 10^{-7} \text{ m}}{3 \times 10^{-4} \text{ m}} = 2 \times 10^{-3} \text{ radians}$$

If the distance from the slit to the screen is 1 m, this represents a distance on the screen of:

$$2 \times 10^{-3} \text{ radians} \times 1 \text{ m} = 2 \times 10^{-3} \text{ m} = 2 \text{ mm}$$

Interference patterns at multiple slits – the diffraction grating

As we have seen, light passing through a single narrow slit produces an image which consists of a bright central band with less intense bands on either side of it. Replacing the single slit by two parallel narrow slits produces the same diffraction pattern as the single slit, but in addition it is crossed by a series of interference bands. What happens if further slits are added? Figure 3.2.20 shows how the pattern changes – note that the slit spacing in each case is the same.

Three parallel slits produce a pattern similar to that produced by two slits, with two important differences. In the three-slit pattern the principal maxima are narrower, and a subsidiary maximum is introduced between each pair of

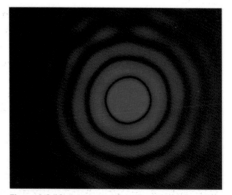

Figure 3.2.18 Fraunhofer diffraction caused by a circular aperture is probably more common than that caused by a single slit, since our eyes and most optical instruments (telescopes and cameras for instance) use circular apertures and lenses. The geometry of this arrangement is more complex than for a simple rectangular slit, and the zeros of intensity (dark bands) occur at angles of 1.22 $n\lambda/a$ from the central maximum. This pattern is effecitvely a slightly 'stretched' version of that shown in figure 3.2.16, rotated about the central point.

In examining the two-slit experiment earlier, we made the (unstated) assumption that the width of each slit was small compared with the wavelength of the light ($a < \lambda$), so that the diffraction pattern produced by each slit was very wide. (Because $\sin \theta = n\lambda/a$, the angle between the centre of the pattern and the first minimum is given by $\sin \theta = \lambda/a$. If $a < \lambda$, $\lambda/a > 1$ and so the central peak of the pattern is so wide that it effectively covers all angles.) This meant that each slit effectively produced an even light intensity over a wide angle, and the pattern of light intensity produced by the two slits was entirely due to interference between them, producing the even light and dark bands of figure 3.2.13.

If the width of the slits is not narrow compared with the wavelength of the light, each slit produces its own Fraunhofer diffraction pattern, and these then interfere to produce an overall pattern. The way in which the distribution of light in this overall pattern is determined is shown in figure 3.2.19 – the graph of intensity versus angle is actually the product of a diffraction curve (describing Fraunhofer diffraction at each slit) and an interference curve (describing the superposition of light from each slit). If I_s is the intensity at a point due to interference and I_d is the intensity at the same point due to diffraction, the resultant intensity I is given by $I = I_s \times I_d$. If I_d is zero at any point, then $I = 0$ at that point regardless of the value of I_s.

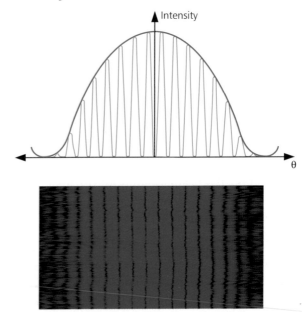

Figure 3.2.19 As a result of Fraunhofer diffraction at each slit, the overall intensity distribution produced by a pair of slits which are wide compared with the wavelength of light looks like this. The photograph shows how the pattern consists of a complex series of bands whose intensity varies widely, rather than the series of light and dark bands produced by a narrow pair of slits.

principal maxima. As more and more parallel slits are added, the principal maxima decrease in width. At the same time the number of subsidiary maxima increases and their intensity decreases.

A **diffraction grating** consists of a set of many evenly spaced slits, in which the slit separation is very small. This means that the principal maxima are very

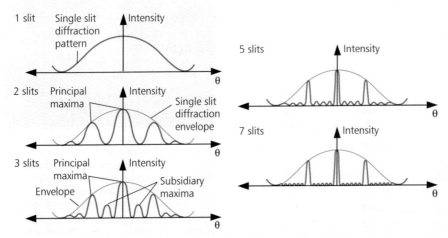

Figure 3.2.20 As the number of slits increases the intensity and sharpness of the principal maxima increase while the intensity of the subsidiary maxima decreases.

narrow, and there are so many subsidiary maxima that they are so faint as to be effectively invisible. A beam of monochromatic light passing through a diffraction grating is split into very narrow maxima, as figure 3.2.21 shows. The maxima are numbered outwards from the centre, with the undeviated maximum referred to as the **zero order** maximum.

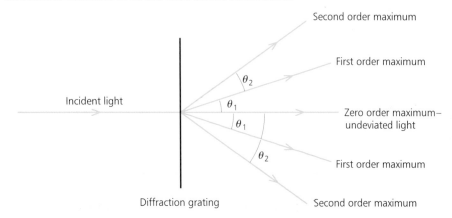

Figure 3.2.21 The number of maxima produced by a diffraction grating depends on the wavelength of the light and the distance between the slits of the grating.

The relationship between the angle at which the maxima occur, the slit separation and the wavelength of light can be obtained as follows. This examination of the diffraction grating assumes that the light strikes the grating with normal incidence.

Each slit in a grating diffracts the incident light, and the diffracted waves then interfere constructively in certain directions only. Figure 3.2.22 shows a small portion of a grating. The wavefronts interfere constructively in the direction shown to produce the first order maximum, since the path difference between each adjacent pair of slits is λ. Light from slit A thus interferes constructively with light from slit B (path difference = λ), slit C (path difference = 2λ), slit D (path difference = 3λ), and so on. From figure 3.2.22, BF = λ and the slit spacing = AB = d.

$$\sin \theta = \frac{\mathbf{BF}}{\mathbf{AB}} = \frac{\lambda}{d}$$

For the second maximum, BF = 2λ, and:

$$\sin \theta = \frac{\mathbf{BF}}{\mathbf{AB}} = \frac{2\lambda}{d}$$

Figure 3.2.22

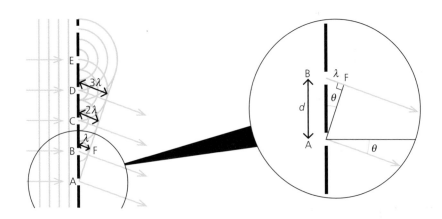

DIFFRACTION AND THE DOUBLE HELIX

In the early 1950s, the race was on among scientists to find the structure of the DNA molecule, which was known to be the substance in the cell that carried genetic information from one generation to another. The story of how the structure of this enormously important molecule was worked out is the story of four scientists.

Information about the structure of crystalline solids (like common salt, or copper sulphate) can be obtained by passing X-rays through them. Because the spaces between the atoms in a crystal are about the same as the wavelength of X-rays, X-rays passing through the crystal are diffracted. The diffracted beams then interfere with one another, and a pattern of constructive and destructive interference is formed. It is this pattern that carries the information about the arrangement of the atoms in the crystal. This technique can also be used for large, complex molecules like DNA.

One year after her arrival at King's College, London, in 1950, Rosalind Franklin had developed a new approach to taking X-ray diffraction photographs of DNA, building a high-resolution X-ray camera, and pulling the DNA into very fine fibres. Maurice Wilkins, her colleague at King's, was also working in this field, but he and Franklin did not get on well, and they spent very little time discussing their work.

While Franklin and Wilkins were busy getting X-ray diffraction evidence for the structure of the DNA molecule, two Cambridge scientists had decided that they too would try to suggest a structure. Francis Crick and James Watson had no experimental data of their own to work on – instead, they based their ideas on Watson's recollections of a seminar about Franklin's work that he had heard her present (though he had not taken any notes). Their first idea for the structure was a disaster. When it was presented to Franklin and Wilkins, Franklin pointed out that the model could not possibly fit the data she had presented at her seminar, and refused to have anything more to do with Crick and Watson.

Some months later, Wilkins showed Watson a copy of Franklin's best X-ray diffraction picture of DNA which provided clear evidence that its structure was a helix. At the same time a Cambridge colleague gave Crick and Watson a copy of a report from the King's research group to the Medical Research Council, in which Franklin summarised her findings and gave data from the X-ray diffraction studies. This was what Crick and Watson needed to complete their work. Within a frenzied few weeks of model-building they had arrived at the double helical structure, and their paper appeared in *Nature* on 25 April 1953, together with supporting papers by Wilkins and Franklin and their co-workers.

In 1962, Watson, Crick and Wilkins shared the Nobel prize for medicine for their work. Franklin had died of cancer, four years earlier, at the age of 37.

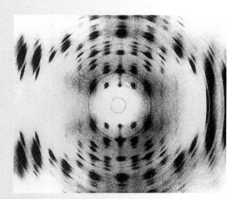

Figure 3.2.23 One of Franklin's X-ray crystallograms of DNA.

Figure 3.2.24 Watson (left) and Crick with their model. Watson was the only biologist in the story told on this page – Crick and Wilkins were both physicists, while Franklin was a chemist.

Figure 3.2.25 Rosalind Franklin decided to become a scientist when she was 15, winning a place at Cambridge three years later. She had a struggle to take up her place – her father did not approve of university education for women, and was only persuaded when her mother and an aunt took Rosalind's side in the ensuing family disagreement.

Figure 3.2.26 Shy and serious, Maurice Wilkins found it hard to get on with Rosalind Franklin. Their relationship was not helped by Wilkins' understanding that Franklin had moved to King's in 1950 to be his assistant – in fact, she had been invited to work at King's on exactly the same terms as Wilkins, having had more experience of X-ray diffraction than him.

In general, the nth maximum will occur at an angle θ_n from the zero order maximum, where θ_n is given by:

$$\sin \theta_n = \frac{n\lambda}{d}$$

The spacing of the slits in a grating is sometimes expressed in terms of the number of slits per metre. For a grating with N slits per metre, the slit spacing is N^{-1}.

To find out the highest order of the principal maxima, we can use the fact that the maximum value of $\sin \theta$ is 1. This means that we can write:

$$\frac{n\lambda}{d} \leq 1$$

so:

$$n \leq \frac{d}{\lambda}$$

Since n must be a whole number, to calculate the highest order spectrum we calculate the value of d/λ and round it down to the next whole number.

Grating calculations – worked example

Yellow light with a wavelength of 5.89×10^{-7} m strikes a diffraction grating with normal incidence. The grating has 5000 slits per centimetre (that is, 5000×100 slits per metre). At what angles will the maxima be seen?

The first order maximum will be when $n = 1$. Since $d = 1/(5000 \times 100)$ m^{-1} we can write:

$$n\lambda = d \sin \theta_n$$

$$1 \times 5.89 \times 10^{-7} \text{ m} = \frac{1}{(5000 \times 100) \text{ m}^{-1}} \times \sin \theta_1$$

so:

$$\sin \theta_1 = 1 \times 5.89 \times 10^{-7} \text{ m} \times (5000 \times 100) \text{ m}^{-1}$$

$$= 0.2945$$

Therefore $\theta_1 = 17.1°$.

Similarly for θ_2:

$$2 \times 5.89 \times 10^{-7} \text{ m} = \frac{1}{(5000 \times 100) \text{ m}^{-1}} \times \sin \theta_2$$

so:

$$\sin \theta_2 = 2 \times 5.89 \times 10^{-7} \text{ m} \times (5000 \times 100) \text{ m}^{-1}$$

$$= 0.589$$

Therefore $\theta_2 = 36.1°$.

In the same way, we can show that a third order maximum appears at an angle of 62°. If the calculation for a *fourth* order maximum is carried out, however, we get a value of 1.178 for $\sin\theta_4$. Since the maximum value that the sine of an angle can have is 1, there is no fourth order maximum visible. This can be shown using the value of d/λ:

$$\frac{d}{\lambda} = \frac{(1/(5000 \times 100)\ \text{m}^{-1})}{5.89 \times 10^{-7}\ \text{m}} = 3.40$$

The highest order maximum visible is thus the third order maximum.

Diffraction grating spectra

When light of more than one wavelength falls on a grating, maxima for each wavelength are produced. Figure 3.2.27 shows the way in which light from a lithium source and a tungsten filament lamp is affected by a diffraction grating. Where the light passing through a grating consists of a range of wavelengths it is more appropriate to talk in terms of **spectra** rather than maxima, since for each order there is a maximum for each wavelength present in the light. There are two particular points to note from figure 3.2.27:

1 Within the spectrum for a particular order, the light with the longest wavelength is diffracted through the greatest angle.

2 The zero order spectrum consists of undeviated light, and is therefore the same colour as the light before passing through the grating, since it contains the same combination of wavelengths.

We shall look at how spectra like this are produced in section 6.5.

Lithium lamp—five wavelengths are present, leading to five lines being seen in the maxima for the first and second orders.

Tungsten lamp—a continuous range of wavelengths is present, leading to a continuous range of wavelengths in the maximum for each order.

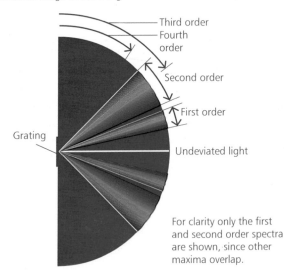

For clarity only the first and second order spectra are shown, since other maxima overlap.

Figure 3.2.27 The effect of a diffraction grating on light from a lithium lamp and a tungsten lamp. The grating has 500 slits per millimetre.

SUMMARY

- **Huygens' construction** views a wavefront as a set of disturbances producing a new wavefront, and can be used to explain the behaviour of waves in motion.

- **Reflection** is the change in direction of a wave when it meets a barrier. The angle of incidence equals the angle of reflection, where the angles are measured between the incident ray and the normal ray and between the reflected ray and the normal ray respectively.

- **Refraction** is the change in direction of a wave travelling from one medium to another, caused by a change in the speed of propagation of the wave in the different media. **Snell's law** says that $(\sin i/\sin r)$ is constant, where i is the angle of incidence and r the angle of refraction. The constant is the **refractive index** n for the medium, which is also equal to the ratio of speeds of the wave in the two media:

$$_1 n_2 = \frac{\sin \theta_1}{\sin \theta_2} = \frac{c_1}{c_2}$$

- Snell's law shows that, for an observer looking down at an object in a medium below a boundary for which the refractive index is n,

$$n = \frac{\text{real depth}}{\text{apparent depth}}$$

- For a wave leaving a medium in which it travels more slowly than in the medium it is entering, when the angle of incidence of the wave is greater than an angle called the **critical angle** θ_c, **total internal reflection** takes place. When total internal reflection occurs, $\sin \theta_c = 1/n$.

- **Diffraction** describes the behaviour of a wave travelling through a gap or round an object. Diffraction occurs when the gap or object is about the same size as the wavelength of the wave.

- Two sets of circular waves can overlap to form an **interference pattern** of areas of waves with large amplitude (waves superpositioned in phase) and areas of zero amplitude (waves superpositioned antiphase).

- For light passing through two narrow slits, the resulting interference pattern is a pattern of light and dark bands called **fringes**. The wavelength of the light λ, the fringe separation w, the slit separation s and the distance from the slits to the screen D are related by the equation $\lambda = ws/D$.

- A **diffraction grating** provides interference patterns from a number of slits. The interference pattern for monochromatic light consists of a few bright principal maxima at positions described by $\sin \theta_n = n\lambda/d$, where n is the order of the maximum (1, 2, 3, etc.) and d the slit separation. For light containing a range of wavelengths, orders of spectra are seen.

Figure 3.2.28 X-ray diffraction provides an important way of exploring the structure of molecules, and has provided large amounts of information about the nature and structure of biological molecules such as DNA.

3

EXAMPLES

1   *A microscope is focused on a scratch at the bottom of a beaker. Turpentine is poured into the beaker to a depth of 4.0 cm, when it is found necessary to raise the microscope lens by a vertical distance of 12.8 mm to bring the scratch back into focus. Calculate the refractive index of the turpentine.*

For this calculation we can use the relationship:

$$_1n_2 = \frac{\text{real depth}}{\text{apparent depth}}$$

The scratch lies 4.0 cm below the surface of the turpentine – this is its *real depth*. Since the lens must be raised 1.28 cm to keep the scratch in focus, its *apparent depth* must be 4.0 cm – 1.28 cm = 2.72 cm.
Thus:

$$_{air}n_{turpentine} = \frac{4.00 \text{ cm}}{2.72 \text{ cm}}$$
$$= 1.47$$

The refractive index of the turpentine is 1.47.

2   *Light with a wavelength of 590 nm is incident normally on a diffraction grating. The angle of the second order maxima is 32°. Calculate the spacing of the lines on the grating. Are there third and fourth order maxima?*

For the grating we know that:
$$n\lambda = d \sin \theta_n$$
In this case $n = 2$, and so:
$$2 \times 5.9 \times 10^{-7} \text{ m} = d \times \sin 32°$$
that is,

$$d = \frac{2 \times 5.9 \times 10^{-7} \text{ m}}{\sin 32°}$$
$$= 2.23 \times 10^{-6} \text{ m}$$

The lines on the grating are 2.23×10^{-6} m apart, which corresponds to approximately 4500 lines per centimetre.
For $n = 3$ we have:
$$\sin \theta_3 = \frac{3 \times 5.9 \times 10^{-7} \text{ m}}{2.23 \times 10^{-6} \text{ m}}$$
$$= 0.794$$
This corresponds to $\theta_3 = 52.5°$ for the third order maxima.
For $n = 4$:
$$\sin \theta_4 = \frac{4 \times 5.9 \times 10^{-7} \text{ m}}{2.23 \times 10^{-6} \text{ m}}$$
$$= 1.058$$
Since $\sin \theta$ is always less than 1, there are no fourth order maxima.

3   *A ray of light enters a pond at an angle of 30° to the horizontal. What is its direction as it travels through the water? The refractive index of water is 1.33.*

A ray travelling at an angle of 30° to the horizontal will make an angle of $(90 - 30)° = 60°$ to the normal ray.

So: $\dfrac{\sin i}{\sin r} = \dfrac{\sin 60°}{\sin r} = 1.33$

$$\sin r = \frac{\sin 60°}{1.33} = \frac{0.866}{1.33} = 0.651$$

This means that angle $r = 41°$.
So the ray travels at an angle of 41° to the normal (or $(90 - 41)° = 49°$ to the horizontal).

QUESTIONS

(Take n_{air} as 1 and n_{water} as 1.33 where necessary.)

1   A ray of light strikes a sheet of plate glass 5 mm thick with a refractive index of 1.5 at an angle of 60° to the glass. Calculate the displacement of the transmitted ray from the path that the incident ray would have followed had the glass not been present.

2   What is the apparent depth of a swimming pool which is filled with water to a depth of 2 m?

3   On a hot day, the distant surface of a road shimmers in such a way that it appears to be covered in water. Explain this.

4   The speed of sound in water is 1500 m s⁻¹, while in air it is 340 m s⁻¹. A person standing on the side of a swimming pool shouts to a swimmer 1 m below the surface of the water 5 m from the side of the pool. Will the swimmer be able to hear the shout? Justify your answer.

5   Why is interference not seen when the beams of a car's headlights overlap?

6   A straight road runs parallel to the line joining two radio transmitting aerials A and B which are 400 m apart, and which both radiate signals at a frequency of 50 MHz. The road is 4 km from the aerials at its nearest point X. A car travelling at a steady speed along the road receives a signal whose intensity varies with a frequency of 0.5 Hz as it passes point X.
   a   Explain why the signal intensity varies like this.
   b   Calculate the speed of the car.

7   Two loudspeakers are connected to a signal generator in order to observe the interference of sound waves. When the signal generator is switched on, a minimum of sound intensity is heard midway between the speakers.
   a   Why is a minimum heard instead of a maximum?
   b   How far apart should the speakers be placed if the signal generator is set to 650 Hz? Justify your answer.
       (Speed of sound in air = 340 m s⁻¹.)

8 Sensitive galvanometers (current measuring devices) use a light beam reflected from a mirror to indicate the angle of rotation of a coil (see figure 3.2.29). Show that if the mirror rotates through an angle θ, the angle between the incident and reflected rays changes by 2θ. How does this increase the sensitivity of the instrument?

Shaft carrying mirror and coil
(coil not shown)

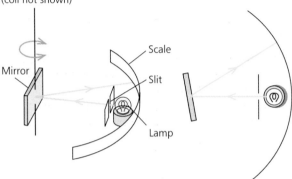

Mirror

Scale

Slit

Lamp

General arrangement   **Plan view**

Figure 3.2.29

9 Light of wavelength 633 nm from a helium neon laser passes through a single slit 0.2 mm wide. What is the width of the central maximum of the diffraction pattern formed on a screen 1.5 m from the slit?

10 A friend inside a house shouts to you from an open window, producing sound waves with a wavelength of 15 cm. If the window has a width of 50 cm, what is the angular width of the central maximum of the beam of sound in a horizontal plane?

11 In a two-slit experiment using light of wavelength 5.89×10^{-7} m, the distance between the two slits and the screen on which the fringes are observed is 1.2 m. If the spacing between the slits is 0.55 mm, calculate the distance between the fringes seen on the screen.

12 A parallel beam of light consisting of light of wavelength 450 nm and light of wavelength 650 nm falls normally on a diffraction grating with 6000 lines per centimetre. Calculate the angular separation between the second order maximum of each wavelength.

13 A filter which transmits light between 650 nm and 600 nm is placed between a source of white light and the slit of a spectrometer 1.7×10^{-6} m wide. Calculate the angular width of the first order spectrum seen.

Developing Key Skills

If you have not already done so, read the focus on page 232.

Robert Merton, a sociologist who studied the way in which scientists work, proposed a set of *norms* which describe the professional values that scientists bring to their work. The values are often referred to as Merton's *four norms of science*. They can be represented by the letters **CUDOS**, which stand for:

- **C**ommunalism – science is concerned with public knowledge. This norm implies that secrecy has no place in the conduct of science.

- **U**niversalism – science is a collective activity. This norm implies that the conduct of science depends on scientists being able to express themselves freely, to communicate with each other freely, and to travel freely, without discrimination.

- **D**isinterestedness – science is emotionally neutral. This norm implies that the conduct of science depends upon the scientist being detached from the object of study.

- **O**rganised **S**cepticism – science involves rational procedures and reserved judgement. This norm implies that a scientist's work is judged against a set of rational criteria before being accepted into the body of scientific knowledge.

Write a short essay answering the following questions:

1 Consider the four people (Watson, Crick, Wilkins and Franklin) in the DNA story. To what extent do you think that they acted in accordance with Merton's four norms?

2 To what extent do you think that the values reflected in CUDOS are essential for the work of scientists?

Reference: Fullick, P. and Ratcliffe, M. (eds) (1996) *Teaching Ethical Aspects of Science*. Southampton: Bassett Press.

[Key Skills opportunities: C]

3.3 Light and sound

In sections 3.1–2 we have seen that oscillations and waves are closely linked and have looked at both stationary and progressive waves and the properties they possess. We shall now concentrate on the two wave motions that are most directly relevant to the lives of those of us who are blessed with the senses of sight and hearing – **light** and **sound**.

Light

A brief history of light

Early ideas

The debate about the nature of light raged from the very earliest times. The Ancient Greek philosopher Democritus believed that objects were visible because the atoms of which they were made 'swarmed' into the air and entered the observer's eyes – in other words, a particle theory of light. Other philosophers of the time disagreed. Empedocles argued that objects became visible when touched by light rays emitted from the eyes, while Plato held that the eyes emitted light rays which intercepted the light rays emitted by objects. This debate, polarised into almost opposing views about the nature of light and vision, continued right up to the twentieth century.

The first wave model

The first person to propose a wave model for light was Leonardo da Vinci, in the late fifteenth century, comparing the reflection of light to the echoing of sounds. This theory was given support by the work of the Italian physicist Francesco Maria Grimaldi, whose paper published in 1665 after his death described his experiments with the diffraction of light, and set out his ideas about light as a wave motion. In the same year, Robert Hooke compared light to waves in water, and Isaac Newton discovered that a prism may be used to split white light into the colours of the rainbow.

Waves or particles?

The end of the seventeenth century saw a fierce debate about the nature of light. Newton argued that light was a stream of particles, and showed how the properties of reflection and refraction could be explained using a particle model. He also argued that if light behaved as a wave it should form 'fuzzy' shadows around objects rather than the sharp-edged shadows seen on a sunny day. (Newton was probably unaware of the earlier work of Grimaldi, and certainly did not realise that the wavelength of light is too small to exhibit such behaviour with any but the smallest everyday objects.) In opposition to this view, the Dutch physicist Christiaan Huygens described in detail the wave theory of light in his *Traité de la Lumière* (Treatise on Light), including the principle of secondary wavelets used in section 3.2.

By around 1700 there was good evidence to suggest that light had properties which could best be explained in terms of a wave motion. This view was supported by eminent scientists of the day like Hooke and Boyle, who used it to explain the colours caused by oil floating on the surface of water in terms

Figure 3.3.1 Chandrasekhara Venkata Raman was born in 1888 and attended the University of Madras where he was an outstanding student. After obtaining his degree, a career in physics did not appear to offer the best opportunities, so Chandrasekhara worked for the Indian Civil Service for 10 years, continuing his physics work in his spare time until eventually he obtained the Chair of Physics at the University of Calcutta. He was knighted in 1929, and was awarded the Nobel Prize in 1930 for his work on the molecular scattering of light. He died in 1970.

of the interference of two waves. Newton rejected these ideas, however, and for the next century or so the particle theory of light was generally accepted by scientists.

Convincing evidence for wave motion

In 1802, Thomas Young published *On the Theory of Light and Colours*, in which he set out his ideas about light, giving his account of two-slit interference (see section 3.2). The evidence from Young's observations – many of which Grimaldi had recorded nearly 200 years previously – made it difficult, if not impossible, to continue to think of light as having a particle nature. This idea was extraordinarily difficult to overthrow however, possibly because Newton himself had argued for it so forcefully. The middle of the century brought proof to convince everyone. In 1853 the French physicist Léon Foucault showed that light travelled more slowly in water than in air. This indicated the death of the particle theory of light, since it required that light must travel more quickly in water than in air to explain refraction (see figure 3.3.2).

Wave–particle duality

But Newton was not entirely wrong. In 1905, Albert Einstein showed that the photoelectric effect (see section 6.4) could be understood if light were thought of as a stream of particles rather than as a wave. Nearly 20 years later, Louis de Broglie produced his theory of **wave–particle duality**, in which he showed that anything which had particle properties could also be shown to have wave properties – even objects like tennis balls and people! De Broglie's theory received confirmation in 1927 when two physicists working independently (Clinton Davisson in the USA and George Paget Thomson in England) showed that electrons could be diffracted by crystals. The modern science of **quantum mechanics** regards light as both a stream of particles and as a wave. Sometimes the wave-like properties are more important than the particle-like properties, and sometimes it is the other way around. The particles of light are called **photons**, and we shall return to them and the intriguing world of quantum mechanics in section 6.

Light as a wave

For the rest of this section, we shall treat light as a wave motion, since it is its wave-like properties that are of interest to us. Remember as we do so, however, that it does behave differently under different circumstances, and we shall investigate these later on.

In the 1860s, the Scottish mathematician and physicist James Clerk Maxwell produced a theory to explain light in terms of electric and magnetic fields, using work on magnetism and electricity previously begun by Michael Faraday. Maxwell reasoned that as a moving magnet could induce a current to flow in a wire and that as a current flowing in a wire was also the cause of a magnetic field, it ought to be possible to produce some sort of combination of an electric field and a magnetic field which was 'self sustaining'. Using some fairly complex mathematics, Maxwell showed that light can be pictured as a combination of a transverse 'electric wave' and a transverse 'magnetic wave' moving through space, as illustrated in figure 3.3.3.

Maxwell modelled the way that the electric field and the magnetic field varied with one another according to equations describing electric and magnetic fields, and was able to show that light waves:

1 travelled through a vacuum with a velocity of 3×10^8 m s^{-1}, agreeing with measurements of the speed of light made by Fizeau in 1849

2 were part of a larger family of waves with a large range of wavelengths.

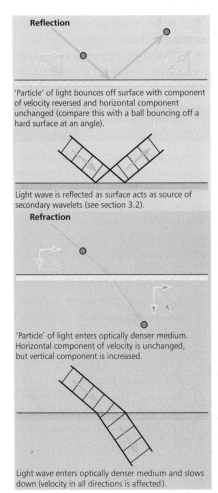

Reflection

'Particle' of light bounces off surface with component of velocity reversed and horizontal component unchanged (compare this with a ball bouncing off a hard surface at an angle).

Light wave is reflected as surface acts as source of secondary wavelets (see section 3.2).

Refraction

'Particle' of light enters optically denser medium. Horizontal component of velocity is unchanged, but vertical component is increased.

Light wave enters optically denser medium and slows down (velocity in all directions is affected).

Figure 3.3.2 Reflection and refraction explained using Newton's and Huygens' ideas. There is no easy way of testing the two theories to compare them in the case of reflection. Refraction, however, can be used to test them, provided that the speed of light can be measured in an optically dense medium such as glass or water.

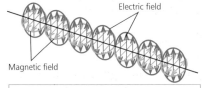

Electric field

Magnetic field

The electromagnetic wave is caused by an oscillating electric charge which sets up an oscillating electric field. This oscillating charge is often an electron. Light waves are the result of electrons moving within atoms, while radio waves are the result of electrons moving in wires (transmitting aerials).
The oscillating electric field causes an oscillating magnetic field.
The electric field oscillates in one plane (vertical in this example) while the magnetic field oscillates at right angles to it. (This relationship is explained further in section 5.5.)
The electric field and the magnetic field are in phase. The plane of polarisation of the wave is the plane in which the electric field oscillates.

Figure 3.3.3 James Clerk Maxwell's model of an electromagnetic wave.

The large family of waves predicted by Maxwell forms the **electromagnetic spectrum**. All the waves in this family travel through a vacuum at the same speed, although there is a vast range of wavelengths from radio waves with wavelengths of several kilometres to gamma rays with wavelengths of as little as 10^{-16} m.

Maxwell's work on electromagnetic waves

Maxwell used earlier work by two distinguished physicists in his model of light waves – Michael Faraday and André-Marie Ampère. Faraday and Ampère had set out laws relating the movement of electric charge (in the form of electric currents) to changes in magnetic fields. When applied to oscillating electric and magnetic fields, these laws showed that:

(1) an oscillating electric field and an oscillating magnetic field travelling through space can be self sustaining (that is, the oscillating electric field produces an oscillating magnetic field and vice versa)

(2) the two oscillating fields can be self sustaining only if they are at right angles to each other and to the direction of propagation, and are in phase

(3) the waves must travel through a vacuum with a speed fixed by two physical constants: ε_0, the **permittivity of a vacuum**, and μ_0, the **permeability of a vacuum**.

$$c^2 = \frac{1}{\mu_0 \varepsilon_0}$$

With such a model, the explanation of the behaviour of electromagnetic waves such as light and radio waves becomes a task of explaining how the oscillating fields interact with matter, as shown in figure 3.3.4.

Reflection: incident wave's oscillating fields set up oscillations of electrons in reflecting surface. This leads to the absorption of the energy of the incident wave by the surface, which re-radiates it.

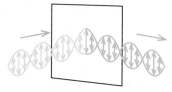

Refraction: as the wave enters the new medium its speed changes. This causes the change in direction shown here. For the speed change to cause the direction change observed in experiments (that is for the wave to obey Snell's law), the wave must *slow down* on entering an optically denser medium. For such a medium (e.g. water) it is known that values of ε and μ are larger than for a vacuum. Maxwell's relationship between these two quantities and the velocity of the wave shows that this leads to the required decrease in speed.

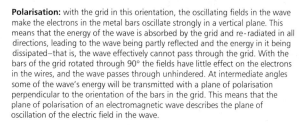

Polarisation: with the grid in this orientation, the oscillating fields in the wave make the electrons in the metal bars oscillate strongly in a vertical plane. This means that the energy of the wave is absorbed by the grid and re-radiated in all directions, leading to the wave being partly reflected and the energy in it being dissipated—that is, the wave effectively cannot pass through the grid. With the bars of the grid rotated through 90° the fields have little effect on the electrons in the wires, and the wave passes through unhindered. At intermediate angles some of the wave's energy will be transmitted with a plane of polarisation perpendicular to the orientation of the bars in the grid. This means that the plane of polarisation of an electromagnetic wave describes the plane of oscillation of the electric field in the wave.

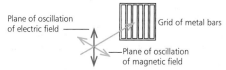

Plane of oscillation of electric field

Grid of metal bars

Plane of oscillation of magnetic field

Figure 3.3.4 Maxwell's explanations of reflection, refraction and polarisation in electromagnetic waves

The electromagnetic spectrum

Light is a small part of the electromagnetic spectrum, consisting only of the wavelengths to which our eyes are sensitive. This is deceptively simple however, for just as within the visible spectrum colours merge into each other so that it is difficult to tell where yellow finishes and orange begins, so the visible spectrum merges at one end into the infra-red and at the other into the ultraviolet, with no definite cut-off point. This is also the case in the rest of the electromagnetic spectrum, where the properties of the waves change gradually as their wavelengths and frequencies change. Figure 3.3.5 shows the electromagnetic spectrum.

Laser light

The word **laser** is an acronym, which stands for **l**ight **a**mplification by **s**timulated **e**mission of **r**adiation. The way in which a laser works is described in section 6.5. Laser light has a number of important properties.

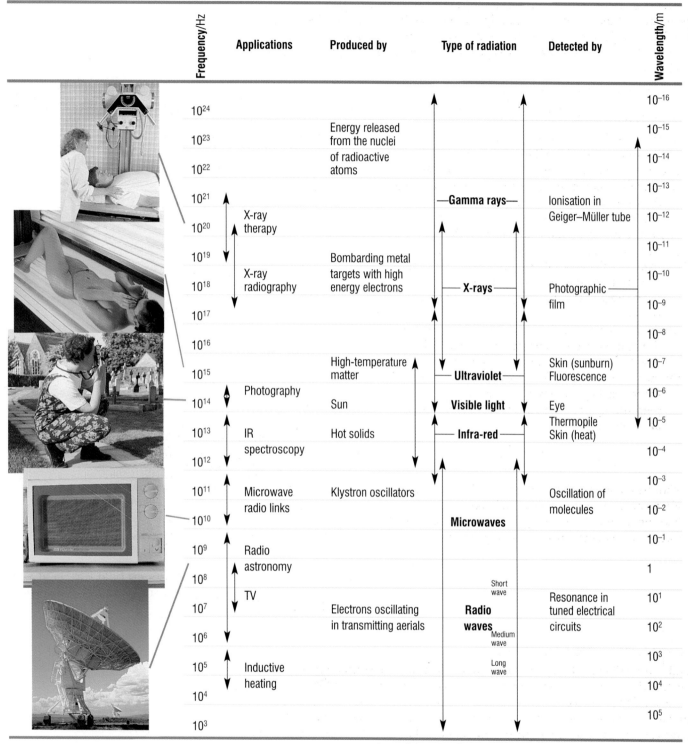

Frequency/Hz	Applications	Produced by	Type of radiation	Detected by	Wavelength/m
10^{24}					10^{-16}
10^{23}		Energy released from the nuclei of radioactive atoms			10^{-15}
10^{22}					10^{-14}
10^{21}			—Gamma rays—	Ionisation in Geiger–Müller tube	10^{-13}
10^{20}	X-ray therapy				10^{-12}
10^{19}		Bombarding metal targets with high energy electrons			10^{-11}
10^{18}	X-ray radiography		—X-rays—	Photographic film	10^{-10}
10^{17}					10^{-9}
10^{16}					10^{-8}
10^{15}		High-temperature matter	—Ultraviolet—	Skin (sunburn) Fluorescence	10^{-7}
10^{14}	Photography	Sun	**Visible light**	Eye	10^{-6}
10^{13}	IR spectroscopy	Hot solids	—Infra-red—	Thermopile Skin (heat)	10^{-5}
10^{12}					10^{-4}
10^{11}	Microwave radio links	Klystron oscillators		Oscillation of molecules	10^{-3}
10^{10}			**Microwaves**		10^{-2}
10^{9}	Radio astronomy				10^{-1}
10^{8}					1
10^{7}	TV	Electrons oscillating in transmitting aerials	**Radio waves** Short wave	Resonance in tuned electrical circuits	10^{1}
10^{6}			Medium wave		10^{2}
10^{5}	Inductive heating		Long wave		10^{3}
10^{4}					10^{4}
10^{3}					10^{5}

Figure 3.3.5 The electromagnetic spectrum

1 A laser can produce a narrow beam of light which is powerful, concentrating a large amount of energy over a small area. The sides of this beam are very nearly parallel, so that the beam can travel quite a long way before the size of the spot it produces becomes much larger than when the beam first left the laser. (In 1969 a beam of laser light a few millimetres across was shone at the Moon. After travelling the 400 000 km to the Moon, the beam was still only 3 km in diameter!)

2 Laser light is monochromatic – it contains light of one wavelength only.

3 The beam of light is perfectly **coherent** – the phase at different times and different positions in the beam are related in a predictable way.

These properties make lasers very useful in a wide variety of applications, from medicine through engineering to telecommunications.

Measuring the velocity of light waves

For many years it was thought that the velocity of light was infinitely large, as attempts to measure it seemed to indicate that the time for light to travel any distance was zero. The first person to realise the nature of the problem confronting anyone setting out to measure the velocity of light was Galileo. Galileo attempted to measure the velocity of light by placing an assistant a known distance away at night and then covering and uncovering a lantern, as figure 3.3.6 shows.

This experiment was planned to provide Galileo with a known time for the light to travel from him to his assistant and back again. Knowing the distance between them, the calculation of the velocity of light should then have been easy. The results were puzzling, however. Galileo found that no matter what the distance between him and his assistant, the time taken for the light to travel from his lantern and back to him was always the same. This appeared to indicate that light must travel infinitely fast. Galileo thought more deeply, however, and proposed that the velocity of light was very large but finite, and the time delay in his experiment was simply the reaction time of his assistant, which was constant no matter what the distance between them.

The history of the measurement of the velocity of light is outlined in figure 3.3.7.

Figure 3.3.6 Galileo uncovered his lantern briefly to send a flash of light to his assistant. When the assistant saw the flash he uncovered his lantern to send a flash of light back to Galileo.

The difficulty in measuring the velocity of light

Because light travels so rapidly, to measure its velocity with any accuracy requires using either large distances or accurate methods of measuring time intervals. Even if a distance of 30 km (3×10^4 m) is used, the time interval to be measured is extremely small:

$$\text{Velocity} = \frac{\text{distance}}{\text{time}} \quad \text{so} \quad \text{time} = \frac{\text{distance}}{\text{velocity}} = \frac{3 \times 10^4 \text{ m}}{3 \times 10^8 \text{ m s}^{-1}} = 10^{-4} \text{ s}$$

The measurement of 0.0001 s is not difficult using modern laboratory equipment, but presented considerable challenges to earlier physicists.

The velocity of light and definitions

The velocity of light is now *defined* as $2.997\ 924\ 58 \times 10^8$ m s^{-1}, and this is used to define the metre as:

The distance light travels in a vacuum in 1/299 792 458 second

The effect of this definition is to make any experiment to measure the velocity of light an experiment to measure distance.

Sound

The nature of sound

The nature of sound has caused far less debate than the nature of light among scientists and philosophers of the past, probably because the connection between vibrating objects and sound is reasonably obvious to a fairly observant individual. Leonardo da Vinci is probably the person to whom the idea of sound as a wave motion can first be attributed, but experiments on the nature of sound waves and to show that a medium was needed for their propagation were not carried out until the time of Newton.

Work on the oscillations and resonance of solid objects was carried out towards the end of the eighteenth century by the German physicist Ernst

1675. In Denmark **Ole Römer** used the eclipses of the moons of Jupiter, which occur at intervals which vary unexpectedly due to the orbiting of the Earth and Jupiter round the Sun. By estimating the diameter of the orbit of the Earth, Römer arrived at a value for the velocity of light of around 300 000 km s^{-1}. His work was ignored by other scientists.

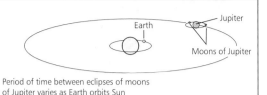

Period of time between eclipses of moons of Jupiter varies as Earth orbits Sun

1728. The English astronomer **James Bradley** explained the slight change in position of stars as the Earth orbits the Sun in terms of the resultant velocity of the Earth travelling round the Sun and the velocity of light. His results confirmed Römer's results.

1848. The Frenchman **Hippolyte Fizeau** measured the velocity of light using a toothed wheel – the first example of a **terrestrial** method.

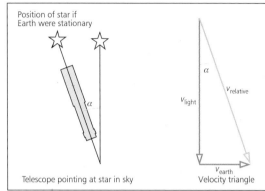

Position of star if Earth were stationary

Telescope pointing at star in sky

Velocity triangle

An arrangement of mirrors and lensés made a light ray travel in one direction through the toothed wheel and back again along the original path. As the speed of rotation of the wheel was increased, the light passed through a gap between two teeth and returned to the wheel when the tooth next to the gap had replaced it. Careful measurement of the speed of rotation of the wheel and the distance travelled by the light ray enabled the speed of light to be calculated.

1853. Léon **Foucault's** method used a rotating plane mirror. An adaptation of the experiment demonstrated that the velocity of light in water is less than that in air, showing that Newton's particle theory of light was wrong.

1926. Albert Michelson measured the velocity of light with error calculated at less than 0.000 01%.

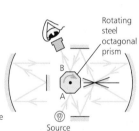

Light from a source bounced off a prism and was then reflected along a long path back to the other side of the prism, where an image was observed using lenses in an eyepiece. As the octagonal prism rotated, the image disappeared (light reflected at A arrived at B when the prism had rotated, and was not reflected into the eyepiece). If the prism was rotated faster, an image again became visible as light reflected at A arrived at B after the prism had rotated through one-eighth of a revolution. Measurement of the distance travelled by the ray together with the rate of rotation of the prism provided the data for the calculation of the velocity of light.

to M

Plane mirror

Ray from source S hit a plane mirror and travelled to another mirror M which reflected it back to the plane mirror. When the ray arrived back the plane mirror had rotated, thus reflecting the ray back along a different path. Measurement of the deflection of the ray together with the speed of rotation of the mirror enabled the speed of light to be calculated.

Chladni, who obtained 'pictures' like that in figure 3.3.8 of the oscillations of glass plates by scattering sand on them and then making them oscillate using a violin bow.

Other physicists have conducted experiments into the properties of sound waves. At the end of the nineteenth century the Irish physicist John Tyndall demonstrated that sound can be refracted by a gas-filled balloon, in much the same way that light is refracted by a lens. However, there is no one individual to whom the construction of the idea of a sound wave as a longitudinal progressive mechanical wave can be attributed, in contrast to James Clerk Maxwell's work on the nature of light.

Figure 3.3.7 The important names and dates in the history of the measurement of the velocity of light. Michelson obtained a final value of 2.997 74 x 10^8 m s^{-1} for the velocity of light shortly before his death in 1931.

Measuring the velocity of sound waves

A wide variety of methods is available for measuring the velocity of sound, including some which are suitable for measuring the velocity in gases other than air and others suitable for use with solids and liquids too. Two methods are illustrated in figure 3.3.9.

Person claps blocks together with a regular gap between the claps so that each clap coincides with the echo of the last clap returning from the wall. Assistant times the elapsed time for (say) 50 claps.

Calculation: Time for 50 claps = 29 s
Distance from person to wall = 100 m
So time between successive claps = 29/49 s (there are 49 gaps between 50 claps)
And in this time sound travels 2 x 100 m (i.e. to wall and back) = 200 m
So velocity of sound = distance/time = 200 m/(29/49) s = 340 m s^{-1} to 2 SF.

Microphone 1 is kept stationary. Microphone 2 is placed next to it and the trace on the oscilloscope is adjusted so that it looks like that in diagram (a). Microphone 2 is now moved away from the loudspeaker. As it does so the phase relationship between the signals produced by the microphone changes as there is a phase difference between the different points of the sound wave. This is shown in diagram (b), where the two microphones are half a wavelength apart. Moving the microphones in this way enables the wavelength of the sound wave to be found. The frequency of the signal produced by the signal generator is known, and this is the same as the frequency of the sound wave.

Calculation: Microphone 2 moved a distance of 3.2 m, in which the signals from the microphones were in phase at 9 points (including the starting position where the microphones were next to each other)
Thus 3.2 m corresponds to 8 wavelengths, i.e. 3.2 m = 8λ, so λ = 0.4 m
Frequency of wave = 850 Hz
So velocity = $f\lambda$ = 850 s^{-1} x 0.4 m = 340 m s^{-1} to 3 SF.

Diagram (a) Microphones coincide – in phase.

Diagram (b) Microphone 2 moving away – signals antiphase. Note that the signal from microphone 2 decreases as it is moved away from microphone 1 as the intensity of sound decreases with distance from the loudspeaker (see section 3.1 page 212 on the inverse square law).

Diagram (c) Microphone 2 further away still – signals in phase again.

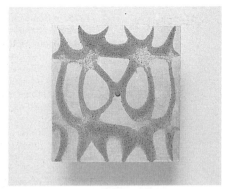

Figure 3.3.8 The patterns obtained by making forced oscillations in a sheet of glass or metal are called **Chladni figures**, after their discoverer. Sand on the sheets collects at the nodes, having been violently displaced from the antinodes by the oscillations.

The difficulty in measuring the velocity of sound

Many methods for measuring the velocity of sound make use of an observer, whose job it is to signal when a sound has been heard. The objection to this is that there is an unknown time between the sound wave reaching the observer's ear and the observer registering the sound – effectively the observer's reaction time. This unknown time introduces a personal element into any calculations from a method involving the use of an observer, and for accurate work some attempt should be made to take this into account.

Figure 3.3.9 Two methods for measuring the velocity of sound in air. (Stationary waves and the production of an interference pattern between two sound sources can also be used – see page 225.)

SUMMARY

- Early ideas about the nature of light included a particle theory and theories about 'rays' emitted by objects or by eyes. In the late seventeenth century there were opposing views about whether light was a wave (supported by Christiaan Huygens) or a stream of particles (Newton). Further experiments by Thomas Young and Leon Foucault in the nineteenth century gave convincing evidence that light is a wave.

- In the early twentieth century **wave–particle duality** was proposed by Louis de Broglie, and today light is regarded as behaving as either a stream of particles or a wave, depending on the phenomenon being described.

- James Clerk Maxwell pictured light as an **electromagnetic wave**, a combination of a transverse electric wave and a transverse magnetic wave at right angles to each other, and predicted other similar waves with a range of wavelengths making the **electromagnetic spectrum**.

- Early attempts to measure the velocity of light were unsuccessful due to its high velocity (around 3×10^8 m s^{-1}) and the reaction times of people involved. The velocity of light is now *defined* as $2.997\ 924\ 58 \times 10^8$ m s^{-1}.

- Experiments to measure the speed of sound include methods involving clapping regularly in time with the echo of the last clap a known distance from a wall, and using microphones to detect the phase difference and hence the wavelength of sound from a signal generator.

QUESTIONS

1 An atom emits light of wavelength 450 nm for a period of 10^{-10} s. How many cycles does the wave train contain?

2 A toothed wheel used in Fizeau's method for measuring the speed of light has 150 teeth, with 150 spaces between them. The teeth and spaces are of equal width. Light travels through a gap between two teeth on the wheel and is reflected back along its path by a mirror 8 km away. At what speed must the wheel rotate for the light to arrive back at the wheel to strike the tooth next to the gap through which it travelled?

3 a When a beam of unpolarised light is incident on a pair of 'crossed' polarising filters, the intensity of transmitted light is zero. Explain this.

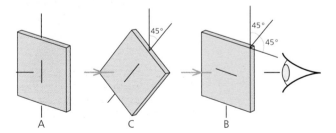

Figure 3.3.10

b When a third polarising filter C is placed at an angle between a pair of crossed polaroids (see figure 3.3.10), some light is observed to pass through filter B. Suggest why this is, and show that the maximum intensity of the light transmitted by filter C is 50% of the intensity of the light incident on it.

4 A student standing at one end of a closed corridor 86 m long blows a short blast on a whistle and notes a series of echoes. If the time from the blast to the fifth echo is 2.5 s, calculate the speed of sound.

5 A vibrating tuning fork appears at rest when illuminated by a light flashing at regular intervals. When a disc with 40 equally spaced radial lines is viewed in the same light, the disc appears to be stationary when rotating at 120 revolutions per minute. What can you deduce about the frequency of vibration of the tuning fork?

6 An observer notes that if she claps her hands sharply in front of a flight of stone steps, she hears a ringing sound.
   a Explain how the ringing sound arises.
   b Calculate the frequency of the ringing sound if each step is 20 cm deep and the speed of sound is 340 m s^{-1}.

Sections 3.1–3 have dealt with the relationship between waves and oscillations and the properties of wave motion. We shall now be concerned with how waves can be used in practical situations. We shall begin by looking at some of the typical components of systems that make use of waves, and then look at some practical applications which involve the use of waves and wave properties.

Handling waves

Mirrors

At least one plane mirror is probably found in most homes, and mirrors are also used in an enormous number of optical instruments. Mirrors are simple in their design. Household mirrors usually consist of a sheet of glass behind which is a thin layer of aluminium, backed by a protective layer of some sort. Yet the physics of mirrors can be quite involved – especially if we also consider mirrors other than plane mirrors.

The image in a plane mirror

The image we see in a plane mirror when we stand in front of it is something of a 'trick', since there is actually nothing there behind the mirror! If you stand 1 m away from a mirror you see a reflection of yourself standing 2 m away from you, as if another 'you' were standing 1 m behind the mirror. The position of the image formed by a plane mirror is easy to show using a **ray diagram** like figure 3.4.1. Such an image is **erect**, it is neither **magnified** nor **diminished**, and it is **virtual** – formed at a point from which light rays *appear* to diverge. A virtual image cannot be cast onto a screen.

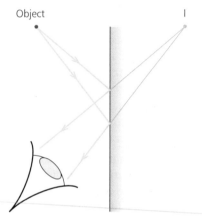

Light rays from the **object** strike the mirror and enter the eye which sends electrical signals to the brain. To the brain, the light rays *appear* to come from point I, the place where the rays cross. This is where we see the **image** of the object.

Figure 3.4.1 The image of an object seen in a plane mirror.

Mirrors and lateral inversion

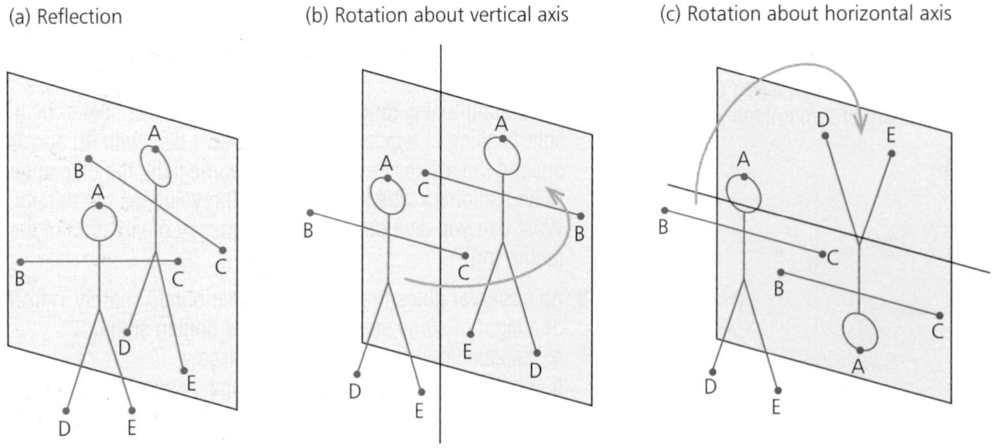

(a) Reflection

(b) Rotation about vertical axis

(c) Rotation about horizontal axis

Figure 3.4.2 Seeing yourself in a mirror gives a different result from actually going round behind the mirror yourself. This is why a photograph of yourself can look quite unfamiliar.

The image in a plane mirror is said to be **laterally inverted**, that is, back to front. This is one reason why you don't quite recognise yourself in a photograph, since you are used to seeing your image in a mirror. People often wonder why, if a mirror inverts something left to right, it doesn't invert it top to bottom as well.

The answer lies in what a mirror does. Figure 3.4.2(a) shows how a mirror takes five points on a person and maps them onto their image, a mathematical transformation called a **reflection**. The diagram shows clearly that any point on the object has a corresponding point on the image directly behind the mirror and the same distance behind the mirror as the object was in front of it.

In thinking about going behind the mirror to compare ourself with our image, we use a different mathematical transformation – a **rotation**. The transformation shown in diagram (b) is a rotation about a vertical axis, and that in diagram (c) is a rotation about a horizontal axis. The important point is that in *neither* case can the object be superimposed on its image.

Curved reflectors

Curved reflectors are found in many objects which use light, such as torches and lamps. Satellite television receivers reflect radio waves in the same way. **Spherical reflectors** have a shape which can be imagined as being cut from a hollow sphere. Their cross-section appears in diagrams as an arc of a circle. Concave spherical reflectors focus waves at a point called their **principal focus**, though if the beam is wide the waves are actually focused at a range of points on a curve called a **caustic**.

Parabolic reflectors can focus waves to a single point. These reflectors have a three-dimensional shape formed from the rotation of a two-dimensional parabola about its axis. All waves travelling parallel to the axis are focused at the principal focus. Figure 3.4.3 explains a little more about curved reflectors.

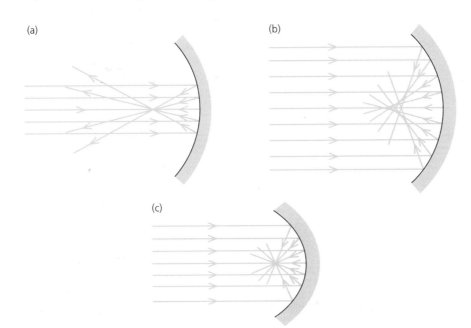

(a)

(b)

(c)

Figure 3.4.3 The effect of using a concave spherical reflector ((a) and (b)) and a concave parabolic reflector (c) to focus waves. The photograph shows a caustic curve produced by light reflected off the inside of a cup onto the surface of the liquid in it.

Using ray diagrams

A ray diagram can be used to show how a mirror (or a lens, as we shall see later) forms an image of an object. For example, the ray diagram in figure 3.4.4 shows how a concave mirror forms an image of a distant object.

Rays representing wavefronts are reversible (it does not matter in which direction the arrow heads point). A source of waves like a lamp placed at the focus of one of these reflectors produces a parallel beam of waves after reflection. A parabolic reflector produces a better parallel beam of rays than a spherical reflector.

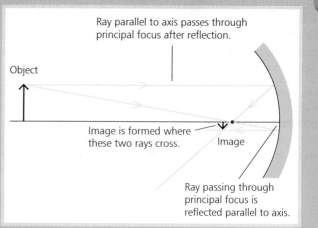

Ray parallel to axis passes through principal focus after reflection.

Object

Image is formed where these two rays cross.

Image

Ray passing through principal focus is reflected parallel to axis.

Figure 3.4.4

Prisms

Dispersion

Glass prisms are probably best known for their ability to split light into the colours of the spectrum. This phenomenon is called **dispersion**, and was first described by Newton in 1665. In a vacuum all electromagnetic waves travel at the same velocity. Dispersion happens because the velocity of electromagnetic waves in some media such as water and certain glasses varies with wavelength. In the case of light in crown glass (a special glass used in the lenses of optical instruments) the refractive index for blue light n_{blue} may be 1.521 and that for red light n_{red} may be 1.510 (exact values will vary according to the composition of the glass). Since $n_{blue} > n_{red}$, blue light will be refracted more than red light, and so the colours will separate.

Total internal reflection

Prisms can also be used to reflect rays, when the angle of incidence is greater than the critical angle.

A prism with angles of 45°, 90° and 45° can be used to reflect light so that it is deviated through 90°, as figure 3.4.7 shows.

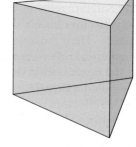

Figure 3.4.5 The word **prism** describes an object with two flat sides at an angle to each other. Prisms are usually met in applications involving light, but they can also be used with other types of wave, for example, paraffin wax prisms are sometimes used with microwaves.

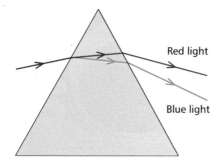

Red light

Blue light

Figure 3.4.6 Blue light entering the prism slows down more than red light, so it is refracted more. The extremes of the spectrum are red and violet, between which the other colours of the spectrum are visible in the order red, orange, yellow, green, blue, indigo, violet.

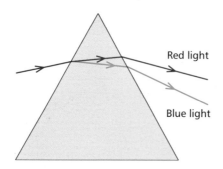

Red light

Blue light

Figure 3.4.7 The ray enters the prism with an angle of incidence of 0° so is not refracted. It meets the opposite side at 45°, where $\theta > \theta_c$, so it is reflected. The ray leaves the prism at 90° to the direction in which it entered.

Rearbows

The physics of the formation of rainbows was first described by René Descartes in 1637, although attempts to understand rainbows through practical experiments with globes of water had previously been carried out by Theodoric of Freibourg, a Dominican monk, as early as 1300.

A rainbow is seen when you stand with the Sun behind you and look at light reflected from water droplets falling through the air some distance in front of you. Although the rainbow appears as an arc, it has no ends (or, unfortunately, pots of gold) – if a rainbow is seen from sufficiently high up it can be seen to be completely circular. Figure 3.4.8 explains the formation of a rainbow.

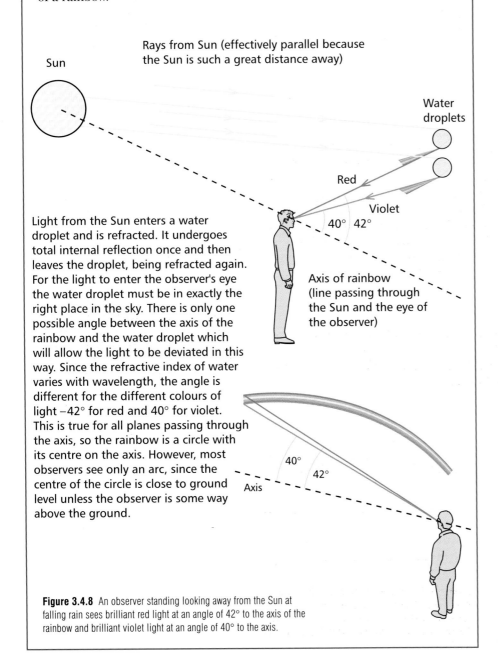

Light from the Sun enters a water droplet and is refracted. It undergoes total internal reflection once and then leaves the droplet, being refracted again. For the light to enter the observer's eye the water droplet must be in exactly the right place in the sky. There is only one possible angle between the axis of the rainbow and the water droplet which will allow the light to be deviated in this way. Since the refractive index of water varies with wavelength, the angle is different for the different colours of light –42° for red and 40° for violet. This is true for all planes passing through the axis, so the rainbow is a circle with its centre on the axis. However, most observers see only an arc, since the centre of the circle is close to ground level unless the observer is some way above the ground.

Figure 3.4.8 An observer standing looking away from the Sun at falling rain sees brilliant red light at an angle of 42° to the axis of the rainbow and brilliant violet light at an angle of 40° to the axis.

The spectrometer

By focusing a telescope on a distant star, the light emitted can be analysed using a **spectrometer**. This instrument effectively consists of three parts – a slit and lens or **collimator**, which admits a narrow beam of light to the instrument, a **diffraction grating**, which deviates the light according to its wavelength as described in section 3.2, page 230, and a **telescope**, which is used to observe the spectra formed. The light from a star is a **continuous spectrum** typical of that from any glowing object, and the range of wavelengths emitted by a star is a precise indication of its temperature. From the **absorption spectrum** of a star it is possible to tell what chemical elements are present in a star's atmosphere and so have some idea of its composition. (The origin of these spectra is explained in section 6.5.)

The Doppler effect

When astronomers first began to look at the spectra of stars in other galaxies during the 1920s, they noticed that the spectra looked very similar to the spectra from stars in our own galaxy but that all the features present were shifted by the same relative amount towards the red end of the spectrum. This phenomenon became known as the **red shift**. This shift is due to the relative motion of the stars and our planet, in an effect called the **Doppler effect**. An observer receiving waves emitted from a moving body observes that the wavelength of the waves has been altered to a new wavelength λ_{obs}.

Figure 3.4.10 shows how the Doppler effect may be understood.

Figure 3.4.9 Cecilia Payne-Gaposchkin (1900–1979) studied the absorption lines in the spectrum of stars, and suggested that these showed that the different temperatures of stars accounted for their different spectra. The great astronomer Henry Norris Russell dismissed her results as 'clearly impossible', and she therefore conceded that her results were 'almost certainly not real'. It took only a few years for astronomers to realise that the young Cecilia had been correct where Russell had been wrong.

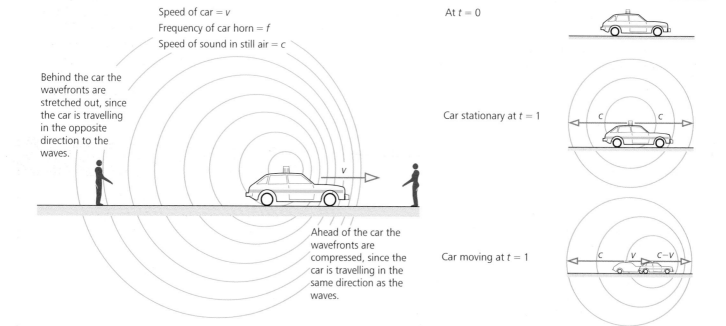

Speed of car = v
Frequency of car horn = f
Speed of sound in still air = c

At $t = 0$

Behind the car the wavefronts are stretched out, since the car is travelling in the opposite direction to the waves.

Car stationary at $t = 1$

Ahead of the car the wavefronts are compressed, since the car is travelling in the same direction as the waves.

Car moving at $t = 1$

Figure 3.4.10

Suppose at time $t = 0$ the car sounds its horn. In one second the sound from the horn travels a distance c. Ahead of the car the waves emitted over this period are spaced over a distance $(c - v)$, since the car and the sound waves are travelling in the same direction. This means that ahead of the car f waves are spread over a distance $(c - v)$. $\lambda = c/f$, so the observed wavelength in front of the car is thus:

$$\lambda_{obs} = \frac{c - v}{f}$$

We may write this as:

$$\lambda_{obs} = \frac{c}{f} - \frac{v}{f}$$

The frequency observed in front of the car f_{obs} is thus given by:

$$f_{obs} = \frac{c}{\lambda_{obs}}$$

$$= \frac{c}{\frac{c}{f} - \frac{v}{f}} = f\left(\frac{1}{1 - \frac{v}{c}}\right)$$

Behind the car the waves emitted are spread over a distance $(c + v)$, so that f_{obs} behind the car is given by:

$$f_{obs} = \frac{c}{\lambda_{obs}} = \frac{c}{\frac{c}{f} + \frac{v}{f}} = f\left(\frac{1}{1 + \frac{v}{c}}\right)$$

Hence a receding star or galaxy emits light which appears to have a lower frequency than expected.

We also experience this effect when, for example, we hear a car coming towards us and driving past at a steady rate. As it approaches, the note of its engine rises to a maximum pitch, and then falls as the car travels away.

Astronomers quickly realised that the red shift implied that galaxies surrounding us were travelling away from us. In 1929 the American astronomer Edwin Hubble published his finding that the size of a galaxy's red shift is proportional to its distance from us – that is, the further away a galaxy is, the faster it is moving. Hubble's paper had the same effect on the twentieth century's view of the Universe as Galileo's work had some 300 years earlier.

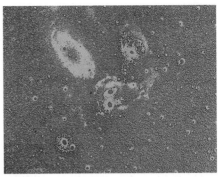

Figure 3.4.11 A false-colour image of a group of galaxies. The colour coding indicates the extent of the red shift (red = greater shift, blue = less shift).

Hubble's law

Hubble's law is very simple to express in mathematical terms. It can be written

$$v = H_0 d$$

where v is the galaxy's velocity, d is its distance from us, and H_0 is a constant called the **Hubble constant**. If d is measured in light-years, modern estimates for the numerical value of the constant lie between 15 and 30 km s^{-1}/(million light-years).

The Doppler effect and relativity

The equation for the Doppler shift is obeyed for sound, and for light waves from nearby galaxies. However, the fact that more distant galaxies are travelling away faster than nearer ones leads to a breakdown in this relationship, since the velocity of the galaxy relative to the Earth begins to approach the velocity of light, a situation dealt with in Einstein's **special theory of relativity**. One of the results of this theory is that the speed of light appears the same to all observers.

Light sources which have speeds approaching that of light are affected by a phenomenon called **time dilation**, in which a moving clock appears to run slow to a stationary observer. To the observer in our example this results in an extra reduction in frequency by a factor of $\sqrt{(1 - v^2/c^2)}$, and this factor must be included in the relationship for the Doppler shift. The exact Doppler shift relationship for a receding object emitting waves of any sort thus becomes:

$$f_{obs} = f\left(\frac{\sqrt{\left(1 - \frac{v^2}{c^2}\right)}}{1 + \frac{v}{c}}\right)$$

Since $1 - v^2/c^2 = (1 + v/c)(1 - v/c)$, this simplifies to:

$$f_{obs} = f\sqrt{\frac{1 - \frac{v}{c}}{1 + \frac{v}{c}}}$$

For the star 3C 147 in figure 3.4.12, the ratio f_{obs}/f is measured to be 1.55. Putting this ratio into the relativistic Doppler relationship gives:

$$\frac{f_{obs}}{f} = 1.55 = \sqrt{\left(\frac{1 - \dfrac{v}{c}}{1 + \dfrac{v}{c}}\right)}$$

Squaring both sides of this relationship gives:

$$1.55^2 = \frac{1 - v/c}{1 + v/c}$$

Rearranging and simplifying:

$$1.4025c = -3.4025v$$

so:

$$v = -0.41c$$

The object is thus receding at 41% of the speed of light (the negative sign indicates that the velocity of the object is in the opposite direction to the velocity of the light).

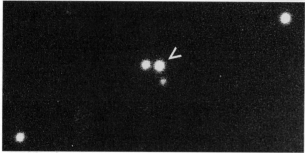

Figure 3.4.12 This distant stellar object (called 3C 147) is receding at almost half the speed of light, producing an enormous Doppler shift.

Doppler shift and sound – worked example

If a car travels at 30 m s^{-1} towards you sounding its horn with a frequency of 300 Hz, what note will you hear? Take the velocity of sound in still air as 340 m s^{-1}.

As the car is travelling towards the observer, f waves will be compressed into a distance $(c - v)$ so that the observed wavelength λ_{obs} is given by:

$$\lambda_{obs} = \frac{c - v}{f}$$

$$= \frac{340 \text{ m s}^{-1} - 30 \text{ m s}^{-1}}{300 \text{ Hz}}$$

$$= \frac{310 \text{ m s}^{-1}}{300 \text{ Hz}}$$

$$= 1.033 \text{ m}$$

The observed frequency f_{obs} will be given by:

$$f_{obs} = \frac{c}{\lambda_{obs}}$$

$$= \frac{340 \text{ m s}^{-1}}{1.033 \text{ m}}$$

$$= 330 \text{ Hz to 2 SF}$$

Cosmology is the study of the Universe – its size and shape, its history and its future. Cosmologists measure the distance of galaxies according to their brightness, in a method that is sometimes called the 'headlamp method' – a nearby galaxy is brighter than a distant one, in the same way as the headlights of a car that is close to us appear brighter than the headlights of a distant car. Astronomers have developed ways of taking into account the fact that there may be a difference in brightness between two galaxies which are at similar distances (in just the same way as two cars may have headlamps of different brightness). Even so, there is still considerable uncertainty in making measurements of distance, leading to corresponding uncertainty in the value of the Hubble constant.

The way in which galaxies are receding can be described very simply. If we think about a firework exploding, the fragments of the firework shoot out in all directions with different velocities. After a time t a fragment with velocity v will have travelled a distance d such that

$$d = vt$$

which can be written

$$v = d/t$$

This means that the fragments with greatest velocity will be those which have travelled furthest from the explosion. The similarity between this relationship and Hubble's law suggests a similar model for the origin of the Universe, in the form of a huge cosmic explosion, which cosmologists call the **Big Bang**.

We can calculate the age of the Universe by comparing Hubble's law with the relationship $v = d/t$. Since $v = H_0 d$ it follows that

$$d/t = H_0 d$$

so

$$t = 1/H_0$$

This gives a figure for the age of the Universe of between 1×10^{10} and 2×10^{10} years.

Using Hubble's law together with some relatively straightforward physics which we shall meet in section 5, cosmologists are able to calculate the fate of the Universe, based on measurements of its density. According to these calculations, if the density of the Universe is less than or equal to 6×10^{-27} kg m^{-3} then the Universe will continue to expand indefinitely, while if the density is greater than this the Universe will eventually cease to expand and will then contract (leading ultimately to a *Big Crunch*). The big problem for cosmologists is finding values for unknown quantities like the Hubble constant. Although much work has been done, it is still not possible to calculate the density of the Universe with sufficient accuracy to be sure what its fate might eventually be.

Figure 3.4.13 Edwin Hubble proposed classifying galaxies according to their shape. The structure of a galaxy reflects what is happening inside it – spiral galaxies are the nurseries of new stars, while elliptical galaxies contain ageing stars.

Figure 3.4.14 Edwin Hubble (1889–1953). Hubble was among the stars in his work and in his private life too. He and his wife were two prominent social figures in Hollywood in the 1930s and 40s. Despite his great scientific and social successes, Hubble was a very modest man – he left instructions in his will that no monuments to him were to be built, and no funeral service was held for him. His remains lie buried in an unmarked grave.

How do we know?

Our knowledge of the world (and the Universe) around us is based on the data we are able to collect. For many hundreds of years the five human senses were the sole means of collecting such information, but this changed as people began to develop scientific instruments which allowed the extension of these senses. In this way, Galileo was able to observe the satellites of Jupiter and the rings of Saturn using his telescope, Hooke saw the cells in a sample of cork bark through a microscope, and Herschel noted the existence of infrared radiation by means of a prism and a thermometer. As science has become ever more sophisticated, scientists have been able to build more and more complex instruments until many scientific observations are no longer made directly by the human senses.

As far as information about space is concerned, until the middle years of the twentieth century astronomers were limited, like Galileo, to making observations using the light waves that arrived at the surface of the Earth. Bigger and bigger telescopes were built to collect the faint light coming from distant stars and galaxies, each one pushing the limits of what was possible using existing technology. In 1948 the Hale telescope at Mount Palomar in California became operational. But the following decade saw the beginnings of radio astronomy, expanding the observational horizons of astronomers by giving them the ability to scour the skies for electromagnetic waves with frequencies lower than those of light.

Detection of information in the form of electromagnetic radiation with frequencies higher than those of light came when it became possible to put satellites into orbit in the 1960s. This led the way to observations of X-ray, ultraviolet and gamma rays coming from space, as well as a greater understanding of the way in which the Earth is bombarded by a constant stream of particles coming from the Sun. This **solar wind** consists of a mixture of protons and electrons streaming out from the Sun at a speed of around 500 km/s. In addition, the Earth is also bathed in a constant stream of particles called **neutrinos** from the Sun. These particles interact only very weakly with matter, so the vast majority of them pass straight through the Earth. Because of this weak interaction with matter, experiments to detect and count neutrinos require very sophisticated techniques. Knowledge of the number of neutrinos passing through the Earth is important to scientists studying the evolution of stars, since it provides information about what is happening at the heart of our nearest star, the Sun, so enabling solar physicists to test their models using real data.

Communicating information – analogue vs digital

Our ability to transmit information from one place to another, whether by radio waves, through copper cables or along optical fibres, revolutionised the world in the latter part of the twentieth century. The majority of information transmitted starts out as a signal that is described as an **analogue** signal, which simply means that the signal varies continuously and directly represents the information from which it came. In many simple cases, an analogue signal will have been produced by means of a potential divider, one part of which contains a device which has a resistance that changes with the property to be measured (a thermistor in the case of temperature, a light-dependent resistor (LDR) in the case of light). The output voltage from the potential divider changes with

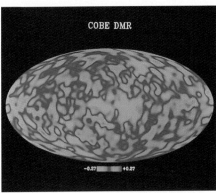

Figure 3.4.15 The COBE satellite was launched in November 1989 to survey the cosmic background radiation – an echo of the birth of the Universe. This photograph shows the unevenness in the background radiation detected by COBE which provides confirmatory evidence for the Big Bang theory. This is a false colour photograph – the satellite detects radiation that we could not know about without its sensitive instruments.

Figure 3.4.16 It was using radio astronomy to pick up weak radio signals from space that led Jocelyn Bell Burnell to discover the first pulsar in 1967 (although her results were not published for another year). Pulsars are rapidly rotating neutron stars whose existence was first predicted in 1938.

the change in the property being measured – in other words, it is an *analogue* of it. Potential dividers are considered in more detail in sections 4.2 and 4.5.

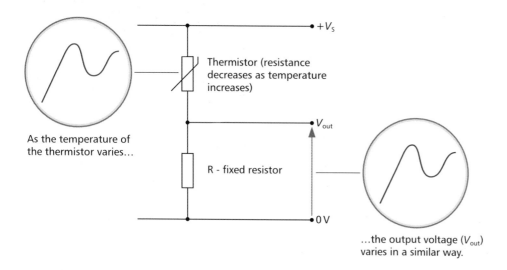

As the temperature of the thermistor varies...

Thermistor (resistance decreases as temperature increases)

$+V_s$

V_{out}

R - fixed resistor

0 V

...the output voltage (V_{out}) varies in a similar way.

Figure 3.4.17 A potential divider provides one way of producing an analogue signal, in which the output voltage varies directly with the quantity being measured.

Analogue signals have been widely used to send information for many years – radio broadcasts are an example of this. Increasingly, however, more and more information is being transmitted as a **digital** signal rather than an analogue one, since this leads to a signal of much higher quality at the receiver. Amplification of a signal is necessary because a signal is **attenuated** (its amplitude is reduced) after travelling a long distance. As it travels, a signal picks up **noise**. This term refers to unwanted signals that become mixed with the wanted signal. Noise occurs for a variety of reasons. Some noise is picked up within the communication system itself, when a signal is amplified by an electronic circuit, for example. Other noise may come from outside the system, as when a signal being carried in one cable is picked up by another cable through electromagnetic induction (a phenomenon called **crosstalk**). Figure 3.4.19 illustrates the difference between digital and analogue signals, and the advantages of digital signals where amplification is needed.

Analogue to digital conversion

In order to convert an analogue signal into a digital one, a process called **pulse-code modulation (PCM)** may be used. This works as follows. The analogue signal to be converted is sampled at regular intervals of time. At each instant it is sampled, the analogue value of the signal is assigned to one of a number of values. Each of these values is expressed by a binary number. If we use an eight-bit number to represent the possible values of the signal, the signal may have any one of $2^8 = 256$ possible values, from 0000 0000 to 1111 1111.

Figure 3.4.18 The global computer communication network called the Internet makes exclusive use of digital technologies to send information around the world, through copper cables, optical fibres, microwave links and by satellite.

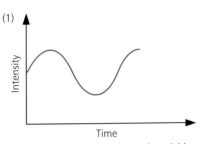

(1)

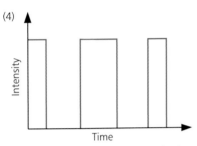

An analogue signal is continuously variable – the output from a microphone is an example of this.

(2)

An attenuated analogue signal contains 'noise'.

(3)

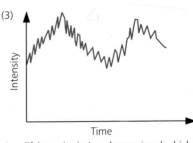

Amplifying a 'noisy' analogue signal which has been attenuated also amplifies the noise.

(4)

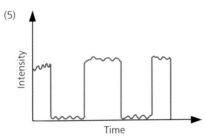

A digital signal consists of a series of pulses, where there is either a signal at a given instant or there is not.

(5)

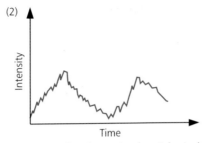

An attenuated digital signal also contains 'noise'.

(6)

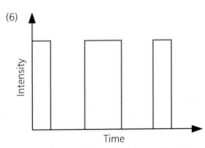

Regenerating a digital signal loses the 'noise' since each pulse is read as either 'signal' or 'no signal', and the original signal is restored.

Figure 3.4.19 The advantage of digital communication channels is the ability to boost the attenuated signal without boosting the noise as well.

Noise

Some of the noise in communication systems comes from the system itself, particularly within electronic components where thermal energy leads to the excitation of electrons and other charge carriers. The random kinetic energy of these particles then leads to the production of random electrical signals, which mix with the wanted signal. The noise caused by this thermal effect can be reduced by keeping components cool, and by limiting the current through devices, since the heat produced is proportional to the square of the current. This problem is made more difficult by further miniaturisation of electronic components, when a halving of cross-sectional area of a component leads to an increase in its resistance by a factor of 4. (These relationships are explored further in section 4.)

The rate of sampling depends on the frequency of the signal to be sampled. As a general rule, an analogue signal of frequency f needs to be sampled at a minimum rate of $2f$ in order to produce a digital signal that accurately represents it. (Transmitting speech by telephone usually involves transmitting frequencies up to about 3500 Hz, so a sampling rate of around 7 kHz is used.)

The digital signal consists of a string of pulses, which can be transmitted as voltage pulses along a wire or as light pulses along an optical fibre.

The process of reconstructing the analogue signal from the digital signal is effectively the reverse of the analogue-to-digital conversion process described here.

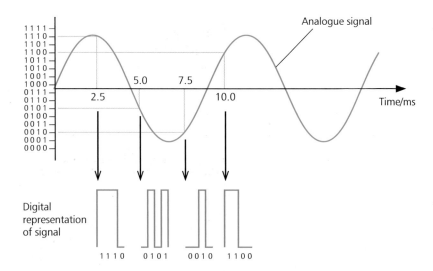

Figure 3.4.20 A simple sinusoidal analogue signal, showing how sampling produces a digital signal. For clarity, the analogue value of the signal has been assigned to one of 16 levels rather than to one of 256 levels. This produces a four-bit number representing the signal, rather than an eight-bit number. The sampling rate here is 400 Hz, one sample every 2.5 ms.

Time-division multiplexing

Digitally encoding an analogue signal greatly improves the quality of the signal, as we have already seen. However, there is another advantage. Think about a person in Southampton talking on the telephone to someone in Birmingham. Their telephone is connected to the local exchange, where the analogue signal is converted into a digital signal using pulse-code modulation, as we have just seen. This digital signal then goes on the next stage of its journey, perhaps by optical fibre. Now imagine that someone else in Southampton also wants to talk to someone in Birmingham. Their telephone is also connected to the local exchange, where again the analogue signal is converted to a digital one. But how will the signal make the next stage of the journey – surely another optical fibre will be needed? With digital signals this is not necessarily the case, since a process called **time-division multiplexing** can be used to send many signals through one optical fibre. The way in which time-division multiplexing works is shown in figure 3.4.21.

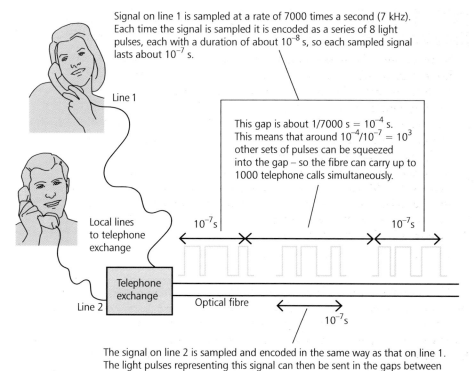

Signal on line 1 is sampled at a rate of 7000 times a second (7 kHz). Each time the signal is sampled it is encoded as a series of 8 light pulses, each with a duration of about 10^{-8} s, so each sampled signal lasts about 10^{-7} s.

This gap is about $1/7000$ s $= 10^{-4}$ s. This means that around $10^{-4}/10^{-7} = 10^3$ other sets of pulses can be squeezed into the gap – so the fibre can carry up to 1000 telephone calls simultaneously.

The signal on line 2 is sampled and encoded in the same way as that on line 1. The light pulses representing this signal can then be sent in the gaps between the pulses representing the first signal.

Note: signals not shown to scale

Figure 3.4.21 Time division multiplexing works by allowing a number of messages to be sent through a communication channel at the same time. This is like allowing a queue of people to use a telephone by letting each one speak for a short period of time before passing the telephone on to the next person in the queue. Using this method of communication for sending computer signals through a single optical fibre, all the text of Shakespeare's 37 plays could be transmitted in a quarter of a second.

Communication channels

In order to transmit information through a communication channel – which may be an optical fibre, a copper cable or a radio wave – it must be **encoded** into a suitable form before transmission. **Decoding** is then necessary at the receiving end. In the case of transmission along an optical fibre, the analogue signal is encoded by conversion into a digital form as we have already seen. It is then possible to transmit this information as a series of very short flashes of light. In the case of radio broadcasts, the information to be transmitted must be combined with a suitable **carrier wave** in order to broadcast it. Before transmission, the carrier wave is mixed with the information to be transmitted, called the **modulating wave**. This wave may be an analogue electrical signal from a microphone, but it may equally well be digital information (for example, a series of pulses produced by a digital computer, or an analogue signal converted to digital form). Figure 3.4.23 shows a block diagram of a transmitting and receiving system which uses electromagnetic waves.

The **bandwidth** of a communication channel is a measure of the rate at which information can be transmitted through it. The wider the bandwidth, the more quickly information can be sent, just as a wider road allows a greater flow of traffic. The *quantity* of information sent through a communication channel in a given time determines the *quality* of the signal received at the other end of the channel. This is because the more information we have about something, the more accurately we can perceive it, as the two pictures in figure 3.4.24 show. Bandwidth is measured in hertz (Hz), since it is a measure of the range of frequencies that a communication channel can carry.

Figure 3.4.22 Minute solid state lasers are used to produce the short pulses of light used in digital communications. These lasers are capable of flashing at a rate of more than 10^{10} times a second.

Figure 3.4.23 A block diagram of a communication system using radio waves. The size of a radio transmitting or receiving aerial must be of the same order as the wavelength to be broadcast. With carrier wave frequencies of around 10^8 MHz used in FM broadcasts, the size of aerial needed for good reception is around 1 m or less.

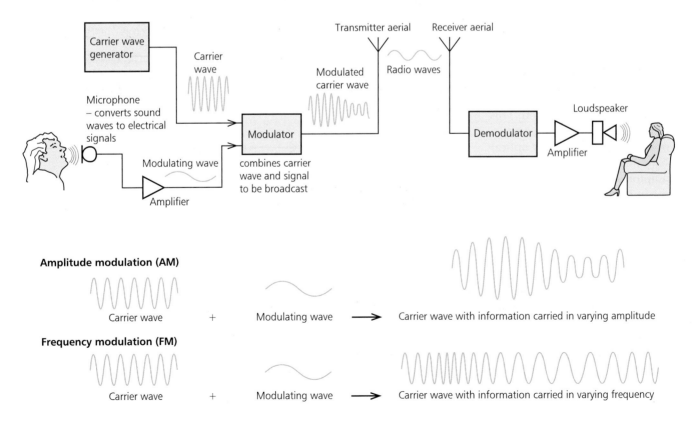

Figure 3.4.24 There is far less information in the first picture than in the second, making it far more difficult to see what it is.

Figure 3.4.25 The **bandwidth** of an optical fibre (and of any other communication channel, such as copper wires or radio waves) is a measure of the rate at which information can be transmitted through it. The wider the bandwidth, the more quickly information can be sent – just as a wider road allows a greater flow of traffic.

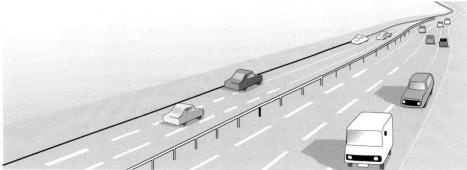

Preventing pulse broadening

There are two major problems in the transmission of light along optical fibres which must be overcome when using them for telecommunications:

1 The light used must be monochromatic, otherwise the differing velocities of different wavelengths will mean that the pulse will be broadened, as different wavelengths will arrive at the end of the fibre at slightly different times.

2 The fibres must be very fine so that the number of paths that the light can follow along the fibre is as small as possible. If many paths are possible, some of the light in a pulse will arrive before the rest of the light. This will again lead to the pulse broadening.

Figure 3.4.26 illustrates these problems.

The problem of non-monochromatic light is solved by using lasers. The digital pulses sent along optical fibres are produced by minute lasers. The radiation these lasers produce is in the infra-red region of the spectrum, with a wavelength of around 8.5×10^{-7} m, and is almost completely monochromatic. The lasers are capable of being switched on and off at a rate of up to 2×10^{8} Hz, so that many millions of pulses can be sent each second.

Non-monochromatic light

Pulse produced at this end contains a range of wavelengths – it can be regarded as a collection of pulses, each with a different wavelength, which are sent simultaneously.

Pulse received is broadened as pulses with different wavelengths arrive at different times. Pulse with longest wavelength is received first and pulse with shortest wavelength is received last.

Range of paths within fibre, known as **multimode propagation**

Monochromatic pulse

Pulse received is broadened as pulses arrive at different times after differing numbers of reflections. Pulse taking most direct route is received first and pulse undergoing reflection greatest number of times is received last.

The problem of multimode propagation is solved in three ways. If the fibre is to be used for fairly narrow bandwidths (sending information slowly over short distances, for example, between two computers 25 m apart) multimode propagation is not a problem, and simple **step-index multimode fibres** are used. For higher bandwidths **graded-index multimode fibres** are used. There are still many modes of propagation in these fibres, but each mode takes the same time to travel along the fibre, since longer paths are in regions of lower refractive index, where the pulse travels faster. For very wide bandwidths (for example, sending large numbers of telephone calls or television signals) **step-index monomode fibres** are used, with only a single mode of propagation. These types of fibres are illustrated in figure 3.4.27.

Choosing a communication channel

The choice of communication channel for transmitting information depends upon a number of factors, including cost. The first decision is whether the information is to be **broadcast** or whether it is to be transmitted to a specific recipient (sometimes known as **narrowcasting**). If broadcasting is desired, then the communication channel chosen will normally be radio waves, since these can be transmitted and received over a wide area. This transmission depends on two kinds of waves – the **groundwave** and the **skywave** (figure 3.4.28).

The groundwave travels along a path close to the Earth's surface. How far it travels depends on the transmitter power, the operating frequency, and the conductivity of the surface over which the wave travels. It also depends very much on the frequency, with low frequency signals travelling greater distances. Because of this, groundwave propagation is mainly important in medium wave (MW) and long wave (LW) broadcasts, with frequencies in the range 200 kHz to 1500 kHz. Groundwaves travel best over sea water. In regions such as the Caribbean, where the sea is particularly salty (and therefore better at conducting electricity), groundwaves may travel up to 1500 km. Groundwave propagation is very stable, which produces consistent reception. It is usually associated only with the daytime (although the groundwave is also present at night), since at night long-distance reception is predominantly via the skywave.

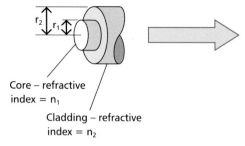

Generalised optical fibre

Core – refractive index = n_1

Cladding – refractive index = n_2

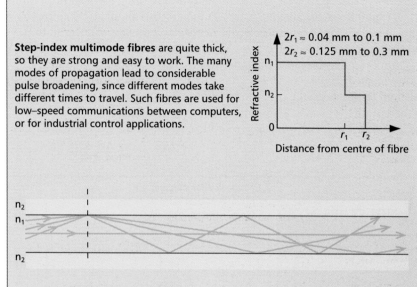

Step-index multimode fibres are quite thick, so they are strong and easy to work. The many modes of propagation lead to considerable pulse broadening, since different modes take different times to travel. Such fibres are used for low–speed communications between computers, or for industrial control applications.

$2r_1 \approx 0.04$ mm to 0.1 mm
$2r_2 \approx 0.125$ mm to 0.3 mm

Refractive index

Distance from centre of fibre

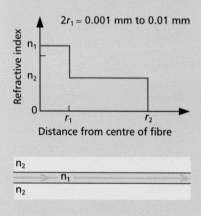

Step-index monomode fibres have only one, straight-through mode of propagation. This gives them a very wide bandwidth, and they are most widely used for telecommunications work. They require complex techniques to join and work them.

$2r_1 \approx 0.001$ mm to 0.01 mm

Refractive index

Distance from centre of fibre

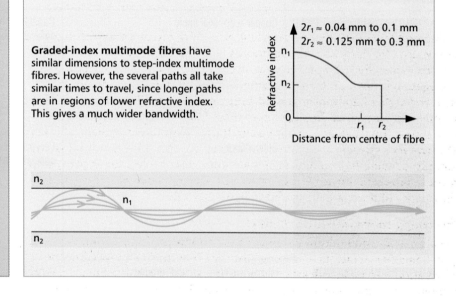

Graded-index multimode fibres have similar dimensions to step-index multimode fibres. However, the several paths all take similar times to travel, since longer paths are in regions of lower refractive index. This gives a much wider bandwidth.

$2r_1 \approx 0.04$ mm to 0.1 mm
$2r_2 \approx 0.125$ mm to 0.3 mm

Refractive index

Distance from centre of fibre

Figure 3.4.27 Different types of optical fibre

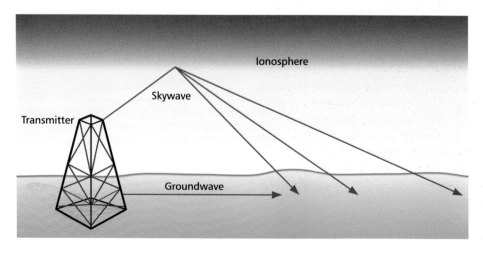

Ionosphere

Skywave

Transmitter

Groundwave

Figure 3.4.28 Radio signals from a transmitter may travel along the ground and can also bounce off the ionosphere, a highly ionised layer of the Earth's atmosphere.

Because of its stable daytime behaviour, medium and long wave radio stations usually arrange their aerials to radiate as much of the signal as they can via the groundwave to maximise the number of people able to listen to the station.

Skywave propagation is much more complicated than groundwave propagation, not least because the behaviour of the ionosphere changes according to the time of day. During the daytime, solar radiation penetrates the atmosphere far enough to ionise the air about 60 km above the Earth's surface (this is called the 'D layer'). This ionised layer almost completely absorbs MW and LW signals. This is why daytime reception is due to the groundwave.

Table 3.4.1 Transmission media

	Communication channel	**Features and usage**
	Copper – twisted pair	Simple and cheap. Suitable for medium bandwidth communication over short distances (<5 km)
	Copper – co-axial cable	Capable of high capacity. Simple technology means relative ease and cheapness of laying and repair
	Optical fibre	Very high bandwidth. More complex technology requires specialist installation and maintenance techniques
	Microwave link – ground–ground	Very high bandwidth. Line of sight propagation only, requiring transmitter and receiver to be placed relatively close together. Parabolic dishes used at transmitter and receiver to focus beam
	Microwave link – satellite	Very high bandwidth. Signals can be sent over long distances. Constant communication between transmitter and receiver requires geostationary satellite. Extremely costly

As night falls, the 'D' layer decreases, so that MW and LW signals can bounce back to the ground from higher parts of the ionosphere, between 100 km and 300 km above the Earth's surface, depending on conditions. This 'bouncing back' is due to the change in refractive index of the ionosphere, which causes the wave to undergo total internal reflection.

Where the groundwave and the skywave meet, the two waves may interfere. Since the intensity of the skywave varies as the behaviour of the ionosphere changes, this interference may lead to quite severe distortion of the signal received, making night-time reception at a distance of about 80 km to 150 km from the transmitter very poor.

Where the signal is not broadcast, the choice of communication channel includes optical fibre, copper cables and microwave links (both ground–ground and ground–satellite). These different methods of information transmission are compared in table 3.4.1.

Radio receiving aerials

Radio waves are generally defined as electromagnetic waves with a wavelength between several kilometres and about 10^{-2} m. To detect radio waves an aerial and an electrical circuit are needed. We shall be looking at electrical circuits in section 4. The properties of radio aerials, however, depend on the wave nature of electromagnetic waves. To detect a radio wave the wave must induce a current in a wire. The role of the radio aerial is to make this current as large as possible. The same principle applies to radio broadcast aerials but in reverse, the object being to use the smallest possible current to produce the largest possible electromagnetic wave.

The size of aerial required to receive or broadcast radio waves is closely related to the wavelength of the wave concerned, as figure 3.4.29 shows. Thus short wave radio broadcasts with wavelengths of the order of a few metres may be picked up using lengths of wire of about the same length, while television

Figure 3.4.29 These aerials are very different in appearance, but all rely on the interaction of the electric and magnetic fields of an electromagnetic wave with a wire capable of carrying a current.

Satellite television aerial

Radar aerial

Television aerial

VHF radio aerial

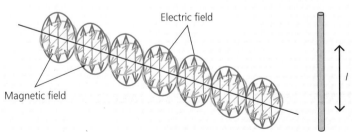
The oscillating electric and magnetic fields cause an oscillating electric current to flow in a wire placed in them. The wire must be parallel to the electric field for this effect to occur (see section 5.5, page 451).

LW/MW radio aerial

aerials, receiving waves with wavelengths of considerably less than a metre, can be much smaller. To overcome the need for lengths of wire up to 1.5 km long for receiving long and medium wave broadcasts, domestic radio receivers use long coils of wire as aerials within the set itself.

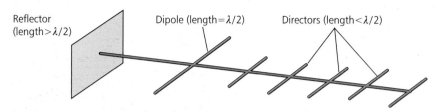

Reflector (length$>\lambda/2$)   Dipole (length$=\lambda/2$)   Directors (length$<\lambda/2$)

Figure 3.4.30 This array is used to receive television signals with a wavelength of around 0.5 m. The directors and the reflector allow a larger current to be induced in the dipole. They also make the aerial highly directional, so it must point exactly in the direction of the transmitter, otherwise the signal it produces will be very weak.

The television and radio aerials are examples of half-wave dipoles, shown in figure 3.4.30. These are usually arranged in arrays, with the main receiving dipole in the middle of a set of directors and radiators.

Small wavelengths can be received by dishes. These are parabolic reflectors with the detector of radio waves at their focal point. The diameter of the dish must be several times larger than the wavelength of the waves concerned to prevent diffraction effects, since the reflector effectively acts as a source of circular waves for the detector.

Resolving power

A receiver designed for receiving waves (light waves, radio waves, sound waves or any other type of wave) can **resolve** two sources of waves when it can detect them as two distinct and separate sources as opposed to one source.

The first stage of any receiver uses an aperture of some sort to admit the waves to it. When two sources are close together, their individual Fraunhofer diffraction patterns caused by this aperture may overlap, and this overlap may make it impossible to distinguish between the two sources.

Experiments suggest that the criterion for two objects to be *just* resolved is that the maximum of the diffraction pattern of one falls over the minimum of the diffraction pattern of the other, as illustrated in figure 3.4.31.

The relationship between wavelength and fringe separation derived in section 3.2, pages 228–9, shows that for two point objects to be resolved by Rayleigh's criterion, $\theta = \lambda/a$, since θ is the angle between the central maximum of the Fraunhofer diffraction pattern and its first minimum ($n = 1$). For a circular aperture, such as the eye or a parabolic receiving aerial, this relationship becomes $\theta = 1.22\,\lambda/a$ (see figure 3.2.18).

Figure 3.4.31 Two point objects are just resolved when the maximum of the diffraction pattern of one falls over the minimum of the diffraction pattern of the other. This is called **Rayleigh's criterion**.

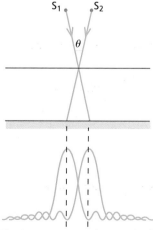

The two sources are easily resolved

The two sources are just resolved

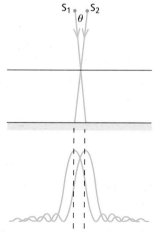

The two sources cannot be resolved

Radio telescopes

Astronomers use radio telescopes to pick up radio waves from space which provide them with information about distant objects. These telescopes use huge parabolic reflectors to capture the radio waves – for example, the telescope shown in figure 3.4.32 is 76 m in diameter. These reflectors are made so large in order to resolve distant objects that appear close together in the sky.

Figure 3.4.32 The radio telescope at Jodrell Bank, Cheshire, has a dish 76 m in diameter.

Resolving power – worked example

If the diameter of the pupil of the human eye is 2 mm in bright light, what is its resolving power with light of wavelength 5.0×10^{-7} m? Would it be possible to resolve two large birds 30 cm apart sitting on a wire 1.5 km away in bright daylight? Would the situation be any different at dusk, when the pupil will dilate to 4 mm diameter?

$$\theta = 1.22 \, \lambda/a$$

a is the diameter of the pupil, which is 2×10^{-3} m, and λ the wavelength of light, which is 5.0×10^{-7} m, so:

$$\theta = \frac{1.22 \times 5.0 \times 10^{-7} \text{ m}}{2 \times 10^{-3} \text{ m}}$$

$$= 3 \times 10^{-4} \text{ radians}$$

So two objects will be just resolved if the angle between them at the eye is 3×10^{-4} radians.

Treating the birds as point sources of light, the rays of light from the birds will make an angle of θ at the eye, where θ is given by:

$$\theta = \frac{\text{distance between birds}}{\text{distance from eye to birds}}$$

$$= \frac{3 \times 10^{-1} \text{ m}}{1.5 \times 10^{3} \text{ m}}$$

$$= 2 \times 10^{-4} \text{ radians}$$

This is smaller than the angle at which two objects can just be resolved, so the birds cannot be resolved in bright daylight.

At dusk, the pupil expands to a diameter of 4 mm. The angle for resolution is now:

$$\theta = \frac{1.22 \times 5.0 \times 10^{-7} \text{ m}}{4 \times 10^{-3} \text{ m}}$$

$$= 1.5 \times 10^{-4} \text{ radians}$$

This is smaller than the angle between the birds, so they can now be resolved.

FOCUS LOOKING INSIDE THE BODY

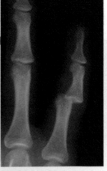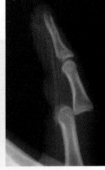

Figure 3.4.33 An X-ray photograph of a dislocated finger. The X-rays have travelled through the air around the finger and through the soft tissue of the finger itself. This has produced the familiar 'shadow picture' in which the dark areas are regions where the film has been exposed to X-rays.

X-rays

X-rays were first discovered by Röntgen in 1895. They are electromagnetic waves with a short wavelength (see page 241) and, just like visible light, they cause a photographic film to become exposed where they fall on it. X-rays carry a lot of energy and can easily pass through the body. They pass less easily through bones and other dense body tissue, and so can be used to form a 'shadow picture' of dense body tissue by placing a photographic film behind the patient, on the side opposite the X-ray source. Because the body tissues absorb some of the energy of the X-rays, the X-rays can damage cells in the body, and the exposure received by a patient must be carefully measured and controlled.

X-rays are produced in an **X-ray tube**, in which high energy electrons are fired at a metal target. The beam of X-rays produced has a characteristic series of lines which are superimposed on a background of continuous radiation. The beam is *hardened* to remove the low energy X-rays which would be absorbed by the patient's body but which would not contribute to the production of a clear picture. (You can find out more about the production of X-rays on pages 547–8.)

The time it took for a practical use for X-rays to be found was astonishingly short. Only three months after Röntgen's announcement of his discovery, an American named Eddie McCarthy became the first person to have a broken bone (in his arm) set with their aid.

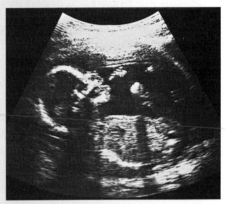

Figure 3.4.34 In the UK, ultrasound examination of pregnant women is carried out as a matter of routine. This ultrasound scan clearly shows the head and body of the unborn baby. If you look carefully you may just be able to see that the baby is sucking his thumb.

Ultrasound

Most people are familiar with the idea of **echo location**, the technique used by animals such as bats and dolphins to navigate using high frequency sound waves which bounce off objects around them. This same technique has been used for many years by fishermen to locate shoals of fish, and by warships to locate submarines – and it is widely used today to produce images of the structures inside the human body.

Ultrasound is high frequency sound above the audible range of human hearing, that is, above about 20 kHz. The frequencies used in medical imaging are much higher than this, usually between 1 and 15 MHz. Ultrasound carries much less energy than X-rays, and as a result it hardly affects the tissues through which it travels. This makes ultrasound examination a very safe procedure, a fact that accounts for its widespread use in examining the developing baby inside its mother (figure 3.4.34).

Ultrasound is produced and detected by a **piezoelectric transducer**, in which the oscillations of a crystal are coupled to a rapidly alternating electric field. The transducer emits ultrasound in pulses, so that when it is not acting as an ultrasound transmitter, the transducer also acts as an ultrasound detector, in which the returning ultrasound pulse produces a voltage across the crystal. Figure 3.4.35 shows how an ultrasound probe emits and then detects pulses, which enables an image of a baby's head to be built up.

By using arrays of transducers connected together, a complex ultrasound 'picture' can be built up which shows a 'slice' through the patient's body, like that in figure 3.4.34. In order to obtain images which are as clear as possible, it

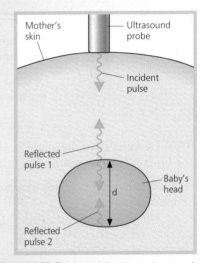

Figure 3.4.35 The ultrasound probe contains a transducer which acts as a transmitter and a detector of ultrasound. Placed on the mother's skin, electronic circuits measure the time taken for pulses of ultrasound to be reflected back to the probe from either side of the baby's head.

is important to select the frequency of ultrasound used in the scan so as to minimise the diffraction of the ultrasound waves. If the ultrasound waves pass through a gap or around an object of about the same size as the wavelength of the ultrasound, diffraction occurs and a blurred ultrasound image is the result. Figure 3.4.36 shows the effect of this diffraction.

Another important use of ultrasound is in blood flow measurement using the Doppler effect, which we met on page 250. In this technique a beam of ultrasound is directed at the blood flowing in a particular vein or artery. As the beam is reflected off the blood, the movement of the blood causes a change in frequency (a 'Doppler shift') of the ultrasound – an increase in frequency if the blood is flowing towards the ultrasound probe, or a decrease if the flow is away from it. This Doppler shift can be used to calculate the velocity of the blood using the relationship

$$\Delta f = \frac{2fv\cos\theta}{c}$$

where c is the speed of the ultrasound and f is its frequency, v is the velocity of the blood flow and Δf is the Doppler shift.

Light – inside the body

We have already seen (pages 259–61) how light is able to travel along an optical fibre due to total internal reflection, something that can happen even when the fibre is bent. Figure 3.4.38 shows the construction of an endoscope. Light from a powerful lamp is passed along a bundle of fibres to the part of the patient's body that is to be examined. This light travels out of the fibre into the patient's body, where some of it is then reflected, via a focusing lens, back into another bundle of optical fibres running alongside the first bundle. This second bundle of fibres then carries this reflected light up to an eyepiece where the image of the interior of the patient is focused. This image can be viewed directly by a doctor, or viewed using a television camera and the image recorded on videotape or computer.

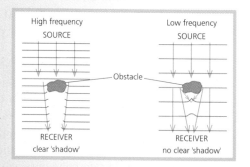
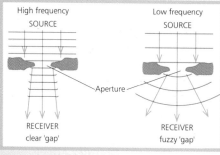

Figure 3.4.36 The effect of diffraction on the sharpness of ultrasound images.

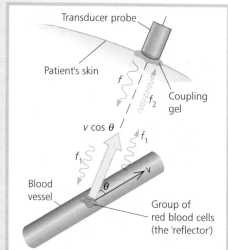

Figure 3.4.37 Using ultrasound to measure the velocity of blood flow.

Figure 3.4.38 Neither X-rays nor ultrasound can provide images of the interior of the body which tell us exactly what it would look like if we were able to open it up and look directly inside it. Using an **endoscope** it is possible to observe tissues such as the lung, the oesophagus and stomach, and the lower part of the intestinal tract.

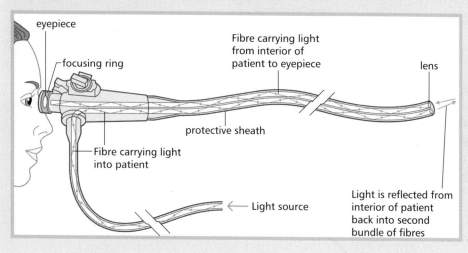

SUMMARY

- The image produced by a **plane mirror** is a **virtual image** – it cannot be cast onto a screen. It is the same distance from the mirror as the object. It is neither magnified nor diminished (it is the same size as the object), it is erect and laterally inverted.

- **Curved reflectors** may be **spherical** or **parabolic**. Parabolic reflectors focus waves from a distant source to their **principal focus**, while if the beam is wide a spherical reflector will focus it to points on a curve called a **caustic**.

- Glass prisms can **disperse** white light (split it into its component colours). This happens because light of different wavelengths has different velocities in glass, which is called a **dispersive medium**. The refractive index for blue light in glass is greater than that for red light.

- Light can be analysed using a **spectrometer**. A **collimator** admits a narrow beam of light to a diffraction grating, which deviates the light according to its wavelength. A telescope observes the spectra produced. When used to observe light from a star, the wavelength of the light gives an indication of the star's temperature.

- A stationary observer hears waves emitted with frequency f from a moving body with a different frequency f_{obs} given by:

$$f_{obs} = f\left(\frac{1}{1 \pm v/c}\right) \quad \text{(+ for receding sources, – for approaching sources)}$$

  where v is the velocity of the source relative to the observer and c the velocity of the wave motion relative to the observer. This shift in frequency is called the **Doppler effect**.

- **Optical fibres** are very thin glass fibres used to transmit pulses of light in telecommunications. The light is totally internally reflected by the surface of the fibre.

- Waves may be detected by **transducers**, which transfer energy from one form to another.

- In a **radio receiving aerial**, a current is induced by an electromagnetic wave in a wire. The current is detected by an electrical circuit. The size of the aerial is related to the wavelength of the waves it is designed to detect.

- A receiver can **resolve** two sources of waves if it can detect them as being separate. Two sources can be resolved if the maximum of the Fraunhofer diffraction pattern of one falls over the minimum of the other. This is called **Rayleigh's criterion**.

- **X-rays** are very short wavelength electromagnetic waves that pass through soft body tissue and form a 'shadow picture' of denser materials, such as bones, on photographic film. They are produced by firing high-energy electrons at a metal target.

- **Ultrasound** is high-frequency sound above 20 kHz, about the limit of human hearing. It carries much less energy than X-rays and is a safe method of examining unborn babies, measuring blood flow, and so on. Ultrasound is produced and detected using a **piezoelectric transducer**.

- In an **endoscope**, a probe inserted into a patient's body comprises one bundle of **optical fibres** carrying light, and another bundle fitted with a lens and eyepiece through which an observer views the illuminated region, either directly or with a camera.

EXAMPLE

A ray of light enters a 60° prism and is just totally internally reflected when it meets the opposite face of the prism. If the refractive index of the prism is 1.5, calculate the angle of incidence of the ray of light on the first face.

The first stop in solving this problem is to represent the information in a diagram, as in figure 3.4.39.

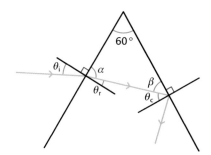

Figure 3.4.39

We know that the ray of light strikes the second face of the prism with an angle of incidence equal to the critical angle, θ_c. Our first step is therefore to calculate this angle.

We have:

$$\sin \theta_c = \frac{1}{n}$$

We know that $n = 1.5$, so

$$\sin \theta_c = \frac{1}{n} = \frac{1}{1.5} = 0.667$$

This gives $\theta_c = 41.8°$.

We know that the sum of the angles in a triangle is 180°. From our diagram, we can therefore write

$$\alpha + \beta + 60° = 180°$$

But we also know that $\beta + 41.8° = 90°$, which tells us that $\beta = 48.2°$.

Therefore

$$\alpha = 180° - 60° - 48.2°$$
$$= 71.8°$$

This now tells us the angle of the refracted ray at the first face, θ_r:

$$\theta_r + 71.8° = 90°$$

So $\theta_r = 90° - 71.8°$
$$= 18.2°$$

From Snell's law we know that

$$\frac{\sin \theta_i}{\sin \theta_r} = n$$

so we can write

$$\frac{\sin \theta_i}{\sin 18.2°} = 1.5$$

and thus

$$\sin \theta_i = 1.5 \times \sin 18.2°$$
$$= 0.469$$

which gives the value of θ_i as 27.9°.

The angle of incidence of the ray of light on the first face is 27.9°.

QUESTIONS

1 Shopkeepers often install convex mirrors in order to see what customers are doing. What is the advantage of convex mirrors over plane mirrors?

2 A car headlamp uses a spherical concave mirror to produce a parallel beam of light. If the filament of the lamp is 5 cm from the mirror, what must be the radius of curvature of the mirror?

3 The refractive index for a particular sample of glass for red light is 1.514 and for blue light is 1.523. Calculate the velocities of red and blue light in the glass if the velocity of light in a vacuum is taken as 2.998×10^8 m s^{-1}.

4 The refractive index of the glass prism shown in figure 3.4.40 is 1.5.
   a Calculate the critical angle for this prism.
   b Show how such a prism may be used to turn a ray of light
      i through 90°
      ii through 180°.

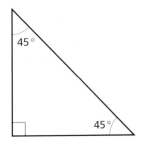

Figure 3.4.40

5 The horn of a stationary car emits sound at a frequency of 440 Hz. What frequency of note will you hear if you drive towards this car at 20 m s^{-1}?
(The speed of sound in air = 340 m s^{-1}.)

6 Two cars drive along the same road towards each other, one at 15 m s^{-1} and the other at 12 m s^{-1}. Each car horn sounds at 256 Hz. Calculate the frequency that the driver of each car hears coming from the other car.

7 Figure 3.4.12 (on page 252) shows a distant object receding at a velocity of 0.41c (41% of the speed of light). Use Hubble's law to calculate how far away this object is from Earth. Take the Hubble constant as 1.7 x 10^4 m s^{-1}/(million light-years).

8 An optical fibre is made of a thin strand of glass with a refractive index of 1.5. If the fibre is surrounded by air, what is the maximum angle a ray of light may make with the glass–air boundary and still remain trapped in the fibre?

9 Glass used to make optical fibres absorbs a small amount of the energy of light travelling through it. The *half-value thickness* of such a piece of glass is the distance through which the light must travel for exactly half of its energy to be absorbed. The half-value thickness of a particular piece of glass used to make optical fibres is 1.2 km at a given frequency. A signal with this frequency travelling along the fibre will need to be processed once two-thirds of the light's intensity has been absorbed by the glass. By plotting a suitable graph, estimate the intervals along the fibre at which this will need to be done.

10 In strong light the pupil of a cat narrows to a vertical slit about 0.5 mm across. Can a cat resolve two white mice sitting 5 cm apart a distance of 20 m away under these conditions?

11 According to press reports, the camera on a 'spy in the sky' aeroplane can distinguish detail as small as a person from an altitude of 27 km. According to Rayleigh's criterion, how large must the camera lens be in order to make this possible?

Developing Key Skills

The ultrasound department of a hospital requires a leaflet for patients which will explain to them
- what ultrasound is,
- how it is used to produce an image of the inside of a patient's body, and
- why it is harmless.

Produce a leaflet suitable for use with patients who have no knowledge of science, and who will require ideas to be explained in simple, reassuring language.

[Key Skills opportunities: C, IT]

1

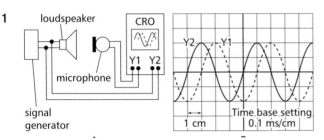

In an experiment to investigate progressive sound waves in air, the output from a signal generator is fed to the Y2 input of a double beam oscilloscope as well as to a loudspeaker, as shown in figure A. The signal picked up by the microphone a short distance from the loudspeaker is applied to the Y1 input of the same oscilloscope.

a i Use the Y2 trace on figure B to determine the frequency of the sound waves.

ii By what fraction of a cycle does the Y1 trace lag behind the Y2 trace?

iii Given that the Y2 trace remains stationary, explain why the Y1 trace moves to the right when the microphone is moved further away from the loudspeaker.

iv When the microphone is moved 34 mm further away from the loudspeaker the Y1 trace moves 10 mm to the right. Calculate the wavelength of the sound waves.

v Calculate a value for the speed of sound waves in air.

(7 marks)

b i State how you could use a single beam oscilloscope to show the phase difference between the two signals.

ii Draw the trace you would expect to see on the screen if the phase difference between the two signals was the same as that shown in figure B. **(2 marks)**

(AQA specimen)

2 a State two features which are common to all sections of the electromagnetic spectrum. **(2 marks)**

b Below is a part-completed table summarising several features of different sections of the electromagnetic spectrum. Complete the table with brief statements for six sections of the spectrum.

radiation	typical wavelength	method of production	a use
gamma (γ)			
	10^{-10} m	stopping high speed electrons at a target	
	10^{-8} m		
light		from very hot objects	sight, photography
infra-red			heat from the Sun
	10 m	high frequency oscillation of electrons	

(13 marks)

(OCR specimen)

3 Sonar is a method of detecting underwater objects by transmitting a pulse of ultrasound and detecting the reflected pulse. An anchored sonar buoy is immersed in water, as shown in the diagram, and sends out waves in all directions.

speed of sound in air $= 330$ m s^{-1}
speed of sound in water $= 1400$ m s^{-1}
speed of sound in rock $= 3200$ m s^{-1}

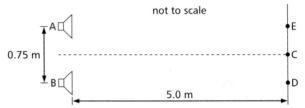

a Explain whether or not total internal reflection can occur for sound waves at
i the water–air interface,
ii the water–rock interface. **(3 marks)**

b Explaining your answers, sketch on a copy of the diagram the directions of sound waves initially travelling in the directions
i SA, after reaching the water surface,
ii SB, after reaching the water–rock interface. **(5 marks)**

(AQA 1999)

4 The diagram shows two identical loudspeakers, A and B, placed 0.75 m apart. Each loudspeaker emits sound of frequency 2000 Hz.

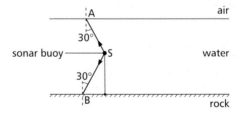

Point C is on a line midway between the speakers and 5.0 m away from the line joining the speakers. A listener at C hears a maximum intensity of sound. If the listener then moves from C to E or D, the sound intensity heard decreases to a minimum. Further movement in the same direction results in the repeated increase and decrease in the sound intensity.

Speed of sound in air $= 330$ m s^{-1}

a Explain why the sound intensity
i is a maximum at C,
ii is a minimum at D or E. **(4 marks)**

b Calculate
i the wavelength of the sound,
ii the distance CE. **(4 marks)**

(AQA 1999)

5 A stretched string on a stringed instrument has a vibrating length of
   1.16 m. It is bowed to set it oscillating and it is observed to undergo
   oscillations, as illustrated in the diagram.

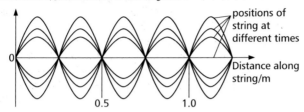

   a i Is this wave a progressive wave or a standing wave?
      ii Is this wave a transverse wave or a longitudinal wave?
                                                              (2 marks)
   b Explain how, as a result of the bow moving the string, this wave
      is formed.   **(4 marks)**
   c From the diagram deduce
      i the distance (metres) between two nodes,
      ii the wavelength (metres) of the wave.   **(2 marks)**
   d Discuss briefly whether such a wave can be polarised. **(3 marks)**
   e Give experimental details of how you would extend the
      investigation described in this question in order to determine the
      speed of the wave on the string.   **(6 marks)**

                                                           (OCR specimen)

6 a State the laws of refraction of light. Illustrate your answer with a
      diagram.   **(3 marks)**
   b Light is travelling in glass X with speed 1.9568×10^8 m s^{-1}. It
      reaches boundary with a different glass Y at an angle slightly
      greater than the critical angle of 87.60° and undergoes total
      internal reflection.
      i Explain, with the aid of a diagram, what is meant by the terms
         1. critical angle,
         2. total internal reflection.   **(3 marks)**
      ii Calculate the speed of light (m s^{-1}) in glass Y. **(4 marks)**
   c Calculations similar to that in **b** are important when considering
      the passage of a pulse of light along an optic fibre. A fibre of
      length 10 km is made out of glass X. Some light is continually
      being reflected by the walls of the fibre, always having an angle
      of incidence equal to the critical angle.
      Calculate the extra distance (metres) travelled by this light when
      compared to light travelling along the axis of the fibre. **(4 marks)**
   d i Explain how the effect described in **c** causes dispersion of a
         pulse.
      ii Suggest how this effect may be minimised.   **(4 marks)**

                                                           (OCR specimen)

7 a i Explain why, in general, a wave crossing a boundary between
         two media at non-normal incidence changes its direction.
                                                              (4 marks)
      ii Define the term *refractive index*.   **(2 marks)**
   b A pair of parallel slits (Young's slits) is illuminated by
      monochromatic light of wavelength 590 nm. It is found that,
      when one slit is covered by a thin film of transparent material of
      refractive index 1.55, the zero-order bright fringe (corresponding
      to equal transit times for waves coming from the two slits) shifts
      to a position previously occupied by the 12th-order bright fringe.

      i Explain how the original position of the zero order fringe
         (before insertion of the transparent material) could be
         established experimentally.   **(4 marks)**
      ii Calculate the thickness of the film.   **(6 marks)**
   c The thin film is removed, and a tube with transparent ends is
      placed in front of one of the slits. The tube can be filled with air
      under pressure. Explain how the apparatus could be used to
      investigate how variations of pressure affect the refractive index
      of air.   **(4 marks)**

                                                              (OCR 1998)

8 a A radio programme is to be received nationwide. It is much
      cheaper to achieve this using AM transmissions on the LW
      waveband than using FM transmissions on the VHF waveband.
      i Explain, with the aid of diagrams (one in each case), what is
         meant by
         1. *AM* transmissions,
         2. *FM* transmissions.
      ii State two reasons why music broadcast on VHF/FM radio
         generally sounds much better than the same music broadcast
         on LW/AM radio.
      iii Suggest why the LW waveband system would be cheaper than
         the VHF waveband system.   **(7 marks)**
   b When a signal is transmitted along a cable or an optic fibre, the
      signal is attenuated.
      i What is meant by *attenuation*?
      ii Suggest why attenuation is a more serious problem when
         transmitting a signal in analogue form than in digital form.
                                                              (4 marks)
   c The diagram illustrates a satellite in geostationary orbit receiving
      signals from the Earth's surface for television broadcasts. These
      signals are re-transmitted back to Earth.

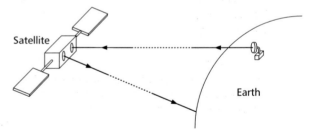

      i State a typical wavelength for the signal transmitted from
         Earth to the satellite.
      ii Give two reasons why the wavelength of the signal received
         by the satellite is made to be different from that transmitted
         back to Earth.
      iii Suggest why an aerial, situated near the Equator to receive
         signals from the satellite, would be inclined at a different angle
         to the horizontal compared with that for a similar aerial near
         the North pole.   **(4 marks)**

                                                              (OCR 1998)

9 Parallel light is incident normally on a diffraction grating.
   a Light of wavelength 5.9×10^{-7} m gives a first order image at
      20.0° to the normal. Determine the number of lines per metre on
      the grating.   **(2 marks)**

b Light of another wavelength gives a second order image at 48.9° to the normal. Calculate this wavelength. **(2 marks)**

c What is the highest order in which both these wavelengths will be visible? Justify your answer. **(2 marks)**

(AQA 1998)

10 When monochromatic light of wavelength λ passes through glass the refractive index, *n*, of the glass is found to depend on λ. The Cauchy equation

$$n = A + \frac{B}{\lambda^2}$$

gives the approximate relation between λ and *n*. *A* and *B* are constants for a particular glass. The table shows corresponding values of *n* and λ for a sample of glass.

λ/nm	361	434	589	768	1200
n	1.5464	1.5333	1.5198	1.5136	1.5074

a A linear graph could be obtained by plotting *n* on the *y*-axis against $1/\lambda^2$ on the *x*-axis.
Calculate values to enable you to plot the linear graph and insert them in a copy of the table. **(2 marks)**

b On graph paper
  i label the axes appropriately,
  ii plot the points for your linear graph, and
  iii draw the best straight line through your points. **(4 marks)**

c **i** State how the values of constants *A* and *B* could be obtained from your graph.
  ii Use your graph to find the values of *A* and *B*, giving the units, if appropriate. **(5 marks)**

d The *dispersive power*, ω, of the glass is its ability to spread out colours. It may typically be defined as

$$\omega = \frac{n_{486} - n_{656}}{n_{589} - 1},$$

where n_{486}, n_{656} and n_{589} are the refractive indices at wavelengths of 486 nm, 656 nm and 589 nm, respectively.
Use the values from your graph to calculate ω. **(2 marks)**

(AQA 1998)

11 The diagram shows water waves, produced by two sources A and B, in a ripple tank. The circles represent adjacent crests at a particular instant.

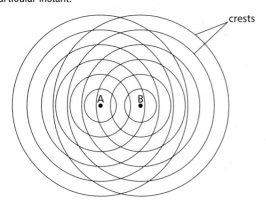

The waves are moving with a speed of 80 mm s⁻¹.

a Using the diagram, make measurements to calculate the wavelength (mm) and the frequency of the waves. Give your answers to two significant figures. **(4 marks)**

b On a copy of the diagram, draw
  i a line joining successive points at which maximum constructive interference takes place. Mark this line C.
  ii a line joining successive points at which the adjacent destructive interference takes place. Mark this line D. **(4 marks)**

(OCR 1998)

12 The diagram shows the path of a ray of monochromatic light through a glass prism.

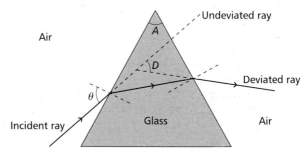

a **i** Describe how you would measure the angle *A* of the prism to within ±0.5%, i.e. to about a quarter of a degree.
  ii It is suggested that the ray shown would follow exactly the same path if its direction were reversed.
  Describe how you would test this suggestion experimentally. **(6 marks)**

b As the angle of incidence θ is varied, the angle of deviation *D* also varies. When *A* is equal to 60.0°, a series of corresponding values of θ and *D* were found experimentally with the following results:

θ/deg	32.5	35.0	37.5	40.0	45.0	50.0	55.0	60.0	65.0
D/deg	44.8	42.4	40.5	39.0	37.5	37.3	37.9	39.0	40.6

  i Plot a graph of *D* against θ.
  Write down the value of the minimum deviation D_m and the corresponding value of the angle of incidence.
  ii When the deviation is a minimum, the ray passes symmetrically through the prism. The refractive index *n* of the glass of the prism is then given by

$$n \sin\left(\frac{A}{2}\right) = \sin\left(\frac{A + D_m}{2}\right)$$

where *A*, here 60.0°, is the angle at the top of the prism.
Use the equation to calculate a value for *n*. **(10 marks)**

  c **i** When the angle *A* of the prism is less than about 10° the prism is a thin wedge of glass. The deviation *D* is then small and is constant over a wide range of values of the angle of incidence. Use the equation in **b ii**, together with the small angle approximation sin *x* ≈ *x* (in radians), to predict how *D* (=D_m) depends on *n* and *A* for thin prisms.

ii The deviation produced by a thin prism, though independent of θ, does depend on the refractive index n of the glass. The value of n depends in turn on the wavelength (colour) of the light. The table below gives the values of n for four colours for a prism with $A = 5.00°$.

Colour	red	green	blue	violet
n	1.520	1.526	1.531	1.538

Draw up a table of corresponding values of n and D for this prism. Plot a graph of D against n. **(8 marks)**
(Total 24 marks)
(Edexcel 1999)

13 a Explain:
i the meaning of *plane-polarization* (of light waves); **(1 mark)**
ii why sound waves cannot be plane-polarized. **(1 mark)**
b Figures A and B show an experiment in which a student observes two parallel beams of light through a Polaroid filter. In A the beam consists of unpolarized light. In B the beam is **partially** plane-polarized.

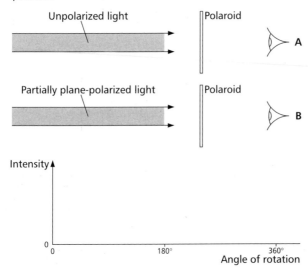

On a copy of the axes shown, sketch **two** graphs, labelled (i) and (ii) respectively, to show how you might expect the intensity of the light reaching the student to vary as the filter is turned through 360° in its own plane. **(5 marks)**
c Give an example of plane-polarization that does not involve light. Explain how the plane-polarization may be detected. **(2 marks)**
(OCR 1998)

14 The diagrams show a device for detecting when the level of liquid in a tank is above a certain level. The device uses a solid glass rod bent into a U-shape. The refractive indices n are shown on the diagram.

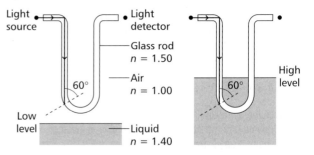

Calculate the critical angle for the glass/air interface.
Calculate the critical angle for the glass/liquid interface. **(3 marks)**
Complete the diagrams to show the path of the ray of light when
i the liquid level is low,
ii the liquid level is high. **(2 marks)**
Explain how the liquid level detector works. **(2 marks)**
(Total 7 marks)
(Edexcel 1999)

15 A piezoelectric probe produces ultrasound pulses with a frequency of 3.5×10^6 Hz.
a A pulse is sent from the probe through soft tissue during a medical examination. An echo of the pulse is detected after $26.6 \, \mu s$.
The speed of ultrasound through soft tissue is $1.54 \, \text{km s}^{-1}$.
i At what depth (metres) is the pulse reflected? **(2 marks)**
ii Calculate the wavelength (metres) of the ultrasound in the soft tissue. **(1 mark)**
b Suggest a type of medical investigation in which it would be advantageous to use a probe with a lower frequency, such as 1.5×10^6 Hz, rather than the higher frequency probe. Explain your suggestion. **(2 marks)**
(OCR 1998)

WAVES CONCEPT MAP

How to use the map

The map is a way of representing the structure of the knowledge contained in this section. It is designed to be used as you get towards the end of the section, when you should begin to see a pattern in the key concepts you have met. The map shows how one area of knowledge builds on another, so that more complex ideas develop as you go through the section.

As you study, try to think about how you learn best. Do you prefer to have understood one idea completely before going on to another? Or do you like to meet several related new ideas and then put these together rather like you might put together several pieces of a jigsaw at once?

The concept map will help you to see how ideas are related. You can use it to help you to put your knowledge and understanding in some sort of order so that you can organise your learning. You can also use it to organise your revision at the end of the section and before your examinations. Alternatively, try drawing up your own concept map as you revise.

Notes on the map

The key ideas in the section are contained in the green boxes. Solid lines with arrows between these boxes show how ideas in the section develop. Where parts of this section relate to other sections, dashed lines with arrows indicate this – the links are described in yellow boxes. Finally, some sections introduce and apply key mathematical skills – this is indicated by purple boxes, with double arrows indicating areas where the skill is applied.

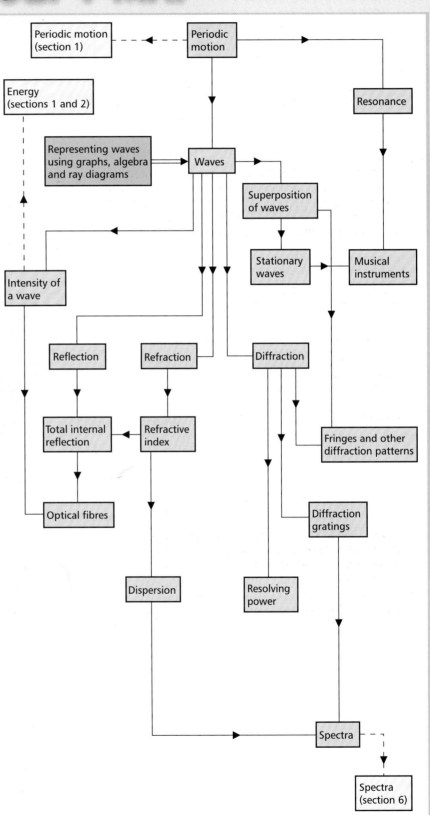

3

4 ELECTRICITY

Introduction

Those of us who live in the developed world take electricity largely for granted – at least, until there is a power cut. Electricity's usefulness lies in its ability to provide energy to run countless different devices, from underground trains to digital watches, and in the ease with which this energy may be transmitted through wires and cables. Electricity is also the secret behind communication using electromagnetic waves, as we saw in section 3.

Electricity has been known from ancient times, when it was discovered that a piece of amber that had been rubbed with cloth or fur would attract small hairs and other light objects. The Ancient Greek word for amber (ελεκτρον) gives us our modern word **electron**. Our understanding of an electric current as a flow of charged particles has developed over many years, although the idea that there are two types of charge, positive and negative, was first proposed over 250 years ago.

In this section we shall begin by reviewing our ideas about electricity, thinking carefully about the terms we use to describe the behaviour of electric circuits and their component parts. Following this, we shall look at the relationships between such variables as current and potential difference in different kinds of circuits, developing the tools which will help us to describe and explain what is happening in them. We shall then take a look at capacitors, essential components in many circuits, especially those where the current through the circuit changes with time – as it does with alternating currents, which we explore next. We finish the section with a brief introduction to the world of electronics.

Figure 4.1 Colourful electronic components of many different shapes and sizes transformed life in the second half of the twentieth century.

FARADAY AND AMPÈRE – A MEETING OF MINDS

Michael Faraday was born in 1791, the son of a blacksmith. The family was so poor that at one stage Michael had to survive with nothing more to eat than a single loaf of bread a week. The Faradays belonged to the Sandemanian Church, an exclusive Christian sect, and Michael received little formal schooling. Apprenticed to a London bookbinder, he took the opportunity to read the scientific books he was binding. He attended free science lectures, and when a client of his master offered him the chance to attend a series of lectures given by the eminent chemist Sir Humphrey Davy, Faraday not only went along, but also illustrated and bound his notes of the occasions. These he sent to Davy, at the Royal Institution in London. Later, when one of Davy's laboratory assistants had a fight with a glass blower, Davy sacked the man and offered Faraday the job. Faraday never looked back.

In 1813, just a year later, Davy invited Faraday to accompany him on a trip to Europe. Faraday greeted the opportunity to travel and meet other European scientists with enthusiasm, in spite of the fact that France and England were at war.

Faraday and Davy met a number of famous scientists on their tour, and one of their most interesting meetings was on 23 November 1813, when André-Marie Ampère visited the British scientists, bringing them a sample of a new and unknown substance he had discovered. In little over two weeks Davy, with help from Faraday, had determined that the substance was a new element, called it iodine and written a paper on the subject – not entirely endearing himself to Ampère! A few years later, both Faraday and Ampère were to be inspired by the work of Hans Christian Oersted, who showed that a compass needle is affected when placed near a wire carrying electric current. This triggered ideas which in Faraday led to the development of the first electric motor, and in Ampère to the measurement of the force between two wires carrying a current.

It is astonishing that one man could work on so many areas of chemistry and physics with such success. Faraday identified new elements, worked on stainless steel and optical glass, made major breakthroughs in our understanding of electricity and electromagnetism, invented the first electric motor and the dynamo, unravelled the mysteries of electrolysis, and made the first steps into field theory. On top of this he ran the Royal Institution and set up the Christmas lectures for young people.

In his private life Michael Faraday was just as dedicated as in his work, but his dedication was to his beloved wife Sarah, his family and his church. Sarah and Michael were close partners all through their marriage. And to the Sandemanian church – demanding, challenging, unyielding – Michael Faraday gave total loyalty, even though at times the conflict between his work and fame and the beliefs of his church community must have been very hard to deal with.

At the end of Faraday's life came the great sadness of his decline into senility. It distressed his wife and family to see his struggle to remember the simplest things. Faraday himself was long aware of and frustrated by the deterioration of his mental powers. But nothing which occurred at the end of his life could dim the brilliance of the legacy that he left behind – a legacy which still affects all our lives today.

Figure 4.1.1 Michael Faraday started the Christmas lectures for young people at the Royal Institution in 1826. Between 1827 and 1862 he personally delivered 19 series of these lectures.

Figure 4.1.2 Professor Susan Greenfield became Director of the Royal Institution in 1998, continuing in Faraday's footsteps. The Christmas lectures continue to this day, reaching millions through the medium of television, made possible by Faraday's work.

Electric current

A flow of charge

The movement of charged particles which we call an **electric current** is something that cannot usually be seen – for example, we cannot observe electrons flowing through a metal wire. We can see the *effect* of an electric current, however, which may cause:

- a magnetic field
- chemical changes (for example, the formation of copper metal when a current flows through a solution containing copper ions)
- an increase in temperature of whatever is carrying the current.

Current and charge

If we have a wire carrying a current I, it seems reasonable to assume that the total amount of charge Q passing a given point in time t will depend on two things, namely I and t. This means that:

$$Q = It$$

The unit of electric current

The unit of electric current is one of the fundamental quantities in physical measurements (see box 'Units', page 7). All the other units used in measuring electrical quantities are derived from it, so they are all defined in terms of the unit of current or another unit derived from it.

The SI unit of current is the **ampere**, which is defined in terms of the force between two wires carrying currents:

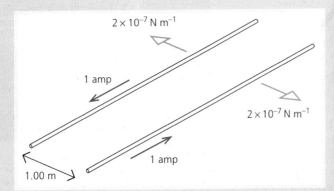

One ampere is the constant current which, when passing through two infinitely long parallel straight conductors of negligible cross-section placed 1 m apart in a vacuum, produces a force between them of 2×10^{-7} N per metre of their length.

Figure 4.1.3 The situation described in the definition of the ampere is not practical, since it would be impossible to achieve and almost impossible to measure the force produced with any degree of accuracy. At the National Physical Laboratory in the UK, this moving-coil balance in a vacuum chamber is used to measure current with great precision. This instrument then functions as a **primary standard** against which other instruments may be calibrated.

The SI unit of charge is the **coulomb** (C), where 1 C = 1 A s, that is, the charge passing a given point in a wire when a current of 1 A flows through the wire for 1 s. We can also write:

$$I = Q/t$$

which shows that *current is the rate of flow of charge*.

Circuits

For an electric current to flow, a complete circuit is needed. In order to explain this, a model is often used in which water flowing through pipes represents electric current. We have already seen in section 2.3 how heat and electricity may both be modelled as fluids. Whilst this is a satisfactory model in some respects it is unsatisfactory in others, and it is as well to recognise this now – like many models, the 'electricity as a fluid' model collapses if pushed too far (see box 'The flow model for electricity' on page 280).

Consider a water circuit in which water causes a turbine to rotate, as in the diagram, figure 4.1.4.

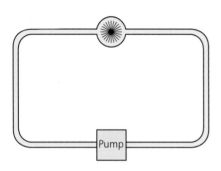
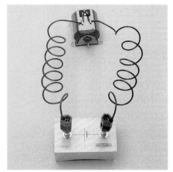

Figure 4.1.4

This situation is similar to a battery driving an electric motor, as shown in the photograph. In each case 'something' travels round a complete circuit. Energy is transferred from one place in the circuit to another by 'something' that moves round the circuit. Studies of the structure of metallic conductors suggest that in metals it is free electrons which make up the current in an electrical circuit – an electric current in a metal is nothing more than a flow of electrons carrying negative charge. Electric current is not always a flow of electrons, however. For example, in an electrolyte (a conducting solution – salt solution, for instance) positive and negative ions act as charge carriers. By convention, electric current flows in the direction of the flow of positive charge, so electrons flow one way round a circuit while conventional electric current flows the other. (The mechanisms by which electric currents flow through conductors are explored in section 4.2.)

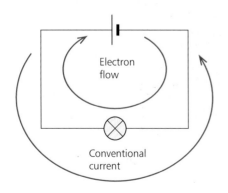
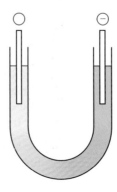

Figure 4.1.5 Conventional current flows from + to − while electrons move from − to +. As long as you are clear about the convention you are using, it does not matter whether you use the direction of flow of electrons or the direction of flow of conventional electric current when referring to the current through a wire – but you must be consistent. In this book we shall use the flow of conventional current in all cases. As current flows through a solution containing blue copper ions and yellow chromate ions, the positive copper ions move in one direction, while the negative chromate ions move in the opposite direction. In this case *both* are involved in the flow of electric current.

Energy and electricity

Electromotive force

Anyone who has carried out simple investigations into electrical circuits is familiar with the need for an energy source to make an electric current flow. In many cases this energy source is a **cell**, in which chemicals react to cause an electric current to flow when the terminals of the cell are joined by a conductor. The energy changes occurring in this situation are sometimes modelled as shown in figure 4.1.6.

The 'cell' in the water circuit provides energy to each bucketful of water passing through it. The amount of energy per bucketful is a measure of the effect of the cell on the flow of water round the circuit. This is true for the electrical circuit too, where we can measure the amount of energy supplied by the cell to each 'bucketful' of charge flowing through it. The amount of energy supplied to each unit of charge is called the **electromotive force** E or e.m.f. of the cell. In the SI system, the unit of e.m.f. is the **volt** (V). A cell is said to have an e.m.f. of 1 V when it supplies 1 J of energy to each 1 C of charge flowing through it, in other words:

$$\mathbf{1\ V = 1\ J\ C^{-1}}$$

Of course, there are other energy changes taking place in a circuit too. The energy stored in the chemicals of a cell can cause charges to flow through a circuit containing a resistance. The energy carried by moving charges can cause (for example) the filament of a lamp to become 'white-hot' and emit infra-red and visible electromagnetic radiation. In this case we refer to a **potential difference** or p.d. across the object in which the energy carried by the current causes a change to occur. Potential difference has the same unit as e.m.f. since it also measures energy transferred per unit charge. We shall see in section 4.2 how energy changes are related to changes in potential difference.

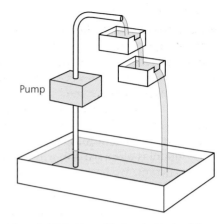

Figure 4.1.6 In this model of an electric circuit the cell is seen as a pump that increases the gravitational potential energy of water in the circuit, which then flows round the rest of the circuit under the influence of gravity.

The flow model for electricity

We have already mentioned the care which must be taken in thinking of electric current too literally in terms of flow. One example will illustrate the problem.

A lamp may be connected to a suitable cell via a switch using leads that are (say) 2 m long. If the switch is closed, the lamp lights. One explanation for this is to say that energy is being transferred from the cell to the lamp, and that this energy is being carried by a flow of electrons. This is very similar to the way water in a central heating system carries energy from the boiler to the radiators – a very straightforward analogy.

The situation seems less straightforward if we note that the lamp lights almost immediately the switch is closed, and then look at the speed at which the electrons travel through the wire. We cannot do this by experiment, but some fairly simple physics leads us to a relationship (the **transport equation** – see section 4.2, page 308) that enables us to carry out a calculation. In the situation just described, with copper wires connecting the cell and lamp, the electrons in the copper are unlikely to be travelling faster than 0.01 mm s^{-1}. This suggests that an electron would take around 2 days to travel from the cell to the lamp – so it seems unlikely that it is the flow of electrons that transfers energy from the cell to the lamp. A practical investigation to measure the speed of an electric pulse along a wire (see section 4.4, pages 346–7) confirms that this speed is very high – close to the speed of light in a vacuum. This suggests that the energy may be carried by an electromagnetic wave or something similar, and that a simple visual model of electrons 'picking up' energy as they pass through the cell and then 'unloading' it as they pass through the lamp is totally inadequate. Instead, we should visualise the cell as causing an electric field in the wires. It is this field that causes the current to flow and provides the means for transferring the energy from cell to lamp.

We shall develop the ideas of electric fields and energy further in section 4.2.

Voltage, p.d. and e.m.f.

A little care is needed when talking about current and voltage in a circuit (the word 'voltage' is often used instead of the terms 'e.m.f.' and 'p.d.'). Since current flows *through* a conductor, it makes sense to say, for example, 'the current through the lamp is 0.2 A'. However, p.d. is measured *across* components in a circuit, so it is sensible to make statements like 'the p.d. across the motor is 2.5 V'. It is particularly important not to talk in terms like 'the voltage *through* the lamp' – such statements are nonsense! However, e.m.f. is usually thought of as a property of a cell or battery in a circuit, so it is reasonable to speak of 'the e.m.f. *of* the battery'.

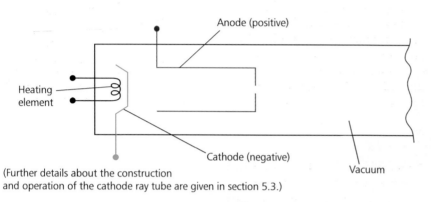

Anode (positive)

Heating element

Cathode (negative)

Vacuum

(Further details about the construction and operation of the cathode ray tube are given in section 5.3.)

Figure 4.1.7 Electron guns have transformed the world in the last 50 or so years – they form the basis of the cathode ray tube, without which televisions and computers would be very different, if they existed at all. The acceleration of electrons also plays a vital role in the production of X-rays, as we shall see in section 6.

Transferring energy in the electron gun

The energy transferred to charges moving through a potential difference in a vacuum is transferred to the charges themselves as kinetic energy. The device that does this is called an **electron gun**, shown in figure 4.1.7. In the electron gun, electrons are 'boiled off' a metal plate in an evacuated enclosure by heating it with an element through which an electric current is passed. The electrons are accelerated towards an anode, which is made positive with respect to the cathode. The overall effect of this is to transfer energy from the power supply to the electrons themselves:

$$\text{Energy transferred to electron} = \frac{\text{charge on}}{\text{electron}} \times \frac{\text{p.d. between}}{\text{cathode and anode}}$$
$$= eV$$
$$= E_k$$
$$= \tfrac{1}{2} m_e v^2$$

While some electrons hit the anode to return to the power supply, others emerge through the hole in the anode with considerable speed.

Figure 4.1.8 Cathode ray tubes, for so long the central component in the construction of televisions and computer monitors, are rapidly being replaced by new 'flat screens'. These use semiconductor technology similar to the light-emitting diodes (LEDs) we shall meet later in this section.

Measuring current and potential difference

Current and potential difference are measured using ammeters and voltmeters respectively. The simplest type of each of these instruments is a **moving-coil meter**, which consists of a coil of many turns of fine wire suspended in a magnetic field by means of a low-friction bearing. This coil rotates through an angle θ when a current passes through it, and the instrument is so arranged that $\theta \propto I$. (The construction of a meter of this type is explained in more detail in section 5.4.)

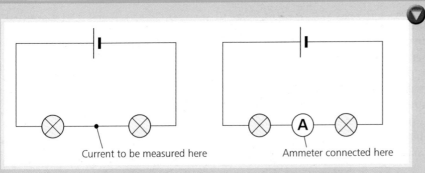

Current to be measured here   Ammeter connected here

Figure 4.1.9 Ammeters are used to measure the current at a specific point in a circuit. They are therefore connected into the circuit in series, at the point where the current is to be measured.

A moving-coil meter like that just described is sometimes referred to as a **galvanometer**. A basic galvanometer may be used to measure a range of currents, from a few microamps up to several amps. To do this, special adaptors called **shunts** are used. There is more about this in section 4.2.

A galvanometer may also be used to measure potential difference. An adaptor of a different kind, called a **multiplier**, is used to enable a range of p.d.s to be measured. Again, this is described in more detail in section 4.2.

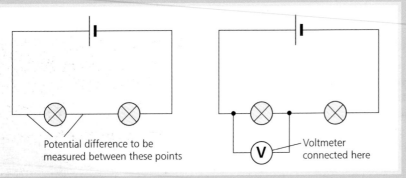

Potential difference to be measured between these points   Voltmeter connected here

Figure 4.1.10 Voltmeters are used to measure the potential difference between two points in a circuit. They are therefore connected into the circuit in parallel, between the points where the potential difference is to be measured.

Digital instruments are becoming increasingly common for measuring currents and p.d.s, since they are accurate, reliable, robust and easy to read.

Resistance

Ohm's law

Although current and p.d. measure different things, they are related to each other. If we connect a battery to a length of resistance wire, we can measure the current through the wire using 1, 2, 3 or 4 cells. Such an investigation leads to results such as those shown in figure 4.1.11 and table 4.1.1.

The results show that there is a simple relationship between the p.d. across the ends of the wire and the current through it – doubling the p.d. doubles the current. Repeating the investigation with other wires gives results showing a similar relationship between p.d. and current – the graphs are always straight

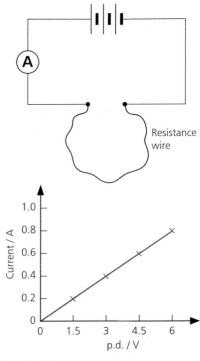

Resistance wire

Figure 4.1.11

Number of cells	p.d. across ends of wire/V	Current/A
1	1.5	0.2
2	3.0	0.4
3	4.5	0.6
4	6.0	0.8

Table 4.1.1

lines through the origin, although the slopes are different. This relationship was first discovered by the German physicist Georg Ohm in 1826 and is called **Ohm's law**:

> **Provided the temperature and other physical factors remain constant, the current through a wire is proportional to the potential difference across its ends.**

If we divide the potential difference across the ends of the wire by the current through it, we get a constant figure for a given piece of wire. The figure is the **resistance** of the wire, and represents the wire's opposition to current. A conductor has a resistance of 1 ohm (1 Ω) if a current of 1 A flows through it when it has a p.d. of 1 V across it. This leads to a very simple mathematical relationship which states Ohm's law:

$$I = V/R$$

The resistance of a conductor

Resistivity

As the simple investigation described above shows, the resistance of two different wires is not necessarily the same. Investigations show that the resistance of a uniform conductor depends on:

- its length (l)
- its cross-sectional area (A)
- the material of which it is made.

The relationship between resistance and these three variables is straightforward:

$$R = \frac{\rho l}{A}$$

where ρ is the **resistivity** of the material from which the conductor is made. In the SI system, resistivity is measured in Ω m. Table 4.1.2 shows the resistivities of some materials, and also how this changes with temperature.

Material	Resistivity ρ/Ω m at 20 °C	Change in ρ per °C/%
Silver	1.6×10^{-8}	$+0.38$
Copper	1.7×10^{-8}	$+0.39$
Aluminium	2.8×10^{-8}	$+0.2$
Constantan	4.9×10^{-7}	$+0.001$
Germanium	4.2×10^{-1}	
Silicon	2.6×10^{3}	
Poly(ethene)	2×10^{11}	
Glass	$\sim 10^{12}$	
Epoxy resin	$\sim 10^{15}$	

Ohm's law – worked example

A wire has a p.d. of 5 V across it, and its resistance is 2 Ω. What is the current through it?

$$I = V/R$$

so:

$$I = 5 \text{ V} / 2 \text{ } \Omega$$
$$= 2.5 \text{ A}$$

Table 4.1.2 Resistivity varies greatly between materials, and is also dependent on temperature. Note the small change in resistivity with temperature for constantan, an alloy of copper and nickel used where it is important to know the resistance accurately. As some materials are cooled to very low temperatures, **superconductivity** may result – this phenomenon is explored in the section 4.2 focus on page 306.

Conductance

Conductance, G, measures the inverse of resistance – the ease with which a conductor will permit a current to flow. Conductance is defined as I/V $(= R^{-1})$, and depends on the same quantities as resistance, except that ρ is replaced by σ, the **electrical conductivity** of the material of which the wire is made:

$$G = \frac{\sigma A}{l}$$

The SI unit of conductance is the **siemens** (S), where $1\ \text{S} = 1\ \Omega^{-1}$. Electrical conductivity is measured in $\Omega^{-1}\ \text{m}^{-1}$.

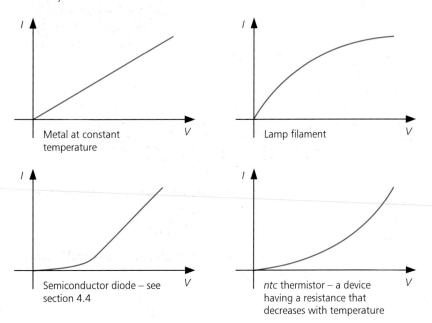

Figure 4.1.12

Ohmic and non-ohmic conductors

Not all circuit elements (conductors) have the simple current–voltage graphs seen in figure 4.1.11. If the current through a conductor and the p.d. across its ends are explored, the relationship is found to vary according to the circuit element, as shown in figure 4.1.12. Conductors for which I–V graphs are straight lines are said to be **ohmic conductors**, for example, a metal at a constant temperature. Where the I–V graph is non-linear, the conductor is said to be **non-ohmic** – a lamp filament and a semiconductor diode are two examples of non-ohmic conductors. The change in resistivity with temperature is explored further in section 4.2, page 303.

Power and work in electrical circuits

If we consider a lamp in a circuit, the potential difference across it measures the energy E transferred to the lamp per unit charge flowing through it, while the current measures the rate of flow of charge through it:

$$V = \frac{E}{Q} \qquad I = \frac{Q}{t}$$

Ohm and his law

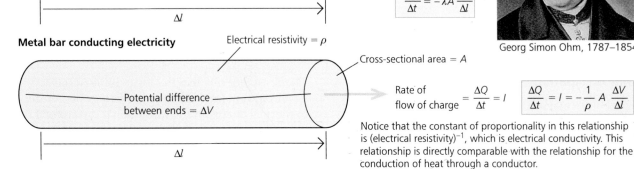

Figure 4.1.13

Ohm was led to his law by reasoning that there was a direct analogy between the conduction of heat and the conduction of electricity, as illustrated in figure 4.1.13. He saw that the electric potential gradient in the conductor is analogous to the temperature gradient, and that electric current is analogous to the flow of heat. His reasoning went like this. The electric field E in the conductor causes the electrons to move with an average velocity (called their 'drift velocity'), v:

$$v \propto E$$

The current flowing through the conductor is proportional to this drift velocity:

$$I \propto v, \text{ so } I \propto E$$

The current is also proportional to the cross-sectional area of the conductor, A:

$$I \propto AE$$

The strength of the electric field in the conductor is $\Delta V / \Delta l$ (see section 5.3, page 418), so:

$$I \propto A\Delta V / \Delta l$$

If a constant of proportionality $1/\rho$ is inserted in this equation we get:

$$I = \frac{1}{\rho} \frac{A \, \Delta V}{\Delta l}$$

If we remember that:

$$R = \frac{\rho \Delta l}{A}$$

then we can write:

$$I = \frac{\Delta V}{R}$$

If we multiply the p.d. and the current together we have the rate at which energy is transferred to the lamp:

$$VI = \frac{EQ}{Qt} = \frac{E}{t}$$

or:

$$P = VI$$

The rate at which energy is transferred to an element such as a lamp in a circuit is called the **power dissipation**. It is measured in **watts**.

Use of the relationship between V, I and R gives us two other relationships for power dissipation:

$$P = VI \quad \text{and} \quad V = IR$$

so:

$$P = (IR)I = I^2R \qquad \text{(relationship 1)}$$

and:

$$I = V/R$$

so:

$$P = V(V/R) = V^2/R \qquad \text{(relationship 2)}$$

Power dissipation – worked examples

A light bulb is marked '3.5 V, 0.1 A'. What will be the power dissipated in the bulb when the p.d. across it is 3.5 V?

$$P = VI = 3.5\ \text{V} \times 0.1\ \text{A} = 0.35\ \text{W}$$

The resistance of a length of wire is measured as 1.5 Ω. At what rate will electrical energy be transferred to thermal energy in the wire when a current of 2 A flows through it, assuming its resistance remains constant?

$$P = I^2R = (2\ \text{A})^2 \times 1.5\ \Omega = 6\ \text{W}$$

Sources of e.m.f.

The most important sources of e.m.f. are batteries, generators, fuel cells and solar cells. Generators will be covered in section 5.5 (page 459) when dealing with magnetic fields and electric current, but we shall consider briefly the important aspects of the other sources here.

Batteries

Batteries store energy in the form of chemicals, the energy being released when a conductor is connected between the terminals of the battery. Batteries are composed of **cells**, which are connected together in series in order to give a larger e.m.f. For example, a car battery consists of six cells, each of which has an e.m.f. of 2 V, so the total e.m.f. of the battery is $6 \times 2\ \text{V} = 12\ \text{V}$. A car battery is an example of a **secondary cell**. When the chemicals inside it have reacted and no more electricity can be drawn from it (the battery is 'flat'), the battery can be recharged by passing a current through it in the reverse direction. A **primary cell** cannot be recharged in this way. Figure 4.1.14 shows some examples of cells and batteries.

Figure 4.1.14 Cells and batteries provide a convenient source of electrical energy, although energy is stored in them as high-energy chemicals, not as electrical charge. A 'dry cell' may store as much as 6 kJ of energy, while a car battery may store up to 2 MJ.

Fuel cells

A **fuel cell** is very similar to a battery, in that it makes use of the energy stored in chemical substances. However, unlike the battery, in the fuel cell neither the high-energy reactants nor the low-energy products are stored inside the cell. The reactants are supplied from outside the cell and the products are removed from it once formed.

Probably the best known type of fuel cell is the type used in spacecraft. These cells 'burn' hydrogen and oxygen, forming water as they do so. The energy released from the hydrogen and oxygen in this process is collected as electrical energy rather than as thermal energy. Fuel cells are compact and clean – the water produced by the fuel cells on the US space laboratory *Skylab* was used for drinking and washing.

Solar cells

Solar cells transfer the energy carried by the electromagnetic waves that make up sunlight directly to an electrical circuit in order to make a current flow. They are made of very thin layers (about 10^{-6} m) of a semiconductor (see section 4.2), and generally produce e.m.f.s of a fraction of a volt. Only small currents can be drawn from the cells, so that large arrays of cells are needed to produce appreciable currents at useful voltages.

Figure 4.1.15 Although fuel cells are still at an early stage of development, they have been used with great success in space missions, where their small size and mass have obvious advantages.

Figure 4.1.16 The energy density of sunlight is low, and as yet solar cells are not very effective at harvesting it. Further work is needed for a significant proportion of our energy needs to be met in this way, especially in the UK!

SUMMARY

- When an electric current I flows through a conductor, the rate at which charge Q flows past a given point in the conductor is given by dQ/dt. For steady currents this may be written as $I = Q/t$.

- The amount of energy transferred when a charge of 1 C moves through a potential difference of 1 V is 1 J. $1\ V = 1\ J\ C^{-1}$.

- **Ohm's law** states that provided the temperature and other physical factors remain constant, the current through a wire is proportional to the p.d. across its ends. This leads to the relationship $I = V/R$, where R is the **resistance** of the wire.

- The **resistivity** ρ of a conductor is a measure of its resistance to current passing through it: $R = \rho l/A$, where l is the length of the wire and A its cross-sectional area.

- The **conductance** G measures how easily a conductor will allow current to flow: $G = \sigma A/l$, where σ is the **electrical conductivity** of the conductor, $= 1/\rho$.

- **Ohmic conductors** have a straight-line graph of I against V, while **non-ohmic conductors** have an I–V graph that is not a straight line.

- The **power dissipation** P is the rate of energy transfer of a device: $P = VI$ or $P = V^2/R$.

QUESTIONS

1 A torch bulb is rated as '2.5 V, 0.03 A'.
  a How much charge flows through the bulb in 1 minute when it is operating at its rated current?
  b At what rate is electrical energy dissipated in the lamp when it is operating at its rated voltage and current?

2 When cranking the engine, the starter motor of a car draws a current of 80 A from a 12 V battery.
  a If it takes 5 s for the motor to start the car, how much energy is delivered from the battery to the motor in this time?
  b If the generator of the car delivers 10 A to the battery as it is recharging, how long will it take for the battery to be recharged?

3 In a torch, two 1.5 V cells are connected in series with a bulb of resistance 8 Ω. Assuming that there is no other resistance in the circuit, how much energy is delivered to the bulb in 30 minutes?

4 The customer of an electricity supply company argues that the company should not charge him for electricity – after all, any electron that enters the wires in his home leaves again at some time and returns to the power station. What would you say in reply to this argument?

5 Table 4.1.3 gives details of two rechargeable batteries. The car battery is a regular cuboid, while the torch battery is a cylinder. The capacity of each battery is expressed in 'amp hours' (Ah), where 1 Ah indicates a current of 1 A for 1 hour.

	Capacity/Ah	Mass/kg	Dimensions/cm
Car battery	70	21	$25 \times 17 \times 15$
Torch battery	0.5	0.025	4.8 long $\times$ 0.8 diameter

Table 4.1.3

Calculate:
  a the energy stored in each of the batteries if the p.d. across the terminals of the car battery is 12 V, while that across the torch battery's terminals is 1.2 V
  b the energy stored per cubic centimetre in each battery
  c the energy stored in each battery per kilogram of battery mass.

6 Calculate the resistance of 2.00 m of constantan wire with a diameter of 1.00 mm (take the resistivity of constantan as 4.9×10^{-7} Ω m).

7 'Jump leads' may be used for starting the engine of one car using the battery in another car. One such set of leads is 4 m long, and consists of copper cables with a cross-sectional area of 13.6 mm^2.
  a What is the voltage drop along the length of one of these cables when it is carrying a current of 100 A? (Take the resistivity of copper as 1.7×10^{-8} Ω m.)
  b In practice, such cables are made of a number of strands of thin copper wire rather than a single strand of thicker wire – why?

8 An aluminium wire has a resistance of 0.20 Ω. The wire is stretched in such a way that its length doubles. What is its new resistance?

9 An iron lightning rod on top of a church consists of a single spike 1.5 m long and 1.5 cm in diameter. During a lightning strike this rod carries a current of 10 000 A. What is the potential difference along the length of the rod while this current flows? (Take the resistivity of iron as 1.0×10^{-7} Ω m.)

10 The resistance of dry skin is about 10^5 Ω cm^2. A man grasps two uninsulated wires in his fists.
  a If each wire has a diameter of 2.0 mm, and the man's fists make contact with them over a length of 9.0 cm, calculate the resistance the man's body offers to a current flowing through him from one wire to the other.
  b Calculate the current flowing through the man's body if the potential difference between the wires is:
    i 2 V
    ii 12 V
    iii 110 V
    iv 240 V
    v 3 kV.
  Comment on the effect the current is likely to have in each case.

11 A short-circuit has occurred somewhere along a pair of telephone cables 10 km long. In order to find the short, a telephone technician measures the resistance between the terminals at each end of the pair of wires. The resistance between the terminals at one end is 25 Ω, while that at the other end is 80 Ω. Where has the short-circuit occurred?

12 Table 4.1.4 shows some data for copper, aluminium and steel.

	Copper	Aluminium	Steel
Density/kg m^{-3}	8900	2700	7700
Electrical resistivity/Ω m	1.7×10^{-8}	2.8×10^{-8}	1.0×10^{-7}
Tensile strength/Pa	2.5×10^8	8×10^7	3.8×10^8

Table 4.1.4

Each overhead conductor in the National Grid consists of a thin core of steel cables surrounded by aluminium cables. Why is this construction used in preference to copper cables? Support your answer with any necessary calculations.

13 A tumble dryer operates at 240 V. When drying a load of clothes the dryer draws a current of 10 A. If the clothes weigh 2.5 kg when dry and 4.3 kg when wet, how long will the dryer take to dry the clothes, assuming all the electrical energy entering the dryer is used to evaporate the water? Take the specific latent heat of vaporisation of water as 2300 kJ kg^{-1}.

4.2 More about electricity

Having met some basic ideas about electricity in section 4.1, we shall now go on to develop these ideas further. In studying circuits it is necessary to have some idea of how the flow of current round a circuit behaves, and how this is related to the e.m.f. and the p.d. across components in the circuit. Connected with this is the need to be able to measure these quantities in practical situations. This section concludes by examining briefly the way in which electric currents are carried through materials, and why some materials are good conductors of electricity while others are not.

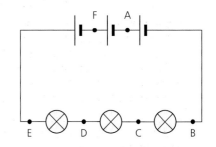

Figure 4.2.1

Circuits containing resistors

Currents in series and parallel circuits

Given three lamps, a source of e.m.f. (say three cells) and connecting wire we might well wish to know how the current flowing round a circuit made of these circuit elements behaves. Let us consider one of the possible ways of connecting these circuit elements.

Figure 4.2.1 shows the lamps connected **in series** (notice that the cells are connected in series too). What is the size of the current flowing at the different points A to F round the circuit? An ammeter inserted in the circuit at these points gives the same reading in each case. This is yet another reminder of the fluid model for electric current which we have seen before, since a flow model implies that whatever is flowing is *conserved* (remains constant) as it travels round the circuit.

A further check on the fluid model is given by connecting up the lamps as in figure 4.2.3, an arrangement in which the lamps are said to be **in parallel**.

In this circuit an ammeter inserted at points A to E in turn will show currents I_A, I_B, I_C, I_D and I_E at these respective points. Analysis of the results of such an investigation shows that:

$$I_A = I_E = I_B + I_C + I_D$$

which is once again in agreement with a flow model for electric current. This behaviour is described by **Kirchhoff's first law**:

> **The total current into any point in a circuit is equal to the total current out of that point.**

Potential differences in circuits

Having examined the size of an electric current as it flows round a circuit, we shall now look at the variation of potential difference between pairs of points round the circuit.

Consider once more the circuit in figure 4.2.1. To measure the p.d. across each lamp in turn we should need to connect a voltmeter between points B and C, then between points C and D, and finally between points D and E. This would give three readings of p.d. which we may call V_{BC}, V_{CD} and V_{DE} respectively. Measuring the p.d. between B and D and between C and E shows that:

$$V_{BD} = V_{BC} + V_{CD}$$

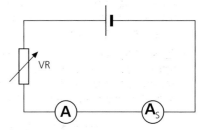

Figure 4.2.2 The fact that the current is constant all the way round a circuit provides us with a way of calibrating an ammeter A against another standard ammeter A_s, which could be a current balance (see figure 4.1.3, page 278) if extremely accurate calibration were required. VR is a variable resistor which allows the current through the circuit to be altered.

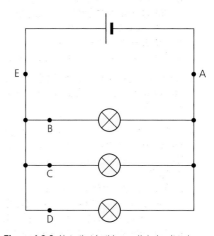

Figure 4.2.3 Note that in this parallel circuit only one cell is used. This causes the lamps to light with the same brightness as when connected in series using three cells. The reason for this will become apparent shortly.

and:

$$V_{CE} = V_{CD} + V_{DE}$$

from which it follows that:

$$V_{BE} = V_{BC} + V_{CD} + V_{DE}$$

Experiment confirms this, and shows that the same rule is obeyed when the p.d. across the cells is measured.

These results show that there is a simple relationship between p.d.s in a circuit, and that they can be regarded as 'adding up' as one goes round a circuit. However, this is not quite the full story, as some careful thought about energy changes in the circuit reveals.

What are the energy changes as current flows round the circuit in figure 4.2.4? The cells transfer electrical energy to the charge flowing through them, and this energy is then transferred in turn to the lamps as the charge flows through them. Clearly more energy cannot be transferred to the lamps than is transferred from the cells, and if no energy is transferred to the connecting wires in the circuit (which will be the case if the resistance of the wires is negligible), then the energy transferred from the cells must equal the energy transferred to the lamps. Since p.d. measures the energy transferred per coulomb of charge, this must mean that the p.d. across the lamps is the same as the p.d. across the cells.

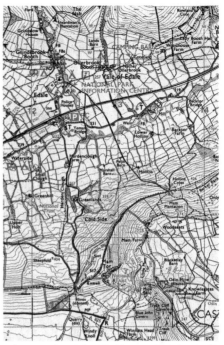

Figure 4.2.4 Going round the circuit with a centre-zero voltmeter produces the results shown here. The total fall in voltage on going from B to E across the lamps is the same as the rise in voltage on going from E to B across the cells. This is not so very different from walking round a closed path from Edale, shown on the map. At the end of the walk we should be most surprised to finish up a different height above sea level!

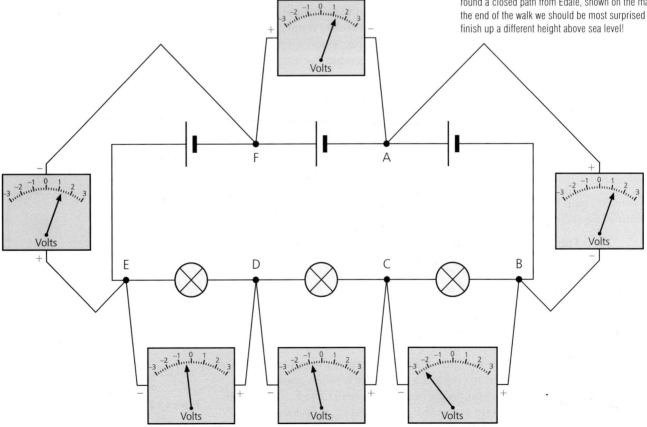

The analogy between the electrical circuit and the circular walk in figure 4.2.4 is a useful one. We can visualise a certain **potential** at point B in the electrical circuit, and another potential at point C. Between points B and C there is therefore a **potential difference**. If we wish to state the potential at any point in the circuit it must be stated with reference to a fixed point elsewhere in the circuit. This fixed point can be chosen anywhere in the circuit, since it is used purely for *comparing* potentials. This is just like the heights on a map, which are always stated with reference to sea level.

As current flows from B to E through the lamps there is a *drop* in potential, as energy is transferred from the charge flowing through the lamps. From E to B through the cells there is a *rise* in potential, as energy is transferred from the cells to the flowing charge. The fall in potential is the same as the rise in potential as we are dealing with a closed circuit, just like the circular walk. This result is known as **Kirchhoff's second law**:

The sum of potential rises and falls around a closed path in a circuit is zero.

Note that the falls in potential occur where energy is transferred *from* the flowing charge, while the rises occur where energy is transferred *to* the flowing charge.

Resistors in series and parallel

When resistors are connected together in a circuit, it is often useful to be able to calculate their combined resistance. Using the principles discussed earlier in this section, this is quite straightforward to do.

Resistors in series

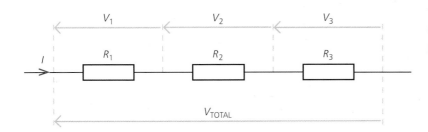

Figure 4.2.5

Consider figure 4.2.5. Since the three resistors are connected in series, we know that they must all have the same current I flowing through them. We also know (from Kirchhoff's second law) that the sum of the p.d.s across the individual resistors must be equal to the total p.d. across all three resistors, that is,

$$V_{TOTAL} = V_1 + V_2 + V_3$$

Dividing both sides of this equation by I gives:

$$\frac{V_{TOTAL}}{I} = \frac{V_1}{I} + \frac{V_2}{I} + \frac{V_3}{I}$$

We know that Ohm's law defines the resistance of each resistor as:

$$R_1 = V_1/I \qquad R_2 = V_2/I \qquad R_3 = V_3/I$$

and the total resistance must be defined as:

$$R_{TOTAL} = V_{TOTAL}/I$$

Comparing these relationships, we can see that:

$$R_{\text{TOTAL}} = R_1 + R_2 + R_3$$

This relationship applies to any number of resistors connected together in series.

Resistors in parallel

Because the three resistors in figure 4.2.6 are connected together in parallel, they must all have the same potential difference V across them. We also know (from Kirchhoff's first law) that the sum of the currents through each individual resistor must be equal to the current through all three resistors in total, that is,

$$I_{\text{TOTAL}} = I_1 + I_2 + I_3$$

Once again we can apply Ohm's law:

$$I_1 = V/R_1 \qquad I_2 = V/R_2 \qquad I_3 = V/R_3$$

and the total current can be calculated as:

$$I_{\text{TOTAL}} = V/R_{\text{TOTAL}}$$

Comparing these relationships, we can see that

$$\frac{V}{R_{\text{TOTAL}}} = \frac{V}{R_1} + \frac{V}{R_2} + \frac{V}{R_3}$$

Dividing both sides of the equation by V gives:

$$\frac{1}{R_{\text{TOTAL}}} = \frac{1}{R_1} + \frac{1}{R_2} + \frac{1}{R_3}$$

This relationship applies to any number of resistors connected in parallel.

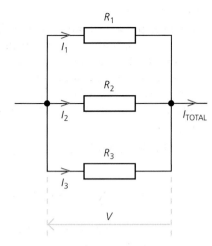

Figure 4.2.6

Solving problems in multiloop circuits

Kirchhoff's first and second laws provide us with two powerful tools for analysing the behaviour of circuits in which there is more than one loop and where the solution is not immediately obvious. As an example, consider the circuit shown in figure 4.2.7.

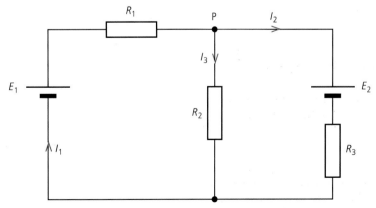

Figure 4.2.7 If $E_1 = 6\,\text{V}$, $E_2 = 2\,\text{V}$, $R_1 = 10\,\Omega$, $R_2 = 5\,\Omega$, and $R_3 = 2\,\Omega$, what is I_3?

As a first step we examine the circuit to see what branches are involved in it. In this case there are two branches, which separate at P. We now assign currents to the branches, which are shown as I_1, I_2 and I_3. (The directions of these currents are not important, since the calculations will show in which direction they flow – if the answer from our circuit calculation is negative, the current flows in the opposite direction to that assigned in our diagram.)

Applying Kirchhoff's first law at point P:

$$I_1 = I_2 + I_3 \qquad \text{(equation 1)}$$

We may now apply Kirchhoff's second law to the two loops in the circuit, noting that:
(1) there is a potential *rise* whenever we go through a source of e.m.f. from the − to the + side
(2) there is a potential *fall* whenever we go through a resistance in the same direction as the flow of conventional current.

Starting at point P and applying Kirchhoff's second law as we go round the left-hand loop:

$$-I_3R_2 + E_1 - I_1R_1 = 0 \qquad \text{(equation 2)}$$

Starting at point P and applying Kirchhoff's second law as we go round the right-hand loop:

$$-E_2 - I_2R_3 + I_3R_2 = 0 \qquad \text{(equation 3)}$$

Substituting the expression for I_1 in equation 1 into equation 2:

$$-I_3R_2 + E_1 - (I_2 + I_3)R_1 = 0 \qquad \text{(equation 4)}$$

Equations 3 and 4 are simultaneous equations, which can be solved to find I_3.

Rearranging equation 3 to find I_2:

$$I_2 = \frac{I_3R_2 - E_2}{R_3}$$

Substituting for I_2 in equation 4:

$$-I_3R_2 + E_1 - \frac{(I_3R_2 - E_2)}{R_3}R_1 - I_3R_1 = 0$$

and substituting values for E_1, E_2, R_1, R_2 and R_3:

$$-5\,\Omega \times I_3 + 6\,\text{V} - \frac{(5\,\Omega \times I_3 - 2\,\text{V})}{2\,\Omega}\,10\,\Omega - 10\,\Omega \times I_3 = 0$$

Solving this equation for I_3 gives $I_3 = 0.4$ A. The positive value of I_3 shows that it flows in the direction we originally assigned to it in figure 4.2.7.

The potential divider

The principle of the **potential divider** is important in many applications which use circuits containing resistors. The volume control on a radio is a potential divider, as are the controls for brightness, contrast and colour balance on a television set. Circuits that sense changes using devices like light-dependent resistors and thermistors (see section 4.5) use potential dividers too.

A potential divider is a device consisting essentially of two resistors. A current I flows through the two resistors, and the effect of this is to split or *divide* the potential difference across the resistors in two. A simple example of a potential divider is shown in figure 4.2.8. Using Ohm's law we may write:

$$V_1 = IR_1 \quad \text{and} \quad V_2 = IR_2$$

Dividing the first equation by the second gives us:

$$\frac{V_1}{V_2} = \frac{R_1}{R_2}$$

which means that the total potential difference V across the two resistors has been divided up in the ratio of their two resistances – hence the name **potential divider**. By choosing appropriate values of R_1 and R_2, any voltage between zero and V can be obtained across either of the two resistors.

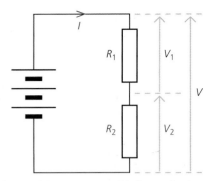

Figure 4.2.8 The voltages on this diagram rise as we go up the diagram. This rise is indicated by the use of single-headed arrows.

The potential divider – worked example

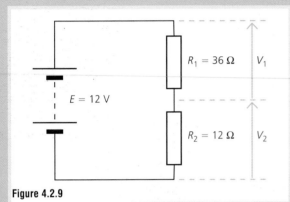

Figure 4.2.9

Figure 4.2.9 shows a battery with an e.m.f. of 12 V with a pair of resistors R_1 and R_2 connected to it. R_1 has a resistance of 36 Ω, while R_2 has a resistance of 12 Ω. What is the p.d. across each resistor?

The total p.d. across the two resistors is 12 V. This is divided up in the ratio of their two resistances:

$$\frac{V_1}{V_2} = \frac{R_1}{R_2} = \frac{36\,\Omega}{12\,\Omega} = 3$$

Since:

$$V_1 = 3V_2 \quad \text{and} \quad V_1 + V_2 = V$$

we know that:

$$3V_2 + V_2 = V, \text{ that is, } V_2 = V/4$$

In this case this gives:

$$V_2 = 12\ \text{V}/4 = 3\ \text{V}$$

and:

$$V_1 = 3V_2 = 3 \times 3\ \text{V} = 9\ \text{V}$$

The potentiometer

Where a continuously variable p.d. is required, the fixed resistors in the potential divider circuit are replaced by a **potentiometer**. This is a device consisting of a length of resistance wire or a carbon track, along which a wiper may be moved – effectively a resistor with a sliding contact. The diagrams in figure 4.2.10 show that as the wiper is moved along, the values of R_1 and R_2 alter, although $R_1 + R_2$ remains constant. In this way, the p.d. appearing across terminals AB can be continuously varied from zero up to the e.m.f. of the supply. Practical potentiometers come in different shapes and sizes, depending on the job they have to do.

Resistances in potential dividers

It can be seen that the factor influencing the p.d. developed across the terminals of a potential divider or a potentiometer is the *ratio* of the two resistances, not the *absolute* value of either resistance. What determines the actual values that might be used in practical circuits?

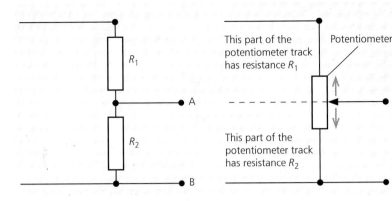

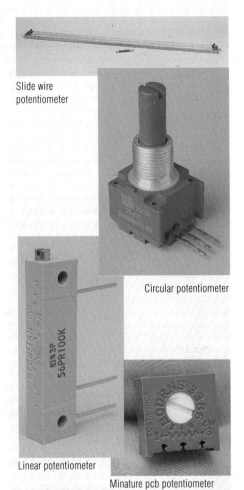

Figure 4.2.10 As the wiper is moved along the potentiometer track, R_1 and R_2 alter (R_1 increases as R_2 decreases and vice versa). The total resistance R of the potentiometer track remains constant, $R = R_1 + R_2$. The photographs of the practical potentiometers shown here are at widely differing scales. At the top is a 1 m length of resistance wire (used in laboratory measurements), while the other photographs show miniature and subminiature potentiometers used in electronic circuits.

Slide wire potentiometer

Circular potentiometer

Linear potentiometer

Minature pcb potentiometer

The answer to this question depends on the current to be drawn from the potential divider. The current drawn from the device should not be an appreciable fraction of the current through the resistors, otherwise the assumption that the currents through R_1 and R_2 are the same will not be valid. Therefore, if an appreciable current is required, a large current must flow through the potential divider itself. This may well be undesirable, since this current does nothing useful, and the energy it carries will be transferred to the resistors of the potential divider, making them hot. This is seldom a problem, however. The usual applications for potential dividers do not draw large currents, and in practice there is little difficulty in using large resistors which lead to a small current through the divider itself, while providing any voltage required between zero and the e.m.f. of the supply. We shall return to the potential divider in section 4.5, and shall look in more detail at the effect of connecting resistances into circuits in the next part of this section.

Circuit measurements and calculations

Connecting ammeters and voltmeters

In connecting a load to a potential divider we have seen that care must be taken that the load does not upset the calculations carried out before it was connected to the divider. This is similar to the situation when connecting meters to circuits in order to make measurements of current and voltage, and one might therefore wonder whether similar problems exist in these circumstances.

An ammeter is placed in a circuit in order to measure the current at that particular point. Current therefore flows through the meter, and so it should have a sufficiently low resistance that it does not significantly affect the current flowing through the circuit. The extent to which an ammeter reduces the current flowing will depend on its resistance compared with the resistance of the other circuit elements. Even quite inexpensive ammeters have resistances as low as 0.01 Ω, which is orders of magnitude less than the resistance encountered in most laboratory circuits, so in the vast majority of situations we are quite justified in ignoring the effect that an ammeter has on a circuit into which it is inserted, as illustrated in figure 4.2.11.

The situation with voltmeters is different. Voltmeters must be connected across two points in a circuit between which we wish to know the potential difference. Once again, the connecting of this measuring device into the circuit should not significantly alter the current flowing through the circuit in any way. In order for this to be so, the voltmeter should have as *large* a resistance as possible in order that as little current as possible should flow through it.

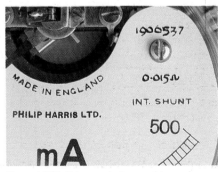

Figure 4.2.11 This ammeter has a resistance of 0.015 Ω. If we wish to measure current in a circuit with an uncertainty of better than 5%, this meter will be quite adequate unless the series resistance of the rest of the circuit is 0.3 Ω or less.

Selecting a voltmeter

Consider making measurements on a potential divider using two voltmeters, a situation shown in figure 4.2.12.

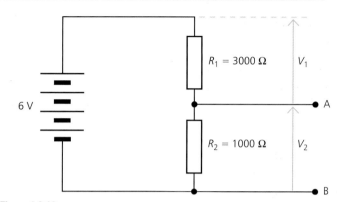

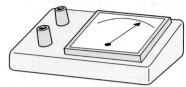

Standard laboratory voltmeter

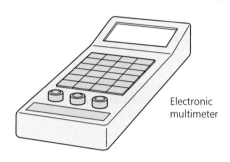

Electronic multimeter

Figure 4.2.12

To begin with, each meter is connected across the terminals of the battery in turn – both give a reading of 6.0 V. When the electronic multimeter is connected to terminals AB, it reads 1.5 V as expected. However, when the other meter is connected to the terminals, it reads only 1.0 V.

The key to understanding this apparent paradox is to realise that connecting the voltmeter between two points affects the potential difference between them. Although the battery has a resistance itself (see internal resistance of power supplies, pages 300–1), this is low compared with the resistance of both meters. However, the resistance of the laboratory meter is comparable to that of R_2 in the potential divider, and so it alters V_2 significantly. This is explained in figure 4.2.13.

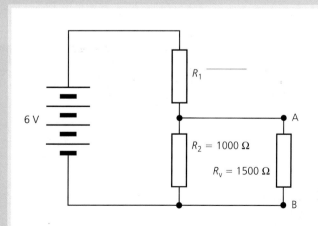

Figure 4.2.13

With the meter connected across terminals AB, the resistance between these two points drops to R_{NEW}:

$$\frac{1}{R_{NEW}} = \frac{1}{1000 \ \Omega} + \frac{1}{1500 \ \Omega}$$

$$= \frac{5}{3000 \ \Omega}$$

so:

$$R_{NEW} = 600 \ \Omega$$

This means that:

$$\frac{V_1}{V_2} = \frac{R_1}{R_{NEW}} = \frac{3000 \ \Omega}{600 \ \Omega} = 5$$

so that V_2 is now 1.0 V.

This does not happen with the electronic voltmeter, since it has a resistance of several million ohms. Connecting this meter across AB changes V_2 by only about one part in a million, which is virtually undetectable! To ensure that a voltmeter does not appreciably alter the p.d. between two points in a circuit it should have a resistance at least 10^3 times greater than the resistance of the circuit element(s) between the two points.

Measuring the properties of systems

As a general rule, it is impossible to make an observation of some property of a system without disturbing it in some way. The examples using voltmeters and ammeters we have just seen show that this is so for electrical circuits – and it is true for other systems too.

If we wish to measure the pressure of the air in a car tyre, for example, it is necessary to connect a pressure gauge to the tyre and draw off some of the air. Similarly, a thermometer must be brought into thermal equilibrium with the system being measured, which results in a transfer of energy from system to thermometer or vice versa. In all these cases the disturbance to the system can be minimised so that the disturbance is negligible in comparison to other uncertainties involved in the measurement, but this does not negate the fact that the disturbance is there.

In all but the most sensitive experiments in the macroscopic world such problems are easily overcome. On a microscopic scale, however, things are much more difficult. How to observe an electron without disturbing it is one of many similar problems that have exercised great minds during the course of this century, even giving rise to a creature called Schrödinger's cat! We shall return to this problem in section 6.5.

Changing the sensitivity of ammeters and voltmeters

From the previous discussions, it may appear that ammeters and voltmeters are different instruments. This is only true to the extent that they have very different resistances. In fact, both are current-measuring devices.

Using shunts with ammeters

An ammeter is inserted in a circuit in order to measure the rate of flow of charge at the point of insertion. In order that a meter can be used to measure a range of currents, **shunts** can divert a proportion of the current through a resistor connected in parallel with the meter. Clearly such shunts must have a low resistance themselves in order to make this happen. Figure 4.2.14 shows a meter that can be adapted to measure two very different currents. To convert this meter to measure (a) currents of up to 500 mA and (b) currents of up to 50 A, two different shunts are needed. The resistance of these shunts is calculated as shown in table 4.2.1 overleaf.

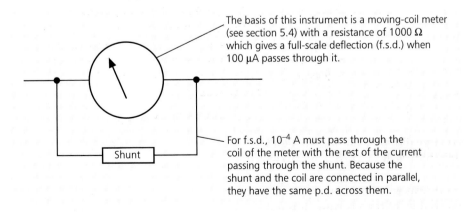

The basis of this instrument is a moving-coil meter (see section 5.4) with a resistance of 1000 Ω which gives a full-scale deflection (f.s.d.) when 100 μA passes through it.

For f.s.d., 10^{-4} A must pass through the coil of the meter with the rest of the current passing through the shunt. Because the shunt and the coil are connected in parallel, they have the same p.d. across them.

Figure 4.2.14

(a) 0–500 mA meter	(b) 0–50 A meter
10^{-4} A passes through meter for f.s.d., so at f.s.d. the current through the shunt $\quad = 5.0 \times 10^{-1}$ A $- 10^{-4}$ A $\quad = 0.4999$ A Applying Ohm's law to the meter to find the p.d. across it: $\quad V = IR$ $\quad\quad = 10^{-4}$ A $\times 1000\ \Omega$ $\quad\quad = 0.1$ V This will also be the p.d. across the shunt, so the resistance of the shunt may be found by using Ohm's law again, since we know the p.d. across it and the current through it: $\quad R = V/I$ $\quad\quad = 0.1$ V/0.4999 A $\quad\quad = 0.2000\ \Omega$ A shunt with a resistance of 0.2000 Ω will convert this meter to measure currents up to 0.5 A.	10^{-4} A passes through meter for f.s.d so at f.s.d. the current through the shunt $\quad = 5.0 \times 10^{1}$ A $- 10^{-4}$ A $\quad = 49.9999$ A Applying Ohm's law to the meter to find the p.d. across it: $\quad V = IR$ $\quad\quad = 10^{-4}$ A $\times 1000\ \Omega$ $\quad\quad = 0.1$ V This will also be the p.d. across the shunt, so the resistance of the shunt may be found by using Ohm's law again, since we know the p.d. across it and the current through it: $\quad R = V/I$ $\quad\quad = 0.1$ V/49.9999 A $\quad\quad = 0.0020\ \Omega$ A shunt with a resistance of 0.0020 Ω will convert this meter to measure currents up to 50 A.

Table 4.2.1

Notice that in both cases the resulting resistance of the meter is very small ($< 0.2\ \Omega$ in the first case, and $< 0.002\ \Omega$ in the second case) as required if the meter is to disturb the circuit into which it is inserted as little as possible.

Using multipliers with voltmeters

A voltmeter is connected across two points in a circuit in order to measure the p.d. between them. Resistors called **multipliers** are connected in series with the meter in order to increase the resistance of the meter so that only a small proportion of the current flows through it. Figure 4.2.15 shows a meter that can be adapted to measure two very different p.d.s. To convert this meter to measure (a) p.d.s of up to 500 mV and (b) p.d.s of up to 5000 V two different multipliers are needed. The resistance of these multipliers is calculated as shown in table 4.2.2.

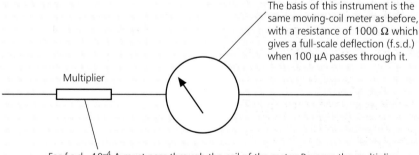

The basis of this instrument is the same moving-coil meter as before, with a resistance of 1000 Ω which gives a full-scale deflection (f.s.d.) when 100 µA passes through it.

Multiplier

For f.s.d., 10^{-4} A must pass through the coil of the meter. Because the multiplier and the coil are connected in series, they have the same current through them. The total p.d. to be measured appears across the coil of the meter and the multiplier.

Figure 4.2.15

In this case the resistance of the meters is large (4000 Ω and 50 000 000 Ω), as it must be if the meters are to have a negligible effect on the circuits to which they are connected.

The resistance of shunts and multipliers is usually calculated and quoted to four significant figures to ensure that the uncertainty of the instrument is not greatly increased by the uncertainty in the resistance of the shunt or multiplier.

(a) 0–500 mV meter	(b) 0–5000 V meter
Resistance of multiplier and meter coil in series $$= R + 1000\ \Omega$$	Resistance of multiplier and meter coil in series $$= R + 1000\ \Omega$$
The p.d. across these for f.s.d. is 5×10^{-1} V, and the current through them is 10^{-4} A, so using Ohm's law gives: $$5 \times 10^{-1}\ \text{V} = 10^{-4}\ \text{A} \times (R + 1000\ \Omega)$$ so: $$R + 1000\ \Omega = \frac{5 \times 10^{-1}\ \text{V}}{10^{-4}\ \text{A}} = 5000\ \Omega$$ so: $$R = 4000\ \Omega$$ A multiplier with a resistance of 4000 Ω will convert this meter to measure p.d.s up to 0.5 V.	The p.d. across these for f.s.d. is 5×10^{3} V, and the current through them is 10^{-4} A, so using Ohm's law gives: $$5 \times 10^{3}\ \text{V} = 10^{-4}\ \text{A} \times (R + 1000\ \Omega)$$ so: $$R + 1000\ \Omega = \frac{5 \times 10^{3}\ \text{V}}{10^{-4}\ \text{A}} = 5 \times 10^{7}\ \Omega$$ so: $$R = 5.000 \times 10^{7}\ \Omega$$ A multiplier with a resistance of $5.000 \times 10^{7}\ \Omega$ will convert this meter to measure p.d.s up to 5000 V.

Table 4.2.2

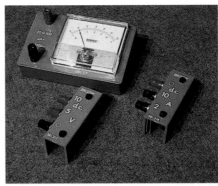

Figure 4.2.16 This galvanometer has a full scale deflection (f.s.d.) of 100 A. The shunts and multipliers shown fit quickly and easily to the meter, enabling it to be used for a wide range of measurements of both current and potential difference.

Uncertainties and errors – systematic and random

When taking readings using instruments, there will always be some uncertainty or error in the measurements an experimenter makes. Although all measurements contain uncertainties, since we can never be sure that an instrument has measured the true value of a physical quantity, faults in instruments and poor experimental technique may also introduce errors. In experimental physics it is important to be able to see where uncertainties and errors may arise in order to deal with them.

Figure 4.2.17(a) shows an ammeter not connected into a circuit. Despite the fact that there is no current flowing through it, the ammeter reads 0.04 A because the needle does not line up with the end of the scale. If this meter is used to make readings of current in a circuit, there will be a **systematic error** of $+0.04$ A in each reading made, resulting in all the readings being 0.04 A too large.

Systematic errors result in all the readings being 'out' in the same direction. Although equipment is often responsible, poor experimental technique may also be to blame. For example, an experimenter who consistently reads a meter while viewing the scale at an angle of 60° introduces a systematic error in the readings made in this way, as shown in figure 4.2.17(b).

Systematic errors may be difficult to detect and measure. Good experimental technique is important, and readings taken with one instrument can be checked using another instrument. Two ammeters in series should read the same, as should two thermometers in the same surroundings. Repeating readings with the same instrument will not eliminate systematic errors – it will simply provide more readings with the same error!

Random uncertainty often arises from the inability of an experimenter to make precise readings (for example, in timing an event with a stopclock, where the observer's reaction time may be unpredictable). It may also arise as a result of natural statistical fluctuations, as in the example of radioactive decay, as we shall see in section 6.2.

4

Random uncertainties produce a scatter of results about a mean, as figure 4.2.17(c) shows. These uncertainties may be treated by using statistical methods – a brief description of this is given in section 6.2, page 495.

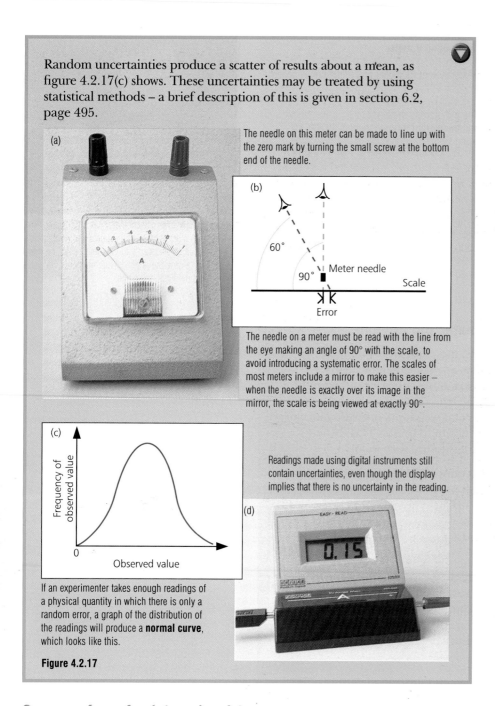

(a)

The needle on this meter can be made to line up with the zero mark by turning the small screw at the bottom end of the needle.

(b)

60°

90°   Meter needle

Scale

Error

The needle on a meter must be read with the line from the eye making an angle of 90° with the scale, to avoid introducing a systematic error. The scales of most meters include a mirror to make this easier – when the needle is exactly over its image in the mirror, the scale is being viewed at exactly 90°.

(c)

Frequency of observed value

0

Observed value

Readings made using digital instruments still contain uncertainties, even though the display implies that there is no uncertainty in the reading.

(d)

EASY - READ

0.15

If an experimenter takes enough readings of a physical quantity in which there is only a random error, a graph of the distribution of the readings will produce a **normal curve**, which looks like this.

Figure 4.2.17

Sources of e.m.f. – internal resistance

A source of e.m.f. always has some resistance to electric current within it, called its **internal resistance**. The internal resistance of a source of e.m.f. has two effects:

1 it results in the voltage across the terminals of the source dropping as a current is drawn from it

2 it results in the source being less than 100% efficient as energy is dissipated in the internal resistance as current flows through it.

The voltage quoted on the label of a source of e.m.f. such as a battery is the voltage measured when no current is being drawn from it, often called the **open-circuit voltage**.

The internal resistance of a source of e.m.f. may be thought of as a resistance r in series with the nominal e.m.f. E, as figure 4.2.19 shows. When a current I is drawn from the source a p.d. ΔV appears across the internal resistance r, so that $\Delta V = Ir$. The voltage V across the terminals of the source falls, so that:

$$V = E - \Delta V = E - Ir$$

The internal resistance of a source of e.m.f. limits the power that can be supplied to an external circuit or **load**. A source of e.m.f. connected to a load will dissipate some of its energy in its internal resistance, and transfer the rest to the load. It is often desirable to transfer as much electrical power as possible from a source to a load, for example when an aerial is connected to a television. Investigations show that in order to do this, the resistance of the load must be equal to the internal resistance of the source, since the power supplied by a source to a load varies as shown in figure 4.2.20.

Figure 4.2.18 For safety, a high tension power supply should not be able to deliver a large current. The current is limited by ensuring that the supply has a suitably high internal resistance.

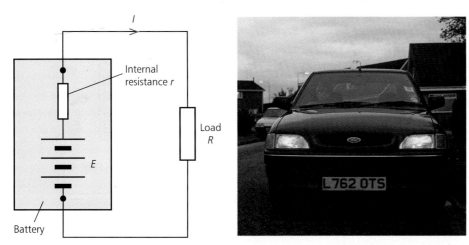

Figure 4.2.19 The internal resistance of a source of e.m.f. results in energy being dissipated within the source itself. This effect can be seen quite clearly when starting a car on a cold, dark morning – turning the starter motor draws a current which may be as large as several hundred amps, producing a significant voltage drop across the internal resistance of the battery. (This voltage drop is sometimes referred to as 'lost volts'.) If a car is started with the headlights on, they can be seen to dim as the p.d. across them drops.

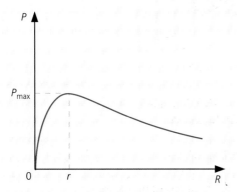

Figure 4.2.20 When a source of e.m.f. delivers power P to a load R, there is a value of R for which the maximum power is transferred, as the graph shows. Calculation shows that this value is equal to r, the internal resistance of the source of e.m.f.

Alternative ways of measuring potential difference and current

It is possible to make measurements of current by measuring potential difference, provided the p.d. is measured across a resistor of known value. Potential difference can be measured using a high resistance voltmeter, as we have seen, or by means of an oscilloscope (or cathode ray oscilloscope, CRO – details of the principles and construction of the CRO are given in section 5.3). In some cases, an arrangement of two potential dividers – called a **bridge circuit** – may be used to measure small changes in current through a circuit.

The oscilloscope is adjusted initially so that the spot is in the exact centre of the screen, with the time base (the circuit that causes the spot to move horizontally across the screen) turned off.

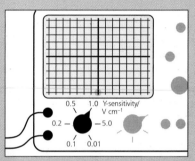

Terminals connected to Y-plates of oscilloscope

Control for adjusting sensitivity of oscilloscope in Y-direction. This is usually calibrated in volts per centimetre (V cm^{-1}).

These diagrams show an oscilloscope connected up to a circuit and measuring p.d. in two different situations.

(a)

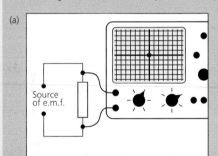

To measure the p.d. across the resistor the oscilloscope is connected across it like this.

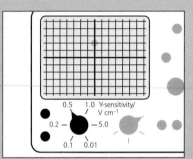

The spot has been deflected up 2 cm from its initial position. The Y-sensitivity is 0.5 V cm^{-1}, so the measured voltage is 2 cm × 0.5 V cm^{-1} = 1.0 V.

The spot has been deflected down 5 cm from its initial position. The Y-sensitivity is 1 V cm^{-1}, so the measured voltage is −5 cm × 1 V cm^{-1} = −5 V.

An oscilloscope has a very high input resistance, and so can be used to obtain quite accurate measurements of p.d. in a circuit. Its chief limitation is in measuring the deflection of the spot, which in practice limits the precision of the measurements made with it. The oscilloscope is particularly useful in measuring *changing* p.d.s, as we shall see in section 4.4.

(b) An arrangement of four resistances known as a **Wheatstone bridge** (invented by Charles Wheatstone in 1843) is used where sensitive measurement of changes in resistance is required. Since it is possible to measure many quantities (temperature and light intensity, for example) by using circuit elements which change their resistance with the quantity to be measured (see section 4.5), Wheatstone bridge circuits find uses in many applications. In this example, a pair of strain gauges is connected to a Wheatstone bridge in order to make accurate measurements of strain.

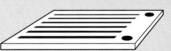

A **strain gauge**. The gauge is made of very fine wire bonded to a support. The support is then attached firmly to the component in which the strain is to be measured, so that the gauge experiences the same strain as the component.

A pair of strain gauges is connected to a Wheatstone bridge circuit – this ensures that changes in resistance due to temperature changes are minimised. The bridge is adjusted so that it is balanced when there is no strain, and so the p.d. across AB is zero. Stressing the active gauge changes its resistance and unbalances the bridge. Previous calibration of the gauge for known strains then enables direct measurement of strain in the component to be made.

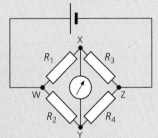

Consideration of the p.d.s across different parts of the Wheatstone bridge circuit shows that when the p.d. across X and Y is zero,

$$\frac{R_1}{R_3} = \frac{R_2}{R_4}$$

In this situation the bridge is said to be 'balanced'.

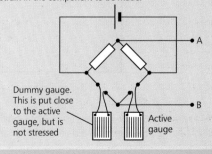

Dummy gauge. This is put close to the active gauge, but is not stressed

Active gauge

Figure 4.2.21 The use of (a) the CRO, and (b) the Wheatstone bridge in making measurements of current and potential difference.

Understanding conduction

We began our consideration of electricity by introducing an electric current as a flow of charge. Having used a flow model to derive the relationships we have seen so far, it is now time to consider the mechanisms by which charge might flow through conductors, and by implication, the reasons why charge is unable to flow through insulators.

Conduction in metals

In section 2.3 we saw that a possible explanation for the high thermal conductivity of metals is the idea that the outermost electrons in the lattice of particles form a sort of 'sea', in which electrons are free to move around. Such a model can explain thermal conductivity quite convincingly, and may also be used to explain the electrical conductivity of metals.

The free electrons in a metal have a motion like the motion of the particles of a gas – in fact, the electrons are often referred to as making up an **electron gas**. The electrons have a velocity of around 10^5 m s^{-1} – to a good approximation this velocity is independent of temperature.

When a source of e.m.f. is connected to the ends of a conductor this causes an electric field across the conductor. This field has the effect of causing the electrons in the conductor to move (see section 5.3 for more details about electric fields and charged particles) with an average velocity known as the **drift velocity**. The size of this drift velocity depends on a number of factors as we shall see shortly, but is typically around 10^{-7} m s^{-1}. The process is outlined in figure 4.2.22.

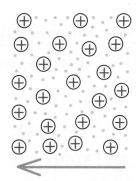

Electrons (·) move through a metal lattice (⊕) in response to an electric field caused by the source of e.m.f. In this process the electrons collide many times with each other and with the metal atoms.

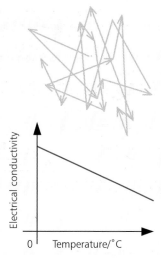

Electrical conductivity

0   Temperature/°C

Even though an individual electron has an instantaneous velocity of many thousands of metres per second, the collisions it makes causes its average velocity to be measured in fractions of a millimetre per second. Electrons moving in an applied electric field have average velocities over time which are oriented in the same direction.

The electrical conductivity of copper falls as its temperature rises. This behaviour is common to most metals.

Figure 4.2.22 The electron gas model for the mechanism of electrical and thermal conduction in metals explains the fall in conductivity with temperature in terms of electron collisions with the metal atoms. The increased amplitude of the vibrations of the metal atoms in the lattice as the temperature increases means that the electrons collide more frequently with the atoms, which impedes their progress. This reduces their drift velocity, which in turn means that the conductivity of the metal is reduced.

Conduction in pure semiconductors

Substances like silicon and germanium have resistivities between those of insulators and those of conductors, as table 4.1.2 shows (see page 283). These substances are known as **semiconductors**, and they form the basis of many devices which we take for granted in a technological society. Pure semiconductors are usually referred to as **intrinsic** semiconductors, since their conductivity arises due to the properties of the atoms in the semiconductor itself. As we shall see very shortly, trace impurities can greatly alter the conductivity of semiconductors.

Electric current is carried by moving electrons in an intrinsic semiconductor, as in the case of metals. However, in addition to electrons, intrinsic semiconductors can also be considered to contain moving *positive* charges which carry current. A simple model for explaining the behaviour of semiconductors is as follows.

Some of the electrons in an atom of intrinsic semiconductor are held less tightly than others. This means that in a piece of intrinsic semiconductor at room temperature, there will always be a few free electrons which have been 'shaken free' of their atoms by thermal excitation – quite simply, they have absorbed energy from their surroundings. When an electron leaves an atom in this way, the atom becomes positively charged. The effect of an electron leaving an atom is therefore to create a positive charge in the semiconductor lattice. This positive charge is called a **hole**. When an electric field is applied to the semiconductor (that is, when it is connected to a source of e.m.f.), the electrons and holes move in opposite directions, and the semiconductor exhibits **intrinsic conduction** because the charge carriers have arisen inside the conductor. Figure 4.2.23 shows this happening.

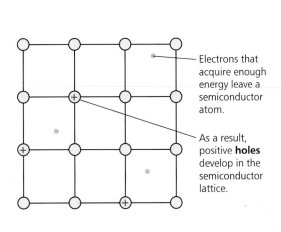

Electrons that acquire enough energy leave a semiconductor atom.

As a result, positive **holes** develop in the semiconductor lattice.

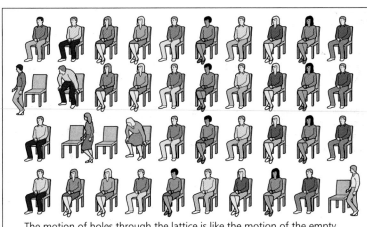

The motion of holes through the lattice is like the motion of the empty chair in this dentist's waiting room. As the people move from right to left, the empty chair moves from left to right.

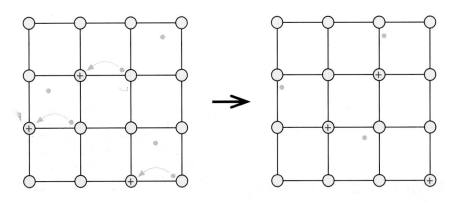

Under the influence of an electric field, electrons move through the lattice. Electrons still bound to atoms in the lattice are able to migrate from an atom to a nearby hole, thus causing the hole to appear to move through the lattice. This motion happens in the opposite direction to the motion of the electrons.

Figure 4.2.23 The current in a pure semiconductor consists of free electrons moving through the semiconductor lattice in one direction, with an equal number of positively charged holes moving in the other direction. Since the number of free electrons (equal to the number of holes) increases as the temperature of the semiconductor increases, the conductivity of an intrinsic semiconductor increases with temperature.

Conduction in 'doped' semiconductors

The use of semiconductors in devices like transistors and diodes and in integrated circuits (see section 4.5) depends on altering their conducting properties by introducing minute quantities of impurities in a process called **doping**. Doping results in an **extrinsic semiconductor**, because the impurity introduces extra charge carriers to the semiconductor lattice. Doping achieves this by replacing atoms in the semiconductor lattice with other atoms of similar size (this is important so as to minimise distortion of the lattice).

The number of free electrons and holes can be altered dramatically by the addition of tiny quantities of impurity. For example, the addition of only one arsenic atom per million silicon atoms increases the conductivity 100 000 times. Arsenic is an example of a **donor** impurity, which releases free electrons into the lattice, increasing the number of *n*egative charge carriers and so producing an ***n*-type semiconductor**. Boron, on the other hand, is an example of an **acceptor** impurity, which traps electrons when introduced into the lattice, resulting in an increase in the number of *p*ositive holes. A semiconductor of this type is called a ***p*-type semiconductor**. Figure 4.2.24 shows how these processes occur.

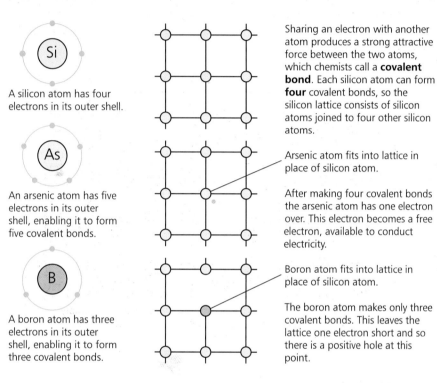

A silicon atom has four electrons in its outer shell.

Sharing an electron with another atom produces a strong attractive force between the two atoms, which chemists call a **covalent bond**. Each silicon atom can form **four** covalent bonds, so the silicon lattice consists of silicon atoms joined to four other silicon atoms.

An arsenic atom has five electrons in its outer shell, enabling it to form five covalent bonds.

Arsenic atom fits into lattice in place of silicon atom.

After making four covalent bonds the arsenic atom has one electron over. This electron becomes a free electron, available to conduct electricity.

A boron atom has three electrons in its outer shell, enabling it to form three covalent bonds.

Boron atom fits into lattice in place of silicon atom.

The boron atom makes only three covalent bonds. This leaves the lattice one electron short and so there is a positive hole at this point.

Figure 4.2.24

Conduction in insulators

An insulator can be thought of as an extreme version of a semiconductor. In a semiconductor, thermal energy excites electrons from atoms in the lattice and enables them to escape from the atom and become free to carry charge. The energy required to do this is sufficiently small that this process is possible at room temperature. In an insulator, the energy required to free an electron from an atom is much greater. As a result, an insulator has so few free electrons that its conductivity is very small indeed.

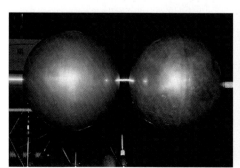

Figure 4.2.25 There are two circumstances in which an insulator may be made to conduct electricity. The first photograph shows two electrodes with a large p.d. between them. Under these circumstances the few free charge carriers that exist in the air between the electrodes are accelerated by the large p.d. and acquire enough kinetic energy to ionise any atoms they hit. These atoms in turn are accelerated and ionise other atoms, resulting in an **avalanche** of charged particles which act as charge carriers and cause the air to become conducting. The second photograph shows a demonstration in which a glass rod is heated to red heat. A p.d. across the rod can then cause a current to flow. The high temperature is sufficient to cause some of the atoms in the glass to lose electrons, which then become available for conduction. (*Do not try this experiment yourself* – it requires high temperatures and large p.d.s.)

The Dutch physicist Heike Kammerlingh Onnes discovered how to liquefy helium (which has a boiling point of just 4.2 K) in 1908, and opened the door to the study of low-temperature physics. Only three years later, Onnes discovered that mercury cooled to 4.15 K completely loses its resistivity and becomes a perfect conductor – a **superconductor**.

Superconductors remained a scientific curiosity for the next few decades, until a practical superconducting wire made of an alloy of niobium and titanium was developed in the 1960s. This **low-temperature superconductor**, which must be cooled below 20 K before it becomes superconducting, has become widely used wherever coils are required to produce large magnetic fields, particularly in magnetic resonance imaging (MRI) machines used in large hospitals.

The temperature to which a material must be cooled in order to become superconducting is called its **critical temperature** (T_c). In the 1980s the development of **high-temperature superconductors**, with critical temperatures of around 100 K, stimulated interest in superconductivity as something that could have enormously important practical applications in uses like electricity generation and transmission, electric motors and electronics.

Although a complete explanation of superconductivity requires a knowledge of quantum mechanics, a simple explanation is possible. When a current flows through an ordinary conductor like copper wire, the outer electrons in atoms move individually from one atom to another. The atoms form a vibrating lattice, and the warmer the metal the more the lattice vibrates. As electrons move through the lattice they collide with tiny imperfections in it, flying off in all directions and losing energy in the form of heat.

Although the vibrating lattice model explains why the conductivity of a metal should decrease with decreasing temperature, it does not explain the sudden fall in resistance at the critical temperature. The BCS theory of superconductivity (named after the scientists who proposed it, John Bardeen, Leon Cooper, and John Schrieffer) explains the fall as being due to electrons forming **Cooper pairs** that can pass all of the obstacles which cause resistance in the conductor.

New applications of superconductors will increase with critical temperature, and the possibility of room-temperature superconductors has the potential to make superconducting devices part of our everyday lives in such areas as electricity generation and transmission, electronics (greatly increasing the speed of computers, for example) and transportation (magnetic levitation for high-speed trains and other vehicles).

Figure 4.2.26 Perhaps the most striking property of superconductors is their ability to act as 'magnetic mirrors'. Here, a small ceramic magnet has been placed above a slice of high-temperature superconductor, cooled by liquid nitrogen. As the magnet falls it induces a current in the superconductor. This current flows through the surface of the superconductor unresisted, in such a direction that a magnetic field is produced which repels the falling magnet. The separation between the magnet and the superconductor is such that the repulsive force of the two magnetic fields exactly equals the weight of the magnet.

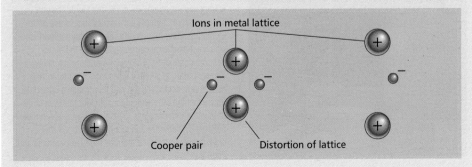

Figure 4.2.27 As an electron passes positively charged ions in the lattice of the superconductor, the lattice distorts, forming a sort of trough. Before the electron passes and the lattice springs back into its normal position, another electron is drawn into the trough, 'linking up' with the first electron to form a **Cooper pair**. By pairing up, the electrons pass through the superconductor more smoothly. Think of the pair of electrons as two cars racing down a motorway. The first car pushes apart the air in front of it. Behind it there is a low pressure area which is quickly filled by air rushing in. The second car, very close behind the first car, can be drawn along with the returning air into this vacuum – it is effectively attracted to the car in front.

Band theory

The conductivities of materials can be explained more fully using the idea of **energy bands** within solids. As section 6.5 will show, the energy each electron in an isolated atom may have is limited to a number of levels, rather like the rungs on a ladder. In a group of atoms these levels broaden out to become bands, and it is the distribution of electrons within these bands that governs the conductivity of the material.

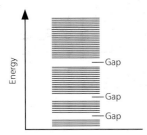

Energy level diagram for an electron moving in a crystal lattice. The permitted energies the electron may have are limited to regions (or **bands**) consisting of closely spaced energy levels separated by forbidden intervals or gaps.

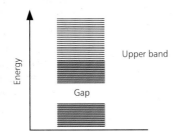

In a **conductor**, the upper energy band is only partly filled with electrons. When these electrons are subjected to an electric field thay are free to move up to unfilled levels slightly higher in the band, absorbing the energy they need to do this from the field. Electrons that do this are free to move through the lattice, so carrying an electric current.

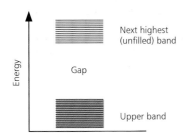

In an **insulator**, the upper band is completely filled with electrons. The gap between this band and the next higher one is too large for electrons to make the transition to higher, unfilled levels, and so conduction is impossible.

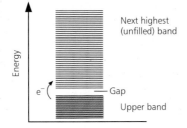

The upper band in an **intrinsic semiconductor** is completely full, as in the case of the insulator. However, in this case the gap between this band and the next is small. Electrons excited by thermal energy may make the transition to the next band. Having done so thay may respond to an electric field and so carry an electric current.

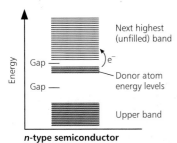

n-type semiconductor

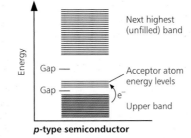

p-type semiconductor

Atoms of impurity added to a semiconductor lattice add additional energy levels. In the case of an n-type semiconductor, these additional levels are just below the next unfilled band. Surplus electrons from the donor atoms can easily enter this band, leading to conduction. In a p-type semiconductor, the additional bands due to the impurity are just above the upper filled band. Electrons from this filled band can move upwards into the additional energy levels of the acceptor atoms, leaving holes in the lower band.

Figure 4.2.28 This theory of conduction in solids is called **band theory**. The full band in an insulator or a conductor is referred to as the **valence band**, while the empty band above it is called the **conduction band**.

The transport equation

Based on the model of a conductor as a material containing charges that are free to move, an expression can be obtained for the drift velocity of the charges and we can use this to make an estimate of its value.

Consider the piece of conducting material shown in figure 4.2.29.

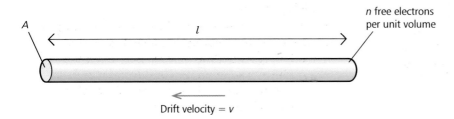

Figure 4.2.29

From the information about the conductor, we may deduce that:

$$\text{Volume of conductor} = Al$$

$$\text{Number of free electrons} = nAl$$

$$\text{Total charge on free electrons } Q = nAle$$

where e is the charge on an electron. If the current through the conductor is I, we know that $I = Q/t$, so:

$$\text{Current through conductor } I = \frac{nAle}{t}$$

But the drift velocity of the electrons v is given by $v = l/t$, so:

$$\text{Current through conductor } I = nAve$$

This is the **transport equation**.

A further quantity J, the **current density**, is sometimes defined as:

$$J = I/A$$

The transport equation can then be simplified as:

$$\text{Current density } J = nve$$

Drift velocities in conductors and semiconductors – worked example

Consider a piece of copper and a piece of silicon with exactly the same cross-sectional area A of 3×10^{-6} m^2. If both the copper and the silicon carry a current of 100 µA, what is the drift velocity of the electrons in each? Assume that the number of free electrons per unit volume for copper n_{copper} is 10^{29} m^{-3} and that for silicon $n_{silicon}$ is 2.6×10^{18} m^{-3}. The charge on the electron e is 1.6×10^{-19} C.

$$I = nAve, \text{ so rearranging:} \quad v = \frac{I}{nAe}$$

Substituting the respective values for copper and silicon gives:

$$v_{copper} = \frac{10^{-4} \text{ A}}{10^{29} \text{ m}^{-3} \times 3 \times 10^{-6} \text{ m}^2 \times 1.6 \times 10^{-19} \text{ C}}$$

$$= 2 \times 10^{-9} \text{ m s}^{-1}$$

$$v_{silicon} = \frac{10^{-4} \text{ A}}{2.6 \times 10^{18} \text{ m}^{-3} \times 3 \times 10^{-6} \text{ m}^2 \times 1.6 \times 10^{-19} \text{ C}}$$

$$= 80 \text{ m s}^{-1}$$

Exploring relationships

Dimensional analysis

In physics we are often interested in establishing relationships between different physical quantities. The derivation of the transport equation shows one way of doing this, by carefully constructing a model based on a number of relevant variables. Another method is **dimensional analysis**, which makes use of the fact that any mathematical relationship involving physical quantities must be dimensionally homogeneous.

As an example, consider a sphere moving through a fluid. Experience, together with a little simple physics, suggests that the drag force on the sphere may depend on a number of factors:

1 the velocity of the sphere, v
2 the radius of the sphere, r.
3 The viscosity of the fluid, η. (Viscosity is a measure of how easily a fluid flows – for example, treacle has a high viscosity, while the viscosity of air is much lower.)

One possible relationship for these quantities might have the form:

$$F = (\eta)^x \, (r)^y \, (v)^z$$

Now the dimensions of these quantities are:

$$[F] = M\,L\,T^{-2} \; [\eta] = M\,L^{-1}\,T^{-1} \; [r] = L \; \text{and} \; [v] = L\,T^{-1}$$

So we may equate the dimensions on each side of the equation:

$$M\,L\,T^{-2} = (M\,L^{-1}\,T^{-1})^x \, (L)^y \, (L\,T^{-1})^z$$

This equation will be dimensionally homogeneous if the powers of M, L and T on each side are equal, so:

For M: $\quad 1 = x$
For L: $\quad 1 = -x + y + z$
For T: $\quad -2 = -x + -z$

which gives:

$$x = 1, y = 1 \text{ and } z = 1$$

So the magnitude of the drag force F on the sphere can be written as:

$$F = k\eta rv$$

Notice that it is necessary to include k, a **dimensionless constant**, in this relationship. The method of dimensions can tell us nothing about such constants, since they depend on the system of units we are using. Using SI units, the constant in this relationship is 6π, so:

$$F = 6\pi\eta rv$$

(This relationship between drag force and velocity is known as **Stokes' law**.)

Using logarithms

In some circumstances, experimental data relating one variable to another may be available. If so, a simple method using logarithms may be used to test the relationship. As an example, consider a set of data which show the time t taken for a marble to fall a distance s in air, starting from rest.

Assume that the relationship between these two variables has the form:

$$t = cs^m$$

where c is a constant and m is a positive or negative number.

We may take logarithms of each side of this equation, giving:

$$\log t = \log c + \log (s^m)$$

which we may write as:

$$\log t = \log c + m \log s$$

If we now plot a graph of $\log t$ (on the vertical axis) against $\log s$ (on the horizontal axis), a straight line should result, as shown in figure 4.2.30.

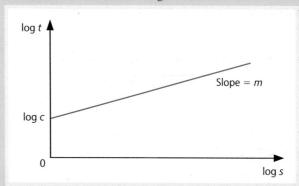

Figure 4.2.30 Comparing the equation for this graph with the general equation for a straight line ($y = mx + c$), the values of m (the slope of the graph) and c (the intercept on the y-axis) may be obtained.

In this case, since we already know that $s = \frac{1}{2}gt^2$, we should expect to find $m = 0.5$ and $c = \sqrt{(2/g)}$.

This method provides a useful way to establish relationships between quantities experimentally, although it may only be used to investigate the relationships between two variables at a time.

SUMMARY

- **Kirchhoff's first law** states that the total current into any point in a circuit is equal to the total current out of that point.
- **Kirchhoff's second law** states that the sum of potential rises and falls around a closed path in a circuit is zero.
- For resistors in series, $R_{TOTAL} = R_1 + R_2 + ...$
- For resistors in parallel, $1/R_{TOTAL} = (1/R_1) + (1/R_2) + ...$
- A **potential divider** is a device with two resistors that divide the p.d. in the ratio of their resistances, $V_1/V_2 = R_1/R_2$.
- An ammeter has a low resistance so that it does not affect the current through it. **Shunts** are resistors connected in parallel to change the full-scale deflection value of an ammeter and thus alter its sensitivity.
- A voltmeter has a very high resistance so that as little current as possible flows through it. **Multipliers** are resistors connected in series with a voltmeter to change its full-scale deflection value.
- The **internal resistance** of a source of e.m.f. can be thought of as a resistance r in series with E, such that $V = E - Ir$.
- The **transport equation** $I = nAve$ gives an expression for the drift velocity v of the electrons, where n is the number of free electrons per unit volume for the material, A the cross-sectional area of the material and e the charge on an electron. The **current density** $J = I/A$, so that $J = nve$.

EXAMPLE

Figure 4.2.31 shows a voltmeter with a resistance of 1800 Ω connected across a 200 Ω resistance. The battery has an e.m.f. of 12 V and an internal resistance of 50 Ω. Calculate the percentage change in the potential difference across the resistor when the voltmeter is connected across it.

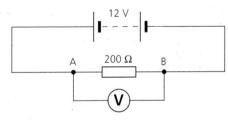

Figure 4.2.31

The current through the circuit without the voltmeter connected across the resistor is given by Ohm's law:

$$I = V/R$$
$$= 12\ V/(200\ \Omega + 50\ \Omega)$$
$$= 0.048\ A$$

The potential difference across the resistor without the voltmeter connected is thus given by:

$$V = IR$$
$$= 0.048\ A \times 200\ \Omega$$
$$= 9.6\ V$$

With the voltmeter connected across the resistor, the resistance between points A and B is given by:

$$1/R = 1/200\ \Omega + 1/1800\ \Omega$$

which gives:

$$R = 180\ \Omega$$

The current through the circuit is now:

$$I = V/R$$
$$= 12\ V/(180\ \Omega + 50\ \Omega)$$
$$= 0.052\ A$$

So the potential difference between A and B is given by:

$$V = 0.052\ 17\ A \times 180\ \Omega$$
$$= 9.39\ V$$

This is a percentage change of:

$$(9.39\ V - 9.6\ V)/9.6\ V \times 100\% = -2.2\%$$

Note: If we note that the potential difference across resistors in a series circuit is in proportion to their resistances, the steps of working out the current through the circuit in this calculation can be omitted. The potential difference across the 200 Ω resistor without the voltmeter connected is then found like this:

$$V = 200\ \Omega/(200\ \Omega + 50\ \Omega) \times 12\ V$$
$$= \tfrac{4}{5} \times 12\ V$$
$$= 9.6\ V$$

1 Give the readings of each ammeter in figure 4.2.32. (Assume that the cells have negligible internal resistance.)

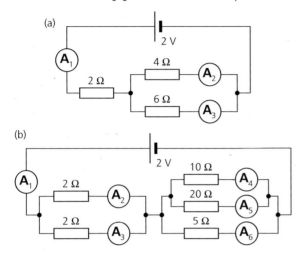

Figure 4.2.32

2 Give the readings of each voltmeter in figure 4.2.33.

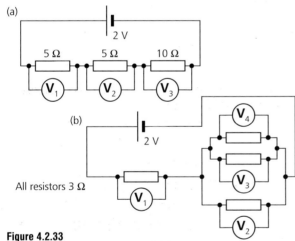

Figure 4.2.33

3 Calculate the resistance between points A and B in the combinations of 3 Ω resistors in figure 4.2.34.

Figure 4.2.34

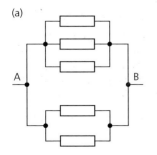

(a)

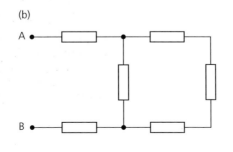

(b)

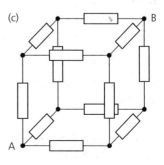

(c)

4 What resistances can be made using four resistors of resistance 5 Ω, 5 Ω, 10 Ω, and 10 Ω?

5 Calculate the marked currents in the circuits in figure 4.2.35.

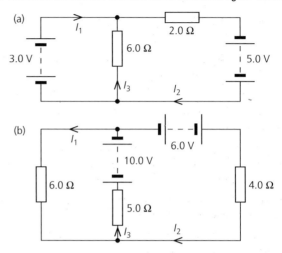

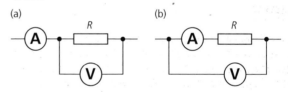

Figure 4.2.35

6 By connecting a voltmeter and an ammeter to a resistor simultaneously, its resistance can be calculated. The circuit may be arranged in two possible ways, shown in figure 4.2.36.

(a)   (b)

Figure 4.2.36

a Why do both of these circuits produce a value of R slightly different from its true value?
b Which circuit should be used for measuring the value of:
   i   a large resistance
   ii a small resistance?
   Explain your answers.

7 A resistor of resistance 2000 Ω is connected to a cell with negligible internal resistance. An electronic voltmeter connected across the resistor reads 10.0 V. What will a moving-coil voltmeter with a resistance of 20 000 Ω read?

8 A cell has an internal resistance of 0.50 Ω and an e.m.f. of 1.5 V. Calculate the current through the circuit and the potential difference across the terminals of the cell when it is connected to:

a a 2 Ω resistor

b a 10 Ω resistor

c the 2 Ω and 10 Ω resistors in parallel.

9 Figure 4.2.37 shows three identical cells connected in a circuit. Each cell has an e.m.f. of 2.0 V and an internal resistance of 2.0 Ω. Calculate the current through the 21 Ω resistor and the potential difference across it.

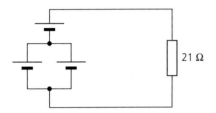

21 Ω

Figure 4.2.37

10 A 12 V battery has an internal resistance of 0.5 Ω.

a The battery is discharged at a steady rate of 1 A through an external resistance. At what rate is energy dissipated in the internal resistance of the battery?

b Repeat the calculation in **a** for a steady current of 10 A. Is the energy in the battery used more efficiently at high currents or low currents?

11 A laboratory EHT power supply produces a potential difference of 3 kV between its output terminals. For safety reasons, the current supplied by the power supply must be limited to no more than 1 mA if a person accidentally touches the terminals of the supply or the leads connected to them. Use your answer to question **10** in section 4.1 to suggest a minimum value for the internal resistance of the supply.

12 The condition of a car battery can be tested by measuring its internal resistance. One way of doing this is to connect a rugged, very low-resistance ammeter across the battery terminals.

a How would you expect the internal resistance of a car battery to affect its ability to start the car's engine? (*Hint*: remember that the starter motor draws a very large current.)

b Show that when the very low-resistance ammeter is connected to the car battery, the current through the ammeter is inversely proportional to the internal resistance of the battery, $I \propto 1/r$.

Developing Key Skills

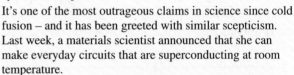

Read the following article, first published in *New Scientist*, 18 July 1998:

Cold reception for superconductivity claim
by Charles Seife

It's one of the most outrageous claims in science since cold fusion – and it has been greeted with similar scepticism. Last week, a materials scientist announced that she can make everyday circuits that are superconducting at room temperature.

Deborah Chung of the State University of New York at Buffalo told the Fifth International Conference on Composites Engineering in Las Vegas that tiny carbon fibres, set into epoxy or cement at high temperature, become "negative" resistors. This means that electrons in a circuit made from the material would be attracted to the side of the circuit with more negative charge and would flow towards it, instead of being repelled by it – rather like water flowing uphill.

Such a system would, in theory, provide a limitless source of energy. But this violates the second law of thermodynamics, which in essence says you can't get something for nothing. "That's part of the dilemma", admits Chung.

By combining negative resistors with normal conductors, Chung says she can create circuits that superconduct – they have zero resistance – at room temperature. The highest temperature at which superconductivity has been confirmed at atmospheric pressure is about –140°C.

Physicists can't understand Chung's claims. Negative resistance is real, but it has only been observed at higher voltages. In these cases electrons don't flow backwards; instead, fewer electrons flow through a circuit as you increase the voltage.

Chung's data come from a voltmeter and an ammeter. Other researchers say they will only be convinced by other key tests of superconductivity – such as showing that the material can be levitated over a magnet. "My suspicion is that there's something wrong with the measurement", says Steven Anlage, a physicist at the University of Maryland at College Park.

Make a list of the technical words and terms used in this article that someone with little or no science knowledge might be expected not to understand. Write a *glossary* to explain these technical words and terms.

[Key Skills opportunities: C, IT]

4.3 Incomplete circuits and capacitors

In sections 4.1 and 4.2 we have looked at the behaviour of complete circuits, and addressed some questions about how charge travels in such situations. Although we have concluded on the basis of some general observations that no charge flows round an incomplete circuit, we have not investigated the behaviour of incomplete circuits in any depth. The first part of this section remedies this, and goes on to look at an important circuit element in many circuits – the capacitor.

A capacitor does not behave in the same way as resistors or the other circuit elements described so far. Capacitors have a wide range of uses which depend on their ability to store charge – they are used in electronic circuits in which voltages vary with time, in power supplies to smooth the rectification of a.c. into d.c., and in circuits where currents are switched, where they may be used to help stop sparks and radio interference.

Incomplete circuits

Some general observations

If we connect up a circuit like that shown in figure 4.3.1 and close switch S_1, nothing appears to happen – the galvanometer shows no current flowing. However, connect a large metal plate (area about 500 cm^2) to each of A and B and place them a small distance apart (about 2–3 mm) and repeat the investigation, and the result is quite different. As the switch is closed, the galvanometer needle shows a brief, small deflection, indicating that a small current has flowed despite the fact that there is no continuous length of conductor.

This simple investigation can be extended by putting a second galvanometer in the circuit, and using a two way switch. Figure 4.3.2 shows the set-up and the results.

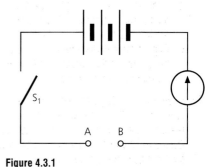

Figure 4.3.1

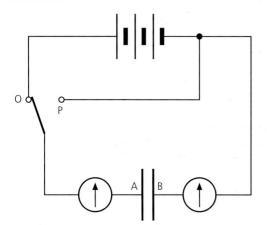

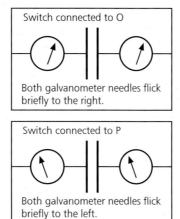

Switch connected to O

Both galvanometer needles flick briefly to the right.

Switch connected to P

Both galvanometer needles flick briefly to the left.

Figure 4.3.2

The behaviour of the galvanometer needles in the investigation suggests that a current flows in the circuit for a brief instant when the position of the switch is changed – in other words, a small charge flows round the circuit.

Since both galvanometers show deflections of similar size and in the same direction when the switch is in a particular position, this suggests that any charge flowing onto one plate is balanced by a similar amount of charge flowing off the other.

In the language of physics, we say that with the switch in position O the plate connected to A becomes positively charged, while the plate connected to B becomes negatively charged. When the switch is in position P, the charge on the plates flows round the circuit, and the plates become **discharged**.

Finally, the effect of changing the arrangement of the two plates may be investigated. This shows that:

1 Increasing the distance between the plates decreases the deflection of the galvanometer needles when the switch position is changed.

2 Decreasing the area of overlap of the plates (by sliding one in relation to the other) decreases the deflection of the galvanometer needles when the switch position is changed.

3 Putting a clean, dry sheet of an insulating material like poly(ethene) or perspex between the plates increases the deflection of the galvanometer needles when the switch position is changed.

The reasons for these observations are discussed later.

Capacitors

The plates in the investigations just described act to store charge. Circuit components which behave like this are called **capacitors**, and form an important part of virtually every electronic circuit. The exact arrangement in the investigation, known as a **parallel plate capacitor**, is not commonly found in electronic circuits, but its miniature equivalent has a similar, if more compact, structure, as we shall see. The circuit diagram symbol for a capacitor is a pair of parallel lines, as shown in figure 4.3.3, which is of course a representation of a parallel plate capacitor.

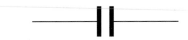

Figure 4.3.3 Capacitor symbol

Investigating the properties of a parallel plate capacitor

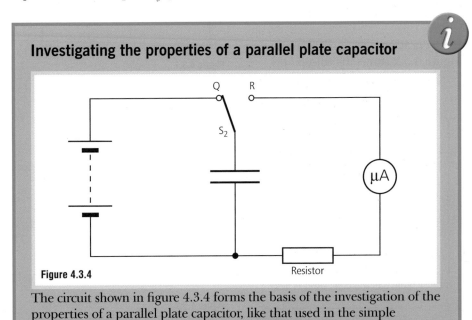

Figure 4.3.4

The circuit shown in figure 4.3.4 forms the basis of the investigation of the properties of a parallel plate capacitor, like that used in the simple investigations described above. S_2 is a single-pole, two-way switch. If S_2 is in position Q, current flows round the circuit and the capacitor becomes charged. If S_2 is now put in position R, the charge on the capacitor flows through the microammeter and resistor, and the capacitor discharges. As this happens the meter needle flicks briefly across the scale. In the investigation, S_2 is a special sort of switch called a **reed switch**, shown in figure 4.3.5.

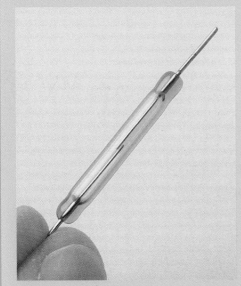

Figure 4.3.5 The reed switch contains a flexible magnetic strip. When the switch is placed in a changing magnetic field, the contact at the centre oscillates at the same rate as the field changes.

S_2 is placed in a solenoid (see section 5.4) through which pulses of current flow. The frequency of the pulses is usually between 50 and 100 Hz. This causes S_2 to oscillate rapidly between Q and R, so the capacitor rapidly charges up from the battery and then discharges though the meter. The rate of discharge (50 to 100 times a second) is sufficient for the meter to show a steady reading. If we assume that:

(1) the capacitor charges fully during the time it is connected to the battery, and

(2) the capacitor discharges completely during the time it is connected to the meter

then we can say that:

(1) the p.d. across the capacitor plates when it is fully charged (i.e. when it is connected to the battery and current has stopped flowing round the circuit) is equal to the battery e.m.f., and

(2) the current I indicated by the meter is equal to nQ, where n is the number of times the capacitor is discharged per unit time and $\pm Q$ are the charges on the capacitor plates when it is fully charged. Thus $Q = I/n$.

Capacitance

Investigations of the behaviour of a parallel plate capacitor show that the charges on the plates are proportional to the p.d. across them, that is,

$$Q \propto V$$

This means that:

$$\frac{Q}{V} = \text{a constant}$$

The constant in this relationship is the **capacitance** C of the capacitor, which is defined as:

the amount of charge stored on the plates per unit potential difference between them:

$$C = \frac{Q}{V}$$

The SI unit of capacitance is the **farad** (F). 1 farad = 1 coulomb per volt ($1\ \text{F} = 1\ \text{C V}^{-1}$). In practice the farad is far too large to be used as a unit, so microfarads (μF) and picofarads (pF) are more commonly used.

Multiples and submultiples of units

It is often convenient to be able to add a **multiplying prefix** to a unit in order to make it a convenient size. The prefixes used are defined as follows:

10^{-18} atto a	[10^1 deca da]	[Those prefixes in square brackets are
10^{-15} femto f	[10^2 hecto h]	not used in scientific work.]
10^{-12} pico p	10^3 kilo k	
10^{-9} nano n	10^6 mega M	
10^{-6} micro μ	10^9 giga G	
10^{-3} milli m	10^{12} tera T	
[10^{-2} centi c]	10^{15} peta P	
[10^{-1} deci d]	10^{18} exa E	

Thus, $1.5\ \text{TJ} = 1.5 \times 10^{12}\ \text{J}$, and $500\ \text{μF} = 5 \times 10^{-4}\ \text{F}$.

Capacitance and permittivity

The capacitance of a parallel plate capacitor depends on the factors described on pages 314–15. Careful investigations show that if a parallel plate capacitor is charged using a constant p.d., the charge Q on it varies in the following ways:

1 $Q \propto 1/d$, where d is the distance between the plates
2 $Q \propto A$, where A is the area of overlap of the plates
3 Q increases when a sheet of insulating material (sometimes called a **dielectric**) is placed between the plates in place of air.

Since V is constant, $C \propto Q$, and so:

$$C \propto \frac{A}{d}$$

The constant of proportionality in this relationship is ε, which is referred to as the **permittivity** of the material between the two plates. Permittivity has SI units of F m^{-1}.

$$C = \frac{\varepsilon A}{d}$$

If the plates are in a vacuum the constant is written as ε_0, and is called the **permittivity of free space**. This has the value $8.854 \times 10^{-12}\ \text{F m}^{-1}$. The idea of permittivity is important, and we shall return to it in section 5.3 when dealing with electric fields.

The term **relative permittivity** ε_r is often used when referring to materials. (Relative permittivity is also called the **dielectric constant**.) The relative permittivity of a material is defined as follows:

$$\varepsilon_r = \frac{\text{capacitance of ideal parallel plate capacitor with the material between its plates}}{\text{capacitance of same capacitor with a vacuum between its plates}}$$

Since ε_r is a ratio, it has no units. Some values of ε_r for different materials are given in table 4.3.1.

Material	Relative permittivity
Vacuum	1 (by definition)
Air	1.0005
Octane	1.95
Poly(ethene) – high density	2.35
Perspex	3.3
Poly(chloroethene)	3.5–4.5
Mica	7
Water	80
Barium titanate	1200

Table 4.3.1

Practical capacitors

Parallel plate capacitors of the type met so far have little practical use since they have capacitances of the order of 10^{-14} F. The capacitors in figure 4.3.6 have a capacitance of many times this – in order to achieve such values, the simple parallel plate capacitor would need to be the size of a football pitch!

Figure 4.3.6 The small size of modern circuits is made possible by using miniature electronic components, including capacitors. The decreasing size of such components has been due to developments in the materials used in their construction and to advances in manufacturing techniques.

The equation $C = \varepsilon A/d$ shows that in order to make a capacitor with as large a capacitance as possible we need to:

1 make the distance between the plates as small as possible
2 make the area of the plates as large as possible
3 use a dielectric between the plates with as large a dielectric constant as possible.

If we wish to make the capacitor reasonably compact, it will be necessary to limit the area of the plates. This therefore means that factors **2** and **3** must be maximised. There is one snag, however. When there is a large potential difference across two plates separated by only a small distance, the dielectric between the plates may **break down** and become conducting. (This effect was described in figure 4.2.25, page 305.) Because of this, there is a limit to how close the plates of the capacitor may be placed for a given p.d. across them. Capacitors are therefore labelled not only with their capacitance but also with their working p.d., in order to prevent breakdown of the dielectric in use.

Figure 4.3.7 shows some practical capacitors.

Figure 4.3.7

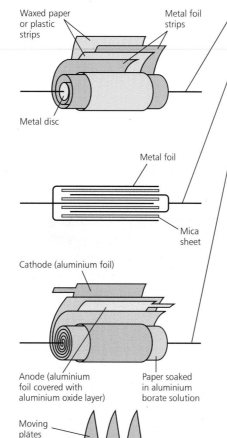

Waxed paper or plastic strips

Metal foil strips

Metal disc

Metal foil

Mica sheet

Cathode (aluminium foil)

Anode (aluminium foil covered with aluminium oxide layer)

Paper soaked in aluminium borate solution

Moving plates

Fixed plates

(a) In a **paper or plastic capacitor**, waxed paper or plastic strips separate strips of metal foil, and are then rolled up like a Swiss roll. Such capacitors can have values of up to a few microfarads.

(b) Mica is a naturally occurring mineral which cleaves (splits) into thin sheets with a very uniform thickness. These sheets are interleaved with metal foil to make up the capacitor. **Mica capacitors** can have values up to around 0.01 μF.

(c) The construction of an **electrolytic capacitor** is very similar to that of a paper or plastic capacitor. It consists of a layer of paper soaked in aluminium borate solution sandwiched between two layers of aluminium foil. When a p.d. is first applied to the plates of the capacitor, a current passes from the anode to the cathode. Oxygen is formed at the anode, and this reacts with the aluminium foil there, forming a layer of aluminium oxide about 10^{-5} m thick. This layer is the dielectric. Because the dielectric is so thin, an electrolytic capacitor has a much larger capacitance than other capacitors of a similar size – values of up to 100 000 μF are possible. The aluminium foil on which the aluminium oxide layer forms acts as the anode of the capacitor, while the aluminium borate solution acts as the other plate (the cathode). Care must be taken to always connect the electrolytic capacitors the correct way round in a circuit – if the capacitor is connected so that the anode becomes negative, the aluminium oxide dielectric will dissolve away and the capacitor will break down. For this reason the polarity is always marked on electrolytic capacitors, and circuit diagrams incorporating such capacitors always indicate which way they should be connected.

The circuit symbol for an electrolytic capacitor. Notice the polarity indicated.

Anode   Cathode

(d) **Variable capacitors** use air as a dielectric. These capacitors contain two sets of plates, one of which can be moved so that the area of overlap can be varied, thus changing the capacitance. These capacitors are used to tune some types of television and radio sets.

Capacitors in circuits

Just as we found simple relationships for the combined resistance of a network of resistors in section 4.2, so we may find simple expressions for the combined capacitance of a network of capacitors.

Capacitors in parallel

Simply by looking at figure 4.3.8, it seems reasonably obvious that the effect of connecting capacitors together in parallel is to add together the area of their plates, and that therefore their capacitances are added together.

Each capacitor has a potential difference V across it. Since $C = Q/V$, the charge on each capacitor is as follows:

$$Q_1 = C_1 V \qquad Q_2 = C_2 V \qquad Q_3 = C_3 V$$

The total charge on all three capacitors is Q_{TOTAL}, and:

$$Q_{TOTAL} = Q_1 + Q_2 + Q_3$$
$$= C_1 V + C_2 V + C_3 V$$

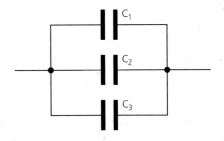

Figure 4.3.8

But $C_{TOTAL} = Q_{TOTAL}/V$, so:

$$C_{TOTAL} = \frac{C_1 V + C_2 V + C_3 V}{V}$$

that is,

$$C_{TOTAL} = C_1 + C_2 + C_3$$

Capacitors in series

Figure 4.3.9 shows three capacitors connected in series. When a potential difference V_{TOTAL} is connected across capacitors connected in series, charge flows onto the plates so that each capacitor carries a charge Q.

The potential difference across the capacitors is V_1, V_2 and V_3 respectively. Since $C = Q/V$, it follows that:

$$V_1 = Q/C_1 \qquad V_2 = Q/C_2 \qquad V_3 = Q/C_3$$

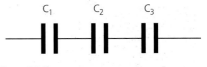

Figure 4.3.9

The p.d. across all three capacitors is V_{TOTAL}, and:

$$V_{TOTAL} = V_1 + V_2 + V_3$$
$$= \frac{Q}{C_1} + \frac{Q}{C_2} + \frac{Q}{C_3}$$

But $1/C_{TOTAL} = V_{TOTAL}/Q$, so:

$$\frac{1}{C_{TOTAL}} = \frac{1}{Q}\left(\frac{Q}{C_1} + \frac{Q}{C_2} + \frac{Q}{C_3}\right)$$

that is,

$$\frac{1}{C_{TOTAL}} = \frac{1}{C_1} + \frac{1}{C_2} + \frac{1}{C_3}$$

Combining capacitors – worked examples

What is the total capacitance of the two arrangements of capacitors in figure 4.3.10?

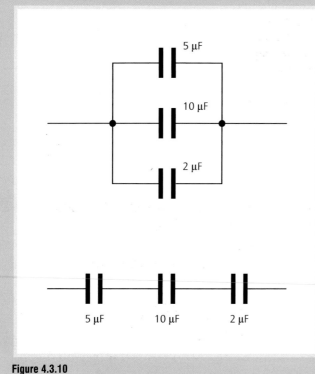

Figure 4.3.10

In parallel:

$$C_{TOTAL} = C_1 + C_2 + C_3$$
$$= 5\,\mu F + 10\,\mu F + 2\,\mu F$$
$$= 17\,\mu F$$

In series:

$$\frac{1}{C_{TOTAL}} = \frac{1}{C_1} + \frac{1}{C_2} + \frac{1}{C_3}$$
$$= \frac{1}{5\,\mu F} + \frac{1}{10\,\mu F} + \frac{1}{2\,\mu F}$$
$$= \frac{2 + 1 + 5}{10\,\mu F}$$
$$= \frac{8}{10\,\mu F}$$

so:

$$C_{TOTAL} = 1.25\,\mu F$$

The energy stored in a capacitor

When a capacitor is connected to a battery a current flows. This suggests that energy transfers are taking place in the circuit – energy is transferred from the source of e.m.f. to the capacitor. Simple investigations like those shown in figure 4.3.11 suggest that a charged capacitor is capable of doing work, so a charged capacitor must therefore be an energy store. How much energy is stored in a charged capacitor?

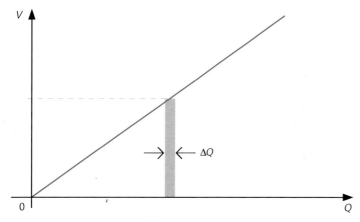

Figure 4.3.12

Figure 4.3.11 Simple investigations show that a charged electrolytic capacitor with a capacitance of about 10 000 μF stores enough energy to drive a motor to raise a small mass a short distance, or to light a lamp for a few seconds.

The energy stored in a charged capacitor must be equal to the energy transferred to it from the battery in the charging process. When the capacitor is completely uncharged, the battery does no work in transferring a small amount of charge to it. However, as positive charge is transferred to one plate of the capacitor and removed from the other, it develops a p.d. across its plates and the battery must therefore do work in charging it. Figure 4.3.12 shows how the p.d. across a capacitor varies as it is charged. In transferring charge ΔQ to the positive plate of the capacitor and removing it from the negative plate, the battery does work equivalent to the area of the shaded strip under the graph, $V\Delta Q$. (This assumes that ΔQ is small enough to ensure that V is effectively constant while the charge on the capacitor increases.) The work done in charging the capacitor is the sum of the area of all such strips under the graph, that is, $\frac{1}{2}QV$. Since $C = Q/V$, we can write:

$$E = \tfrac{1}{2}QV = \tfrac{1}{2}CV^2 = \tfrac{1}{2}Q^2/C$$

Capacitors and energy – worked example

A 10 000 μF capacitor is described as having a maximum working voltage of 25 V. How much energy can this capacitor store? If this capacitor were connected to a motor so that it could lift a mass of 100 g, what is the *maximum* height to which this could be raised?

$$E = \tfrac{1}{2}CV^2$$
$$= \tfrac{1}{2} \times 10\ 000 \times 10^{-6}\ \text{F} \times (25\ \text{V})^2$$
$$= 3.125\ \text{J}$$

If all this energy were transferred to the mass as gravitational potential energy, then:

$$3.125\ \text{J} = mg\Delta h$$
$$= 0.1\ \text{kg} \times 9.8\ \text{N kg}^{-1} \times \Delta h$$

So:

$$\Delta h = \frac{3.125\ \text{J}}{0.1\ \text{kg} \times 9.8\ \text{N kg}^{-1}}$$
$$= 3.2\ \text{m}$$

The mass could be raised over 3 m if all the energy in the capacitor were to be transferred to it as gravitational potential energy.

Discharging capacitors

In the investigation described in figure 4.3.4, we neglected the time taken for the capacitor to discharge and assumed that it did so instantaneously. We can investigate the discharge of a capacitor using the circuit shown in figure 4.3.13.

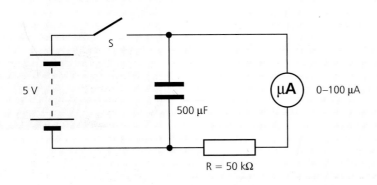

Figure 4.3.13

Batteries are excellent at storing electricity as chemical energy, although they are not so good at giving and receiving. Charge a battery too fast and it is likely to overheat and become useless. Drain it too quickly – by blasting away from the traffic lights in your new electric car, for example – and you are just as likely to damage it. This is where capacitors come in. Because they store energy in an electric field, they can be charged and discharged extremely rapidly, time after time. Yet despite their name, capacitors generally have only very small capacities, giving enough energy to fire the flash tube in your camera, but not enough to do something really big like accelerate a car. The arrival of **supercapacitors** is likely to change all that, as a result of work carried out in the Department of Materials at the University of Leeds.

All capacitors rely on the principle of storing energy in an electric field produced through the separation of electric charge. The amount of charge that can be stored by a capacitor depends on three factors – the area over which the charge is stored, the separation distance of the electric charge, and the **permittivity** of the medium or **dielectric** between the charges (the larger the permittivity, the more charge can be stored). Some supercapacitors have been produced through the development of new dielectrics with much larger permittivities than before. One of these dielectrics is a compound of lead, magnesium and niobium which has a relative permittivity of up to 75 000, some 60 times larger than dielectrics used previously. **Solid state capacitors** like this are very robust and last virtually for ever.

Another approach to producing supercapacitors is to make use of the charge separation between a conductor and an electrolyte (conducing solution) in contact with it. These **electric double layer capacitors** use specially treated carbon as the electrodes, a substance which may have a surface area of as much as $2000\,m^2\,g^{-1}$. When an external voltage is applied, charge building up on the electrodes is balanced by the movement of ions in the electrolyte. This leads to the separation of charge over distances comparable with the size of molecules, over a very large surface area. As a result, a capacitor which is only 10 cm long and 4 cm in diameter may have a capacity of up to 800 F, and may be able to store as much as 2.9 kJ of energy.

Supercapacitors are likely to find many uses. Unlike batteries, they can be very rapidly discharged and charged again, which will make their use as 'load levellers' (devices that can supply surges of demand for electricity or make up for dips in electricity supply) very widespread. In many cases the capacitors will be used in conjunction with conventional batteries, helping to increase the life of the battery by ensuring that the current drawn from it remains relatively steady. Other uses may be in transport, where the next generation of electric vehicles employs **regenerative braking**, which can capture and store some of the energy that would otherwise be dissipated as heat in the braking system during deceleration. One such vehicle is already in production, made by the Honda motor company. At present the electricity produced by the generator is used to charge the battery, but in the near future supercapacitors will provide a way of using this electricity much more effectively, making it available for rapid acceleration following braking.

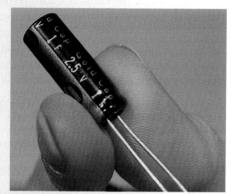

Figure 4.3.14 The capacity of capacitors like this is usually a few tens of microfarads (μF). With a capacitance of 1 F, this supercapacitor can store thousands of times as much energy as a conventional capacitor of the same size.

Figure 4.3.15 Possible uses of supercapacitors include portable power tools and stores for electricity produced by photovoltaic cells, an application that could also lead to potentially dramatic improvements in living standards in the developing world, making it possible to power refrigerators and other appliances very cheaply.

The capacitor is charged by closing the switch S. When the switch is closed, the microammeter reads $100\,\mu A$ ($I = 5\,V/50\,k\Omega = 10^{-4}\,A$). At the instant S is opened, this reading begins to fall.

The p.d. across the capacitor, the charge on it and the current through the circuit at any instant are related by two equations:

$$V = IR \quad \textbf{and} \quad C = Q/V$$

We also know that the current through the circuit at any instant is the rate of flow of charge from the capacitor at that instant, so we can write:

$$I = -\frac{\Delta Q}{\Delta t}$$

(The negative sign shows that the charge on the capacitor *decreases* as time increases.)

The instantaneous current through the circuit is also related to the p.d. across the capacitor and the resistance of the circuit:

$$I = \frac{V}{R}$$

And the p.d. across the capacitor at any instant is related to the charge on it at that instant and its capacitance:

$$V = \frac{Q}{C}$$

Bringing these three equations together:

$$I = -\frac{\Delta Q}{\Delta t} = \frac{Q}{RC}$$

Rearranging this:

$$\Delta Q = -\frac{Q}{RC}\Delta t$$

We can now use this relationship to calculate the charge on the capacitor at 5-second intervals as it discharges, and to calculate the current at those times too. Figure 4.3.16 shows how this is done for the example in figure 4.3.13.

The graphs of current and charge versus time have a constant period in which a quantity (in this case charge or current) halves. This is characteristic of an **exponential decay**, in which the rate of decrease of a quantity is proportional to the quantity itself.

(Note that the p.d. across the capacitor is directly related to the charge on it, and that the current through the circuit is directly related to the p.d. across the capacitor – therefore all these quantities vary in a similar way.)

Calculus is required to investigate fully the relationships involved in the discharge of a capacitor, but some very simple mathematics together with a graphical treatment using techniques like those used in figure 4.3.16 show that:

- The time taken for the capacitor to discharge from voltage V to voltage $V/2$ is proportional to RC (the resistance of the circuit multiplied by the capacitance of the capacitor) – the quantity RC is called the **time constant** of the circuit.
- The decay of charge on the capacitor has a constant half-life of just over two-thirds of the time constant (actually $0.693RC$).
- After it has been discharging for a time RC, the charge on a capacitor has fallen to a little over one-third of its initial value (actually $0.37Q_0$).

4

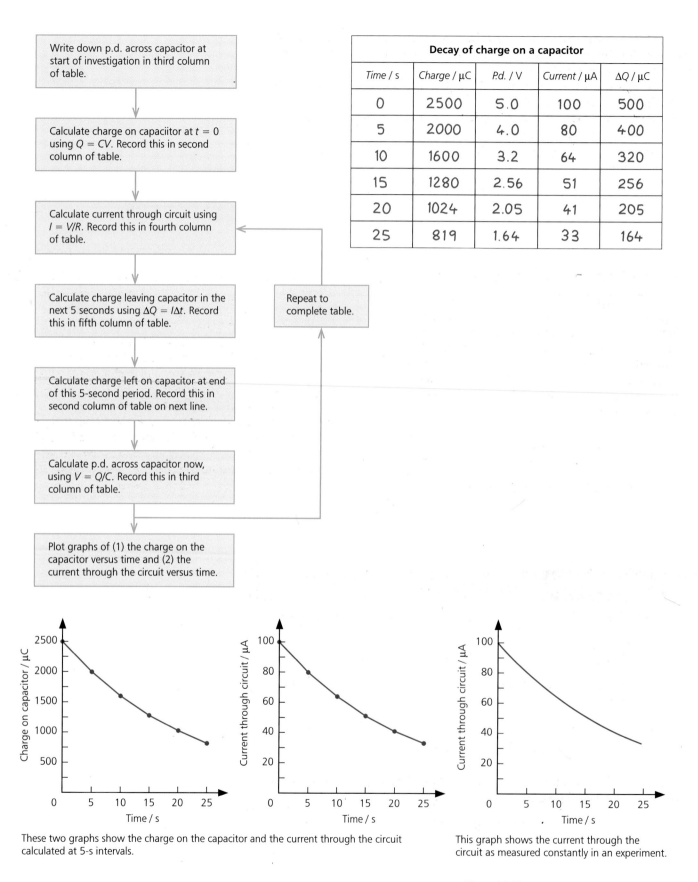

Decay of charge on a capacitor				
Time / s	Charge / μC	P.d. / V	Current / μA	ΔQ / μC
0	2500	5.0	100	500
5	2000	4.0	80	400
10	1600	3.2	64	320
15	1280	2.56	51	256
20	1024	2.05	41	205
25	819	1.64	33	164

Write down p.d. across capacitor at start of investigation in third column of table.

Calculate charge on capaciitor at $t = 0$ using $Q = CV$. Record this in second column of table.

Calculate current through circuit using $I = V/R$. Record this in fourth column of table.

Calculate charge leaving capacitor in the next 5 seconds using $\Delta Q = I\Delta t$. Record this in fifth column of table.

Repeat to complete table.

Calculate charge left on capacitor at end of this 5-second period. Record this in second column of table on next line.

Calculate p.d. across capacitor now, using $V = Q/C$. Record this in third column of table.

Plot graphs of (1) the charge on the capacitor versus time and (2) the current through the circuit versus time.

These two graphs show the charge on the capacitor and the current through the circuit calculated at 5-s intervals.

This graph shows the current through the circuit as measured constantly in an experiment.

Figure 4.3.16

At first it may seem surprising that the time constant RC is a measure of the time taken for the capacitor to discharge. However, a little thought suggests that this is not unreasonable, since:

- Increasing R decreases the current through the circuit, thus increasing the time the capacitor takes to discharge.
- Increasing C increases the charge on the capacitor for a given p.d. across it, without changing the current through the circuit.

In addition, multiplying resistance by capacitance results in a quantity with the units of time:

$$\Omega \times F = V\ A^{-1} \times C\ V^{-1} = V \times (C\ s^{-1})^{-1} \times C\ V^{-1}$$
$$= s$$

The reed switch experiment revisited

In the investigation of the factors affecting the capacitance of a parallel plate capacitor described in figure 4.3.13, the assumption was made that the capacitor was fully discharged in each cycle. Was this justified? The area of the plates was about 500 cm^2 and the space between them (filled with air) was around 3 mm. This suggests that the capacitance C of this capacitor was:

$$C = \frac{\varepsilon_0 A}{d} = 8.85 \times 10^{-12}\ F\ m^{-1} \times \frac{500 \times 10^{-4}\ m^2}{3 \times 10^{-3}\ m}$$

$$= 1.5 \times 10^{-10}\ F\ \text{(that is, about } 10^{-10}\ F\text{)}$$

If the resistance of the circuit was 50 kΩ, $RC = 5 \times 10^4\ \Omega \times 10^{-10}\ F = 5\ \mu s$. The capacitor will completely discharge to all intents and purposes in about $5RC$ (although note that because the decay is exponential, the capacitor will *never* be fully discharged – see the graph in figure 4.3.16), that is, about 25 μs. The capacitor will also take a finite time to charge up – this can be shown to be the same as the time to discharge. So the capacitor will take about 50 μs to charge and discharge again. Since the reed switch was operating at a maximum rate of 100 Hz, this allowed 10^{-2} s for each charge/discharge cycle – about 200 times longer than required. So the assumption that the capacitor was fully discharged in each cycle was justified.

Discharging a capacitor

From considering the discharge of a capacitor we know that we can write:

$$\frac{\Delta Q}{\Delta t} = -\frac{Q}{RC}$$

If we now let $\Delta t \to 0$, the differential equation which results may be solved by integration:

$$\int_{Q_0}^{Q} \frac{dQ}{Q} = -\int_{0}^{t} \frac{dt}{RC}$$

The limits of the integration are chosen so that the charge on the capacitor is Q_0 when $t = 0$ and Q when $t = t$.

Integrating this relationship gives the result:

$$\left[\log_e Q\right]_{Q_0}^{Q} = -\left[\frac{t}{RC}\right]_0^t$$

When these two expressions are evaluated between their limits, we get:

$$\log_e Q - \log_e Q_0 = -t/RC$$

Since $\log x - \log y = \log (x/y)$, this becomes:

$$\log_e \frac{Q}{Q_0} = -\frac{t}{RC}$$

or:

$$Q = Q_0\, e^{-t/RC}$$

The time taken for the capacitor to lose half its charge is known as the **half-life** $t_{1/2}$ of the decay process. In this case, $Q = Q_0/2$ when $t = t_{1/2}$, so:

$$\log_e \frac{Q_0/2}{Q_0} = -\frac{t_{1/2}}{RC}$$

or:

$$\log_e \frac{1}{2} = -\frac{t_{1/2}}{RC}$$

Since $-\log_e \frac{1}{2} = \log_e 2$ this can be rearranged:

$$t_{1/2} = RC \log_e 2$$

$$\approx 0.693 RC$$

When t = the time constant, RC:

$$Q = Q_0\, e^{-RC/RC} = Q_0\, e^{-1}$$

$$\approx 0.37 Q_0$$

Thus RC is the time for the charge on the capacitor to fall to 0.37 times its initial value, as we have already seen.

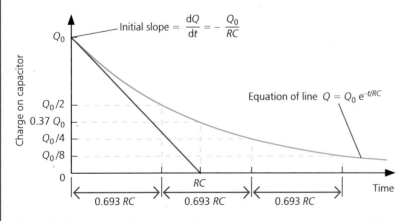

Figure 4.3.17 The exponential decay curve of the charge on a capacitor shows a constant half-life of $RC \log_e 2$. The graph also illustrates how the capacitor would fully discharge in time RC if it continued to discharge at its initial rate, and how the actual charge remaining on it after this time is $0.37Q_0$.

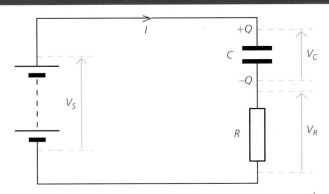

Figure 4.3.18

A similar process enables the charging of the capacitor to be modelled. In the circuit shown in figure 4.3.18, Kirchhoff's second law (see page 291) tells us that:

$$V_{\mathrm{S}} = V_{\mathrm{R}} + V_{\mathrm{C}} = IR + \frac{Q}{C}$$

As the capacitor charges, I and Q will change while V_{S} and C will not, so that in a time interval of Δt we can write:

$$\frac{\Delta V_{\mathrm{S}}}{\Delta t} = 0 = \frac{\Delta I\, R}{\Delta t} + \frac{1}{C}\frac{\Delta Q}{\Delta t}$$

But $\Delta Q/\Delta t = I$, so:

$$0 = \frac{\Delta I\, R}{\Delta t} + \frac{I}{C}$$

Rearranging gives us:

$$\frac{\Delta I}{\Delta t} = -\frac{I}{RC}$$

If $\Delta t \to 0$, this produces a differential equation:

$$\frac{\mathrm{d}I}{\mathrm{d}t} = -\frac{I}{RC}$$

This is exactly the same form of the equation we saw before in the case of the decay of charge on the capacitor. The solution to this equation is also obtained by integration:

$$\int_{I_0}^{I} \frac{\mathrm{d}I}{I} = -\int_{0}^{t} \frac{\mathrm{d}t}{RC}$$

This produces the solution:

$$I = I_0\, \mathrm{e}^{-t/RC}$$

Now when $t = 0$, we know that:

$$I = I_0 = V_{\mathrm{S}}/R, \text{ since at } t = 0, V_{\mathrm{C}} = 0$$

We also know that $I = V_R/R$, so:

$$I = \frac{V_R}{R} = \frac{V_S}{R} e^{-t/RC}$$

that is,

$$V_R = V_S e^{-t/RC}$$

Now the p.d. across the capacitor is given by:

$$V_C = V_S - V_R$$

so:

$$V_C = V_S - V_S e^{-t/RC}$$
$$= V_S(1 - e^{-t/RC})$$

and:

$$Q = CV_S(1 - e^{-t/RC})$$

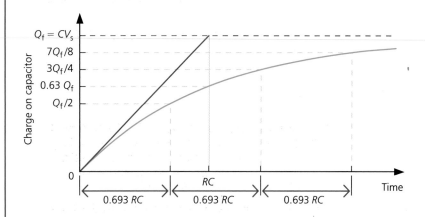

Figure 4.3.19 The curve of the increase of charge on a capacitor has similar characteristics to the decay curve for the same capacitor. Notice that the increase in charge has a constant half-life of $RC \log_e 2$. The graph also illustrates how the capacitor would fully charge to a charge Q_f in time RC if it continued to charge at its initial rate, and how the actual charge on it after this time is $(1 - 0.37)Q_f = 0.63Q_f$.

SUMMARY

- A **capacitor** stores a charge of $+Q$ on one plate and a charge of $-Q$ on the other plate.
- The **capacitance** C of a capacitor is the amount of charge stored on the plates per unit p.d. between them, $C = Q/V$. Capacitance is measured in **farads** F, $1\ \text{F} = 1\ \text{C V}^{-1}$.
- $C = \varepsilon A/d$ where ε is the **permittivity** of the material between the plates, A the area of overlap and d the distance between the plates.
- For capacitors in parallel, $C_{\text{TOTAL}} = C_1 + C_2 + \ldots.$

- For capacitors in series, $1/C_{\text{TOTAL}} = (1/C_1) + (1/C_2) + ...$
- The energy stored in a charged capacitor $E = \frac{1}{2}Q^2/C = \frac{1}{2}CV^2$.
- The discharge of a capacitor is an example of exponential decay, since $Q = Q_0 e^{-t/RC}$ where RC is the **time constant** of the circuit and is a measure of the time taken for the capacitor to discharge.

EXAMPLE

A 50 µF capacitor is discharged through a 10 000 Ω resistance. How long will it take for the potential difference across the capacitor to fall to 40% of its initial value?

We know that for a capacitor C discharging through a resistor R, the charge remaining after time t has elapsed is given by:

$$Q = Q_0 e^{-t/RC}$$

where Q_0 is the charge on the capacitor at $t = 0$.
Since $C = Q/V$, it follows that $V \propto Q$, and we may also write:

$$V = V_0 e^{-t/RC}$$

or:

$$\log_e V = \log_e V_0 - \frac{t}{RC}$$

This can be simplified to:

$$\frac{t}{RC} = \log_e \frac{V_0}{V}$$

In this case, $V = 0.4V_0$, $R = 10\ 000\ \Omega$ and $C = 50 \times 10^{-6}$ F, so:

$$\frac{t}{10\ 000\ \Omega \times 50 \times 10^{-6}\ F} = \log_e \frac{V_0}{0.4\ V_0}$$

so:

$$t = (10\ 000\ \Omega \times 50 \times 10^{-6}\ F) \times \log_e 2.5$$
$$= 0.46\ s$$

The potential difference across the capacitor falls to 40% of its initial value in 0.46 s.

QUESTIONS

1 A capacitor consists of two discs of metal 10 cm in diameter 1 mm apart in air. (Take $\varepsilon_0 = 8.85 \times 10^{-12}$ F m^{-1}.)
Calculate:
  a the capacitance of the capacitor
  b the charge on each plate of the capacitor if it is connected to a battery with an e.m.f. of 24 V.

2 If the capacitor plates in question **1** are moved 1 mm further apart while the capacitor remains connected to the battery, what happens?

3 Figure 4.3.20 shows a variable capacitor like that used in some radio tuners.
  a The capacitor can be thought of as several capacitors connected together. Are these connected in series or parallel?
  b What happens to the capacitance of the capacitor as the knob is turned anticlockwise?

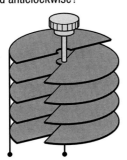

Figure 4.3.20

4 You have a sheet of polythene ($\varepsilon_r = 2.3$) 0.25 mm thick. If this polythene is to be used in a capacitor by sandwiching it between two sheets of aluminium foil, what area must the sheets have if the capacitor is to have a capacitance of 0.5 µF? (Take $\varepsilon_0 = 8.85 \times 10^{-12}$ F m^{-1}.)

5 Calculate the capacitance between points A and B in figure 4.3.21.

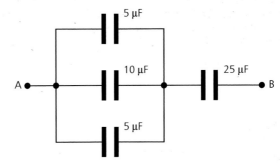

Figure 4.3.21

6 What capacitances can be made using four capacitors of 0.5 µF, 1.0 µF, 2.5 µF and 8.0 µF?

7 A 5.0 µF capacitor and an 8.0 µF capacitor are charged separately to 12 V. The two capacitors are then connected as shown in figure 4.3.22. Calculate the charge on the plates of each capacitor after they have been connected.

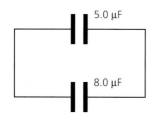

Figure 4.3.22

8 A 10 μF capacitor is connected to a source of e.m.f. of 2×10^4 V.
  a Calculate the energy stored in the capacitor.
  b Comment on your answer.

9 A 10 000 μF capacitor is charged by connecting it to a 12 V power supply. The capacitor is then discharged by connecting it to a length of copper wire of mass 1.5 g. If all the energy in the capacitor is dissipated as thermal energy in the wire, calculate the maximum temperature rise of the wire. (Take the specific heat capacity of copper as 390 J kg^{-1} K^{-1}.)

10 A discharge lamp consists of gas at low pressure surrounding two electrodes. When it is not glowing, the gas in the lamp has a very high resistance. The gas does not conduct electricity until the potential difference across the lamp reaches a certain minimum value V_{min} (sometimes called the 'striking voltage'). Once conducting, the gas glows, and its resistance falls – it will continue to glow until the potential difference across it falls to around $0.75V_{min}$. Use this information to explain the observation in figure 4.3.23, and sketch a graph of the reading on the voltmeter.

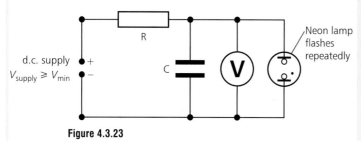

Figure 4.3.23

11 A timing device is to be made using a capacitor that is to discharge through a fixed resistor. Time is to be measured using the potential difference across the capacitor. If a resistor of 5×10^4 Ω is available, what value capacitor will be appropriate for measuring times of around 10 s?

12 A charged capacitor will discharge slowly, even if its terminals are 'open circuit', that is, not connected to anything. This occurs because the dielectric between the two plates of the capacitor acts as a very poor conductor, allowing a very small leakage current to flow between the two plates, thus discharging them. A capacitor consists of two plates of area
50 cm^2, separated by a sheet of polythene 0.1 mm thick. The capacitor is briefly connected to a power supply, producing a potential difference between the plates of 15 V. Calculate:
  a the capacitance of the capacitor
  b the electrical resistance of the dielectric between the two plates
  c the initial leakage current through the capacitor when it is disconnected from the power supply
  d the time taken for the p.d. across the capacitor plates to fall to 7.5 V. (Take ε_r for polythene as 2.3, ε_0 as 8.85×10^{-12} F m^{-1} and the resistivity of polythene as 2×10^{11} Ω m.)

Developing Key Skills

If you have not already done so, read the focus on page 322.

Write a press release for a company that has just developed a supercapacitor with a higher capacitance than any similar product produced by its competitor.

Hints: A press release should make a newspaper editor really *want* to publish an article on what you are writing about, and should always include information concerning **who** (has made the new product), **what** (is the new product), **where** (it is made), **when** (it will be available) and **why** (it is important). You should be able to use the Internet to find information about producing a really good press release.

[Key Skills opportunities: C, IT]

So far we have looked at simple circuits through which a current flows in one direction. Whilst this is an ideal situation in which to develop an understanding of the basic principles of electricity, it overlooks the single most important influence of electricity in the lives of most of us – the supply of an **alternating current** for lighting, heating, cooking, etc. through the mains. We shall now look at some of the principles by which alternating currents of electricity can be understood, and we shall return to some of these and develop them further in section 5.5, when we shall be concerned with electromagnetic induction.

Describing alternating currents

A.c. in simple circuits

As in d.c. circuits, in a.c. circuits there is a simple relationship between the current through the circuit and the p.d. across it, as the investigation in figure 4.4.2 shows.

Figure 4.4.1 The impact of electricity on our lives can easily be taken for granted.

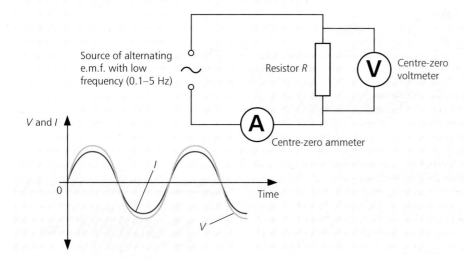

Figure 4.4.2

Observation of the meter needles as low frequency a.c. flows through the circuit shows that the current through the resistor and the p.d. across it vary with time in exactly the same way – they are **in phase**, as the graph shows.

Using an oscilloscope to measure alternating voltages

Figure 4.4.3 shows how an oscilloscope may be used to measure the frequency of an alternating current. (The use of a CRO to measure p.d.s was dealt with in section 4.2, page 302.) With the CRO connected across the resistor, the time base is adjusted so that several complete cycles of the p.d. appear on the screen. The distance between two identical

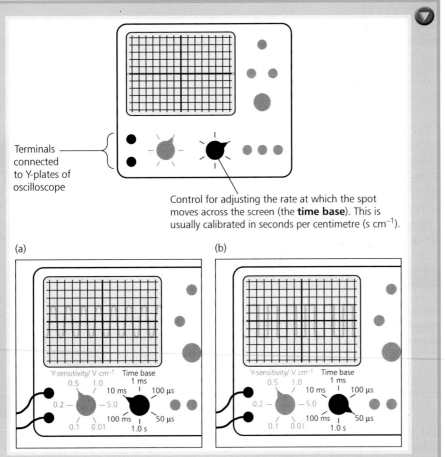

Figure 4.4.3

points in two successive cycles can then be measured, and the time base setting used to convert this to a time measurement. Diagrams (a) and (b) show this process for two different alternating p.d.s:

- In (a) the p.d. varies sinusoidally. The distance representing one complete cycle is 2 cm, and the time base is set to 10 ms cm^{-1}. The time for one complete cycle is thus 2 cm × $(10 × 10^{-3})$ s cm^{-1} = 0.02 s. As $f = 1/T$, the frequency of the alternating p.d. is 1/0.02 s = 50 Hz.

- In (b) the p.d. is a square waveform. The distance representing one complete cycle is 2.5 cm, and the time base is set to 50 μs cm^{-1}. The time for one complete cycle is thus 2.5 cm × $(50 × 10^{-6})$ s cm^{-1} = $1.25 × 10^{-4}$ s. The frequency of the alternating p.d. is 1/($1.25 × 10^{-4}$ s) = 8000 Hz.

The mains supply

The p.d. of the mains supply varies with time as the trace on the oscilloscope screen in figure 4.4.4 shows. If the trace on the screen is transferred to a carefully drawn graph, using the settings on the oscilloscope to obtain the values on the x- and y-axes, the plot shown in figure 4.4.5 is the result.

Although the mains supply in the UK is referred to as a 240 V supply, the oscilloscope trace shows that the supply voltage varies from +340 V to –340 V (measured with respect to the neutral wire), with a period of 0.02 s. The

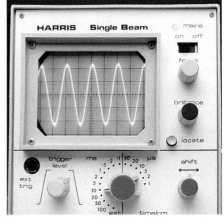

Figure 4.4.4 The supply of mains electric current to our homes is alternating, in order to overcome the problems of energy loss in transmitting large currents at low voltages. If the p.d. of the mains electricity supply is displayed on an oscilloscope screen the trace looks like this.

Figure 4.4.5

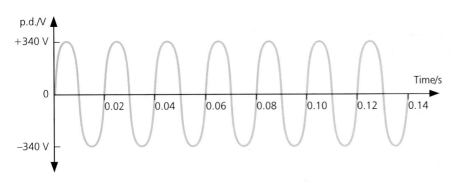

difference of 680 V between the maximum positive and the maximum negative values of the trace is called the **peak-to-peak voltage**. The mean value of the supply voltage is zero. The variation appears to be **sinusoidal**, and we shall prove in section 5.5 that this is indeed so. Since the period of one cycle is 0.02 s, the supply frequency is 1/0.02 s = 50 Hz. The supply voltage therefore follows a relationship which can be expressed as:

$$V = V_0 \sin (2\pi ft)$$

where V_0 = 340 V and f = 50 Hz. This is the general way of describing a sinusoidal supply, in which V_0 is called the **peak voltage** (which is equal to exactly half the peak-to-peak voltage) and f is the **supply frequency**.

Comparing alternating and direct currents

The UK mains supply voltage is usually quoted as 240 V, although we saw above that neither the peak value of the supply (340 V) nor its mean value (zero) corresponds to this figure. In fact 240 V is the **root mean square** of the supply voltage. This is used as a way of comparing an alternating current with a direct current.

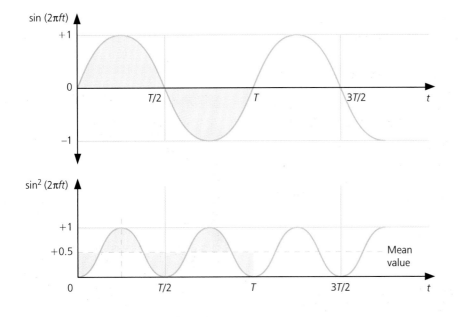

Figure 4.4.6 The average of sin (2π*ft*) over *n* complete cycles is zero, since the function consists of a series of peaks and troughs which vary equally on either side of the *x*-axis. Over the same period the average value of sin² (2π*ft*) is 0.5, since the graph of this function consists of a series of peaks and troughs which are equally spaced above and below the dotted line.

Consider a resistor connected to an alternating supply voltage. The resistor has a p.d. V across it which varies with time as:

$$V = V_0 \sin (2\pi ft)$$

The power dissipated in a resistor R with a p.d. V across it is V^2/R, so in this case

$$P = \frac{V_0^2 \sin^2 (2\pi ft)}{R}$$

The *average* rate of dissipation of energy in the resistor will be the quantity we need if we wish to compare the effect of the alternating p.d. across this resistance with that of a constant p.d. Since V_0^2/R is constant, the average power dissipated in the resistor can be found by finding the average of $\sin^2 (2\pi ft)$. As figure 4.4.6 shows, this is 0.5, so:

$$P = \frac{\frac{1}{2}V_0^2}{R}$$

This rate of energy dissipation could be obtained using a steady p.d. V_S, in which case:

$$P = \frac{V_S^2}{R}$$

V_S and V_0 are related by the expressions for energy dissipation in the resistance, so:

$$P = \frac{\frac{1}{2}V_0^2}{R} = \frac{V_S^2}{R}$$

and thus:

$$V_S^2 = \frac{V_0^2}{2}$$

or:

$$V_S = \frac{V_0}{\sqrt{2}}$$

Thus an alternating p.d. dissipates energy in a resistance R at an *average* rate of $\frac{1}{2}V_0^2/R$. If a *constant* p.d. were used to do this, the p.d. would have to be $V_0 / \sqrt{2}$, because:

$$\frac{\left(\frac{V_0}{\sqrt{2}}\right)^2}{R} = \frac{\frac{1}{2}V_0^2}{R}$$

Thus the peak voltage of 340 V which is used for the UK mains electricity supply is equivalent to a steady voltage of 340 V$/ \sqrt{2}$ = 240 V, which is why the mains voltage is referred to in this way.

The root-mean-square (r.m.s.) value of the p.d. can be defined in words:

The root-mean-square value of an alternating potential difference is the square root of the mean value of the square of the potential difference over a complete cycle. The r.m.s. potential difference is numerically equal to the constant p.d. which would dissipate energy at the same rate as the alternating p.d. when applied across a given resistor.

Note that the factor of $\sqrt{2}$ which is used in the conversion of peak value to r.m.s. value applies only to quantities which vary sinusoidally. For a square wave p.d. with peak value V_0 the r.m.s. value of the p.d. is also V_0, as figure 4.4.7 shows.

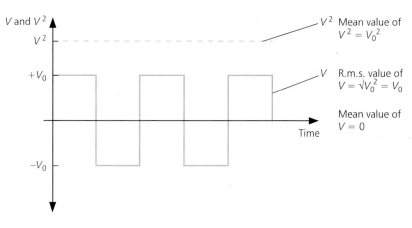

Figure 4.4.7

V² Mean value of $V^2 = V_0^2$

V R.m.s. value of $V = \sqrt{V_0^2} = V_0$

Mean value of $V = 0$

The power dissipated in a resistor

The same set of relationships apply to the current through a resistor as to the p.d. across it, since the current and p.d. vary in phase, as figure 4.4.2 showed. This means that we can write:

$$V = V_0 \sin (2\pi ft) \qquad I = I_0 \sin (2\pi ft)$$

for the p.d. across a resistor and the current through it.

Because the current and p.d. are in phase for a resistor, the power dissipated at any instant in a resistive load carrying a.c. can be written as the product of the current through the load and the p.d. across it, that is,

$$P = IV$$

Now the *maximum* power dissipated in the resistor will be given by the product of the maximum p.d. across the resistor and the maximum current through it, that is,

$$P_{max} = I_0 V_0$$

Similarly, the *mean* power dissipated in the resistor will be given by the product of the two r.m.s. quantities:

$$P_{mean} = I_{r.m.s.} V_{r.m.s.}$$

Since:

$$I_{r.m.s.} = I_0 / \sqrt{2} \quad \text{and} \quad V_{r.m.s.} = V_0 / \sqrt{2}$$

we can write:

$$P_{mean} = \frac{I_0}{\sqrt{2}} \times \frac{V_0}{\sqrt{2}} = \frac{I_0 V_0}{2}$$

This means that for a resistive load:

Mean power dissipated = $\frac{1}{2}$ × peak power dissipated

Comparing alternating and direct currents by eye

The apparatus in figure 4.4.8 can be used to compare an alternating and a direct current. The brightness of a lamp is a measure of the power dissipated in it. An oscilloscope measures the potential difference

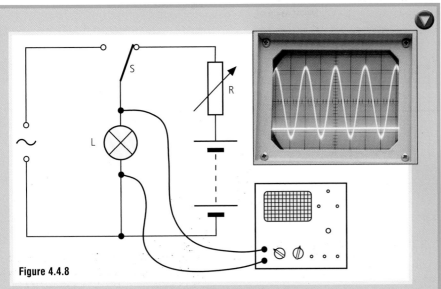

Figure 4.4.8

across lamp L, which is lit using either a direct current or an alternating current, depending on the position of switch S. S is moved between its two positions so that the lamp is lit first by a.c., then by d.c., and then by a.c. again, and so on. The variable resistor R is used to vary the direct current so that the lamp appears to be the same brightness when lit by both a.c. and d.c. (This is usually best done by switching S quite rapidly between its two positions, at a rate of about 1–2 Hz.) Observation of the oscilloscope traces shows that when the lamp is the same brightness when lit by both a.c. and d.c., the peak voltage of the a.c. supply is about 1.4 ($\sqrt{2}$) times the voltage of the d.c. supply.

More complex circuits

Capacitors and a.c.

The behaviour of a capacitor in a circuit carrying an alternating current is rather different from its behaviour in a d.c. circuit. If a capacitor and a lamp are connected in series to a battery the lamp does not light, since the capacitor is effectively a break in the circuit. If the battery is replaced by a 50 Hz supply from a power pack, the lamp lights. Why this difference? Figure 4.4.9 provides the explanation.

Figure 4.4.9

Supply may be either a.c. or d.c.

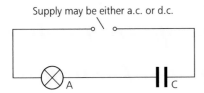

The capacitor is effectively a break in the circuit, through which a current cannot flow. When a battery is connected to the circuit, charge flows round the circuit until the capacitor is charged and then stops. This brief flow of current *may* be sufficient to light lamp A briefly if C is very large – but it will not light constantly.

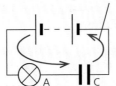

With an alternating supply, charge flows first one way round the circuit and then the other, so the capacitor first charges, then discharges and charges up in the opposite way, and lamp A lights steadily.

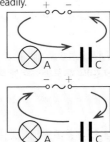

Capacitors in a.c. circuits also behave differently from resistors. This can be shown by repeating the investigation described in figure 4.4.2, adding a capacitor to the circuit in place of the resistor. (See figure 4.4.10.)

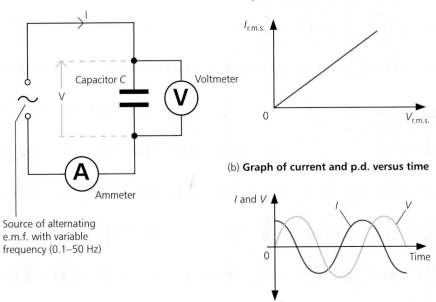

(a) **Graph of r.m.s. current through the capacitor versus r.m.s. p.d. across it**

(b) **Graph of current and p.d. versus time**

Figure 4.4.10 This investigation is similar to that described in figure 4.4.2. If a p.d. with a frequency of about 50 Hz is used with an a.c. voltmeter and a.c. ammeter in the circuit (a reasonably high frequency is needed in order to give a steady reading on the meters), the relationship between p.d. and current may be explored and graph (a) obtained. If frequencies between 0.1 and 2 Hz are used with centre-zero meters, the relationships between p.d., current and time may be explored and graph (b) obtained.

Graph (a) shows that the r.m.s. current through a capacitor is directly proportional to the p.d. across it, so we can write:

$$\frac{V_{r.m.s.}}{I_{r.m.s.}} = \text{constant}$$

This looks at first sight just like Ohm's law for resistors. Graph (b) shows that this is not strictly true, however, since the current and p.d. do not vary in phase as they do in a resistor – the current through a capacitor is $\pi/2$ radians *ahead* of the p.d. across it. This is an important point – we shall see why shortly.

The reason why the current through a capacitor and the p.d. across it are out of phase can be understood if we consider how charge flows round a circuit containing a capacitor. Figure 4.4.11 shows how the charge on a capacitor, the p.d. across it and the current through the circuit are related.

This model for flow of charge in a circuit containing a capacitor suggests that the ability of a capacitor to allow an alternating current to flow depends on the frequency of the current and on the capacitance of the capacitor. If either variable increases, the current round the circuit increases, since:

1 If the current frequency increases, the capacitor charges and discharges more frequently, and the quantity of charge flowing per second increases.

2 If the capacitance of the capacitor increases, the charge stored on its plates increases, so the charge flowing per second also increases.

The opposition that a capacitor presents to a current flowing through it is called its **reactance** X_C, and is given by the relationship

$$X_C = \frac{1}{2\pi f C}$$

where f is the frequency of the current and C is the capacitance of the capacitor.

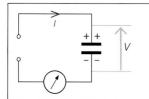

To relate current *I* and p.d. *V* in a capacitor circuit, we must first define the direction in which each is to be taken as positive. In keeping with the convention used earlier in this section, voltages will be taken as positive going up the diagram.

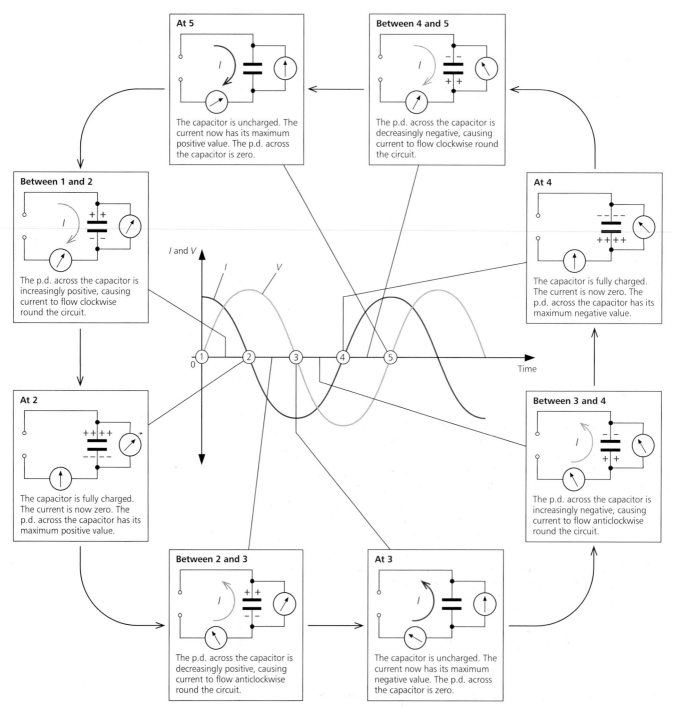

At 5

The capacitor is uncharged. The current now has its maximum positive value. The p.d. across the capacitor is zero.

Between 4 and 5

The p.d. across the capacitor is decreasing negative, causing current to flow clockwise round the circuit.

At 4

The capacitor is fully charged. The current is now zero. The p.d. across the capacitor has its maximum negative value.

Between 1 and 2

The p.d. across the capacitor is increasingly positive, causing current to flow clockwise round the circuit.

At 2

The capacitor is fully charged. The current is now zero. The p.d. across the capacitor has its maximum positive value.

Between 2 and 3

The p.d. across the capacitor is decreasingly positive, causing current to flow anticlockwise round the circuit.

At 3

The capacitor is uncharged. The current now has its maximum negative value. The p.d. across the capacitor is zero.

Between 3 and 4

The p.d. across the capacitor is increasingly negative, causing current to flow anticlockwise round the circuit.

I and *V*

Time

Figure 4.4.11

The mathematics of reactance

The current through a circuit is equal to the rate of flow of charge, or:

$$I = \frac{dQ}{dt}$$

We also know that $C = Q/V$, so we can write:

$$I = \frac{d(CV)}{dt} = \frac{CdV}{dt} \quad \text{since} \quad \frac{dC}{dt} = 0$$

This tells us that when the current has its maximum value, the rate of change of p.d. across the capacitor will be at its greatest too. In more rigorous terms, if $V = V_0 \sin (2\pi ft)$ then:

$$I = C \frac{d}{dt} (V_0 \sin (2\pi ft))$$

$$= CV_0 2\pi f \cos (2\pi ft)$$

This can be written as:

$$I = I_0 \cos (2\pi ft), \text{ where } I_0 = 2\pi fCV_0$$

By the very nature of these functions, the phase of I must therefore be $\pi/2$ radians ahead of V, that is,

$$I = I_0 \cos (2\pi ft) = I_0 \sin (2\pi ft + \pi/2)$$

The expression for I_0 also tells us something about the relationship between current through a capacitor and the p.d. across it. We can rearrange the expression for I_0 above to show that:

$$\frac{V_0}{I_0} = \frac{1}{2\pi fC}$$

This looks similar to Ohm's law at first sight. The relationship confirms our earlier observation that (for an alternating current of constant frequency) the current through a given capacitor is proportional to the p.d. across it. However, here p.d. divided by current cannot represent resistance, since the two quantities are $\pi/2$ radians out of phase: V_0/I_0 only defines resistance when the two quantities are in phase. In this case V_0/I_0 represents a quantity called the **reactance** of the capacitor, X_C. Like resistance, reactance is measured in ohms. The quantity $X_C = 1/2\pi fC$ has units ohms because $2\pi f$ has units s^{-1}, C has units $C\,V^{-1} = A\,s\,V^{-1}$, so $1/2\pi fC$ has units $1/(s^{-1} \times A\,s\,V^{-1}) = V\,A^{-1} = $ ohms. Whether one defines reactance using the peak voltage and current or the r.m.s. voltage and current does not matter, since $V_{r.m.s} = V_0/\sqrt{2}$ and $I_{r.m.s} = I_0/\sqrt{2}$, so:

$$\frac{V_{r.m.s.}}{I_{r.m.s.}} = \frac{V_0/\sqrt{2}}{I_0/\sqrt{2}} = \frac{V_0}{I_0} = X_C$$

Note that these arguments apply only to *sinusoidal* a.c. supplies.

FOCUS ALTERNATING CURRENTS AND ELECTRIC SHOCK

Electric shock

The term 'electric shock' describes a range of effects connected with the passage of electricity through the body. An electric shock is usually painful, and may cause physical damage to the tissues of the body. Victims of shock describe the sensation as a prickling or stabbing pain where the electric current enters and leaves the body, although the exact sensation depends on the size of the current, and probably also varies from person to person. The nerves and muscles of the body function by means of tiny electric currents, and the physiological effects of electricity are directly related to the way in which the passage of electricity affects the function of these parts of the body.

Electric currents and muscles

Serious electric shock is nearly always associated with alternating currents (a.c.). As electricity travels through the body, the excitation of nerves produces contractions in muscles. As a result of such contractions, a person gripping a live wire may be unable to let go of it if the current through their body is greater than a minimum value (called the 'let-go current'). Alternatively, if someone touches a live conductor without actually gripping it, the muscles in their legs and back may contract so violently that they are thrown backwards, which may cause a fall and consequent injury.

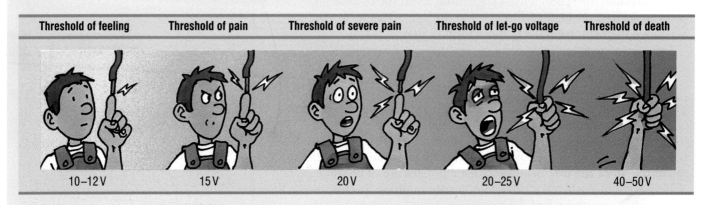

Threshold of feeling	Threshold of pain	Threshold of severe pain	Threshold of let-go voltage	Threshold of death
10–12 V	15 V	20 V	20–25 V	40–50 V

The let-go current for a.c. at mains frequency is around 10 mA, although for some individuals the figure may be as little as 7 mA. Obviously, the magnitude of the current flowing through the body depends on its resistance to the flow of electricity. This is very variable, and depends particularly on the area of skin through which the current flows and whether the skin is wet or dry. For this reason it is difficult to be precise about the dangers of particular voltages, and the data in Figure 4.4.12 are only approximations.

Figure 4.4.12 The effects of different voltages at 50 Hz. The voltages shown are based partly on experiments to determine the minimum voltages required to cause certain effects, and partly on experience of electrical accidents. They are for dry conditions only. (*Source:* W. Fordham Cooper, *Electrical Safety Engineering*, Butterworth & Co, London 1989)

Electric currents and the heart

The human heart consists of a bag of muscle which is about the size of a clenched fist. It beats continually throughout life, with an average of about 70 beats per minute, although in small children the heart rate is much higher. In the very early embryo, cells which are destined to become the heart begin contracting rhythmically long before the actual organ forms. An adult heart removed from the body will continue to contract as long as it is bathed in a suitable oxygen-rich fluid. This basic **intrinsic rhythm** has evolved to ensure that the vital, continuous sequence of contraction and relaxation is maintained without conscious control. The intrinsic rhythm of the heart is around 60 beats per minute.

One of the most important ways in which the body controls the rate at which the heart beats is by using electrical impulses. The intrinsic rhythm of the heart is maintained by a wave of electrical excitation like a nerve impulse that spreads through special tissue in the heart muscle.

Since the heart is controlled by electrical signals just like other muscles, it is not surprising that an electric current travelling through the body close to the heart can disrupt this control. An electric shock is most dangerous if current flows from one hand to the oppostie foot, thereby passing close to or even through the heart. The effect of an electric current flowing in this way depends not only on the magnitude of the current flowing but also on the length of time for which it flows.

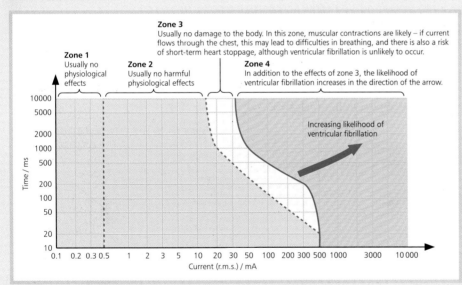

Figure 4.4.13 The time/current zones of effects of a.c. currents (15–100 Hz) on people

As figure 4.4.13 shows, the larger the current and the longer its duration, the greater the risk of disruption to the heart. A small shock may lead to stoppage of the heart for a short time, when the heart will be able to restore its natural rhythm on its own. The greatest danger is that the passage of electric current may lead to **ventricular fibrillation**, when the muscles of the heart contract in a completely disorganised and uncoordinated way. A fibrillating heart cannot pump blood around the body, and so the tissues of the body become starved of oxygen and die. The fibrillating heart remains in a state of fibrillation – it will not right itself. Unless treatment is given rapidly, as shown in figure 4.4.14, death follows.

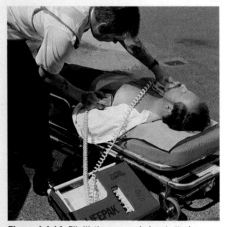

Figure 4.4.14 Fibrillation occurs in heart attack victims as well as people suffering from electric shock. It can be stopped by giving the heart a controlled electric shock, which must be of exactly the right current, frequency and duration. This brings the heart to rest, when the impulses from the sinoatrial node can once again produce coordinated contractions, provided no permanent damage to the tissue of the heart has been done as a result of fibrillation. The electric shock needed for defibrillation requires special equipment and must be administered by qualified medical staff.

Worked example

Calculate the current through a 25 μF capacitor when the r.m.s. voltage across it is 5 V and the frequency of the supply is 60 Hz. What effect would doubling the supply frequency have?

For a 60 Hz supply:

$$2\pi f = 377 \text{ rad s}^{-1} \text{ (to 3 SF)}$$

$$X_C = \frac{1}{2\pi f C} = \frac{1}{377 \text{ rad s}^{-1} \times 25 \times 10^{-6} \text{ F}}$$

$$= 106 \ \Omega$$

$$I_{\text{r.m.s.}} = \frac{V_{\text{r.m.s.}}}{X_C} = \frac{5 \text{ V}}{106 \ \Omega} = 47 \text{ mA}$$

Doubling the supply frequency will *halve* the reactance of the capacitor, which will double the current to 94 mA.

Energy dissipation in capacitors

In capacitors the current is $\pi/2$ radians out of phase with the p.d. This means that although energy is stored in a charged capacitor, energy is returned to the circuit as the p.d. across the capacitor changes, so there is no net dissipation of energy. In the capacitor, energy transfer occurs between electrical energy and energy stored in the electric field between the plates of the capacitor. The direction and magnitude of this transfer vary according to the part of the cycle, so that the net transfer of energy over one complete cycle is zero, as shown in figure 4.4.15.

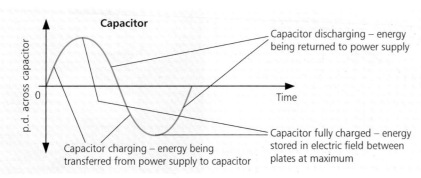

Figure 4.4.15 Over one complete cycle, there is no net exchange of energy between a capacitor and the power supply.

RC circuits – impedance

Figure 4.4.16(a) shows a circuit which contains a resistor and a capacitor. By definition, the current at all points in this circuit must have the same value. However, the relationship between the potential differences in the circuit is more complex.

The graph (b) shows, as we expect, that the voltage across the resistor V_R is in phase with the current through it, and that the voltage across the capacitor V_C is $\pi/2$ radians behind the current through it. (This means that V_C is also $\pi/2$ radians behind V_R.) These quantities are represented by the rotating vectors, called **phasors**, shown in figure 4.4.16(c).

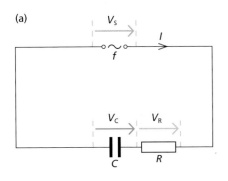

(a)

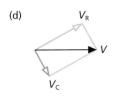

(c)

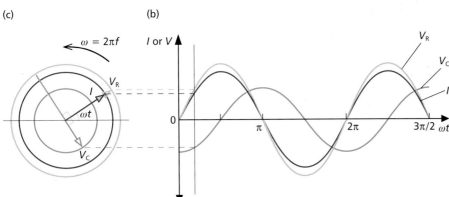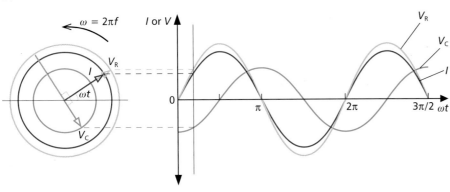

(b)

(d)

Figure 4.4.16 A circuit (a) containing a capacitor and a resistance, through which an alternating current passes. The graph (b) shows the relationship between the current through the circuit and the voltage across the resistor and capacitor. This graph is the projection of the rotating vectors (called **phasors**) which represent these quantities (c). The two potential difference vectors V_R and V_C can be added using the techniques of vector addition we met in section 1.

The opposition that the capacitor and the resistor present to the current flowing in this circuit is called their **impedance** Z, and is the combination of the resistance of the resistor, R, together with the reactance of the capacitor, X_C. Since each of these is measured in ohms, it might seem that all we have to do is add them together to find Z, but a few moments' thought shows that this is not so.

The impedance of the circuit is defined by the equation

$$Z = V / I$$

Because the potential difference across the resistor V_R and the potential difference across the capacitor V_C are perpendicular to each other, we find their sum using vector addition, so, applying Pythagoras' theorem to Figure 4.4.16(d),

$$V = \sqrt{V_R^2 + V_C^2}$$

This means that

$$Z = \frac{\sqrt{V_R^2 + V_C^2}}{I}$$

$$= \sqrt{\left(\frac{V_R}{I}\right)^2 + \left(\frac{V_C}{I}\right)^2}$$

$$= \sqrt{R^2 + X_C^2}$$

Calculate the impedance of a 500 ohm resistor in series with a 5 μF capacitor with a supply frequency of 50 Hz.

We know that $X_C = 1/2\pi fC = 1/(314\text{ rad s}^{-1} \times 5 \times 10^{-6}\text{ F})$

$$= 637\text{ ohms (to 3 SF)}$$

So total impedance $= Z = \sqrt{R^2 + X_C^2}$

$$= \sqrt{500^2 + 637^2}$$

$$= \sqrt{250\,000 + 405\,769}$$

$$= 810\text{ ohms}$$

Filters

Since the impedance of a capacitor changes with frequency, it is possible to construct a frequency-dependent potential divider using a capacitor and a resistor, as figure 4.4.17 shows. This circuit can be used as a very simple kind of **filter**, in which the potential difference between points A and B varies according to the supply frequency.

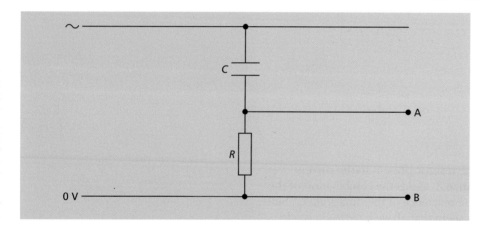

Figure 4.4.17 The reactance of the capacitor decreases as the supply frequency increases. This means that as the supply frequency increases, the potential difference across the resistor increases – so the circuit functions as a **high-pass** filter. You should be able to suggest how a **low-pass** filter might be constructed.

Rectification

A.c. to d.c.

Although a.c. is the most convenient and efficient way to produce and distribute electricity (see section 5.5 for an explanation of this), few of the many devices that we take for granted as part of modern living can use a.c. This is particularly true of devices that use electronic components – these circuit elements *must* have a source of d.c. in order to function properly. The conversion of an a.c. into a d.c. is called **rectification**, and may be done using a **junction diode**. A junction diode allows current to flow through it in only one direction, as shown in figure 4.4.18.

A rectifier makes use of a device called a **junction diode**, which consists of a piece of *n*-type semiconductor joined to a piece of *p*-type semiconductor (see section 4.2) – a **p-n junction.** This junction allows current to flow through it in one direction but not the other.

Figure 4.4.18 The basic principles of rectifying a.c.
(continues overleaf)

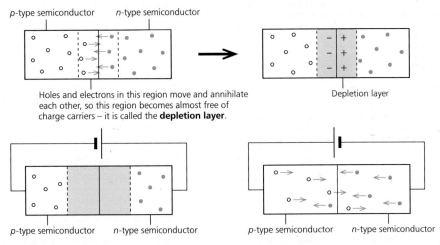

p-type semiconductor   *n*-type semiconductor

Holes and electrons in this region move and annihilate each other, so this region becomes almost free of charge carriers – it is called the **depletion layer**.

Depletion layer

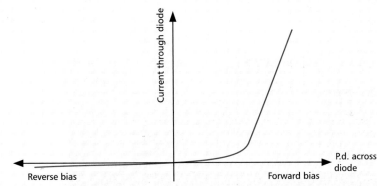

p-type semiconductor   *n*-type semiconductor

p-type semiconductor   *n*-type semiconductor

A source of e.m.f. connected to the *p-n* junction like this repels electrons and holes from the junction and widens the depletion layer. Under these conditions the diode is said to be **reverse biased**. Only a tiny current flows through the depletion layer, carried by minority charge carriers formed when bonds in both *n*- and *p*-type materials break due to thermal energy.

A source of e.m.f. connected to the *p-n* junction like this narrows the depletion layer. As the p.d. across the junction increases, a threshold value is reached when the depletion layer disappears and a large current can flow. Under these conditions the diode is said to be **forward biased.**

 A diode is represented in circuit diagrams like this. The arrow indicates the direction in which the device will permit current to flow.

Current through diode

P.d. across diode

Reverse bias   Forward bias

The current through a junction diode when it is forward biased is many times greater then when it is reverse biased.

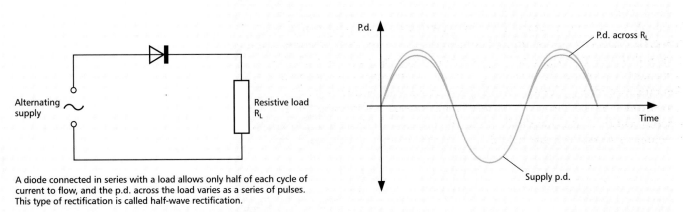

Alternating supply

Resistive load R_L

P.d.

P.d. across R_L

Supply p.d.

Time

A diode connected in series with a load allows only half of each cycle of current to flow, and the p.d. across the load varies as a series of pulses. This type of rectification is called half-wave rectification.

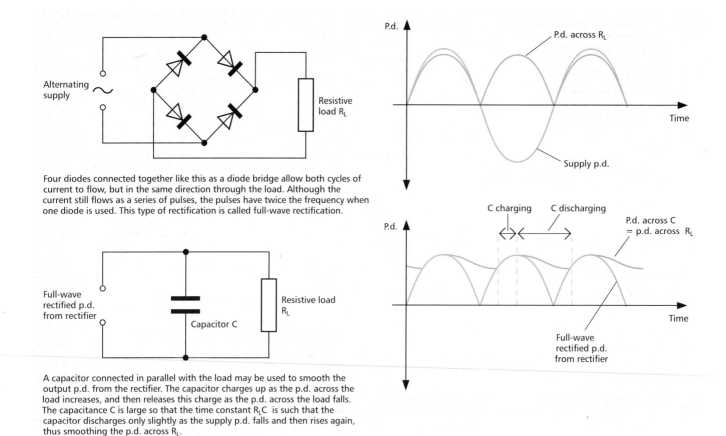

Four diodes connected together like this as a diode bridge allow both cycles of current to flow, but in the same direction through the load. Although the current still flows as a series of pulses, the pulses have twice the frequency when one diode is used. This type of rectification is called full-wave rectification.

A capacitor connected in parallel with the load may be used to smooth the output p.d. from the rectifier. The capacitor charges up as the p.d. across the load increases, and then releases this charge as the p.d. across the load falls. The capacitance C is large so that the time constant R_LC is such that the capacitor discharges only slightly as the supply p.d. falls and then rises again, thus smoothing the p.d. across R_L.

Figure 4.4.18 The basic principles of rectifying a.c. *(continued)*

How fast does electricity travel?

This question was an important one in the last century, as the sending of messages along long cables using an electric current was used more and more, first with the telegraph and then with the telephone. It rapidly became apparent that electric pulses such as those sent by a telegraph operator travel extremely fast through a cable. The work of James Clerk Maxwell and Heinrich Hertz later in the century showed that in fact such pulses are electromagnetic waves. This being so, the pulses travel along a cable with a speed of the order of that of light through free space. Modern equipment can confirm this quite easily, as shown in figure 4.4.19.

A coaxial cable, like that used to connect a television aerial to the set, is connected to the Y_1- and Y_2-plates of a double-beam oscilloscope. The length of the cable needs to be about 200 m. If a pulse generator is used to send a square pulse along the cable, the Y_1-channel of the oscilloscope records when the pulse is sent, while the Y_2-channel records when it reaches the other end. The time for this to happen is of the order of 1 μs, which gives the speed of the pulse through the cable as around 2×10^8 m s^{-1}.

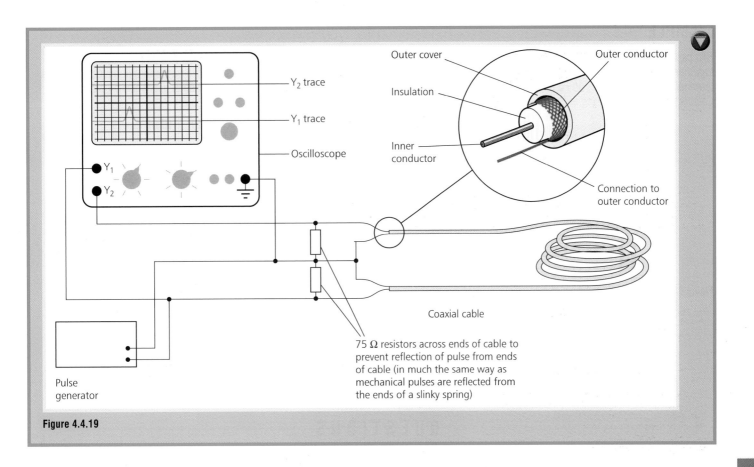

Figure 4.4.19

SUMMARY

- The **peak-to-peak voltage** of an alternating voltage is the difference
  between the maximum and minimum values of the voltage. The
  voltage–time relationship is sinusoidal in the mains supply:
  $V = V_0 \sin(2\pi f t)$, where V_0 is the **peak voltage** (half the peak-to-peak
  voltage) and f the frequency of the supply.

- The **root-mean-square value** of an alternating current is the value of
  direct current that dissipates energy in a resistance at the same rate as the
  alternating supply. For a sinusoidally varying p.d., $V_{r.m.s.} = V_0/\sqrt{2}$,
  $I_{r.m.s.} = I_0/\sqrt{2}$.

- The current through a resistor and the p.d. across it are in phase.

- The mean power dissipated in a resistor is half the peak power dissipated:
  $P_{mean} = \frac{1}{2}I_0V_0$.

- In a capacitor the current and p.d. are not in phase – the current is $\pi/2$
  radians ahead of the p.d. The opposition of a capacitor to an alternating
  current flowing through it is its **reactance** $X_C = 1/2\pi f C$.

- The conversion of a.c. to d.c. is called **rectification** and may be achieved
  using a **junction diode**, a device that allows current to flow in only one
  direction.

EXAMPLE

Two capacitors, each with a capacitance of 10 μF, are connected together in series. The capacitors are then connected across the terminals of a 110 V r.m.s., 60 Hz supply (see figure 4.4.20). Calculate the current flowing in the circuit.

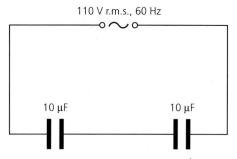

110 V r.m.s., 60 Hz

10 μF   10 μF

Figure 4.4.20

To calculate the current flowing in this circuit, the reactance of the capacitors must be calculated. The two capacitors connected in series effectively behave as one capacitor with capacitance C given by:

$$\frac{1}{C} = \frac{1}{10\ \mu F} + \frac{1}{10\ \mu F}$$

so:

$$C = 5\ \mu F$$

The reactance of this capacitance X_C is given by:

$$X_C = \frac{1}{\omega C}$$
$$= \frac{1}{2 \times \pi \times 60\ Hz \times 5 \times 10^{-6}\ F}$$
$$= 531\ \Omega$$

Since by definition $X_C = V_{r.m.s.}/I_{r.m.s.}$, it follows that:

$$I_{r.m.s.} = \frac{110\ V}{531\ \Omega}$$
$$= 0.21\ A$$

The r.m.s. current flowing in the circuit is 0.21 A.

QUESTIONS

1 Obtain as many details as possible from the oscilloscope trace in figure 4.4.21.

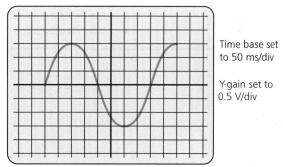

Time base set to 50 ms/div

Y-gain set to 0.5 V/div

Figure 4.4.21

2 By sweeping your eye quickly along the tube of a fluorescent lamp, you can perceive a flicker – the frequency of this flicker is 100 Hz. You can see no such flicker in a filament lamp. Explain these observations.

3 A lamp is lit by a sinusoidal a.c. supply with a peak e.m.f. of 15 V. What d.c. supply would be required to light an identical bulb to the same brightness?

4 The e.m.f. produced by a generator has the form $\mathcal{E} = 5\ V \sin (200\pi\ Hz)t$. Considering this e.m.f., what is:
a the peak e.m.f.
b the r.m.s. e.m.f.
c the frequency of the e.m.f.?
d What peak current will the generator supply when connected to a 10 Ω resistor?

5 The element of an electric kettle for use with an a.c. supply is rated as '2400 W'.
a What is the r.m.s. current through the element when it is connected to the UK mains supply of 240 V?
b What is the maximum current through the element under these conditions?
c What is the resistance of the element?
d The kettle is taken to the USA, where the mains power supply is 110 V a.c. with a frequency of 60 Hz. How does this affect the performance of the kettle?

6 A sinusoidal alternating current with an r.m.s. value of 10 A flows in a copper wire with a diameter of 1 mm, causing the electrons in the wire to oscillate with SHM. If the frequency of the current is 50 Hz, calculate an electron's:
a maximum drift velocity
b amplitude of oscillation
c maximum acceleration.
(Take the number of free electrons in 1 m^3 of copper as 10^{29}, and the magnitude of the charge on one electron as 1.6×10^{-19} C.)

QUESTIONS

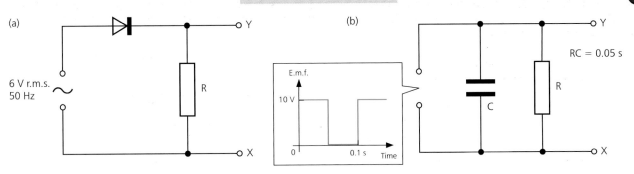

Figure 4.4.22

7 The customer in question **4** of section 4.1 now realises that electrons in a wire carrying a.c. oscillate to and fro. He therefore argues that, as no electrons from the power station enter his home, he should not have to pay the electricity company any money. How would you answer him this time?

8 Sketch graphs of the potential difference between X and Y against time for the circuits shown in figure 4.4.22.

9 A 250 ohm resistor is connected in series with a 10.0 μF capacitor. Calculate the reactance of the capacitor and the impedance of the circuit for alternating currents with frequencies of
  a 100 Hz,
  b 200 Hz.
  Express your answers to an appropriate level of accuracy.

10 A circuit carrying an alternating current with a frequency f consists of a 15 μF capacitor in series with a 36 ohm resistor. If the impedance of the circuit is 43 ohms, calculate the value of f.

11 A filament lamp is connected in series with a capacitor across an a.c. supply.
  a What happens to the brightness of the lamp if the frequency of the supply is doubled?
  b How could a second capacitor be included in the circuit to increase the brightness of the lamp?
  c Why is controlling the brightness of the lamp in this way preferable to using a resistor?

Developing Key Skills

The tables contain data taken from a sample of people attending accident and emergency departments in large hospitals in the UK during 1997, seeking treatment for injuries caused by electrical equipment. (Source: *Home Accident Surveillance System: 1997 Data*. London: Department of Trade and Industry.)

Present these data using a variety of methods (charts, tables, graphs, etc.) and use these to produce a short safety leaflet providing advice for people about electrical safety in the home, targeting people who may be particularly at risk.

Analysis of electrical accidents by:

Location in the home		Activity of patient at the time	
25	Kitchen	18	Household activity
2	Bathroom/toilet	114	DIY/maintenance
30	Living/dining area	0	Shopping
14	Bedroom	0	Education/training
1	Hall	0	Sport
1	Porch	32	Play/hobby/leisure
2	Other indoors	37	Basic needs
112	Unspecified indoors	0	Travelling/touring
42	Garden/lawn	131	Other
13	Drive/path	**332**	**Total**
9	Garage		
2	Shed		
10	Other outdoors		Age and gender
69	Unspec. indoors/outdoors		

		M	F	U
332	**Total**			
		0–4	19	10	0
[Key Skills opportunities: C, A, IT]		5–14	17	10	0
		15–64	189	77	1
		65–74	4	1	0
		75+	1	1	0
		Unknown	0	2	0
		Total 332			

At the beginning of section 4.1, mention was made of the impact electricity has on the lives of all of us in the developed world – to be able to summon up light or heat (or even cold) at the touch of a switch is an incredible achievement. But there is another area of technology in which development would have been impossible without electricity – the wide and varied field of electronics. The impact of this application of physics is at least as great as that of other applications of electricity, in both work and leisure.

Developments in the construction of electronic devices mean that it is now possible to fit in a small case machines that 25 years ago would have filled large rooms – due to the science of **microelectronics**. Our modern world is shaped by the power of microelectronics to control our environment. Microelectronics make possible the fine tuning of the modern internal combustion engine to minimise the (still very considerable) pollution it causes, the instant transfer of funds from a bank account to the account of a store when using a credit or debit card, the control of home appliances such as washing machines, dishwashers and microwaves. This section provides a simple introduction to this world, and will give a brief insight into the way many modern electronic devices work.

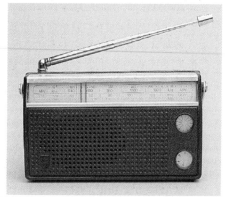

An introduction to electronics

Analogue versus digital

We live in a world in which things are seldom black or white – there are often many shades between. If we wish to represent a varying light level, for example, by a voltage, we might need to use any voltage between two fixed limits. Any system which represents things in this way is called an **analogue** system – the system has some variable that varies in proportion to the property being modelled.

By contrast, we might represent a varying light level by assigning it a number between two fixed limits – in fact, this is not very different from representing it by a voltage. This number could be expressed in **binary notation** as a series of noughts and ones. These noughts and ones can then be represented in electrical circuits as low and high voltages (usually around 0 V and +5 V respectively), and the light level is thus represented as a string of electrical pulses. This method of representing variables is known as a **digital** system – the system represents a variable as a string of digits.

We commonly use both analogue and digital electronic systems in our lives. The CD player which may provide the music to accompany your study uses digital representations of musical notes. These are processed using **digital** electronics and then converted to analogue electrical signals which are amplified by an analogue electronic amplifier. Television and radio sets use analogue electronics (although digital techniques are being introduced increasingly in communications – see section 3.4, pages 255–6 for the reasons for this), while the computers many of us use for writing essays and playing games process data in a digital form. In this section we shall be concerned with both types of system.

Figure 4.5.1
Electronics has developed rapidly in the last 40 years and continues to do so. Miniaturisation of components, possible due to greater knowledge of materials and increasingly complex manufacturing techniques, means that electronic equipment becomes ever smaller and more powerful.

Inputting information – sensors and other devices

Both analogue and digital systems have a number of elements in common, among them the need to be able to make measurements of variables in the physical world (of quantities such as temperature and light level, for example). Having processed these input signals, the system must have the ability to provide some kind of output signal, perhaps to function as an indicator or to make something happen. We shall first examine how the real world outside an electronic circuit can be sensed.

Figure 4.5.2 Four examples using the potential divider to produce a varying potential as different variables change. Only in the first case does the sensing circuit produce one of two states which could be treated as a logical 0 or 1. In the others a variable voltage is produced, which may be converted to a number which can be expressed in binary digits, or the voltage may be compared with another voltage to decide whether it has a high or a low value.

The potential divider may be constructed in two ways, with the transducer placed in two different positions.

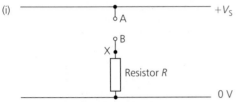

(i)

The supply rails from the power supply are usually labelled $+V_S$ and 0 V. By convention the negative terminal of the supply is usually taken as having zero potential.

With the transducer between X and the positive supply rail, as the resistance of the transducer rises, the p.d. across it increases, and so the potential at X falls.

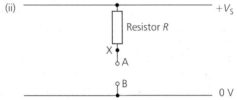

(ii)

With the transducer between X and the 0 V rail, as the resistance of the transducer rises, the p.d. across it increases, and so the potential at X rises.

In both (i) and (ii) the exact value of the potential at X will obviously depend on the ratio of $R_{transducer}$ to R. In practical circuits R is usually a variable resistor to allow adjustment of the potential at X under given circumstances – effectively this provides a way of adjusting the sensitivity of the sensor.

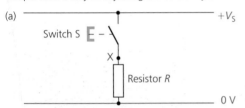

(a)

In this potential divider, when switch S is pressed the potential at point X becomes the same as that of the positive supply rail, i.e. $+V_S$. This sensor might be used as a position sensor, for example to show if a door is open or shut.

Light-dependent resistor (LDR). This semiconductor device has an extremely high resistance (of the order of several million ohms) in the dark. Its resistance falls to only a few hundred ohms when bright light falls on it.

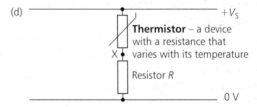

(b)

In this potential divider, when light falls on the LDR its resistance drops and the p.d. across it falls too. This makes the potential at point X fall.

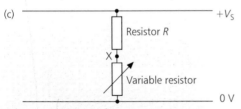

(c)

Rotary potentiometer used as variable resistor (the middle terminal connected to the wiper, plus one of the two end terminals is used). As the position of the shaft varies, the resistance of the variable resistor changes, and the potential at point X rises and falls. This might be used to sense rotary motion, for example the oscillations of a pendulum.

(d)

Thermistor – a device with a resistance that varies with its temperature

This particular thermistor is a n.t.c. (negative temperature coefficient) thermistor, whose resistance falls as its temperature rises (compare this with the resistance of a piece of metal). In this case, as the temperature of the thermistor increases, the potential at X rises as its resistance decreases and the p.d. across it gets smaller.

4

The basic circuit element used in sensing is the potential divider, which we met in section 4.2. Such an element provides a way of sensing a variety of variables, combined with a transducer with a resistance that varies with the quantity to be measured, as shown in figure 4.5.2.

Sensors like those shown in figure 4.5.2 may be used to provide the input for digital electronic systems only if the voltage output from them is converted to digital form. This may be done by comparing the voltage with a reference voltage to decide whether it is high or low, and then representing it by a single bit – usually 0 for low and 1 for high. Alternatively, **analogue-to-digital conversion** may be used. This process converts the analogue voltage to a number (with, for example, eight bits) that can be represented by a string of pulses. The electronics for doing this are much more complex than those needed for the simple conversion of a signal to a single-bit number, and we shall not be concerned with them here.

Providing an output

While sensors like those described above give an input for electronic systems, other devices are usually needed as well to provide an output. To take two simple examples, an output might have a visual form (for example, in a warning device or in a digital clock), or some kind of motion might be required. Most electronic devices are only capable of providing an output of a few milliamps, which means that devices like lamps and motors cannot be driven directly from electronic circuits, since they require currents which are too large.

For these reasons, **light-emitting diodes** (**LEDs**) are commonly used where an electronic circuit has to produce a visual output. LEDs are smaller than filament lamps, have a longer life, and most importantly they draw much smaller currents than filament lamps (around 20 mA for LEDs compared with around 200 mA for small filament lamps). A light-emitting diode has a construction very similar to the junction diode introduced in figure 4.4.18, pages 345–6. Figure 4.5.3 gives details of how an LED works, and shows how it may be used in a circuit.

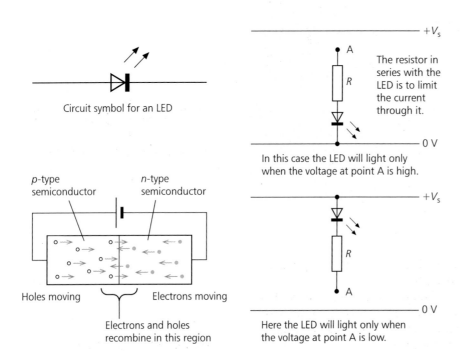

Circuit symbol for an LED

p-type semiconductor

n-type semiconductor

Holes moving

Electrons moving

Electrons and holes recombine in this region

The resistor in series with the LED is to limit the current through it.

In this case the LED will light only when the voltage at point A is high.

Here the LED will light only when the voltage at point A is low.

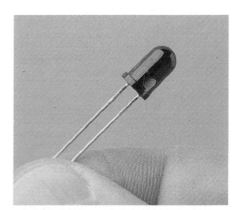

Figure 4.5.3 When a junction diode is forward biased, holes and electrons recombine at the boundary between the p-type and n-type semiconductors. Energy is transferred in this process, causing the junction diode to become warm. In a light-emitting diode, however, the junction is formed very close to the surface of the diode and the recombination of holes and electrons results in the transfer of energy as light. When an LED is forward biased, therefore, the junction between the p- and n-type materials glows.

Where a large current is required to operate, say, a motor or a heating element, a **relay** may be used. A relay makes use of the magnetic effect of an electric current in order to operate a switch – the switch then operates the high-current device, which has its own power supply. (More details about the use and construction of relays are included on pages 439–40 and figure 5.4.19.)

Digital electronics

Making decisions – logic gates

Information from an enormous variety of sources, whether sensors, keyboards or other input devices, may be encoded in binary form and transmitted as a series of pulses. The information may be processed using electronic circuits built up from elements known as **logic gates**, capable of performing operations that make simple decisions about an output based on one or more inputs. Logic gates find uses in an enormous range of applications, including pocket calculators, systems to monitor and control the performance of car and lorry engines, and microwave ovens. It is difficult today to find an item of equipment that does *not* use logic gates in some way! Figure 4.5.4 shows some examples of logic gates.

The NOT gate is the simplest logic gate, having only one input and one output. A table known as a **truth table** shows how the output of the gate varies with the input. The physical inputs and outputs of logic gates are voltages which may be either 'high' (close to the supply voltage of the gate) or 'low' (near to zero). These are represented by the digits 1 and 0 respectively, usually referred to as **logical 1** and **logical 0**. Figure 4.5.5 shows the circuit symbol and table 4.5.1 the truth table for a NOT gate.

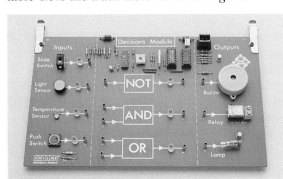

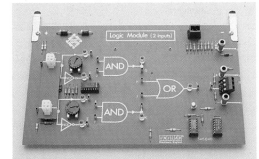

Figure 4.5.4 Three different ready-made pieces of equipment for investigating the behaviour of logic gates in the physics laboratory. The microchip contains *four* logic gates, and connections are made to them via the 'legs' of the chip.

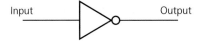

Figure 4.5.5 Circuit symbol for a NOT gate

A NOT gate is often known as an **inverter**, since its output is always the opposite of its input – a 0 becomes a 1 and a 1 becomes a 0.

Other gates have more than one input, although for the moment we shall consider only gates with two inputs. All gates have only one output, no matter how many inputs they have. Table 4.5.2 shows the truth tables and circuit symbols for the six gates most commonly encountered.

Input	Output
0	1
1	0

Table 4.5.1 Truth table for a NOT gate

Inputs		OR	EXOR	NOR	EXNOR	AND	NAND
A	B						
0	0	0	0	1	1	0	1
0	1	1	1	0	0	0	1
1	0	1	1	0	0	0	1
1	1	1	0	0	1	1	0

Table 4.5.2 Six logic gates and their truth tables

The behaviour of the gates is reasonably straightforward to remember:
- The OR gate has a high output if one *or* both of the two inputs is high, while the NOR gate is the reverse of this.
- The EXOR (short for exclusive-OR) gate behaves almost like an OR gate, except that the output is high if A or B is high *but not if both are high*. The EXNOR (exclusive-NOR) gate is the reverse of the EXOR gate. (EXOR may also be abbreviated as EOR or XOR.)
- The EXOR gate is sometimes called a **difference gate**, since its output is logical 1 if the inputs A and B are different. The EXNOR gate is sometimes called a **parity gate**, since its output is a logical 1 if the inputs A and B are the same.
- The AND gate has a high output if input A *and* input B are high. The NAND gate is the reverse of this.

Using logic gates

In practical situations, logic gates may be used where a system is required to *make decisions* about something that needs to be controlled. As an example, imagine the cooling system of a car engine. The electric cooling fan needs to be switched on when the ignition switch is on *and* when the engine gets too hot – which gives a clue about the logic required. Table 4.5.3 gives the truth table.

Inputs		Output (1 = fan on)
From temperature sensor (1 = hot)	From ignition switch (1 = on)	
0	0	0
0	1	0
1	0	0
1	1	1

Table 4.5.3 This truth table shows how the control circuit must work – comparing the inputs and outputs with those in table 4.5.2 shows that an AND gate is required.

The final design shown in figure 4.5.6 is only one possibility – the temperature sensor could, for example, have been arranged to give a low rather than high output when hot. In this case a NOR gate would have been needed with the signal from the ignition switch fed to it via a NOT gate.

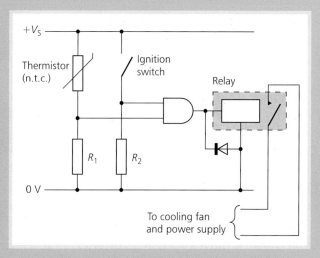

Figure 4.5.6 Circuit diagram showing the gate and its connection to the inputs and outputs. Note the protective diode across the relay – the reason for this is explained in section 5.4. For simplicity the power supply connections to the gate itself are not shown.

Combining logic gates

Gates may be used in combination with each other – for example, an AND gate followed by a NOT gate is equivalent to a NAND gate. Combinations of gates are capable of an enormous number of different uses, not least of which is the microcomputer. As an example, consider a circuit for adding two bits.

There are four possible results from the addition of two bits:

$$0 + 0 = 00 \quad 0 + 1 = 01 \quad 1 + 0 = 01 \quad 1 + 1 = 10$$

This can be done using two NOR gates and an AND gate in combination, as table 4.5.4 and figure 4.5.7 show.

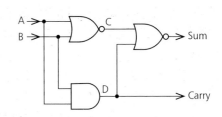

Figure 4.5.7 Circuit diagram for a half adder

A	B	C	D	Carry	Sum
0	0	1	0	0	0
0	1	0	0	0	1
1	0	0	0	0	1
1	1	0	1	1	0
First bit	+ Second bit		=	Left-hand digit	Right-hand digit

Table 4.5.4 Two bits are added with a combination of gates known as a **half adder**. The right-hand digit is obtained from the sum output, while the left-hand digit comes from the carry output.

When two binary numbers consisting of several digits are added together, a series of **full adders** is required, to add not only the two digits themselves but also the carry digit from the previous addition. A full adder is obtained by combining two half adders. Table 4.5.5 and figure 4.5.8 show how this works.

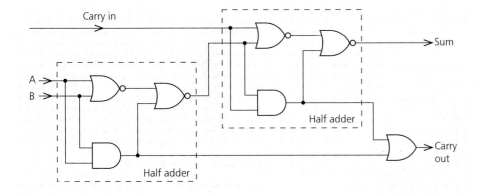

Figure 4.5.8 Circuit diagram for a full adder

Inputs			Outputs	
A	B	Carry in	Carry out	Sum
0	0	0	0	0
0	1	0	0	1
1	0	0	0	1
1	1	0	1	0
0	0	1	0	1
1	0	1	1	0
0	1	1	1	0
1	1	1	1	1

Table 4.5.5 A full adder is made from two half adders plus an OR gate. Adding two binary numbers is then a matter of adding each digit together and then adding the carry digit from the previous addition.

Logic gates do not have to be electronic circuits, or even electrical ones. Any device that has an output state which can be altered by changing one or more input states can be made to behave as a logic gate. In some situations where electricity would be hazardous, pneumatic valves are used for logic work. In other situations, simple switches may do.

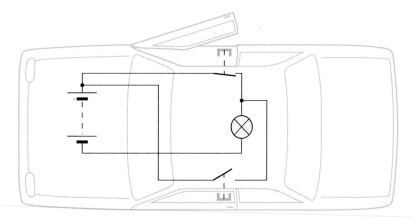

When either one *or* both of the doors is opened, the light in the car is switched on.

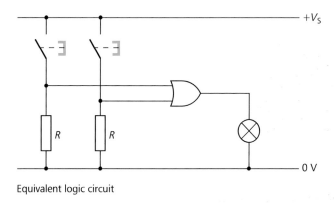

Equivalent logic circuit

Figure 4.5.9 The two switches controlling the interior light in a two-door car act as a two-input OR gate.

Although in principle it would be possible to build circuits to add numbers and to control machines using switches, the current consumption and size of such circuits would make them impractical. For this reason, logic circuits make use of electronic components. The circuits may be made from individual ('discrete') components, or they may be etched into a single silicon crystal – an **integrated circuit** (**IC**). The miniaturisation made possible by ICs means that circuits containing thousands of circuit elements like logic gates can be crammed into a tiny volume.

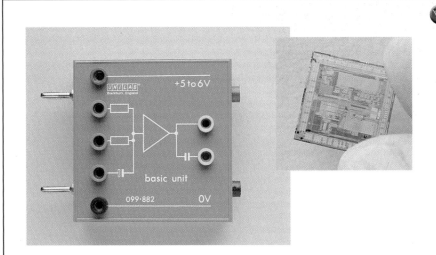

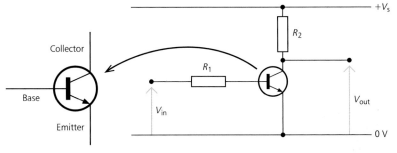

This circuit element is a **transistor**. When a small current flows into the transistor through the **base** lead, it allows a much larger current to flow through the transistor from the **collector** to the **emitter**. In this way a transistor can act as either an amplifier or a switch. In both cases a small change in the input to the transistor gives rise to a large change in the output.

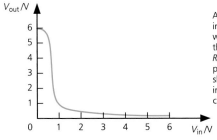

As V_{in} rises, the current through R_1 into the base of the transistor increases, which causes an increase in the current through R_2. As a result, the p.d. across R_2 increases, so that V_{out} falls. This produces the input/output characteristic shown in the graph. A high input results in a low output and vice versa – the circuit acts as an inverter or NOT gate.

Figure 4.5.10 The main photograph shows a logic gate constructed from discrete electronic components. The smaller photograph shows an integrated circuit containing hundreds of such gates. The diagram explains how a transistor acts as a NOT gate when connected in this way.

Memory – bistable circuits

As well as processing information, it is often necessary to store digital information in an electronic system. **Magnetic media** such as disks (both floppy and hard) and tape may be used for long-term storage, but data also need to be stored in electronic circuits so that the information may be readily accessed and processed. One way of storing information electronically is to use a combination of two logic gates to form a **bistable circuit** or **flip-flop**.

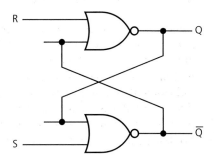

Figure 4.5.11 Circuit diagram of an RS flip-flop from a pair of cross-coupled NOR gates

As its name implies, a bistable circuit has two stable states. It may be made to *flip* from one state to the other by applying a brief voltage pulse to one of the inputs. Table 4.5.6 shows the changes in output states of a bistable made from a pair of NOR gates connected as in figure 4.5.11, as the inputs are momentarily changed.

Momentary inputs		Subsequent outputs	
R	S	Q	$\bar{Q}$
0	0	1	0
		0	1
0	1	1	0
1	0	0	1
1	1	0	0

Table 4.5.6 This type of bistable circuit is known as a **set-reset (RS) bistable**. Inputs R and S may be made high or low, and outputs Q and $\bar{Q}$ ('not Q') vary according to the momentary inputs to R and S and the previous state of the circuit. Note that, except when R and S are both high, the two outputs Q and $\bar{Q}$ are **complementary** – when Q is high $\bar{Q}$ is low, and vice versa.

When the power supply to the bistable circuit is first switched on, it is a matter of chance whether output Q is high and $\bar{Q}$ is low or whether Q is low and $\bar{Q}$ is high. If input R is made high, output Q must go low, which in turn will make $\bar{Q}$ go high. Since the output from $\bar{Q}$ is fed back to the upper gate, this will make the bistable stay in this state, even when the inputs R and S are allowed to 'float' (that is to say, when R and S are not connected to anything). In order to reverse the values of the outputs, S must be made to go high momentarily.

The bistable circuit thus has two distinct states between which it may be flipped by applying a momentary high potential to either R or S. The bistable may thus function as an area of memory, the two distinct states representing the bits 0 and 1.

Pulses and timing

All computers have an internal clock, responsible for generating pulses that control the operations of the different areas of the computer. The pulses are generated at a very high frequency, of the order of 25 MHz, using an oscillator which contains a crystal of the mineral **quartz**. Clock pulses generated in this way have a waveform which is almost exactly square, and can be used to trigger a bistable circuit to flip from one state to the other – this is the basis of the **binary counter** used in digital clocks, and in computers too. Circuits that generate pulses like this have two possible states, neither of which is stable. As a result, the circuit continually oscillates from one state to the other, giving it the name of an **astable vibrator**.

Such triggered bistables are very similar to the bistable circuit seen in figure 4.5.11, with the addition of a small number of extra components which cause the bistable to flip between its two states as pulses are applied to its input. The flipping may occur either when the positive-going edge of a pulse arrives at the input, or when a negative-going pulse arrives, but *not* both. (See figure 4.5.12 for an explanation of 'positive-going' and 'negative-going' pulses.) The effect of arranging a series of triggered bistables into which pulses are fed is shown in figure 4.5.12.

As the example in figure 4.5.12 shows, the frequency of the output from a bistable is exactly *half* the frequency of the pulses arriving at its input. If the three indicator lamps represent three binary digits, it can be seen that this counter is capable of counting up to eight pulses (000 to 111).

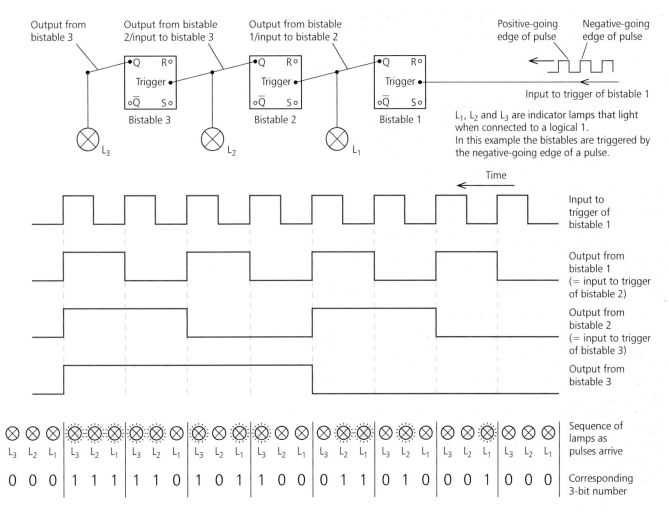

Figure 4.5.12

The operational amplifier

Introduction – the ideal op-amp

The **operational amplifier** (op-amp) is an electronic device developed in the 1960s to carry out mathematical operations like multiplication and integration, hence its name. The first op-amps were made up from discrete components, but they are now available as single components, with the circuit elements contained on a single chip.

Figure 4.5.15 shows the connections to an op-amp and its output voltage for the different input conditions. The **gain** A of an op-amp is the ratio of its output voltage to the input voltage, V_{out}/V_{in}. Under **open-loop** conditions, where the output is not connected to an input, this ratio is called the **open-loop gain** A_o.

The op-amp has two inputs. If a very small positive voltage $+V_{in}$ is applied to the non-inverting input while the inverting input is grounded (that is, held at 0 V), a positive output voltage equal to $+A_oV_{in}$ appears between the output terminal and 0 V. Similarly, a negative input voltage $-V_{in}$ produces a negative output $-A_oV_{in}$ while the inverting input is grounded. The reverse is true for the inverting input – a positive input $+V_{in}$ produces a negative output $-A_oV_{in}$, and a negative input produces a positive output $+A_oV_{in}$, the non-inverting input being grounded in both cases. This is illustrated in figure 4.5.16.

THE ELECTRONICS REVOLUTION

People in the 1950s and 1960s trying to predict what life would be like at the end of the century usually got it spectacularly wrong! One of the reasons is that no-one predicted the pace of the electronics revolution.

The rapid development of electronic devices has meant that our power to control the things around us has increased enormously. A motor mechanic magically transported from the 1950s would find a modern motor car almost impossible to understand, due to its complex electronic systems controlling the car's electrics, which include the control of the ratio of fuel:air admitted to the cylinders and the precise point at which a spark ignites the mixture. This complex system of electronics ensures that today's cars emit far less in the way of pollutants than cars a generation ago – and that they require highly qualified people to service them. A telecommunications technician from the 1950s would find the modern telephone system equally baffling, with its use of optoelectronic devices which make use of laser light to transmit telephone and other signals down a strand of glass thinner than a human hair.

In 1968 Gordon Moore co-founded the Intel corporation to make microprocessor chips. Moore based his business on the idea that the computing power of the most powerful chips that can be made doubles every 18 months, while the cost of such chips remains constant. The years in the latter part of the twentieth century showed Moore to be correct in his thinking – the Intel corporation prospered and his idea became known as **Moore's Law**.

The rate at which the computing power of a microchip grows shows little sign of slowing, leading some people to suggest that the time is not far away when it will be possible for the human nervous system to be enhanced by means of computer chips. In the UK the first steps towards this have already been taken by Professor Kevin Warwick of Reading University. A small transponder (consisting of a number of silicon chips connected to a coil contained in a glass capsule 23 mm long and 3 mm in diameter) was implanted in Warwick's left arm in 1998. This transponder was programmed to respond to a radio signal emitted from transmitters placed in various doorways in the Department of Cybernetics. When Warwick approached one of the doorways, the radio signal induced a small current in the coil which caused the chips to produce an identifying signal that the coil then transmitted. This signal was then picked up by a receiver in the doorway which was connected to a computer. This computer then controlled various devices attached to it, so that the door Warwick was approaching was opened automatically, his telephone calls were automatically re-routed, and his computer announced how many e-mails were waiting for him as he walked into his office – after greeting him personally.

The next stage in this research will see the much closer integration of computer technology with the nervous system, so that nervous impulses can be recorded by an implanted microchip, which may then play them back or broadcast them to a computer. Such an application of electronics might eventually make it possible to treat people who have restricted movements due to damage to their nervous system, and to treat people who are suffering from degenerative diseases which affect muscles and nerves. But it also raises some interesting questions about who we are. For example, if people's brains are linked to each other via silicon implants and the Internet, where does one individual end and the other start?

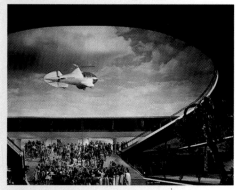

Figure 4.5.13 Half a century ago, the predictions made about life in the year 2000 usually focused on dramatic changes in personal transport. The real changes were rather different – it is personal communication that has changed dramatically, thanks to developments in electronics.

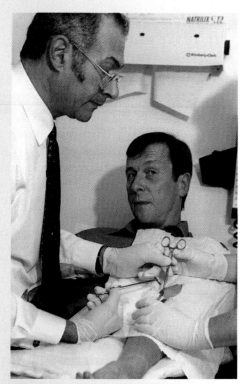

Figure 4.5.14 Professor Kevin Warwick's implant was inserted in a 20-minute operation on 24 August 1998. It was left in place for nine days before being removed.

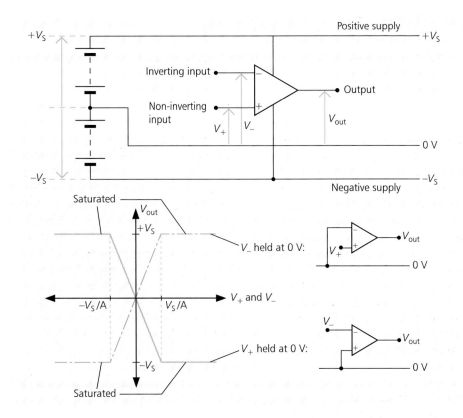

Figure 4.5.15 An integrated circuit op-amp. The diagram shows the general symbol for an amplifier, with the five op-amp connections to it. The graph shows the **transfer characteristics** of the op-amp – the way the output voltage varies with input voltage for the inverting and non-inverting inputs. Note that the range of the output voltage is between $+V_S$ and $-V_S$. For simplicity, the supply connections to the op-amp are usually omitted in circuit diagrams.

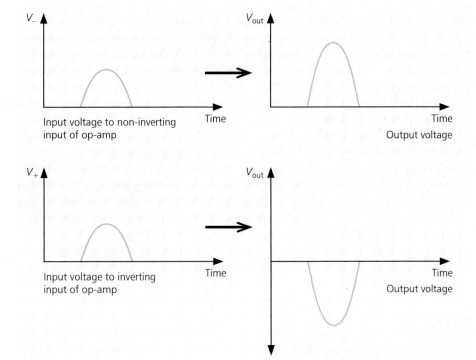

Figure 4.5.16 The output from the operational amplifier is in phase with the input if the non-inverting input is used, and antiphase if the inverting input is used.

The transfer characteristics of the operational amplifier shown in figure 4.5.15 indicate that there is a very small region in which the input voltage is proportional to the output voltage. Beyond this region the output voltage is constant, and the op-amp is said to be **saturated**.

This character is due to the op-amp's high gain. If $V_{out} = \pm 12$ V and the open-loop gain of the op-amp is 10^5, then:

$$V_{out} = \pm 12 \text{ V} = 10^5 \times V_{in}$$

that is,

$$V_{in} = \frac{\pm 12 \text{ V}}{10^5}$$

$$= \pm 120 \, \mu\text{V}$$

This means that the range of input voltage for which the op-amp is not saturated is $\pm 120 \, \mu$V.

An ideal operational amplifier has three important properties:

1 a very high gain. The open-loop gain A_o is typically around 10^5 for d.c. and low frequencies, decreasing as frequency increases.

2 a very high **input resistance**, typically $10^{12} \, \Omega$. This means that the amplifier has little effect on any voltage connected across its input terminals.

3 a very low **output resistance**, typically $10^2 \, \Omega$. This means that the output voltage may be transferred to a load of around $10^3 \, \Omega$ with little loss.

A centre-tapped d.c. supply is needed for an op-amp. The centre tap is used as the 0 V reference level for input and output voltages, and V_s is usually between 5 V and 15 V.

The op-amp as a linear device

The transfer characteristics of the op-amp show that for a limited range of outputs where $-V_s \leq V_{out} \leq +V_s$, the output voltage is proportional to the input voltage. Within these limits the op-amp operates as a **linear** or **analogue** device – these words simply state the fact that $V_{out} \propto V_{in}$. Outside the limits, the op-amp behaves as a **digital** device. The term 'digital' here means 'having two states', high and low output, corresponding to logical 1 and logical 0.

So far we have seen what happens to an op-amp's output when one of the op-amp inputs is grounded and the input voltage to the other is varied. The operational amplifier actually amplifies the *difference* between the two input voltages, so:

$$V_{out} = A_o (V_+ - V_-)$$

If the op-amp is operating as an analogue device, then V_{out} has a value somewhere between about $+10$ V and -10 V (V_s typically lies somewhere between ± 5 V and ± 15 V). If we take the open-loop gain as 10^5, then:

$$-10 \text{ V} \leq 10^5 (V_+ - V_-) \leq +10 \text{ V}$$

which means that:

$$-10^{-4} \text{ V} \leq (V_+ - V_-) \leq +10^{-4} \text{ V}$$

that is, V_+ and V_- have values within about $100 \, \mu$V of each other. Thus we may make the approximation that $V_+ \approx V_-$. We shall use this approximation later on.

The op-amp as a comparator

The op-amp amplifies the difference between two input voltages, so that $V_{out} = A_o (V_+ - V_-)$. Since A_o is so large, the output from the amplifier saturates if $(V_+ - V_-)$ is greater than about $100 \, \mu$V. The amplifier thus acts as a device that compares the input voltages V_+ and V_-, producing a voltage V_{out} which is around $+V_s$ if $V_+ > V_-$, and around $-V_s$ if $V_+ < V_-$. The op-amp is acting here as a **digital** device; figure 4.5.17 shows two examples of the use of an op-amp in this way.

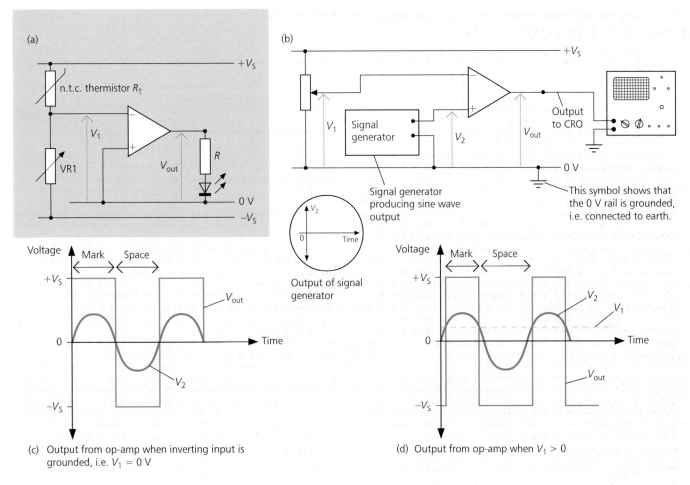

(a)

(b)

Signal generator producing sine wave output

This symbol shows that the 0 V rail is grounded, i.e. connected to earth.

Output of signal generator

(c) Output from op-amp when inverting input is grounded, i.e. $V_1 = 0$ V

(d) Output from op-amp when $V_1 > 0$

Figure 4.5.17

In figure 4.5.17(a), variable resistor VR1 is adjusted so that at the required temperature, the resistance of VR1 is equal to that of the thermistor R_T. (This makes $V_1 = 0$.) If the temperature now rises, R_T falls and so $V_1 > 0$. Since $V_{out} = A_o (V_+ - V_-)$, V_{out} is negative, the LED is reverse biased and so does not light. If the temperature falls, R_T rises and $V_1 < 0$. Now V_{out} is positive, and the LED lights – the arrangement acts as a low temperature warning device.

In figure 4.5.17(b), the non-inverting input of the op-amp is given a sine wave input. With $V_1 = 0$ V (or 'grounded'), V_{out} switches between $+V_s$ and $-V_s$ with $V_2 \approx 0$ V, and a train of square pulses is the result (figure 4.5.17(c)) – note the mark:space ratio of 1 in these pulses. If V_1 is made more positive this switching occurs at a different point, affecting the shape of the pulses and reducing the mark:space ratio to less than 1 (figure 4.5.17(d)).

Amplifying circuits – feedback

An operational amplifier may be used as an amplifier to increase an input voltage, just as the amplifier in an audio system does. The op-amp circuits we have seen so far are not at all suited to this purpose for a number of reasons. First, the range of input voltages over which the amplifier gives a linear response (in which output voltage $\propto$ input voltage) is far too small, so that even a moderate input causes the amplifier to saturate. Second, the amplifier tends to be unstable in this region, and liable to fluctuations that vary with temperature. Third, the gain is frequency dependent, and fourth, the gain may vary considerably from op-amp to op-amp.

These problems can be overcome by the use of **negative feedback**, which reduces the gain of the amplifier and also makes the gain much more predictable. Further, the gain is much more uniform over a wide range of frequencies (referred to as the **bandwidth** of the amplifier), and the op-amp becomes more stable and less prone to temperature-sensitive fluctuations.

Negative feedback – an important principle

Negative feedback is used in systems to increase their stability. It is used wherever output depending on one or more inputs is controlled, not just in electronic systems.

Living organisms have complex control systems which depend on negative feedback to stabilise their life processes. For example, one of the ways in which humans regulate their body temperature is by controlling the flow of blood to the surface of their skin. As a person's temperature rises, the amount of blood passing through the blood vessels near the skin's surface increases. This allows heat to flow out of the blood into the air surrounding the body, and so cools the person down. As a person's temperature falls, less blood is passed to the surface of the skin, less heat is lost, and the person warms up. Body

temperature is also regulated by controlling the amount of sweat produced and the rate of energy transfer in the cells of the body as food is broken down (the **metabolic rate**). Both of these other processes involve negative feedback, just like the control of blood flow.

If a person's temperature rises above a certain point (as it may do if they have a very severe illness which gives them a high fever, for example), the negative feedback in these control systems breaks down and is replaced by **positive feedback**. In this situation an increase in body temperature causes an increase in metabolic rate which in turn increases the body temperature even more, which causes a further increase in metabolic rate. The 'runaway' nature of this process is typical of the instability positive feedback can cause in a system.

Negative feedback is obtained in the op-amp by connecting the output of the device to its inverting input, via a resistor, as figure 4.5.18 shows.

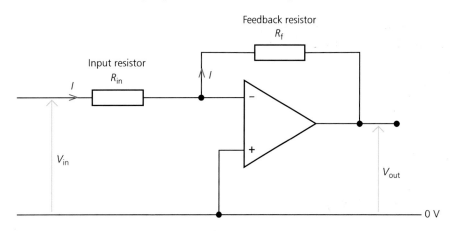

Figure 4.5.18 Negative feedback may drastically reduce the gain of an op-amp, but greatly increases its stability.

The **closed-loop gain** of the amplifier with its input and feedback resistors R_{in} and R_f is given by the relationship:

$$A = \frac{V_{out}}{V_{in}} = -\frac{R_f}{R_{in}}$$

Thus for a gain of –10, one might choose values of $R_{in} = 5\ k\Omega$ and $R_f = 50\ k\Omega$. Notice that the gain of the amplifier under these circumstances does not depend on the open-loop gain of the op-amp itself, only on the values of the two resistors.

The expression for the closed-loop gain of an op-amp with negative feedback depends on an approximation called the **virtual earth** approximation. This works as follows:

(1) The potential at the inverting input of the op-amp must be close to zero, since the maximum value of V_{out} is V_s, which is of the order of 10 V. Thus the maximum potential at the inverting input is around 10 V/$A_o \approx 10^{-4}$ V. This point in the circuit is thus a **virtual earth** – its potential is at, or close to, that of the earth.

(2) R_f has a value of the order of 10^5 Ω. This compares with an input resistance of the order of 10^{12} Ω for the op-amp itself. Because of this, the input current flowing through R_{in} will also flow through R_f, with only a negligible fraction of it flowing through the op-amp.

Applying Ohm's law, we can write:

$$I = \frac{V_{in}}{R_{in}} = -\frac{V_{out}}{R_f} \quad \text{(the negative sign shows that } V_{in} \text{ and } V_{out} \text{ are antiphase)}$$

But $A = V_{out} / V_{in}$, so:

$$A = -\frac{R_f}{R_{in}}$$

Op-amps and voltage measurement

An operational amplifier can be used as a non-inverting amplifier with a gain of 1 to increase the input resistance of a voltmeter. Figure 4.5.19 shows how this may be done.

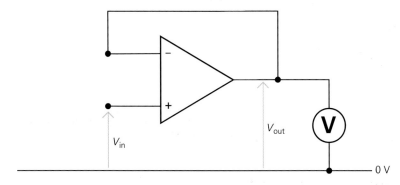

Figure 4.5.19 An operational amplifier may be used as a **buffer** between source and load.

If the op-amp is used as an analogue device, that is, with $V_{out} < V_s$, then $V_+ = V_-$ to a very good approximation (see box 'The op-amp as a linear device', page 362). In this case, $V_+ = V_{in}$ and $V_- = V_{out}$, so $V_{out} = V_{in}$, and the gain of the op-amp is 1. At first sight an amplifier with a gain of 1 seems a pretty useless device – but it is not! Its usefulness stems from its properties. Since the op-amp has a very high input resistance, the circuit to which it is connected 'sees' a very large resistance. The op-amp itself will drive a load with quite a low resistance that may draw a current of around 20 mA – this circuit therefore acts as a **buffer** between the source and the load, and an op-amp used in this way is called a **buffer amplifier**. (It is also sometimes called a **voltage follower**, since this describes how the output of the amplifier follows the input, provided of course that $V_{in} < V_s$.) This type of circuit is used where a voltage must be measured and an absolute minimum of current must be drawn from the circuit to which it is connected, so that a moving-coil laboratory meter can be used to measure voltages in an electronic circuit, for example.

SUMMARY

- In an **analogue system**, a signal may have any value between a maximum and a minimum. In a **digital system**, a signal may have one of only two possible values.
- In a simple **control system**, an input signal is processed to produce an output signal. **Negative feedback** may be used to increase the stability of the system, as shown in figure 4.5.20.

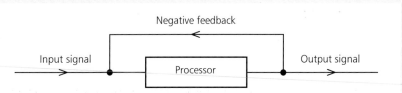

Figure 4.5.20

- **Logic gates** are devices that make simple decisions by applying rules to one or more inputs.
- The **open-loop gain** A_o of an operational amplifier is given by $A_o = V_o/(V_+ - V_-)$.
- For an inverting amplifier, $V_{out} = (-R_f/R_i) V_{in}$.

EXAMPLE

Find the output voltage of the circuit shown in figure 4.5.21.

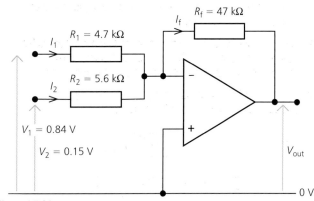

Figure 4.5.21

The input of the op-amp is a virtual earth. The current through the op-amp itself is negligible, so:

$$I_1 + I_2 = I_f$$

Using Ohm's law:

$$I_1 = V_1/R_1$$

$$I_2 = V_2/R_2$$

$$I_f = -V_{out}/R_f$$

SO:

$$-\frac{V_{out}}{R_f} = \frac{V_1}{R_1} + \frac{V_2}{R_2}$$

that is,

$$-\frac{V_{out}}{4.7 \times 10^4 \, \Omega} = \frac{0.84 \, V}{4.7 \times 10^3 \, \Omega} + \frac{0.15 \, V}{5.6 \times 10^3 \, \Omega}$$

$$= 0.1787 \, mA + 0.0268 \, mA$$

SO:

$$V_{out} = -0.2055 \, mA \times 4.7 \times 10^4 \, \Omega$$
$$= -9.66 \, V$$

This is the same as the sum of the individual outputs on their own – the op-amp is acting as a **summing amplifier**. (In this case it is a **weighted summing amplifier**, since the values of R_1 and R_2 are different. The calculation shows how this difference weights the effect of the two input voltages on the output voltage.) One practical use of this is in recording studios, where it is necessary to mix several signals from difference sources together.

1 Write down the state of the output P for each combination of gates in figure 4.5.22.

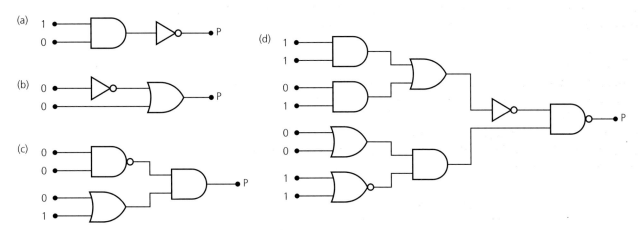

Figure 4.5.22

2 Draw up a truth table for each of the combinations of gates in figure 4.5.22.

3 Show that the combination of gates in figure 4.5.23 is equivalent to an EXOR gate.

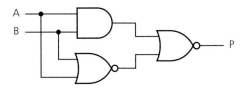

Figure 4.5.23

4 A parity gate gives a high output if both inputs are the same, and a low output if both inputs are different. Design such a gate using only AND, OR and NOT gates.

5 A two-input AND gate gives a high output only if both inputs are high. A three-input AND gate gives a high output only if all three inputs are high.
  a Draw up a truth table for a four-input AND gate.
  b Design such a gate.

6 Figure 4.5.24 shows the use of an OR gate to produce a device called a **latch**. Explain why the output from the gate goes high and remains high when a momentary high input is applied to A.

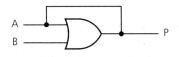

Figure 4.5.24

7 Design a warning device that will alert the driver of a car if any of the doors, boot or bonnet of a four-door car is not properly shut. Assume that each of these is fitted with a switch producing a logical 1 unless the door/boot lid/bonnet is closed.

8 a Draw out a table showing the sequence of colours as a set of traffic lights changes from red through to green and back to red again.
  b Use your table and figure 4.5.14 to help you to work out how an astable multivibrator and a triggered bistable can be used to produce the sequence of red and amber combinations.
  c By using a suitable combination of logic gates, show how the green light can be operated using the logic states of the red and orange lights.

9 Draw a circuit diagram to show how an operational amplifier may be used together with a thermistor and any other components necessary to switch off a kettle when it boils.

10 Figure 4.5.25 shows an inverting operational amplifier. Calculate the voltage gain of this amplifier.

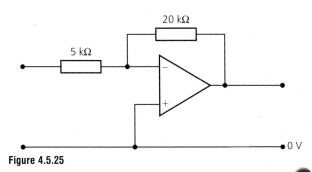

Figure 4.5.25

11 Figure 4.5.26 shows an operational amplifier used as a summing amplifier. Calculate the output voltage provided by this arrangement if $V_1 = 0.75$ V, $V_2 = 0.23$ V and $V_3 = 0.34$ V.

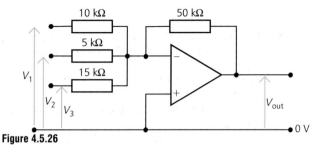

Figure 4.5.26

12 Figure 4.5.27 shows an inverting operational amplifier connected to a supply p.d. of ± 15 V.

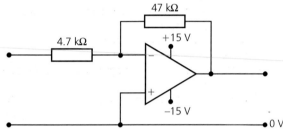

Figure 4.5.27

  a Calculate the gain of this arrangement.
  b An alternating p.d. is applied to the input of the amplifier. Sketch graphs, using appropriate scales, to show the input and output voltages for inputs of:
    i 0.5 V r.m.s. with a frequency of 50 Hz
    ii 5.0 V r.m.s. with a frequency of 10 Hz.

13 Figure 4.5.28 shows an inverting operational amplifier with the feedback resistor replaced by a capacitor C.

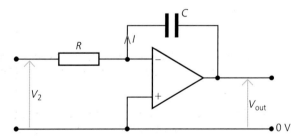

Figure 4.5.28

  a The op-amp has an extremely high resistance. Explain why this means that:
    i effectively all the input current flows into the capacitor C
    ii the potential difference across the capacitor is equal to the output voltage V_{out} from the op-amp.

  b Using the virtual earth approximation, show that the current I flowing into the capacitor is given by $I = V_{in}/R$, assuming that V_{in} is constant over time Δt.
  c If charge ΔQ flows into the capacitor C in time Δt, write down:
    i an expression relating Q to the current flowing into C in time Δt
    ii an expression relating Q to the change of potential difference ΔV_{out} across C in this time.
  d Use your expressions to show that:

$$\Delta V_{out} = -\frac{1}{RC} V_{in} \Delta t$$

(If this expression is integrated, it becomes:

$$V_{out} = -\frac{1}{RC} \int_0^t V_{in}\, dt$$

This circuit is often known as an **integrator** – it integrates the input voltage over a time interval.)
  e Sketch a graph of V_{out} against t for a constant value of V_{in}. Another name for this circuit is a **ramp generator**, due to the shape of this graph.

14 In figure 4.5.29 the feedback resistor of an inverting operational amplifier has been replaced with a non-linear device D.

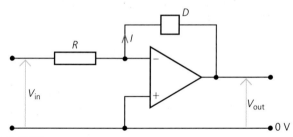

Figure 4.5.29

The current I through D varies with the potential difference across it according to the relationship:

$$I = I_0\, e^{-kV}$$

where I_0 and k are constants.
  a Write down expressions for the current through D:
    i in terms of the output voltage V_{out}
    ii in terms of V_{in} and R.
  b Use these expressions to show that:

$$V_{out} = \frac{1}{k} \log_e \left(\frac{I_0 R}{V_{in}} \right)$$

(Take $\varepsilon = 8.854 \times 10^{-12}$ F m^{-1})

1 a i Give, in words, the equation which is used to define charge.
   ii State the SI unit of charge.
   iii Define potential difference and its unit, the volt. **(5 marks)**
 b In circuit A, the 6.0 V d.c. supply has negligible internal resistance.

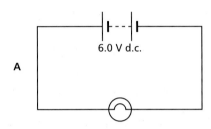

6.0 V d.c.

A

   i On a copy of circuit A show, by means of arrows
    1 the conventional current in the circuit (label this arrow C)
    2 the electron flow in the circuit (label this arrow E). **(2 marks)**
   ii Calculate the energy transfer (in joules, J) in the bulb when a charge of 15 C passes through it. **(2 marks)**
 c Circuit B shows a 12 V d.c. supply of negligible internal resistance connected to an arrangement of resistors.

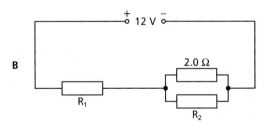

+ 12 V −

B

2.0 Ω

R$_1$

R$_2$

The current in resistor R1 is 5.0 A and the current in the resistor of resistance 2.0 Ω is 4.0 A. Calculate
   i the p.d. (V) across the resistor of resistance 2.0 Ω, **(2 marks)**
   ii the resistance (Ω) of resistor R2, **(3 marks)**
   iii the p.d. (V) across resistor R1, **(1 mark)**
   iv the resistance (Ω) of resistor R1. **(2 marks)**
   (OCR specimen)

2 A radiant heater consists of four heating elements connected in parallel across a power supply as shown in the diagram.

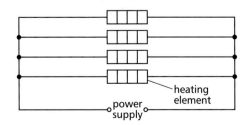

heating element

power supply

Each heating element is made of wire of length 0.60 m and cross-sectional area 4.0×10^{-7} m^2. The wire has resistivity 8.0×10^{-5} W m at room temperature.
 a i Show that the resistance of one heating element at room temperature is 120 Ω. **(3 marks)**
   ii Calculate the total resistance (Ω) at room temperature of the radiant heater. **(3 marks)**
   iii Calculate the power output (W) from the radiant heater when it is connected to a 230 V supply. **(3 marks)**
   iv Calculate the energy output of the heater in kWh if it is kept on for 8 hours. **(2 marks)**
 b The wire in one of the elements of the radiant heater breaks. State and explain the effect on
   i the total resistance of the heater,
   ii the power output of the heater. **(4 marks)**
 c i Sketch a typical current–voltage characteristic for a metallic heating element.
   ii Explain the shape of your graph. **(4 marks)**
   (OCR specimen)

3 a State what is meant by
   i the electromotive force (e.m.f.) of a battery,
   ii the internal resistance of a battery. **(4 marks)**
 b A student is asked to design a circuit to obtain potential differences of 4.0 V and 8.0 V from a 12 V supply of negligible internal resistance. A number of identical resistors is available.
   i Copy and complete the diagram to show a potential divider arrangement which could be used.

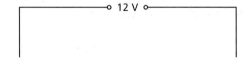

12 V

   ii On your copy of the diagram show the connections made to the circuit for each potential difference. **(3 marks)**
   (OCR specimen)

4 In the circuit shown, A$_1$, A$_2$ and A$_3$ are ammeters of negligible resistance, and V is a high resistance voltmeter. R$_1$ is a 6.0 Ω resistor. R$_2$ and R$_3$ are resistors of unknown value.

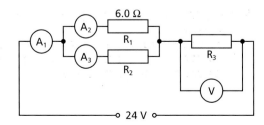

6.0 Ω

A$_2$

A$_1$

R$_1$

A$_3$

R$_2$

R$_3$

V

24 V

The power supply is a battery of e.m.f. 24 V and negligible internal resistance. A_1 reads 4.0 A and A_2 reads 3.0 A.

a i Calculate the reading of A_3. **(1 mark)**
  ii Name the law you have used to obtain your answer. **(1 mark)**
b Calculate:
  i the resistance (Ω) of R_2; **(2 marks)**
  ii the reading of the voltmeter V; **(1 mark)**
  iii the resistance (Ω) of R_3. **(1 mark)**

(OCR 1998)

5 A 100 W tungsten filament lamp operates from the 230 V mains. Calculate its resistance. **(2 marks)**
The drift speed of the electrons in the filament is much higher than the drift speed of electrons in the rest of the circuit. Suggest and explain a reason for this. **(4 marks)**
(Total 6 marks)

(Edexcel 1999)

6 a i State what is meant by *resistivity*. **(1 mark)**
  ii Write down a relation **in words** between the resistance of a wire and the resistivity of its material. **(1 mark)**
b An electrical cable for use in a new aircraft is to be 50 m long with a resistance of $0.020\,\Omega$.
The designer of the aircraft has to choose between copper and aluminium conductors for the cable.
Some data for copper and aluminium are shown below.

	Density (kg m^{-3})	Resistivity (Ω m)
Copper	8.9×10^3	1.7×10^{-8}
Aluminium	2.7×10^3	3.2×10^{-8}

  i Show that the mass of copper needed to make the cable is 19 kg. **(2 marks)**
  ii The mass of aluminium needed to make the cable is 11 kg. Use the above data, and the masses of copper and aluminium needed, to suggest an advantage of choosing copper rather than aluminium. **(1 mark)**

(OCR 1998)

7 A strain gauge is made from a constantan wire of original length 25 mm. If the wire stretches its resistance changes. The gauge is attached to an object that is then placed under tension, which causes the length of the constantan wire to increase. The resistance, R, was measured for various lengths, I, and the following results were obtained:

R/Ω	99.96	100.64	101.76	102.80	103.85	104.71
$I/10^{-2}$ m	2.500	2.508	2.523	2.536	2.548	2.557

When the wire is stretched, it may be assumed that for small extensions $R \propto I^2$.
a Copy and complete the table showing the value of I^2 for each value of R. **(2 marks)**
b Plot a graph of R on the y-axis against I^2 on the x-axis. **(4 marks)**

c Use your graph and a value of $49 \times 10^{-8}\,\Omega$ m for the resistivity of constantan to find the diameter of the wire when its resistance is $103.40\,\Omega$. **(5 marks)**
d Define tensile strain. Use your graph to determine the strain when the resistance of the wire is $103.40\,\Omega$. **(2 marks)**

(AQA specimen)

8 A d.c. power supply of e.m.f. 20.0 V and of negligible internal resistance is used in a circuit to charge a 12.5 V battery of internal resistance $1.00\,\Omega$. A filament lamp is placed in the circuit to limit the charging current.

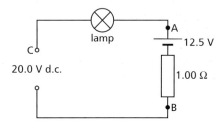

The graph shows how the current through the lamp varies with voltage across it.

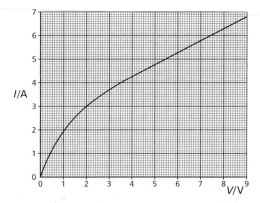

a What is the polarity of terminal C of the power supply? **(1 mark)**
b Calculate the magnitude of the charging current given that the voltage across the battery terminals AB is 16.5 V. **(2 marks)**
c A second identical battery is connected in parallel across the terminals AB so that both batteries are charging. Calculate the magnitude of the current through the lamp. You may assume that there is a linear relationship between current and voltage for the lamp for voltages greater than 3.5 V. **(6 marks)**

(AQA 1999)

9 A very high resistance voltmeter reads 20 V when connected across the terminals of a d.c. power supply. The high resistance meter is disconnected and a second voltmeter of resistance 1.0 kΩ is then connected across the supply. The second meter gives a reading of 16 V.
  i State the e.m.f. of the power supply.
  ii Calculate the current which flows through the second meter.
  iii Calculate the internal resistance of the power supply.
  iv Show the current is equal to 0.080 A when the supply is short circuited. **(5 marks)**

(AQA 1999)

10 An uncharged capacitor of capacitance $2.2\,\mu\text{F}$ is connected in series with a resistor of resistance $11\,\text{k}\Omega$ and a d.c. power supply of 12 V with negligible internal resistance, as shown in the figure.

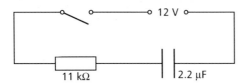

a At one instant after the switch is closed, the charging current in the circuit is 0.40 mA. For this instant, calculate

  i the potential difference (V) across the resistor,

  ii the potential difference (V) across the capacitor,

  iii the charge on the capacitor. **(6 marks)**

b After some time, the capacitor becomes fully charged. Calculate the energy which is then stored in the capacitor. **(2 marks)**

(OCR 1998)

11 The diagram shows the main parts of a capacitor microphone. Terminal A is connected to a flexible metal plate which oscillates when a sound wave strikes it. Terminal B is connected to a fixed metal plate with small holes in it.

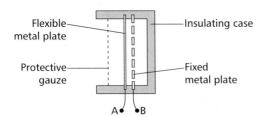

a The flexible plate has a natural frequency of 60 Hz. Draw a graph showing how the amplitude of oscillation of this plate varies with frequency when the frequency of the incident sound waves varies from 30 Hz to 200 Hz.

Explain what is meant by mechanical resonance. Give one other example of mechanical resonance. **(5 marks)**

b i Describe and explain how the capacitance of the microphone varies as a sinusoidal sound wave strikes it.

  ii One such microphone has a plate area of $8.0\,\text{cm}^2$ and a capacitance of 40 pF. Calculate the separation of the metal plates in this microphone. **(5 marks)**

c A 40 pF microphone is connected in series with a $150\,\text{M}\Omega$ resistor and a d.c. source.

  i Draw a circuit diagram of this arrangement and calculate the time constant of the circuit.

  ii An oscilloscope connected across the $150\,\text{M}\Omega$ resistor produces the trace shown when a sound wave of frequency 5000 Hz is incident on the microphone.

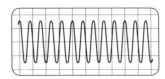

What is the setting, in $\mu\text{s div}^{-1}$, of the time-base of the oscilloscope? **(6 marks)**

(Total 16 marks)

(Edexcel 1999)

12 a A capacitor is made from two parallel metal plates of the same area, separated by an air gap. It is connected across a battery of constant e.m.f.

The plates are moved further apart, maintaining the same area of overlap, whilst the battery remains connected. State and explain what change, if any, occurs to

  i the potential difference across the plates,

  ii the capacitance of the capacitor,

  iii the charge on each plate of the capacitor,

  iv the energy stored by the capacitor. **(4 marks)**

b A thunder cloud and the earth beneath it can be considered to form a parallel plate capacitor. The area of the cloud is $8.0\,\text{km}^2$ and it is 0.75 km above the earth.

  i Calculate the energy stored if the potential difference between the cloud and the earth is 200 kV.

  ii The air suddenly conducts, allowing all the charge to flow to earth in $120\,\mu\text{s}$. Calculate the mean current flowing between the cloud and the earth when this happens. **(6 marks)**

(AQA 1999)

13 a The expression for the capacitance, C, of a parallel-plate capacitor is $C = \varepsilon A/t$ where A is the area of overlap of the plates and t is the separation of the plates.

  i Define *capacitance* of a capacitor. **(1 mark)**

  ii What quantity is represented by ε? **(1 mark)**

  iii Use the expression to derive a unit for ε. **(1 mark)**

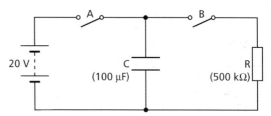

b In the circuit shown, the $100\,\mu\text{F}$ capacitor, C, is charged from the 20 V d.c. supply by briefly closing switch A, with switch B open. C is then discharged through the $500\,\text{k}\Omega$ resistor, R, by opening switch A and closing switch B.

Show that 30 s after B is closed, the potential difference (p.d.) across C is 11 V. **(3 marks)**

c In an attempt to monitor the p.d. across C, the procedure of **b** is repeated with a moving-coil voltmeter connected across C.

  i Suggest why, 30 s after closing B, the reading of the voltmeter is considerably less than 11 V. **(2 marks)**

  ii The moving-coil voltmeter is removed and the procedure in **b** repeated. Suggest how it could be shown that the p.d. across C at 30 s is 11 V. **(1 mark)**

(OCR 1998)

14 The e.m.f. of the electricity supply to a remote cottage is 230 V. The resistance of the cables to the cottage may be considered as the internal resistance of the supply. When an electric cooker is used in the cottage, the measured voltage across the cooker is 210 V. The resistance of the cooker is $35\,\Omega$.

a Calculate

  i the current (A) to the cooker,

  ii the power (W) of the cooker,

  iii the resistance (Ω) of the cables to the cottage. **(4 marks)**

4

b Explain why the voltage measured at the cooker is less than the supply voltage when the cooker is in use. **(2 marks)**

c Suggest two disadvantages of this power supply. **(2 marks)**

(OCR 1998)

15 Electric power is transmitted from generating stations to consumers on high voltage overhead power lines supported by metal pylons, which are earthed. Each conductor is suspended vertically below the pylon structure by an insulator which is 3.5 m long. The distribution voltage is 380 kV r.m.s. It may be assumed that the voltage waveform applied to each conductor is sinusoidal.

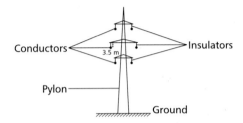

a i Calculate the peak voltage applied to each of the conductors.

  ii Estimate the magnitude of the maximum electric field strength between a conductor and the pylon structure, if the field could be assumed to be uniform. **(3 marks)**

b Under certain atmospheric conditions it is possible to hear sharp, crackling noises coming from the region around the conductors.

  i State the atmospheric conditions under which the effect would become more pronounced and explain your answer.

  ii Suggest an explanation for this effect. **(4 marks)**

c 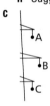 The potential V of conductor B varies with time according to the equation $V = V_0\cos 2\pi ft$ where V_0 is the value you have obtained in **a i** and the frequency, f, is 50 Hz. The potentials of conductors A and C vary with time in a similar manner, having the same peak value and frequency, but the wave carried by A leads on that carried by B by 120°, whilst that on C lags behind that on B by 120°.

Calculate

  i the potential of conductor B when $t = 0.10$ s,

  ii the phase difference between the a.c. waves carried by conductors A and C, indicating whether it is a lead or a lag,

  iii the potential difference between conductors A and C when $t = 0$. **(4 marks)**

(AQA specimen)

16 a The graph shows the variation with frequency f of the voltage gain G, without feedback, of an ideal operational amplifier (op-amp).

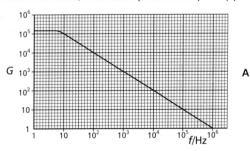

The op-amp is used in the amplifier circuit of figure B.

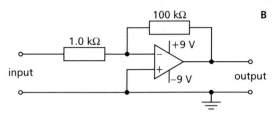

i State

  1 the type of amplifier shown in figure B,

  2 what is meant by *negative feedback*.

ii Calculate

  1 the bandwidth of the amplifier,

  2 the peak output voltage for an input signal of peak value 0.2 V and frequency 1.0×10^5 Hz. **(7 marks)**

b Figure C shows a system in which a warning light (LED) is operated by switches S_1 and S_2.

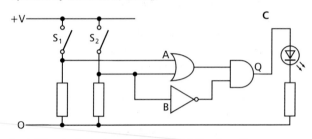

i 1 What is the logic state at A when S_1 is closed?

  2 Copy and complete the table for the circuit of Figure C.

A	B		Q
0	0		
0	1		
1	0		
1	1		

ii The circuit in figure C is modified so that inputs A and B are controlled by a thermistor R_T and an LDR R_L, as shown in figure E.

  1 The logic state at A changes when R_T is cooled. State whether R_T is hot or cold for logic 1 at A.

  2 The logic state at B changes when R_L is put in darkness. State whether R_L is in light or darkness for logic 1 at B.

  3 Hence deduce the environmental conditions for the light-emitting diode to be conducting.

iii State how the circuit in E may be modified so that the environmental conditions for the light-emitting diode to conduct may be varied. **(8 marks)**

(OCR 1998)

ELECTRICITY CONCEPT MAP

How to use the map

The map is a way of representing the structure of the knowledge contained in this section. It is designed to be used as you get towards the end of the section, when you should begin to see a pattern in the key concepts you have met. The map shows how one area of knowledge builds on another, so that more complex ideas develop as you go through the section.

As you study, try to think about how you learn best. Do you prefer to have understood one idea completely before going on to another? Or do you like to meet several related new ideas and then put these together rather like you might put together several pieces of a jigsaw at once?

The concept map will help you to see how ideas are related. You can use it to help you to put your knowledge and understanding in some sort of order so that you can organise your learning. You can also use it to organise your revision at the end of the section and before your examinations. Alternatively, try drawing up your own concept map as you revise.

Notes on the map

The key ideas in the section are contained in the green boxes. Solid lines with arrows between these boxes show how ideas in the section develop. Where parts of this section relate to other sections, dashed lines with arrows indicate this – the links are described in yellow boxes. Finally, some sections introduce and apply key mathematical skills – this is indicated by purple boxes, with double arrows indicating areas where the skill is applied.

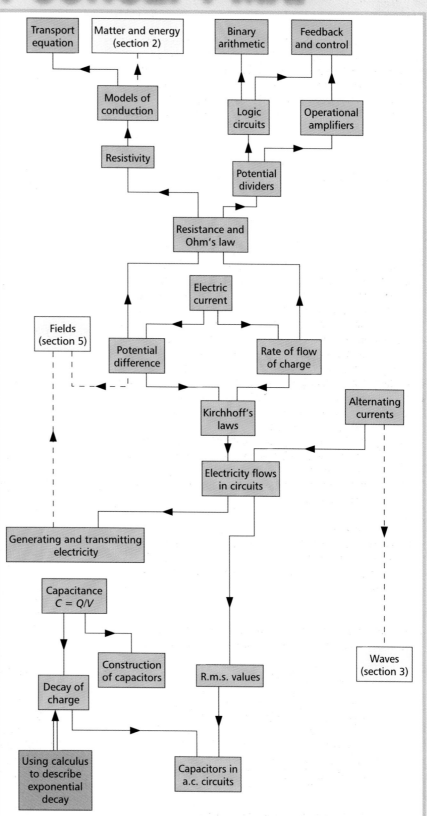

4

5 FIELDS

Introduction

So far we have not thought very seriously about the way in which gravitational and electrical forces work, and have regarded the force between a satellite and the Earth or between the charges on the plates of a capacitor as examples of **action at a distance**. This explanation is not very satisfactory (how can two things which are not touching exert forces on each other?), as Newton realised when he wrote 'It is inconceivable, that inanimate brute matter, should, without the mediation of something else, which is not material, operate on and affect other matter without mutual contact.' He concluded: 'Gravity must be caused by an Agent acting constantly according to certain Laws; but whether this Agent be material or immaterial, I have left to the consideration of my readers.'

Our modern view of gravitational and electrical interactions uses the idea of a **field** as the agent acting between 'brute matter'. A massive or electrically charged body produces a gravitational or electric field around itself. This field pushes and pulls as appropriate on another body whenever it comes into contact with it.

In this section of the book we shall be concerned first with developing an understanding of gravitational fields, basing these on Newton's laws which were formulated over 300 years ago. We shall then consider electric fields, which bear many similarities to gravitational fields, since both obey an inverse square law. This will provide us with the tools we need to go on and study magnetism to gain some insight into the behaviour of magnets, and the relationship between electricity (moving electric charge) and magnetic fields.

Figure 5.1 A plasma globe is simply a large glass sphere which contains a gas at low pressure. An intense electric field between the centre of the sphere and its outside accelerates electrons. These electrons collide with atoms of the gas, transferring some of their kinetic energy to the atoms as they do so. As the atoms lose this energy, they emit light with characteristic frequencies. Distorting the electric field (for example, by touching the glass) intensifies it, and produces the beautiful streamers seen here.

MEASURING AND USING VARIATIONS IN *g*

At some time in your physics career you have probably measured the acceleration due to gravity, *g*. If so, you will probably have been very happy to get a value with an uncertainty of about 0.5%. Compare this with the measurements that geophysicists make, which involve variations in *g* of 0.1 ppm (parts per million) or less.

Geophysicists make measurements with this degree of accuracy using very sophisticated equipment – although the technique involves measuring the acceleration of an object in free fall, just like the practical carried out in the school laboratory. In order to make measurements with the required precision, the apparatus makes use of the interference of laser light (figure 5.1.1).

As the mirror falls under the influence of the local gravitational field, the detector 'sees' alternating lightness and darkness as the waves arriving first interfere constructively and then destructively, due to the changing path length. By linking the number of light/dark transitions detected to an accurate measurement of time, the acceleration of the mirror can then be calculated.

Geophysicists are interested in local variations in the acceleration due to gravity. There is considerable variation in *g* over the surface of the Earth. One variation is due to latitude, which causes *g* to vary because the Earth's radius varies with latitude and because the centripetal acceleration of an object decreases as its distance north or south of the equator increases. Another variation is due to the differing heights above sea level, when *g* decreases with increasing altitude. However, the variations of *g* in which geophysicists are interested are due to differences in the density of rocks that lie beneath the Earth's surface. To obtain a measure of this for a particular point, geophysicists calculate the **gravity anomaly** for that point. This is the difference between the expected value of *g* (after making allowance for factors related to height and radius) and the measured value.

A *gravity anomaly map* provides a picture of the way in which the gravity anomaly varies in different geographical regions. Gravity anomaly is measured in parts per million (ppm), and varies from about –60 ppm to around +180 ppm in the British Isles. A positive gravity anomaly indicates that the density of the rocks below the surface is greater than expected, while a negative anomaly indicates rocks with lower density. It is these differences in density that provide evidence for interesting geological features.

Measurements involving gravitation can also provide evidence about the deep inner structure of the Earth. Newton's law of gravitation sets out the relationship between the gravitational force between two masses, their distance apart, and a constant, *G*. By measuring *g* and *G* experimentally, the mass of the Earth can be calculated, along with its density. The density of the Earth calculated in this way is approximately 5500 kg m^{-3}. Rocks in the Earth's crust have a density of around 2700 kg m^{-3}, while those in the mantle vary in density from about 3300 kg m^{-3} to around 5000 kg m^{-3}. The fact that the mean density of the Earth is greater than any of these figures provides strong supporting evidence for the idea that the core of the Earth contains molten iron under great pressure, with a density of around 13 000 kg m^{-3}.

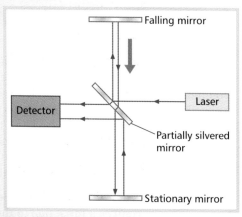

Figure 5.1.1 The absolute gravity meter uses interference between light waves to measure *g* to an uncertainty of the order of parts per billion.

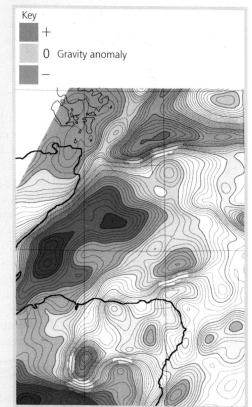

Figure 5.1.2 This map clearly shows the negative gravity anomaly under the North Sea, running up into the Moray Firth. This anomaly is caused by large amounts of oil and gas trapped in the rock layers, reducing the overall density of the rock.

5.1 Action at a distance

An introduction to fields

What is a field?

A **field** is a model used by physicists to help them understand how objects not in direct contact with each other can affect each other's behaviour. The most common kind of field we all experience is probably a **gravitational field**. We all know that the Earth exerts a force on us (in a direction we call 'down'), and we call this force our **weight**. We also know that this force acts on any object on or just above the Earth, and that it causes objects to fall when they are dropped or thrown – 'what goes up must come down'. From simple observations like these, a physicist would describe a gravitational field something like this:

> **A gravitational field is a region of space in which a mass experiences a force due to the presence of another mass.**

Notice that this description tells us (1) what kind of field we are talking about, (2) what property an object must have in order to be influenced by the field – in this case, mass – and (3) what has given rise to the field.

It is obviously just good sense to ensure that we know what type of field we are talking about. The other two pieces of information, about objects influenced by the field and the cause of the field, are also important to ensure that the description of the field is clear.

What kinds of fields are there?

From day to day we experience an astonishing array of different forces. Our weight, the force of a seat belt on us as a car brakes sharply, the tension in a rubber band as we stretch it, the force of the wind on a blustery day, the force of a magnetic catch on a door, the force between a balloon that has been rubbed on a woollen jumper and another balloon – all these and many more are common experience.

As well as these forces which act at a familiar, macroscopic, level, there are many others which act at a microscopic level. These include intermolecular and interatomic forces like those seen in section 2, attracting and repelling molecules and atoms one to another. There are forces within the nucleus of the atom holding the protons and neutrons together, and strange forces which act for the briefest of instants when tiny subatomic particles collide.

All these forces are in fact examples of only four types of force, known as the **four fundamental interactions**. These interactions are the gravitational force, the electromagnetic force, the 'strong' force and the 'weak' force.

Gravitational force	Electromagnetic force	Strong force	Weak force
Acts on mass	Acts on electric charge	Acts on nuclear particles	Acts on most elementary particles
$F = 10^{-34}$ N	$F = 10^2$ N	$F = 10^4$ N	$F = 10^{-2}$ N
Range = ∞	Range = ∞	Range = 10^{-15} m	Range < 10^{-17} m

Table 5.1.1 The behaviour and effects of the four fundamental interactions. In each case, the strength of the force acting between two protons separated by a distance equal to their diameter (2×10^{-15} m) is given.

The Earth's gravitational force pulls this sky diver down towards the Earth.

The strong force causes thermonuclear fusion, the process which fuels the Sun and (indirectly) keeps us warm.

Electric forces between atoms and molecules cause the contact forces between the racquet and the ball.

The weak force is involved in some radioactive decay reactions.

Figure 5.1.3 The four fundamental interactions

As we have seen, the **gravitational force** is an attractive force acting between all masses. It is the weakest of the four interactions in terms of their effect on elementary particles – the interaction between two neighbouring protons due to the gravitational force is insignificant compared to the other three forces – yet it is the gravitational force that plays the greatest role in our everyday lives. The reason for this is that although the interaction between the individual particles in our bodies and those in the Earth is tiny, the number of these particles is enormous, and all the interactions between them add up to give a large force.

The **electromagnetic force** acts between electric charges, and may be repulsive or attractive. These interactions are responsible for all the forces that act whenever one piece of matter is in contact with another. This includes contact forces, surface tension, frictional forces and many other forces, all of which are nothing more than the interaction between the charged particles that make up matter (this is explained further in section 6).

The **strong force** is really important only within the nuclei of atoms, acting as the subatomic 'glue' that prevents particles with the same charge from flying apart (and also prevents them from getting too close together). This interaction is the strongest of the four interactions, and can be either attractive or repulsive. It acts over a limited range – up to a distance of about 10^{-15} m.

The **weak force** is observed in many radioactive decay reactions involving the spontaneous break-up of a particle into other particles. It acts over a very limited range – up to about 10^{-17} m.

In this and following sections we shall concern ourselves with gravitational fields, electric fields and magnetic fields.

Gravitational fields

Gravitational field strength

We saw in section 1.2 that the magnitude of the strength of a gravitational field at a particular point is defined in terms of the magnitude of the force exerted per unit mass at that point, that is,

$$g = \frac{F}{m}$$

At the surface of the Earth, the gravitational field strength is approximately 9.8 N kg^{-1}, although its exact value varies according to latitude. This figure appears to be the same as the figure for the acceleration due to free fall, and a simple comparison between two relationships suggests a reason for this.

From Newton's second law, force = mass × acceleration, $F = ma$.

From the definition of gravitational field strength, the force on a mass in a gravitational field = mass × gravitational field strength, $F = mg$.

Comparing these two relationships suggests that $mg = ma$, and so $g = a$, that is, the acceleration due to gravity is the same as the gravitational field strength. (You should be able to prove to your own satisfaction that gravitational field strength and acceleration have the same dimensions.)

This simple exercise is based on an assumption which may not be immediately obvious – the assumption that we may use inertial mass for the gravitational force equation. Whilst this may seem quite reasonable, we should think more carefully before we do it. The reason will be explored later, in the box 'Inertial and gravitational mass' on pages 385–6.

Figure 5.1.4 The four fundamental interactions, different as they are, all have one thing in common – they are all responsible for **action at a distance**. The action of the gravitational force can have quite spectacular effects – the rise and fall of the tides is caused by the gravitational field of the Sun, 150 million kilometres distant!

Picturing fields – field lines

Field lines are used to visualise how a field affects the behaviour of a mass. For example, the gravitational field around a planet can be represented as shown in figure 5.1.5(a).

The field lines show the direction in which a small test mass would experience a force if placed in the field. For this reason, the lines are sometimes called **lines of force**. In this case the lines converge on the centre of the planet – the field is **radial**.

Although the field around the planet is not uniform, since the field strength decreases as one travels further away from the planet, at the surface of the planet the field lines appear to be parallel as shown in figure 5.1.5(b). Over small distances the field strength does not change very much, and so the field *can* be regarded as uniform.

Newton's law of universal gravitation

The development of the law

Galileo's work in the early seventeenth century showed that a force is necessary to keep an object travelling in a path other than a straight line, and so paved

Figure 5.1.5

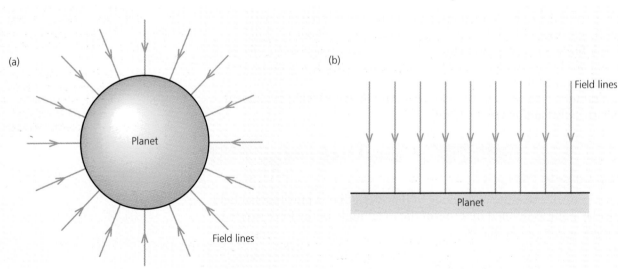

(a)

Planet

Field lines

(b)

Field lines

Planet

Johannes Kepler (1571–1630)

Isaac Newton
(1642–1727)

Figure 5.1.6 The German astronomer Johannes Kepler formulated three laws governing the behaviour of the planets, based on meticulous analysis of data collected by the great Danish astronomer Tycho Brahe. It was Kepler's laws that seventeenth century physicists sought to explain, and which led Newton to the conclusion, confirmed by calculations on the orbit of the Earth's own moon, that the force holding the planets in their orbits obeys an inverse square law. Newton published his theories in his three-volume work *Principia*, infuriating his fellow scientist Robert Hooke, who believed that he had discovered the inverse square law first. Newton and Hooke continued a bitter feud about this and other matters over many years, just one of many disputes with fellow academics in which Newton was involved.

The painting is 'The Orrery' by Joseph Wright. An orrery is a model showing the motion of the planets in the Solar System. These were very popular in the eighteenth century, reflecting the success that physicists had had in explaining planetary motion during the previous century.

the way for the development of a theory to explain the nature of the force keeping the Moon and planets in their orbits. Newton developed his theory of gravitation as a direct result of his attempts to understand this motion.

As we saw in section 1.6, Newton investigated the motion of the Moon round the Earth by considering the motion to have two components, one at a tangent to its orbit (the direction in which the Moon would move without the influence of the Earth), and the other towards the Earth. Newton calculated the rate at which an object falls towards the Earth at the Earth's surface, and then compared this with his calculated rate at which the Moon fell towards the Earth. This comparison led him to the conclusion that the force keeping the Moon in its orbit round the Earth varied inversely with the square of the distance from the Earth, that is,

$$F \propto \frac{1}{r^2}$$

In full, Newton's law states:

> **Every particle attracts every other particle with a force directly proportional to the product of their masses and inversely proportional to the square of the distance between them.**

Mathematically, the magnitude of the gravitational force that two masses m_1 and m_2 separated by a distance r exert on each other can be written as:

$$F = \frac{Gm_1m_2}{r^2}$$

where G is a constant called the **gravitational constant**. The value of G is 6.67×10^{-11} N m^2 kg^{-2}.

Newton's theorem

The gravitational force varies according to an inverse square law, like those governing the intensity of sound and light. Although the force decreases with distance, it never entirely reaches zero, and so every particle in the Universe

Measuring G

The measurement of G is difficult since the force between two masses of a size convenient to use in a laboratory is extremely small, and so very sensitive techniques are required. The first measurement of G was carried out by the English physicist and chemist Henry Cavendish in 1798, using a design of torsion balance invented by Coulomb for his work investigating the forces between two electric charges. Figure 5.1.7 shows a diagram of the apparatus, taken from Cavendish's original paper.

Two small masses m and m' are attached to a light horizontal beam suspended from a fine fibre. Left undisturbed, the beam settles into an equilibrium position so that the fibre is untwisted. Two large, equal masses M and M' are then brought up to m and m', and the beam rotates clockwise as a result of the

gravitational attraction between the masses. The beam then settles into a new equilibrium position, in which the couple caused by the gravitational attraction is exactly opposed by the couple exerted by the twisted fibre. If measurements are made to determine the couple exerted by the fibre for a given small angular displacement, then G can be calculated.

Modern methods, based on Cavendish's apparatus, give G as 6.673×10^{-11} N m^2 kg^{-2}, with an uncertainty of about one in 10 000 (0.01%). Most other fundamental constants are known to a much greater degree of accuracy than this. Fortunately, this is not important in most situations where accurate calculations are needed since the force exerted by a body depends only on the product of G and the mass of the body. This product can usually be determined very precisely from direct measurements.

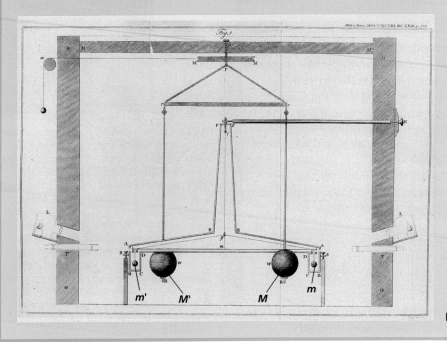

Figure 5.1.7 Cavendish's torsion balance.

attracts every other particle. The force is entirely unaffected by any mass that happens to be between the two particles under consideration, so for example, a cricket ball at Lord's attracts another cricket ball at the Sydney Oval with exactly the force calculated from the equation above, even though the mass of the Earth lies between them.

The fact that intervening masses have no effect on the gravitational force between two particles has an important result, known as **Newton's theorem**. This theorem states that the gravitational field around a spherical mass can be found by treating the sphere as if all the mass were concentrated at its centre, that is, considering it as a **point mass**. The full mathematical proof of this assumption involves some complex mathematics, but a simple justification of it can be made in terms of symmetry, as shown in figure 5.1.8.

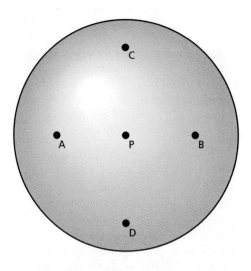

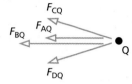

The points A, B, C and D represent equal masses, m.

AP = BP
CP = DP

Figure 5.1.8 Since the sphere is uniform, for every point like A or C there is always another point like B or D such that the two points are exactly symmetrically placed about the centre of the sphere P. This means that the mass of the sphere can be regarded as if it were all concentrated at point P, as far as its effect on a mass at point Q is concerned. This is also true if the density of the sphere varies with its radius, as in the case of the Earth.

The masses at points A and B exert a force on Q as if they were a single point mass $2m$ at P.

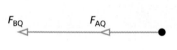

The masses at points C and D also exert a force on Q as if they were a single point mass $2m$ at P.

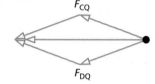

If we consider a small mass m at the surface of the Earth, the mass will experience a force F acting towards the centre of the Earth, along a line joining its centre of mass to the Earth's centre. The magnitude of this force F is given by:

$$F = \frac{GM_{\text{E}}m}{r_{\text{E}}^2}$$

This force will give rise to an acceleration if the mass is dropped – the acceleration due to gravity. Since $a = F/m$, and in this case $a = g$, we can write:

$$g = \frac{GM_{\text{E}}}{r_{\text{E}}^2}$$

---

g at the surface of some celestial bodies

Using the relationship:

$$g = \frac{GM}{r^2}$$

the following calculations show the magnitude of the gravitational field strength at the surface of Jupiter and the Earth's Moon.

Data for Jupiter:

Mass = 1.91×10^{27} kg

Radius at equator = 7.14×10^7 m

$$g_{\text{Jupiter}} = \frac{6.67 \times 10^{-11} \text{ N m}^2 \text{ kg}^{-2} \times 1.91 \times 10^{27} \text{ kg}}{(7.14 \times 10^7 \text{ m})^2}$$

$$= 25.0 \text{ N kg}^{-1}$$

Data for Moon:

Mass = 7.4×10^{22} kg

Radius at equator = 1.74×10^6 m

$$g_{\text{Moon}} = \frac{6.67 \times 10^{-11} \text{ N m}^2 \text{ kg}^{-2} \times 7.4 \times 10^{22} \text{ kg}}{(1.74 \times 10^6 \text{ m})^2}$$

$$= 1.63 \text{ N kg}^{-1}$$

'The Eagle has landed'

This was the message that told controllers at the Manned Spacecraft Center, Houston, Texas that the lunar module from the Apollo 11 spacecraft had landed on the Moon. The time was 3.18 pm (Houston time) on 20 July 1969.

This event was the outcome of a research and development programme costing 24 billion dollars. Astronaut Buzz Aldrin (the second man to step onto the surface of the Moon) later wrote the following reflections:

> The moon was a very natural and very pleasant environment in which to work. It had many of the advantages of zero-gravity, but it was in a sense less *lonesome* than zero G, where you always have to pay attention to securing attachment points to give you some means of leverage. In one-sixth gravity, on the moon, you had a distinct feeling of being *somewhere*, and you had a constant, though at many times ill defined, sense of direction and force …
>
> As we deployed our experiments on the surface we had to jettison things like lanyards, retaining fasteners, etc., and some of these we tossed away. The objects would go away with a slow, lazy motion. If anyone tried to throw a baseball back and forth in that atmosphere he would have difficulty, at first, acclimatizing himself to that slow, lazy trajectory; but I believe he could adapt to it quite readily.

> Source: *First on the Moon. A Voyage with Neil Armstrong, Michael Collins, Edwin E. Aldrin Jr.* written with Grace Farmer and Dora Jane Hamblin, Epilogue by Arthur C. Clarke, Boston and Toronto, Little Brown, 1970.

Figure 5.1.9 Buzz Aldrin on the surface of the Moon.

This relationship thus provides a way of calculating the magnitude of the gravitational field strength at the surface of the Earth (or indeed, at the surface of any other celestial body, such as the Moon or Mars). Alternatively, it provides a relationship from which M_E may be calculated provided that g, G and r_E are known. The circumference of the Earth was first calculated by Eratosthenes of Cyrene around 240BC, with a result close to that accepted today. Cavendish's experiment to measure G (see box 'Measuring G', page 380) is often described as 'weighing the Earth'.

Variations in g on the Earth

The variation of g with latitude

If g is measured at the poles and at the equator, it is found to have different values. This happens for two reasons:
- The Earth is not a perfect sphere – it 'bulges out' slightly at the equator. This means that the polar radius, r_p, is slightly smaller than the equatorial radius, r_e.
- The surface of the Earth at the equator is moving in a circle of radius r_e with a period of 24 hours (this is a tangential velocity of over 450 m s^{-1}), whilst at the poles there is no circular motion of this sort.

Consider a mass m resting on the surface of the Earth at one of the poles. The forces acting on it will be:

1 GM_Em/r_p^2 towards the centre of the Earth due to gravity
2 mg_p away from the centre of the Earth due to the force exerted on the mass by the ground (that is, a force equal in size and opposite in direction to the *weight* of the mass: see section 1.2, page 26).

These two forces are in equilibrium, so:

$$\frac{GM_Em}{r_p^2} - mg_p = 0$$

that is, the magnitude of g_p is given by:

$$g_p = \frac{GM_E}{r_p^2}$$

At the equator, a mass resting on the surface of the Earth will also have two forces acting on it. In this case, however, the two forces are *not* in equilibrium, but provide the centripetal acceleration towards the centre of the Earth (see section 1.6, page 79). Thus:

$$\frac{GM_E m}{r_e^2} - mg_e = \frac{mv^2}{r_e}$$

that is, the magnitude of g_e is given by:

$$g_e = \frac{GM_E}{r_e^2} - \frac{v^2}{r_e}$$

Comparing the two expressions for g_p and g_e, it can be seen that $g_e < g_p$ since $r_e > r_p$ and the gravitational attraction of the mass to the Earth must also provide the centripetal acceleration v^2/r.

Experimental investigations give the magnitude of g_p as 9.83 N kg^{-1}, while g_e is measured as 9.78 N kg^{-1}.

The variation of *g* with depth

As we travel upwards from the Earth's surface, our distance from the centre of the Earth increases and the value of *g* decreases in accordance with the relationship we have already seen. What happens as we travel downwards, into the Earth?

In order to answer this question we need to examine the situation carefully, initially setting the condition that we shall assume the density of the Earth is constant with depth – which is an over-simplification.

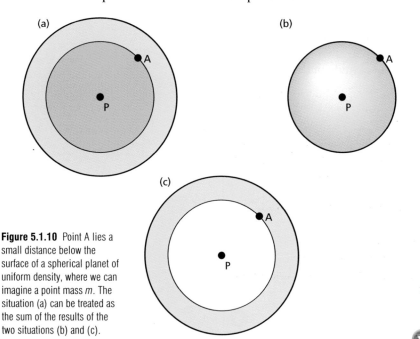

Figure 5.1.10 Point A lies a small distance below the surface of a spherical planet of uniform density, where we can imagine a point mass *m*. The situation (a) can be treated as the sum of the results of the two situations (b) and (c).

From figure 5.1.10, we can see that the gravitational pull of the planet on
the mass can be thought of in two parts – the pull of a sphere of radius PA,
and the pull of a shell of material with interior radius PA. From what we
have seen so far, it is clear that the magnitude of the force of the sphere of
material on the mass m will be given by:

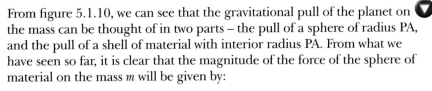

$$F_{sphere} = \frac{GM_{sphere}m}{r^2_{sphere}}$$

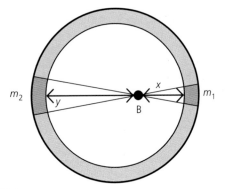

Figure 5.1.11

What about the shell? Figure 5.1.11 shows a point B inside a shell of matter
with a radius PA, as in figure 5.1.10(c). Two imaginary cones spread out
from point B and subtend sections of the shell with masses m_1 and m_2 at
respective distances x and y from B. The masses m_1 and m_2 are proportional
to the cross-sectional areas of the sections of the shell subtended by the
cones, which in turn are proportional to the distance from point B. (This is
the same argument used in developing the inverse square law in section
3.1, page 212.) Therefore:

$$\frac{m_1}{m_2} = \frac{x^2}{y^2} \quad \text{or} \quad \frac{m_1}{x^2} = \frac{m_2}{y^2}$$

If the cones are very narrow and the shell of matter is very thin, m_1 and m_2
can be considered as point masses. A point mass m_3 may then be sited at B,
and Newton's law of gravitation used to find the magnitude of the forces
acting on it:

$$F_1 = \textbf{magnitude of force on } m_3 \textbf{ due to } m_1$$

$$= \frac{Gm_1m_3}{x^2}$$

$$F_2 = \textbf{magnitude of force on } m_3 \textbf{ due to } m_2$$

$$= \frac{Gm_2m_3}{y^2}$$

But we know that:

$$\frac{m_2}{y^2} = \frac{m_1}{x^2}$$

so:

$$F_2 = \frac{Gm_1m_3}{x^2}$$

$$= F_1$$

Thus the resultant force on m_3 is zero.

This process can be repeated for the whole of the shell, (integral calculus is used to carry out the tedious calculation of the sum of the forces on m_3), which shows that the total gravitational field strength at any point inside the shell is zero.

Since we can ignore the shell, this process shows us that the gravitational field strength at any point inside a uniform sphere is proportional to the distance from the centre of the sphere, with the result that gravitational field strength varies as shown in figure 5.1.12.

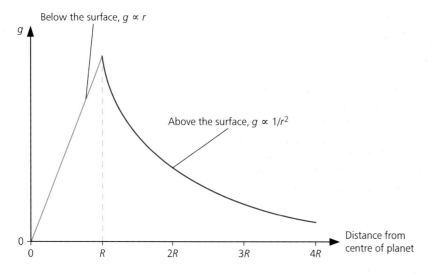

Figure 5.1.12 The gravitational field strength of a planet reaches a maximum at its surface, when $r = R$.

Inertial and gravitational mass

The definition of mass we met in section 1.2, page 25, was based on the comparison of the acceleration of an unknown mass with that of a standard mass when an identical force acted on each of them. Mass measured in this way is clearly associated with inertia (the opposition to a change in state of motion), and is sometimes referred to as **inertial mass**.

On the other hand, in most common situations and in this section of the book, we are concerned with the force exerted on a mass in a gravitational field, for example measuring mass by observing the deformation of a spring – **gravitational mass**.

It is extremely important to verify that these different methods of measuring mass are in agreement, a process which involves highly accurate experimental work.

On page 378 we showed that the numerical value of gravitational field strength and the acceleration due to gravity were the same, by equating the statement of Newton's second law of motion with the definition of gravitational field strength:

$$ma = mg, \quad \therefore a = g$$

The cancelling of m on both sides of the equation assumes the exact equivalence of inertial mass (on the left-hand side) with gravitational mass (on the right-hand side). Is this fair?

Clearly the gravitational field strength at a given point in a gravitational field is the same for any piece of matter, so the answer to this question hinges on whether all masses accelerate at the same rate at a given point in a gravitational field.

Newton and Galileo were the first to try to answer this question experimentally. In the early part of this century much more precise experiments were carried out by the Hungarian physicist Roland von Eötvös, who compared the acceleration of free fall of many different substances. More recently still, work has shown that the acceleration of free fall of samples of gold and aluminium are identical to within one part in 10^{12}, which suggests that the inertial and gravitational mass of a body are probably exactly equal.

As observed in section 1.2, the universal nature of free-fall acceleration leads to the apparent weightlessness of an observer in a freely falling lift, and more generally to the observation that, within a frame of reference like a lift or a spacecraft, it is impossible to tell whether apparent gravitational field strength is caused by the influence of a gravitational field or by acceleration.

The concept of a field provides a useful model to understand how force varies with position. Wherever we find forces and displacements, we inevitably think of work and energy. Section 5.2 addresses these topics, and develops some ideas that will be used when we come to examine electric fields in section 5.3.

SUMMARY

- A **field** is a model used in physics to describe how objects that are not in contact with each other can exert a force on one another.
- The **four fundamental interactions** responsible for action at a distance are the **gravitational force**, the **electromagnetic force**, the **strong force** and the **weak force**.
- **Gravitational field strength** g is the force exerted per unit mass at a point, $g = F/m$.
- The magnitude of the force F that two masses m_1 and m_2 a distance r apart exert on each other is given by the expression $F = Gm_1m_2/r^2$, where G is the **gravitational constant**.

- The magnitude of the gravitational field strength g a distance r from a mass M is given by $g = GM/r^2$. The direction of the gravitational field is always radially in.
- Gravitational field strength g varies over the surface of the Earth such that $g_{\text{equator}} < g_{\text{poles}}$.

QUESTIONS

(Take G as 6.67×10^{-11} N m^2 kg^{-2}.)

1 A large 'supertanker' loaded with oil may have a mass of 500 000 tonnes. Two such tankers are travelling on parallel courses a distance of 1 km apart. Calculate the gravitational force exerted by each tanker on the other, treating both tankers as point masses.

2 The mean distance from the Earth to the Moon is known to an accuracy of 40 cm. To three significant figures it is 384 000 km, while the mean distance from the Earth to the Sun is 150 000 000 km. The mass of each of the three bodies is as shown in table 5.1.2.

	Sun	Moon	Earth
Mass/10^{22} kg	200 000 000	7.4	600

Table 5.1.2

Calculate the resultant force due to the Sun and the Earth acting on the Moon:
a at first quarter (when the Moon is at the right angle of a right-angled triangle, the Earth and the Sun being at the other vertices)
b at new Moon
c at full Moon.

3 The asteroid called Ceres has a diameter of 785 km and a mass of about 10^{20} kg. Calculate:
a the strength of the gravitational field and
b the gravitational potential
at the surface of Ceres.

4 The planet Jupiter is 318 times more massive than the Earth, and rotates with a period of 9 hours 55.5 minutes. This rapid rotation causes considerable flattening of Jupiter at the poles – its North–South diameter is 133 500 km, while its equatorial diameter is 142 800 km. Taking the mass of the Earth as 6×10^{24} kg, calculate:
a the strength of Jupiter's gravitational field at its poles
b the acceleration due to gravity at Jupiter's poles
c the strength of Jupiter's gravitational field at its equator

d the straight-line speed of a point on Jupiter's equator
e the force that the gravitational field of Jupiter must exert on a 1 kg mass in order to just keep it in contact with the surface of the planet at its equator
f the acceleration due to gravity at Jupiter's equator. How rapidly would Jupiter need to rotate for the planet to literally fly apart?

5 The density of the Earth is not uniform, but varies with depth. Figure 5.1.13 is a very simple way of representing the structure of the Earth, with a uniformly dense core surrounded by a less dense crust.

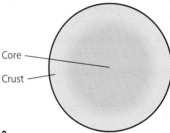

Core

Crust

Figure 5.1.13

Using this information, sketch a graph showing how the gravitational field strength varies with distance from the Earth's centre to a distance of 6 Earth radii.

6 A cricketer can bowl a ball at a speed of 150 km h^{-1}. This cricketer stands on the Moon and throws the ball.
a If he throws it vertically upwards, to what height will it travel?
b If he throws it horizontally, where will it hit the ground?
c What is the maximum distance he could throw the ball? (The gravitational field strength at the Moon's surface is approximately one-sixth of the gravitational field strength at the Earth's surface.)

7 Somewhere between the Earth and the Moon there is a point where the Earth's gravitational field exactly balances that of the Moon. Use the data in question 2 to find out where this point is.

5.2 Gravitational fields and energy

In this section we shall look in a little more depth at some of the ideas about gravitational fields met in section 5.1. In particular, we shall be concerned with the transfer of energy in gravitational fields, and we shall use some of the ideas concerned with this energy transfer to examine some of the physics behind space travel and satellites.

Energy transfers in gravitational fields

Potential energy – some complications

In section 1.5, pages 63–4, we saw that it is possible to calculate the change in potential energy of a mass m when its position in a gravitational field changes. To do this we used the simple relationship:

$$E_p = mg\Delta h$$

where Δh was the change in the vertical displacement of the mass in a gravitational field with magnitude g.

We noted at the time that this relationship actually gives the *change* in potential energy of the mass, but this is not its only simplification. When considering the change in potential energy in a situation like this, we need to recognise that gravitational field strength varies with position in the field. To assume, as this relationship does, that g can be treated as constant will not be a fair assumption in all situations. Furthermore, we need to think very carefully about the mathematical signs given to the various quantities in the relationships and how we can compare potential energies in different situations. This first part of the section looks at these problems and gives the solutions physicists use.

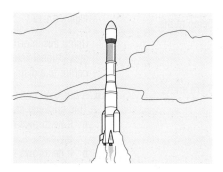

Figure 5.2.1 In most everyday situations it is reasonable to assume that g is constant when calculating transfers of potential energy, and it is also quite easy to keep track of whether potential energy has increased or decreased. In other situations it may not be quite so straightforward.

Comparing potential energies

Consider the simple case of three identical masses m resting on the surface of the Earth. As each mass is raised above the Earth its potential energy increases. If mass A is raised to a height h_1, mass B to a height h_2 and mass C to a height h_3 above the Earth, each mass will have a potential energy E_{p1}, E_{p2} and E_{p3} respectively. If we assume that the strength of the gravitational field is constant over a small area of the Earth's surface, we might represent the situation as shown in figure 5.2.2.

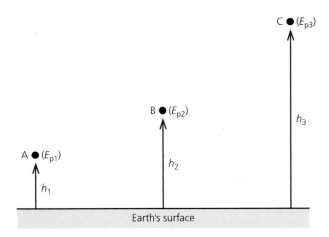

Figure 5.2.2

In dealing with this situation we have used the Earth's surface as a point from which to measure changes in potential energy, assigning a potential energy of zero to any mass resting on the surface. This is perfectly reasonable if all we wish to do is to compare the potential energies of masses at different heights above the Earth – but it becomes more complex if we wish to compare potential energies more generally.

Consider a space mission which is to travel from Earth to a distant planetary system (here we shall ignore the problems in travelling such vast distances in terms of the time taken). Once at the system the mission is to visit two of its planets (X and Y) before returning to Earth. The planetary system is so far distant that when the spacecraft is half-way between it and the Solar System, it can be considered to be infinitely far away from all other matter in the Universe.

In order to leave the Earth, work must be done on the spacecraft to overcome the pull of the Earth's gravitational field – this work increases the potential energy of the spacecraft. If the spacecraft then lands on another planet, X, with a gravitational field less strong than that of the Earth, its gravitational potential energy will decrease from its value in space, but will still be greater than on the Earth.

Work will again have to be done on the spacecraft to remove it from the gravitational field of planet X, so its gravitational potential energy again increases as it travels into space. If it then lands on planet Y, with a *stronger* gravitational field than the Earth, its gravitational potential energy will then be *less* than on the Earth. Figure 5.2.3 shows this situation.

Taking the potential energy of the spacecraft as zero at the surface of the Earth is one way of dealing with the changes of potential energy. But this would not seem very practical when on the surface of planet X and thinking about the journey to the surface of planet Y. The common point of reference in this situation is the potential energy at the midpoint of the journey, that is, when the spacecraft is remote from all other mass in the Universe – and it makes most sense to use this point as our reference point (or **datum**) for calculating potential energy. The potential energy of the spacecraft at this point is at a maximum, since the craft is as far as possible from any other masses in the Universe.

By convention, the potential energy of an object is considered to be *zero* at infinite distance from all other masses, so that its potential energy becomes increasingly *negative* as it approaches another mass. This is exactly the same situation as we saw in section 2.1, when potential energy was set equal to zero at

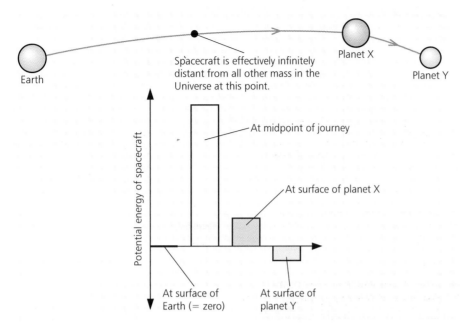

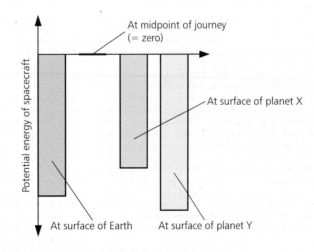

Figure 5.2.3

infinite separation for atoms and molecules. Figure 5.2.4 shows the effect of this convention on the values of potential energy for the spacecraft – compare it with the graph in figure 5.2.3. Taking the potential energy as zero at infinity has the convenient effect that the potential energy of an object is always zero or less. This avoids the situation in figure 5.2.3, in which the spacecraft's potential energy may be zero, positive or negative.

Figure 5.2.4

Calculating gravitational potential energy

How can we calculate the change in potential energy when a mass is moved away from the Earth's surface into space? This calculation is not as straightforward as calculating the change in potential energy for a small distance moved, since we cannot assume that gravitational field strength remains constant. But since we *can* assume that gravitational field strength is constant for a small change in displacement, we can use a method for calculating the change in potential energy that we have seen before.

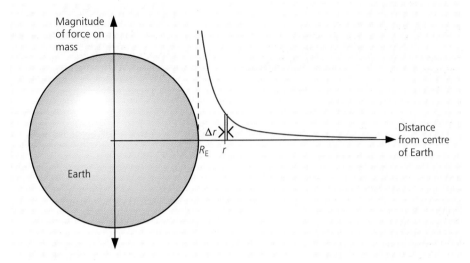

Figure 5.2.5

At or above the Earth's surface, at a distance r from the centre of the Earth, the magnitude of the gravitational force on the mass m is given by Newton's law of gravitation:

$$F = \frac{GM_E m}{r^2}$$

If the mass is now moved a very small distance Δr away from the Earth, we can reasonably assume that the force of attraction of the Earth on the mass remains constant, since the gravitational field strength will change very little over a small distance. Therefore the work done on the mass, which is equal in magnitude to the change in its potential energy, will be given by:

$$\Delta W = \Delta E_p = F \Delta r = \frac{GM_E m}{r^2} \Delta r$$

This is the area of the shaded strip shown in figure 5.2.5. To calculate the *total* change in potential energy in moving the mass from the surface of the Earth to infinity, we must calculate the area under the force–separation curve between the values on the x-axis of r and infinity. The width of the strips used to calculate the area will have an effect on the accuracy of the answer obtained – the narrower the strips, the greater the accuracy, as we saw in section 1.1, page 10.

Using integral calculus (see box 'Force, gravitational field strength and potential energy' on pages 392–4), we can obtain an expression that will enable us to make a precise calculation of the area under the graph. If we consider a mass m a distance r from the centre of a large mass M, the work done on the mass when it moves from r to infinity is given by:

$$W = \frac{GMm}{r}$$

This means that when m is moved from r to infinity, its potential energy increases by an amount GMm/r. Using the convention that the potential energy of the mass at infinity is zero, the potential energy of the mass at r must be $(0 - GMm/r)$, that is, $-GMm/r$. We can now write an expression for the potential energy E_p of a mass at a point r in a gravitational field around a mass m:

$$E_p = -\frac{GMm}{r}$$

Calculating gravitational potential energy – worked example

How much energy would need to be supplied to a person with a mass of 50 kg in order to remove the person completely from the Earth's gravitational field? $G = 6.67 \times 10^{-11}$ N m^2 kg^{-2}, $r_E = 6.4 \times 10^6$ m, $M_E = 6.0 \times 10^{24}$ kg.

To answer this question we need to find out the change in potential energy in going from the surface of the Earth to infinity, which we can do using the equation we have just seen. The energy required is equal to the change in the person's potential energy in going from a distance r_E from the centre of the Earth to infinity, which is given by:

$$E_p = -\frac{GM_E m}{r_E}$$

E_p is the potential energy of the person at the Earth's surface relative to infinity, so the energy that must be supplied in order to move them from r_E to infinity is:

$$E = \frac{GM_E m}{r_E}$$

$$= \frac{6.67 \times 10^{-11} \text{ N m}^2 \text{ kg}^{-2} \times 6.0 \times 10^{24} \text{ kg} \times 50 \text{ kg}}{6.4 \times 10^6 \text{ m}}$$

$$= 3.1 \times 10^9 \text{ J}$$

So just over 3000 MJ of energy would be required to take a 50 kg person from the Earth's surface to infinity.

Force, gravitational field strength and potential energy – vectors and sign conventions

So far in this section, we have used relationships to calculate the *magnitude* of quantities when masses are acted on in gravitational fields. Before going any further, we should look carefully at the relationships we have obtained, thinking a little more carefully about the *directions* and *signs* of the changes they represent.

Consider Newton's law of gravitation. This gives the force F acting on a mass m when it is a distance r from the centre of a mass M. Both force and displacement are vector quantities. We should therefore write the mathematical expression of Newton's law of gravitation as:

$$\boldsymbol{F}_{\mathbf{m}} = -\frac{GMm}{r^2} \boldsymbol{r}_{\mathbf{0}}$$

where $\boldsymbol{r}_{\mathbf{0}}$ is a vector of unit length (sometimes called a 'unit vector') in a direction radially outwards from the centre of M, as shown in figure 5.2.6. The minus sign indicates that $\boldsymbol{F}_{\mathbf{m}}$ and $\boldsymbol{r}_{\mathbf{0}}$ are in opposite directions, that is, that $\boldsymbol{F}_{\mathbf{m}}$ acts radially *inwards* towards the centre of M. This also applies to the expression for gravitational field strength, for which we may write:

$$\boldsymbol{g} = -\frac{GM}{r^2} \boldsymbol{r}_{\mathbf{0}}$$

Using the expression for $\boldsymbol{F}_{\mathbf{m}}$, we can now obtain an expression for the potential energy of the mass m a distance r from the mass M, considering the work done in moving the mass m from r to infinity as before, but this time making use of integral calculus.

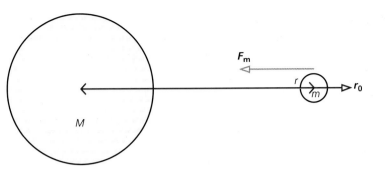

Figure 5.2.6 The force on mass m is written as $\boldsymbol{F_m}$ to make it clear that it is a vector quantity. $\boldsymbol{r_0}$ is a vector of unit length. The right-hand side of the equation is multiplied by $\boldsymbol{r_0}$ in order to give it direction.

First, consider the work done by us in moving a mass m through a small displacement $\Delta \boldsymbol{r}$ away from a mass M. In order to do this, we must exert a force $\boldsymbol{F_{us}}$ on the mass m. The work done by us is given by the expression:

$$W = \Delta E_p = \boldsymbol{F_{us}} . \Delta \boldsymbol{r}$$

where $\boldsymbol{F_{us}} . \Delta \boldsymbol{r}$ represents the **scalar product** of the two vectors $\boldsymbol{F_{us}}$ and $\Delta \boldsymbol{r}$. Figure 5.2.7 explains how we arrive at this scalar product.

When we calculate work done by multiplying force by displacement, we are multiplying two vector quantities to produce a scalar quantity. This process is known as calculating a **scalar product**. The scalar product is sometimes known as the **dot product**, from the way it is written.

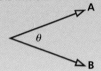

$$\boldsymbol{A}.\boldsymbol{B} = |\boldsymbol{A}| \times |\boldsymbol{B}| \times \cos\theta$$

where $|\boldsymbol{A}|$ is the magnitude of $\boldsymbol{A}$ (this is always positive).

Example 1 – Circular motion

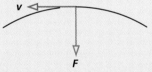

Centripetal force and instantaneous velocity are perpendicular to one another. The rate at which the centripetal force does work
= $\boldsymbol{F}.\boldsymbol{v}$, so:
$\boldsymbol{F}.\boldsymbol{v} = |\boldsymbol{F}| \times |\boldsymbol{v}| \times \cos 90°$
$= 0$ because $\cos 90° = 0$
The centripetal force therefore does no work.

Example 2 – Integration and the unit vector

Calculating the work done by a gravitational force involves an expression in which the dot product $\boldsymbol{r_0}.\boldsymbol{dr}$ appears. Since both $\boldsymbol{r_0}$ and $\boldsymbol{dr}$ both act in the same direction,
$\boldsymbol{r_0}.\boldsymbol{dr} = 1 \times dr \times \cos 0°$
$= dr$

Figure 5.2.7

The work W done by us in moving the mass m from r to infinity is:

$$W = \Delta E_p = E_p(\infty) - E_p(r)$$

$$= \int_r^\infty \boldsymbol{F_{us}} . \mathrm{d}\boldsymbol{r}$$

Now:

$$\boldsymbol{F_{us}} = -\boldsymbol{F_m}$$

$$= -\left(-\frac{GMm}{r^2}\boldsymbol{r_0}\right)$$

$$= \frac{GMm}{r^2}\boldsymbol{r_0}$$

So the work done by us in moving the mass from r to infinity is given by:

$$W = \int_r^\infty \frac{GMm}{r^2}\boldsymbol{r_0}.\boldsymbol{dr}$$

$$= \int_r^\infty \frac{GMm}{r^2}\,\mathrm{d}r$$

$$= \left[-\frac{GMm}{r}\right]_r^\infty$$

$$= -0 + \frac{GMm}{r}$$

$$= \frac{GMm}{r}$$

Now since $E_p(\infty) = 0$ by definition,

$$W = \frac{GMm}{r}$$

$$= 0 - E_p(r)$$

from which it follows that:

$$E_p(r) = -\frac{GMm}{r}$$

Note that $E_p(r)$ is actually the *mutual* potential energy of the masses M and m when their centres are a distance r apart, since when one mass moves the other moves as well and momentum is conserved (that is, the centre of mass stays in the same place). However, if $M \gg m$, its movement is small compared with that of m, and we can regard $E_p(r)$ as the potential energy of m at a distance r from the centre of M which remains approximately fixed in space. In this expression, the minus sign is concerned with the magnitude of E_p (since it is a scalar quantity, it cannot have direction), showing that E_p is always less than or equal to zero.

Because electric fields obey a law with a form very similar to Newton's law of gravitation, this method of calculating potential energy at a point can also be used for electric fields, replacing masses M and m with charges Q and q and replacing G with a constant appropriate to electric fields. We shall consider electric fields in section 5.3.

Gravitational potential

Gravitational potential and gravitational potential energy

In section 5.1 (page 377) the idea of field strength was introduced to give a measure of the force a field would exert on a given mass. The gravitational field strength at a point is expressed in terms of force per unit mass, and so it is independent of the mass placed in the field – in other words, it is a property of the field itself, not of the field and a particular mass.

As we have just seen, a mass in a gravitational field has gravitational potential energy, which may be calculated. It would be useful to have a property similar to field strength, that is, a property per unit mass, that would enable us to calculate the potential energy of a mass in a field. Such a property is **gravitational potential**. Gravitational potential at a point is the potential energy per unit mass of a mass placed at that point, and is given the symbol V.

Since the potential energy of a mass at a point is given by:

$$E_p = -\frac{GMm}{r}$$

it follows that V at that point will be given by:

$$V = -\frac{GM}{r}$$

which is simply E_p/m, that is, the gravitational potential energy of the mass divided by the mass. Note that because of the way it is defined, V follows the same conventions as E_p and is taken as zero at infinity. The SI units of gravitational potential are J kg^{-1}.

The gravitational potential at the Earth's surface

We can use the relationship we have just seen to calculate the potential at the Earth's surface:

$$V = -\frac{GM_E}{r_E}$$

Substituting:

$$V = \frac{-6.67 \times 10^{-11} \text{ N m}^2 \text{ kg}^{-2} \times 6.0 \times 10^{24} \text{ kg}}{6.4 \times 10^6 \text{ m}}$$

$$= -6.3 \times 10^7 \text{ J kg}^{-1}$$

This tells us that a 1 kg mass would require 63 MJ of energy to move it from the Earth's surface to infinity. This is consistent with the answer we obtained on page 392 for the energy required to move a 50 kg person the same distance.

Gravitational potential and field strength

Equipotentials join points with the same potential. Figure 5.2.8 shows the equipotentials a short distance above a small area of the surface of the Earth. The equipotentials represent the potential at 1 m intervals above the surface. The potential energy of a 1 kg mass increases by 9.8 J for every 1 m increase in height above the Earth just above its surface ($E_p = mg\Delta h$). This means that the equipotentials in figure 5.2.8 are spaced at 9.8 J kg^{-1} intervals, since potential is the potential energy per unit mass.

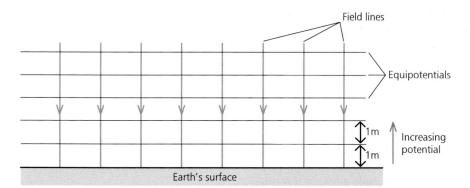

The rate of increase of potential with displacement perpendicular to the equipotential at a given point is called the **potential gradient** at that point. Potential gradient and field strength are related, as the space between the equipotentials in figure 5.2.8 implies – for the magnitude of the gravitational field strength we can write:

$$g = \frac{dV}{dr}$$

Since gravitational field strength is a vector quantity, the derivation of the relationship between g and potential gradient requires the use of vectors. The relationship is derived in the box below.

Gravitational field strength and potential gradient

If we apply a force F_{us} to a mass m to move it a small displacement Δr parallel to the potential gradient, the potential of the mass increases by an amount ΔV. The increase in potential energy for such a change in displacement is given by:

$$m\Delta V = \Delta E_p = F_{us}.\Delta r = -mg.\Delta r$$

The change in potential ΔV must be:

$$\Delta V = -mg.\Delta r/m$$
$$= -g.\Delta r$$

Now $\Delta r = \Delta r r_0$, where r_0 is a unit vector perpendicular to the equipotential in the direction of increasing potential. This means that the expression above may be written as:

$$\Delta V = -g.\Delta r r_0$$

We may write ΔV as:

$$\Delta V = \frac{\Delta V}{\Delta r} \Delta r \, r_0.r_0, \text{ since } \frac{\Delta V}{\Delta r} \Delta r = \Delta V, \text{ and } r_0.r_0 = 1$$

Comparing these two relationships involving ΔV, it follows that:

$$-g.\Delta r r_0 = \frac{\Delta V}{\Delta r} \Delta r \, r_0.r_0$$

and so the gravitational field strength is given by:

$$g = -\frac{\Delta V}{\Delta r} r_0$$

Remembering that we are dealing with vector quantities, the minus sign indicates that gravitational field strength is in the opposite direction to r_0. In the limit, as $\Delta r \to 0$ we can write

$$g = -\frac{dV}{dr}r_0$$

where $(dV/dr)r_0$ is the potential gradient. Hence:

Gravitational field strength = – potential gradient

Equipotentials and the gravitational field around the Earth

Figure 5.2.9 shows the field lines and equipotentials round the Earth, as calculated from $V = -GM/r$. Notice that the equipotentials and the field lines become further apart as the distance from the Earth's centre increases, indicating the decrease in gravitational field strength.

At the Earth's surface the gravitational potential is -63 MJ kg^{-1}. Since $V \propto 1/r$, this value increases to around -30 MJ kg^{-1} at a height above the Earth slightly more than one Earth radius, that is, at a height of about 7000 km.

The inset diagrams in figure 5.2.9 show the spacing between some of the equipotentials around the Earth. Either side of the equipotential passing through point A are two other equipotentials. The potential gradient between these is:

$$\frac{-39\,990 \text{ kJ kg}^{-1} - -40\,010 \text{ kJ kg}^{-1}}{5000 \text{ m}}$$

= 4.0 J m^{-1} kg^{-1} in a direction radially outwards

This means that the field strength at this point is 4.0 N kg^{-1} in a direction radially inwards.

Question 4 on page 407 involves calculating the field strength at point B.

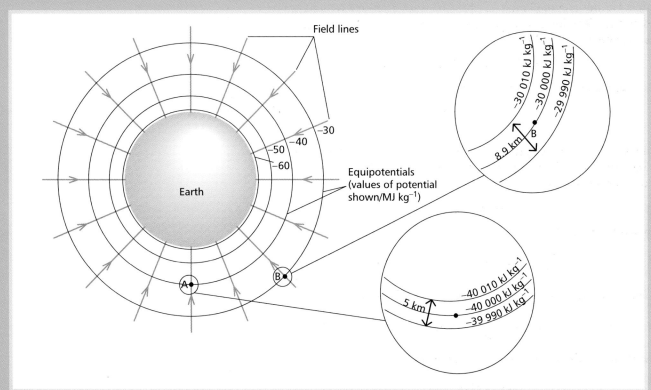

Figure 5.2.9

Potential surfaces

A stationary spaceship far from the Earth experiences an attractive force towards the Earth. As the spaceship begins to accelerate and falls towards the Earth, its potential energy decreases (that is, becomes more negative) and its kinetic energy increases, in exactly the same way as a ball rolling downhill or a stone dropped into a well.

Figure 5.2.11 shows this situation in one dimension, with the spaceship travelling along a straight line towards the centre of the Earth. The graph shows variation in potential along the line. This potential is referred to as a **potential well**, by analogy with the stone.

If we consider the potential around the Earth in two dimensions instead of one, we get a **potential surface** like that shown in figure 5.2.12. The study of potential surfaces is of great importance when considering the motion of objects through space, whether they be spacecraft or comets. The final part of this section looks at the physics of orbits.

Figure 5.2.10 Contour lines join points where the equipotential surfaces around the Earth intersect the surface of the Earth, so the points on a contour line are at a constant height. In this case the reference point against which all others are judged is mean sea level at Newlyn, Cornwall, where there is an Ordnance Survey Tidal Observatory (this is marked on the map). Heights above this level are taken as positive, those below it are negative.

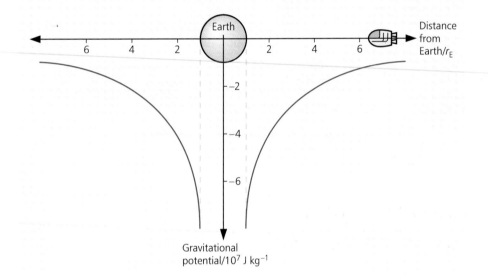

Figure 5.2.11 The gravitational potential well around the Earth.

Energy and trajectories

In the example above, it was assumed that the spaceship started with only a small amount of energy. Clearly this may not always be the case for objects entering the influence of a gravitational field (for example, comets and meteorites) – how does the initial energy of an object affect its path?

The energy of a mass in a gravitational field has two contributions – kinetic and potential, E_k and E_p. The path of a mass travelling into a potential well depends on the sum of these two contributions and their relative values, as figure 5.2.13 shows.

Figure 5.2.12 The gravitational potential at points on a plane surrounding a mass can be represented as a potential surface.

Figure 5.2.13 The path (or orbit) of a mass travelling into a potential well depends on the total energy of the mass.

$E_k + E_p < 0$		$E_k + E_p = 0$	$E_k + E_p > 0$
General case	**Special case if** $E_k = -\frac{1}{2}E_p$		
If the total energy of the mass is negative, its path is an ellipse. The total energy determines the size of the ellipse but not its shape – all the orbits here have the same total energy.	Where the kinetic energy of the mass is equal to half the magnitude of its potential energy, its path is circular (a circle is simply an ellipse with both axes equal in size).	A mass with zero total energy travels in an ellipse which reaches all the way to infinity – a parabola. (At infinity the mass comes to rest, because $E_p(\infty) = 0$.)	With positive total energy, the path of the mass again extends to infinity, this time as a hyperbola. (At infinity the mass will have a non-zero velocity, and will then continue to move in a straight line.)

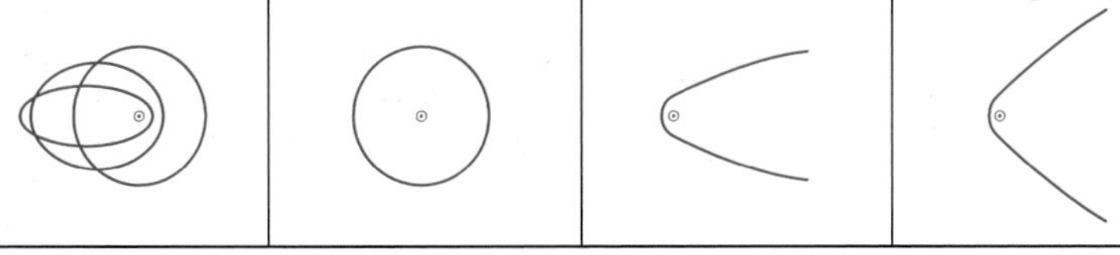

Travelling through gravitational fields

Escape velocity

The **escape velocity** from a point in a gravitational field is the minimum velocity a small mass must have in order to escape from the field and reach infinity. If a mass is given its exact escape velocity it will reach infinity with a velocity of zero.

Since the potential energy of a small mass a distance r from the centre of a large mass M is given by:

$$E_p = -\frac{GMm}{r}$$

E_p is the amount of energy the mass will require in order to just escape from the gravitational field. If the mass is projected with a speed v, it follows that it will escape if:

$$\tfrac{1}{2}mv^2 \geq \frac{GMm}{r}$$

that is,

$$v^2 \geq \frac{2GM}{r}$$

Thus the escape velocity v has magnitude given by:

$$v = \sqrt{\left(\frac{2GM}{r}\right)}$$

We already know that the magnitude of the gravitational field strength at a point is given by:

$$g = \frac{GM}{r^2}$$

so it follows that:

$$v = \sqrt{(2gr)}$$

Escape from planet Earth – worked example

What is the escape velocity from the surface of the Earth, given that at the surface $g \approx 10$ N kg^{-1} and $r_E \approx 6.4 \times 10^6$ m?

$$v = \sqrt{(2gr)}$$
$$= \sqrt{(2 \times 10 \text{ N kg}^{-1} \times 6.4 \times 10^6 \text{ m})}$$
$$= 1.1 \times 10^4 \text{ m s}^{-1}$$

So a mass would need to be projected with a velocity of around 11 km s^{-1} from the surface of the Earth in order to escape from the Earth's gravitational field. In practice, projection from the surface of the Earth in this way is unlikely to be used to send any spacecraft out into deep space. Why?

The motion of satellites

Any small mass which orbits a larger one is a **satellite**, although we are accustomed to thinking only of artificial masses orbiting the Earth when we talk about satellites. Just as the Moon is the Earth's satellite, so the Earth and the other planets are the Sun's satellites.

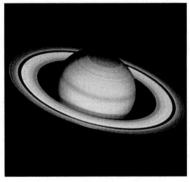

Figure 5.2.14 Anagrams were frequently used by seventeenth-century scientists to send messages announcing new discoveries to other scientists. Galileo is believed to have sent the message 'ALTISSIMUM PLANETUM TERGEMINUM OBSERVAI' to Kepler in 1610, scrambled as 'SMAISMRMILMEPOETALEUMIBUNENGTTAVIRAS'. It means 'I have observed the most distant planet to have a triple form', and concerned the discovery of Saturn's rings, made by Galileo using a telescope of his own design. The discovery that celestial bodies other than the Earth possessed satellites was powerful evidence for the Copernican model of the Universe (see section 1.6, page 85), and led eventually to the overthrow of the model of the Universe in which the Earth was at the centre.

If we consider the orbit of a satellite to be circular, we can analyse its motion quite easily using our knowledge of gravitation and of circular motion. Figure 5.2.15 shows a satellite of mass m in orbit around a mass M ($M \gg m$).

The centripetal force keeping the satellite moving in a circle is provided by the gravitational attraction of the mass M. These two forces are in equilibrium, so:

$$mr\omega^2 = \frac{GMm}{r^2}$$

that is,

$$\omega^2 = \frac{GM}{r^3}$$

For circular motion we know that the period of motion $T = 2\pi/\omega$, so $\omega = 2\pi/T$:

$$\frac{4\pi^2}{T^2} = \frac{GM}{r^3}$$

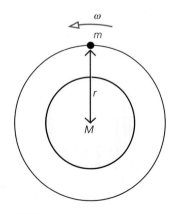

Figure 5.2.15

Rearranging this gives an expression for the period of the satellite's orbit:

$$T = \sqrt{\left(\frac{4\pi^2 r^3}{GM}\right)}$$

The motion of a satellite – worked example

Calculate the period of a satellite in orbit 500 km above the Earth.
$G = 6.67 \times 10^{-11}$ N m^2 kg^{-2}, $r_E = 6.4 \times 10^6$ m, $M_E = 6.0 \times 10^{24}$ kg.

$$T = \sqrt{\left(\frac{4\pi^2 r^3}{GM}\right)}$$

Substituting:

$$T = \sqrt{\left(\frac{4 \times \pi^2 \times (6.4 \times 10^6 \text{ m} + 5.0 \times 10^5 \text{ m})^3}{6.67 \times 10^{-11} \text{ N m}^2 \text{ kg}^{-2} \times 6.0 \times 10^{24} \text{ kg}}\right)}$$

$$= 5.69 \times 10^3 \text{ s}$$

So the satellite has a period of 95 minutes.

By positioning a satellite far enough from the Earth, it is possible to make the period of the satellite's orbit equal to the period of rotation of the Earth, that is, 24 hours. If the satellite is directly above the equator it then appears to be stationary to an observer on the surface of the Earth, and it is said to be in a **geosynchronous** orbit.

As above:

$$T = \sqrt{\left(\frac{4\pi^2 r^3}{GM}\right)}$$

so we can write:

$$(24 \times 3600) \text{ s} = \sqrt{\left(\frac{4\pi^2 r^3}{6.67 \times 10^{-11} \text{ N m}^2 \text{ kg}^{-2} \times 6.0 \times 10^{24} \text{ kg}}\right)}$$

which rearranges to:

$$r^3 = \frac{(24 \times 3600)^2 \text{ s}^2 \times 6.67 \times 10^{-11} \text{ N m}^2 \text{ kg}^{-2} \times 6.0 \times 10^{24} \text{ kg}}{4\pi^2}$$

$$= 7.57 \times 10^{22} \text{ m}^3$$

giving:

$$r = 4.2 \times 10^7 \text{ m}$$

This means that a satellite in geosynchronous orbit is some 42 000 km from the centre of the Earth, that is, about 35 000 km above its surface. Communications satellites are placed in geosynchronous orbits, making telecommunication between different continents possible.

5

DETECTING GRAVITY WAVES

In 1969, Professor Joseph Weber reported that he had detected large amounts of gravitational radiation from space. Weber had produced a detector consisting of a large aluminium alloy bar suspended from a wire in a vacuum chamber. **Gravity waves** (see pages 404–5) passing the bar would cause infinitesimal changes in its dimensions, which were measured using sensitive **strain gauges** (see page 302) fastened to the bar. The signals from these gauges were amplified by electronic circuits and the signal passed to recording equipment.

Weber's findings suggested that he had detected gravitational radiation at an intensity which was orders of magnitude greater than that predicted by established cosmological theories. Repeating his experiments a number of times using a series of ingenious modifications, Weber persuaded other physicists that it was worth constructing other gravity wave detectors to test his results. These results were by no means easy to obtain or interpret. Even though the detector is isolated by containing it inside a vacuum and by using an ingenious suspension mechanism, the signal recorded by the equipment still shows a level of **thermal noise** – spikes in the signal trace caused by the thermal energy of the various components in the equipment. To observe the effect of a gravity wave, a signal above the level of the noise has to be recorded, and a decision has to be made about the level at which a signal counts as a detected gravity wave rather than as noise. If the difference between signal level and noise level (the **signal:noise ratio**) is low, making this decision may not be straightforward.

By 1972 three other research groups had obtained results from their own gravity wave detectors that failed to confirm Weber's findings. Yet physicists involved in this work were reluctant to conclude that Weber had not detected gravity waves, and it was some time before the physics community accepted the idea that Weber's work was flawed. Why was this?

Imagine a piece of practical work carried out by a student to measure the velocity of sound. By checking a student's results with the known answer for the speed of sound, a teacher can check whether the student's work has been carried out effectively. But it is very different when the experimental work involves measuring something about which little is known, like gravity waves. Here the correct answer depends on whether gravity waves are passing the Earth. This can only be measured if we build an effective gravity wave detector and employ good experimental techniques when we use it to detect gravity waves. But we will only know that we have a good gravity wave detector that has been used well if we get the correct answer. And we will only know the correct answer when we have built an effective gravity wave detector … and so on.

This difficulty in resolving what has actually been observed is sometimes called *the experimenter's regress*. In this case, the experimenter's regress was finally broken when one group of physicists 'came off the fence' and stated clearly and unambiguously that they had not detected gravity waves with their detector and that they did not believe that Weber had detected them either. This led other physicists to support the idea that gravity waves had not been detected, and the physics community concluded that Weber had not in fact seen what he claimed to have seen.

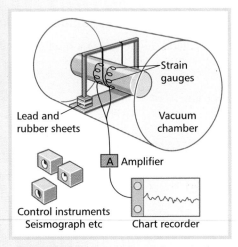

Figure 5.2.16 Weber's gravity wave detector at the University of Maryland, USA. The bar is suspended from a wire which in turn is fastened to a support mounted on lead and rubber sheets. This helps to isolate the bar from vibrations travelling through the ground. The whole setup is contained in an evacuated chamber.

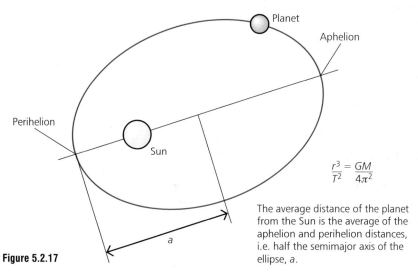

Perihelion

Aphelion

Planet

Sun

$$\frac{r^3}{T^2} = \frac{GM}{4\pi^2}$$

The average distance of the planet from the Sun is the average of the aphelion and perihelion distances, i.e. half the semimajor axis of the ellipse, a.

a

Figure 5.2.17

Planet	$a/10^{10}$ m	$T/10^6$ s	a^3/T^2/m^3 s^{-2}
Mercury	5.79	7.60	3.36×10^{18}
Venus	10.8	19.4	3.35×10^{18}
Earth	14.9	31.6	3.31×10^{18}
Mars	22.8	59.4	3.36×10^{18}
Jupiter	77.8	374	3.37×10^{18}

Table 5.2.1

The planets actually move in elliptical orbits around the Sun. Kepler was able to show from Brahe's data on planetary movements (see section 5.1, page 379) that the squares of the periods of the planets are proportional to the cubes of their average distances from the Sun measured along the major axis of the ellipse of their orbits. This is illustrated in figure 5.2.17 and table 5.2.1. This relationship is known as Kepler's third law of planetary motion. The law is consistent with an inverse square law for gravitational attraction, as the relationship derived above shows. Table 5.2.1 gives a test of Kepler's third law using current data for the first five planets.

Figure 5.2.18 The astronaut, the sandwich and the orbiting spacecraft are in free fall towards the Earth. The universality of the rate of free fall (see section 5.1, page 386) means that all fall at the same rate, so the astronaut and the sandwich appear to be weightless.

A strange observation

Most people are familiar with the fact that an object entering the Earth's atmosphere at high speed experiences friction from the atmosphere which causes the object to get very hot. This friction with the upper atmosphere causes a satellite in a low orbit to decay, so that the satellite loses energy and the radius of its orbit decreases. Less familiar is the fact that this reduction in total energy of the satellite is accompanied by an increase in its kinetic energy.

Why should this be? It may be understood by looking at the way the energy of a satellite is split between potential energy (E_p) and kinetic energy (E_k). The total energy of the satellite (E) is the sum of the potential and kinetic energies:

$$E = E_\text{p} + E_\text{k}$$

$$= \frac{-GMm}{r} + \tfrac{1}{2}mv^2$$

We know from page 400 that:

$$mr\omega^2 = \frac{mv^2}{r} = \frac{GMm}{r^2}$$

so:

$$\tfrac{1}{2}mv^2 = \frac{GMm}{2r}$$

which means that:

$$E = \frac{-GMm}{r} + \frac{GMm}{2r} = -\frac{GMm}{2r} = -\tfrac{1}{2}mv^2$$

Figure 5.2.19 shows E, E_p and E_k plotted on a graph. It can be seen that E_p decreases at twice the rate that E_k increases – so as the radius of the orbit decreases, the total energy decreases, although the satellite's kinetic energy increases, making it speed up.

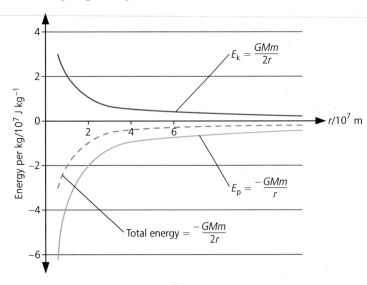

Figure 5.2.19 As the orbit of a satellite decays, its kinetic energy increases.

The picture of gravity

The picture of gravitation that we have just seen is essentially one that Newton himself would recognise – it is based entirely on classical physics. Newton's theory is astoundingly successful (NASA engineers use Newton's theories when they send spacecraft into orbit, for example), yet by the end of the nineteenth century scientists were concerned that it could not explain discrepancies in the orbit of Mercury that had been known about since the time of Newton.

Sitting in the Patent Office at Berne in 1907, Albert Einstein thought deeply about the problems associated with Newton's description of gravitation. His ideas led him eventually to formulate a theory of gravitation which described the behaviour of matter solely in terms of space and time. This theory solves the difficulty with the orbit of Mercury, and predicts the existence of **gravity waves**.

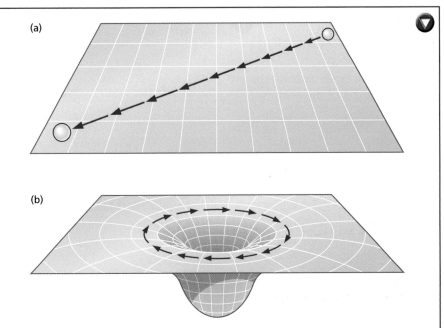

(a)

(b)

Figure 5.2.20 Imagine space as represented by a two-dimensional rubber sheet. (a) If a ping pong ball is rolled across the sheet, it travels in a straight line. (b) Now imagine that a large mass (like a snooker ball) is placed on the sheet, distorting it. This model simulates the way in which general relativity describes how a large mass distorts space around it. An object travelling close to the mass can be captured by it and travels in a closed path around it, doing so purely by virtue of the curvature of space.

General relativity predicts that when large masses accelerate, ripples in the fabric of space spread out like waves across the surface of a pond when a stone is thrown in. In principle the gravitational radiation, or gravity waves, can be detected as they tug to and fro on masses they pass as they travel outwards from their origin. However, the interaction of these gravity waves with mass is very weak, and detecting them is far from easy (see page 402).

SUMMARY

- In a uniform gravitational field, the change in potential energy ΔE_p of a mass m with change in height Δh is given by $\Delta E_p = mg\Delta h$.

- The gravitational potential energy E_p of a mass m a distance r from a mass M is given by $E_p = -GMm/r$. By convention, the gravitational potential energy of a mass is taken as zero at infinite distance from all other masses.

- **Gravitational potential** V at a point in a gravitational field is the gravitational potential energy per unit mass at that point.

- The **gravitational potential** V at a distance r from a mass M is given by $V = -GM/r$.

- The **potential gradient** at a point in a field is the rate of change of potential with displacement. The potential gradient is always in the direction of increasing potential.

- Gravitational field strength = –potential gradient. (Remember that both are vectors – the negative sign shows that gravitational field strength and potential gradient are in opposite directions.)

- The **escape velocity** v from a point in a gravitational field at distance r from the centre of the large mass M is the minimum velocity a small mass m must have to reach infinity, $v = \sqrt{(2GM/r)} = \sqrt{(2gr)}$.
- For a satellite in orbit a distance r from the centre of a large mass M, the angular velocity ω is given by $\omega^2 = GM/r^3$. The period T of the orbit is $T = \sqrt{(4\pi^2 r^3/GM)}$.

EXAMPLE

A planet has half the density of the Earth, but twice the radius. What is
a *the magnitude of the gravitational field strength at its surface, and*
b *the speed of a satellite skimming the surface of the planet (which has no atmosphere)?*

(Take $R_E = 6400$ km, and $g_E = 9.8$ N kg^{-1}.)

a For the Earth, we can write:

$$g_E = \frac{GM_E}{R_E^2} \qquad \text{(equation 1)}$$

and:

$$M_E = \tfrac{4}{3}\pi R_E^3 \rho_E \qquad \text{(equation 2)}$$

For the planet, we can write:

$$g_P = \frac{GM_P}{R_P^2} \qquad \text{(equation 3)}$$

and:

$$M_P = \tfrac{4}{3}\pi R_P^3 \rho_P \qquad \text{(equation 4)}$$

We know that $R_P = 2R_E$, and that $\rho_P = \rho_E/2$, where ρ_P and ρ_E are the densities of the planet and the Earth respectively.

Substituting for R_P and ρ_P in equation 4 we get:

$$M_P = \tfrac{4}{3}\pi(2R_E)^3 \rho_E/2$$
$$= 4 \times (\tfrac{4}{3}\pi R_E^3 \rho_E)$$
$$= 4M_E$$

Substituting for M_P and R_P, equation 3 becomes:

$$g_P = \frac{G(4M_E)}{(2R_E^2)}$$
$$= \frac{GM_E}{R_E^2}$$
$$= g_E$$

The gravitational field strength at the surface of the planet is the same as that at the surface of the Earth.

b For a satellite orbiting a planet, the centripetal force is provided by the pull of the planet on the satellite. If the mass of the satellite is m, then:

$$\frac{mv^2}{R_P} = mg_P$$

so:

$$v^2 = g_P R_P$$

Substituting for g_P and R_P, we get:

$$v^2 = 9.81 \text{ N kg}^{-1} \times (2 \times 6.4 \times 10^6 \text{ m})$$
$$= 1.256 \times 10^8 \text{ m}^2 \text{ s}^{-2}$$

This gives the speed of the satellite as $\sqrt{(1.256 \times 10^8 \text{ m}^2 \text{ s}^{-2})} = 1.12 \times 10^4$ m s^{-1}.

QUESTIONS

(Take $G = 6.67 \times 10^{-11}$ N m^2 kg^{-2}, $M_E = 6.0 \times 10^{24}$ kg, $r_E = 6.4 \times 10^6$ m)

1 In a popular physics demonstration, lead shot is allowed to fall the length h of a vertical cardboard tube stoppered at both ends. Once the shot has fallen, the tube is then inverted and the shot is allowed to fall again. This process is repeated perhaps 50 times. At the end of the demonstration, the temperature of the lead shot is measured, when it is found to have increased.

   a Write down an expression for the gravitational potential energy of a mass m of lead shot a distance h above the surface of the Earth.

   b Write down an expression for the temperature rise $\Delta\theta$ of the same mass of lead shot when energy ΔE is transferred to it.

   c Using your answers to **a** and **b**, obtain an expression which relates $\Delta\theta$ to h.

   d If the specific heat capacity of lead is 128 J kg^{-1} K^{-1}, what is the minimum number of times a 1 m-long tube must be inverted if the lead in it is to increase in temperature by 10 K?

2 The writer Jules Verne suggested that it would be possible to send a craft to the Moon by firing it from the barrel of a giant gun. Use your answer to question 7 on page 387 to calculate:
   a the velocity with which such a craft would need to be launched in order to reach the Moon (*Hint:* With what velocity should this craft reach the point at which the gravitational fields of the Earth and Moon exactly balance?)
   b the length of the muzzle of the gun necessary for the launch, if its acceleration were to be limited to 5g.
   Does the scheme seem practical?

3 Given the mass of the Moon as 7.4×10^{22} kg and its radius as 1738 km, calculate the escape velocity from the Moon's surface.

4 Consider the equipotentials either side of point B in figure 5.2.9.
   a Calculate the change in potential between these two equipotentials.
   b Hence calculate the potential gradient at B, including its direction.
   c What is the gravitational field strength at B?

5 A ballistic missile is a missile that is propelled upwards by its motors for a distance, and then coasts up to a maximum height before returning to its target on the Earth's surface. One such missile is propelled to a vertical height of 100 km when its motors stop. At this point it is travelling vertically upwards at 5.0 km s^{-1}.
   a What will be the maximum height of this rocket above the Earth's surface?
   b What will be its speed of impact on its target?
   Neglect air resistance in both cases.

6 In 1961 the Russian Yuri Gagarin was carried into space by *Voskhod 1*. This craft of mass 4.7×10^3 kg orbited the Earth once, reaching a maximum height of 327 km. Taking the radius of the Earth as 6400 km and assuming that *Voskhod 1*'s orbit at its maximum distance from the Earth can be treated as circular, calculate:
   a the speed and
   b the orbital energy
      of *Voskhod 1* at its maximum height above the Earth.

7 According to a newspaper report, a communications satellite was placed in orbit as shown in figure 5.2.21. What is wrong with this diagram?

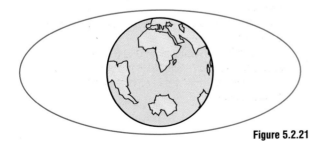

Figure 5.2.21

8 The potential well around the Earth can be modelled using a large funnel and a marble. Look directly downwards onto the top of the funnel. If a marble is held at the top of the funnel and released, it runs directly down into the funnel, behaving in a similar way to an object travelling radially towards the Earth.
   a What path does the marble follow if it is given a small impulse at an angle to the centre of the funnel (figure 5.2.22)?
   b After being given the initial impulse, the marble had a total energy E given by:

$$E = E_p + E_k$$

   i   When the marble is travelling round the funnel, what can you say about E_p if E_p at the lip is taken as zero?
   ii If friction is neglected, what can you say about E during the marble's motion?
   iii How does this explain the behaviour of the marble during its motion?
   c The marble can be made to move in a circle around the funnel. Over a period of time, the radius of this circle decreases, and the marble appears to spiral in to the centre of the funnel. What would make a satellite behave like this?

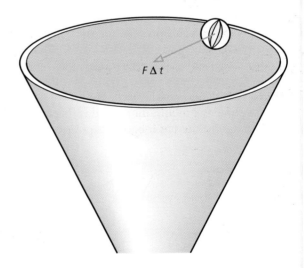

$F \Delta t$

Figure 5.2.22

Having looked in some detail at gravitational fields, this section examines another type of field which we have already met in the context of the flow of electric current through a circuit. Electric fields have similarities with gravitational fields, although there are differences too – not least of which is the great strength of the electric force compared with that of the gravitational force.

Charges and forces

Static charge

We have seen in section 4.1 that the Ancient Greeks knew that a piece of amber would attract small pieces of straw or hair when rubbed, and we have described the contribution of scientists such as Benjamin Franklin to our modern understanding of charge. The study of static electricity is called **electrostatics**.

Using current ideas of physics, charging by friction is understood by thinking of the process of charging with reference to the structure of atoms. Generally speaking, atoms are electrically neutral – that is to say, they contain equal numbers of positive charges (on the protons in the nucleus) and negative charges (on the electrons around the nucleus). When, say, a glass rod is rubbed by a piece of silk, the glass becomes positively charged while the silk becomes negatively charged. In this process, the silk 'rips off' some of the electrons from the surface of the glass, although how this happens is very poorly understood. It seems that other factors also play a part in the process of charging by friction, since if glass is rubbed with an absolutely clean piece of silk, the glass becomes negatively charged. Even air may have an effect, since experiments show that platinum rubbed with silk in a vacuum becomes negatively charged, whereas it becomes positively charged in air.

Figure 5.3.1 Once an object (in this case a glass rod) has been charged by friction, it may be used to charge other bodies by induction.

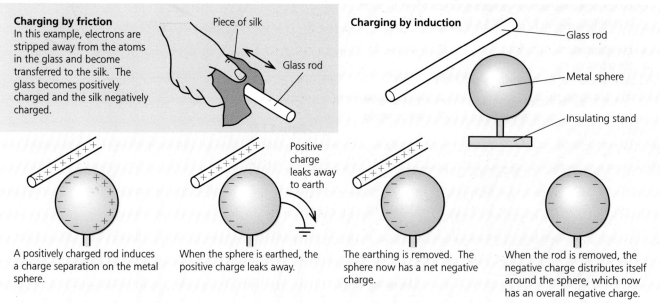

Charging by friction
In this example, electrons are stripped away from the atoms in the glass and become transferred to the silk. The glass becomes positively charged and the silk negatively charged.

Piece of silk

Glass rod

Charging by induction

Glass rod

Metal sphere

Insulating stand

Positive charge leaks away to earth

A positively charged rod induces a charge separation on the metal sphere.

When the sphere is earthed, the positive charge leaks away.

The earthing is removed. The sphere now has a net negative charge.

When the rod is removed, the negative charge distributes itself around the sphere, which now has an overall negative charge.

Having charged a body by friction, the charged body may then be used to charge other bodies by **induction**. Figure 5.3.1 shows this process. Several points are worth noting.

1 The removal of positive charge from the far side of the sphere is usually referred to in terms of the positive charge flowing or leaking away. An alternative way of thinking of this is as the positive charge being neutralised by negative charge (electrons) flowing *onto* that side of the sphere. As with representing current in current electricity, these are simply two alternative ways of explaining the same phenomenon.

2 The metal sphere in figure 5.3.1 is on an insulating stand. Because the sphere is metal, it is quite reasonable to think of the charge flowing freely over it, since we know that metals are good conductors. Measurements with a high-resistance voltmeter and a coulombmeter (simply a capacitor with a high-resistance voltmeter connected across it) in this type of experiment show that the sphere may be charged to a potential of 1000 V, and have around 10^{-9} C of charge on it. If the stand has a resistance of 10^9 Ω, then the initial current through it will be given by Ohm's law:

$$I_{\text{initial}} = V/R$$
$$= 10^3 \text{ V} / 10^9 \text{ }\Omega$$
$$= 10^{-6} \text{ A } \text{ or } \text{ } 1 \text{ } \mu\text{A}$$

This is a tiny current – but the charge on the sphere is tiny too. If all the charge were to leak away at this rate, the sphere would be discharged in time t:

$$I = Q/t$$

so:

$$t = Q/I$$
$$= 10^{-9} \text{ C} / 10^{-6} \text{ A}$$
$$= 10^{-3} \text{ s}$$

Now even though the sphere will not continue to discharge at this initial rate, it will discharge in the same order of magnitude as this, that is, very quickly indeed! For this reason, insulators used in electrostatics experiments must have very high resistivities – plastic and glass are usually suitable.

3 In any investigation of this sort, the total amount of electric charge is found to be constant. Thus, if a piece of silk is used to rub a glass rod so that they both become charged, the magnitude of the charge on the silk is found to be the same as that on the rod. This is referred to as **conservation of charge**.

Conservation of charge and quantisation

Experiments like that described in the text give good evidence for the conservation of charge, and far more accurate work also confirms it. There is a myriad of subatomic charged particles known to physics, and many more ways in which these particles may interact. However, in all such interactions the total amount of charge remains constant, even when particles are destroyed.

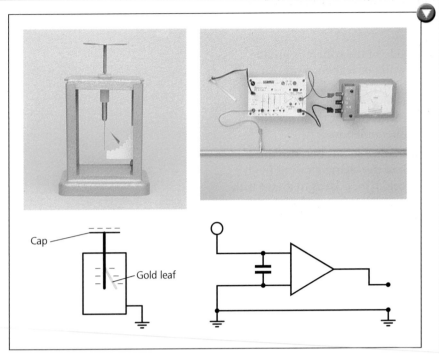

Figure 5.3.2 The measurement of large potential differences and small charge differences is not easy. The **gold-leaf electroscope** may be used as a very high-resistance voltmeter, the deflection of the leaf being proportional to the potential difference between the cap and the case of the instrument. It may also be used to measure charge, since it is effectively a capacitor whose charge may be determined by measuring the p.d. across it. The operational amplifier, with an input resistance of maybe $10^{12}\ \Omega$, provides the basis of a more convenient instrument for the measurement of charge. Such an instrument is called an **electrometer**. The object whose charge is to be measured is connected to a capacitor of known capacitance connected across the input terminals of the operational amplifier, one of which is earthed. The known capacitance is arranged to be much larger than that of the object, so that effectively all the charge flows from the object onto the capacitor. Measurement of the p.d. across the capacitor then enables the charge on it to be found (since the input resistance of the operational amplifier is so high, there is ample time to make this measurement even though the amount of charge involved is so small, often as little as 10^{-9} C).

All known subatomic particles have charges that are an integer multiple of the charge on the electron e, so that the charges found are always 0, $\pm e$, $\pm 2e$, $\pm 3e$, etc. – no fractional charges have ever been found. This is despite extensive searches for charges of $\frac{1}{3}e$ and $\frac{2}{3}e$, the charges of the **quarks**, which physicists believe may be the elementary particles that form the constituents of protons and neutrons. The fact that charge exists in discrete packets is described as the **quantisation** of charge. We have already mentioned the quantisation of energy in section 2.4, and shall return to the subject again in section 6.

Coulomb's law

By the mid-eighteenth century, Franklin and other scientists had established that there are two sorts of charges, and that opposite charges attract while like charges repel. This work, and that of the English scientist Joseph Priestley, was developed by the French military engineer turned physicist Charles Augustin de Coulomb, who investigated in detail the force between charged particles. Coulomb used a torsion balance of his own design, shown in figure 5.3.3, and was able to obtain precise measurements showing the inverse square relationship for charges.

Coulomb's work showed that the magnitude of the force acting on a charge

q_2 a distance r from q_1 (the small balls used in his experiment can be effectively regarded as point charges) follows the expression:

$$F = \frac{kq_1q_2}{r^2}$$

The constant k is usually written as $1/4\pi\varepsilon_0$, where ε_0 is the permittivity of free space, 8.854×10^{-12} F m^{-1}. (This constant was introduced in section 4.3 when considering the space between the plates of a capacitor – we shall return to the reasons why $k = 1/4\pi\varepsilon_0$ very shortly, on pages 420–1.) Thus:

$$F = \frac{1}{4\pi\varepsilon_0}\frac{q_1q_2}{r^2}$$

Notice how similar Coulomb's law is to Newton's law of gravitation (page 379) – we shall use this fact in obtaining expressions for electric potential energy and electric potential.

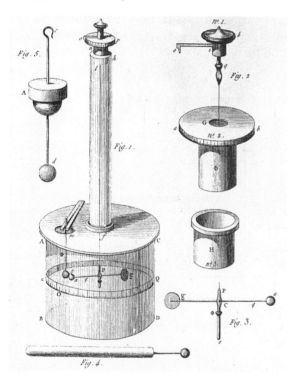

Figure 5.3.3 Coulomb's apparatus. A small charged ball a is fixed to a horizontal beam q suspended from a vertical fibre f. On the other end of the beam is an uncharged counterweight g. A second charged ball t is brought up to a, when the electrostatic force rotates the fibre. The force between the balls can be calculated from the angle through which the fibre twists and the torsional constant of the fibre.

The direction of the electric force

The direction of the electric force is described by the use of a unit vector $\boldsymbol{r_0}$, as in the case of the gravitational force. In this case $\boldsymbol{r_0}$ is parallel to a line passing through the centres of q_1 and q_2, and in the direction from q_1 to q_2 (see figure 5.3.4).

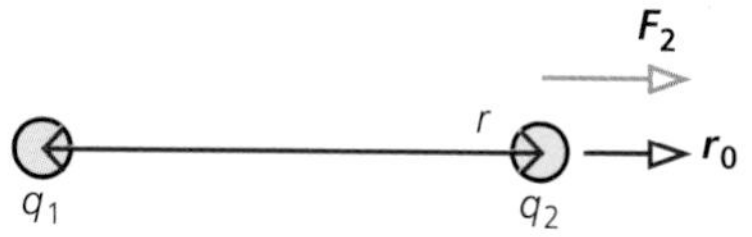

Figure 5.3.4 Two charged particles q_1 and q_2 a distance r apart. The unit vector $\boldsymbol{r_0}$ is directed parallel to the line joining q_1 and q_2.

Charge q_1 exerts a force F_2 on charge q_2. We may then write Coulomb's law as:

$$\boldsymbol{F_2} = \frac{1}{4\pi\varepsilon_0}\frac{q_1q_2}{r^2}\boldsymbol{r_0}$$

This expression gives us both the magnitude and the direction of $\boldsymbol{F_2}$. If q_1 and q_2 are of similar sign, the product q_1q_2 will be positive and $\boldsymbol{F_2}$ acts in the same direction as $\boldsymbol{r_0}$ (repulsive). If q_1 and q_2 are of opposite sign, the product q_1q_2 will be negative, and $\boldsymbol{F_2}$ is the opposite direction to $\boldsymbol{r_0}$ (attractive).

Experimental verification of Coulomb's law

Coulomb's law may be verified experimentally using reasonably simple apparatus. Measurements must be taken quickly, in order to avoid the problem of charge leaking away (see page 409). Figure 5.3.5 shows the details of the investigation.

From the free body diagram it can be seen that when the ball is in equilibrium:

$$F = T \sin \theta$$

and:

$$W = T \cos \theta$$

Dividing the first equation by the second we get:

$$\frac{F}{W} = \frac{T \sin \theta}{T \cos \theta} = \tan \theta$$

so:

$$F = W \tan \theta$$

Now $\tan \theta \approx x/l$ if θ is small, so:

$$F = \frac{Wx}{l}$$

Thus for small deflections, the horizontal deflection of the ball from its equilibrium position (from its position when no other charged body is present) is directly proportional to the electrostatic force F. Confirmation of Coulomb's law is obtained from graphs like those shown in the figure.

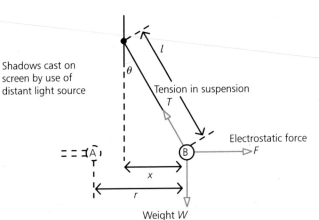

Free body diagram for suspended ball

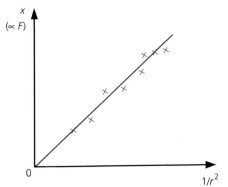

EHT supply

Light insulating filament

Shadows cast on screen by use of distant light source

Insulating rod

Graph paper

Sphere A is charged to constant potential from EHT supply. Sphere B is charged by touching it with a flying lead from EHT supply to differing potentials V_B, giving different charges on it. Since $Q_B = CV_B$, the charge on B is proportional to its potential.

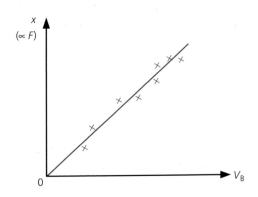

Graphs showing how results from the investigation may be plotted to verify Coulomb's law

Figure 5.3.5 Apparatus to verify Coulomb's law. Very fine nylon thread may be used to suspend the ball. The balls are usually made of expanded polystyrene painted with aluminium paint to give them a conducting layer. Glass is suitable for the insulating rod.

Comparing the magnitudes of electrostatic and gravitational forces – worked example

Calculations suggest that there are around 10^{29} electrons and the same number of protons in the body of a 70 kg person. Taking the charge on an electron as -1.6×10^{-19} C, calculate the magnitude of the electrostatic force F_e between the electrons in one 70 kg person and the protons in another 70 kg person standing 2 m away. Compare this with the size of the gravitational force F_g between the two people.

Total charge on electrons in first person =
$$10^{29} \times -1.6 \times 10^{-19} \text{ C} = -1.6 \times 10^{10} \text{ C}$$
Total charge on protons in second person =
$$10^{29} \times +1.6 \times 10^{-19} \text{ C} = +1.6 \times 10^{10} \text{ C}$$

So the magnitude of the electrostatic attractive force F_e on each person is:

$$F_e = \frac{1}{4\pi\varepsilon_0} \frac{q_1 q_2}{r^2}$$

$$= \frac{1}{4\pi \times 8.854 \times 10^{-12} \text{ F m}^{-1}} \frac{(1.6 \times 10^{10} \text{ C}) \times (1.6 \times 10^{10} \text{ C})}{(2 \text{ m})^2}$$

$$= 5.75 \times 10^{29} \text{ N}$$

By comparison, the magnitude of the gravitational attractive force F_g on each person is:

$$F_g = \frac{Gm_1 m_2}{r^2}$$

$$= \frac{6.67 \times 10^{-11} \text{ N m}^2 \text{ kg}^{-2} \times 70 \text{ kg} \times 70 \text{ kg}}{(2 \text{ m})^2}$$

$$= 8.2 \times 10^{-8} \text{ N}$$

The electrostatic force is nearly 10^{37} times bigger than the gravitational force, although of course the attractive electrostatic force between the electrons and protons is cancelled exactly by the repulsive force between the two sets of protons (or the two sets of electrons).

The electric field

Electric field strength

The **electric field** is a model physicists use to explain the effect one charge has on another charge some distance away. An electric field is a region in which an electric charge experiences a force. As with gravitational fields, we may define electric field strength E at a point in the electric field in terms of the force per unit positive charge at that point:

$$E = \frac{F}{q}$$

Since there are two sorts of charge, it is important to specify which sort q is – by convention it is taken as *positive* charge. The direction of an electric field is therefore that of the force on a small positive charge placed in the field.

From Coulomb's law it follows that the force on a small positive charge $+q$ in a field due to a single larger positive charge $+Q$ is given by:

$$F = \frac{1}{4\pi\varepsilon_0} \frac{Qq}{r^2}$$ in a direction radially outwards from the centre of $+Q$

so the field strength of the electric field around the charge $+Q$ at this point is:

$$E = \frac{F}{q} = \frac{1}{4\pi\varepsilon_0} \frac{Q}{r^2}$$ radially outwards from the centre of $+Q$

The principle of field strength

Taking Coulomb's law using the unit vector notation introduced on pages 392–4, we can write:

$$F = \frac{1}{4\pi\varepsilon_0} \frac{Qq}{r^2} \, r_0$$

Therefore the electric field strength around $+Q$ is:

$$E = \frac{F}{q} = \frac{1}{4\pi\varepsilon_0} \frac{Q}{r^2} \, r_0 \quad \text{(i.e. radially outwards)}$$

If we wish to measure the strength of an electric field, the test charge we use must be very small so that it does not affect the field at the point of measurement, hence the field strength is defined in terms of force *per* unit charge rather than the force *on* unit charge. The expression for field strength should properly be written as:

$$E = \lim_{q \to 0} \frac{F}{q}$$

Just like gravitational field strength, electric field strength varies according to an inverse square law, and the field is radial, as figure 5.3.6 shows.

In practice, the measurement of the force per unit charge is difficult to perform. Conveniently, as electric field strength varies according to an inverse square law in the same way as gravitational field strength, we can measure it by measuring the potential gradient, so that the magnitude of the electric field strength is given by:

$$E = \frac{dV}{dr}$$

We shall see the theoretical justification for this very shortly, and its practical application later in this section.

Electric potential energy and electric potential

Just as we considered the potential energy of a mass at a point in a gravitational field, so we may consider the potential energy of a charge at a point in an electric field. We shall use the same convention for a zero of energy as for the gravitational field (the potential energy of a small charge an infinite distance away from a large charge will be taken as zero). We must also bear in mind that we have to deal with two sorts of charge – we shall begin by considering only positive charge and then generalise the situation.

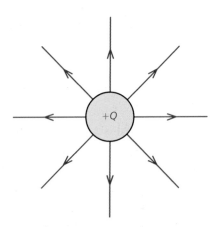

Figure 5.3.6 The field around a positive charge $+Q$. Note that the field around a negative charge of the same magnitude would be identical except that its direction would be reversed.

The potential energy of a charge at a point in an electric field is defined as the work done on the charge in order to move it to that point from infinity. This is the same as the definition of gravitational potential energy given in section 5.2 (see box, pages 392–4). However, whereas the work done in moving a mass to a point in a gravitational field from infinity is always negative (because the gravitational force is always attractive), the work done in moving a charge to a point in an electric field may be positive or negative because the electrostatic force may be attractive or repulsive.

Because both Coulomb's law and Newton's law of gravitation have the same form, the expressions for potential energy and electric potential at a point in an electric field must be similar to the expressions for these quantities in a gravitational field. So if we consider the work done in moving a small positive charge q from infinity to a distance r from a large positive charge Q, the expression for the potential energy of q must be:

$$E_p = \frac{1}{4\pi\varepsilon_0} \frac{Qq}{r}$$

And since electric potential is the potential energy per unit charge, the expression for this must be:

$$V = \frac{1}{4\pi\varepsilon_0} \frac{Q}{r}$$

Note that both these expressions are positive, since in this case we are dealing with a repulsive force. Both these expressions can be derived from Coulomb's law in the same way that the expressions for gravitational potential energy and gravitational potential were derived from Newton's law of gravitation in section 5.2.

Field strength and potential gradient

We noted above that the similarity between electric and gravitational fields leads us to suppose that electric field strength is related to the potential gradient. By analogy with the gravitational field, we may then write:

$$\mathbf{F} = -\frac{\mathrm{d}V}{\mathrm{d}r}\mathbf{r_0}$$

where $\mathbf{r_0}$ is once again a unit vector directed radially outwards. This means that we can write:

Electric field strength = – potential gradient

Figure 5.3.7 summarises the relationship between field and potential gradient for gravitational and electric fields.

The SI units of potential gradient are V m^{-1}. Now 1 V = 1 J C^{-1} and 1 J = 1 N m, so V m^{-1} may also be written as (N m C^{-1}) m^{-1} = N C^{-1}. The units of field strength may therefore be either N C^{-1} (that is, the force per unit charge) or V m^{-1} (that is, the potential gradient) – these units are entirely equivalent.

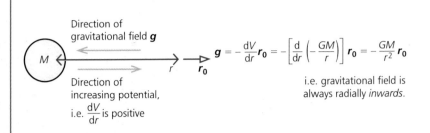

Direction of gravitational field **g**

Direction of increasing potential, i.e. $\dfrac{dV}{dr}$ is positive

$$\mathbf{g} = -\frac{dV}{dr}\mathbf{r_0} = -\left[\frac{d}{dr}\left(-\frac{GM}{r}\right)\right]\mathbf{r_0} = -\frac{GM}{r^2}\mathbf{r_0}$$

i.e. gravitational field is always radially *inwards*.

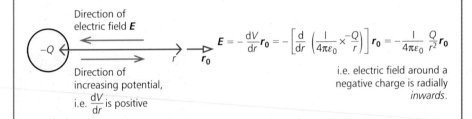

Direction of electric field **E**

Direction of increasing potential, i.e. $\dfrac{dV}{dr}$ is positive

$$\mathbf{E} = -\frac{dV}{dr}\mathbf{r_0} = -\left[\frac{d}{dr}\left(\frac{1}{4\pi\varepsilon_0}\times\frac{-Q}{r}\right)\right]\mathbf{r_0} = -\frac{1}{4\pi\varepsilon_0}\frac{Q}{r^2}\mathbf{r_0}$$

i.e. electric field around a negative charge is radially *inwards*.

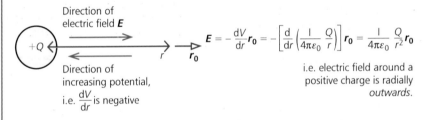

Direction of electric field **E**

Direction of increasing potential, i.e. $\dfrac{dV}{dr}$ is negative

$$\mathbf{E} = -\frac{dV}{dr}\mathbf{r_0} = -\left[\frac{d}{dr}\left(\frac{1}{4\pi\varepsilon_0}\frac{Q}{r}\right)\right]\mathbf{r_0} = \frac{1}{4\pi\varepsilon_0}\frac{Q}{r^2}\mathbf{r_0}$$

i.e. electric field around a positive charge is radially *outwards*.

Figure 5.3.7 The laws governing the behaviour of gravitational and electric fields are very similar, although there are important differences as there is only one type of mass but two types of charge.

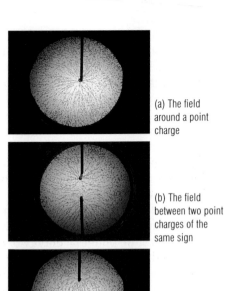

(a) The field around a point charge

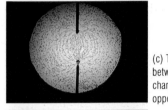

(b) The field between two point charges of the same sign

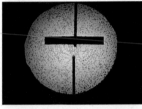

(c) The field between two point charges of opposite sign

(d) The field between a point charge and an earthed plate

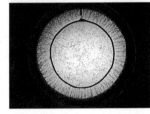

(e) The field between two oppositely charged plates – note how uniform it is, except at the edges.

(f) The field around a circular electrode. The random arrangement of the semolina grains inside the ring shows that the electric field is zero here, in much the same way as the gravitational field is zero inside a hollow sphere. In this way, a charged sphere can be treated as a point charge at its centre.

Figure 5.3.8 Electric fields in different situations. These fields were made visible by producing a field on the surface of castor oil and then sprinkling semolina grains on the surface of the oil, rather like using iron filings to see magnetic field lines. The semolina grains have a dipole induced on them and line up along the field lines.

Investigating electric fields

Field lines in an electric field show the direction in which a positive charge experiences a force in the field. Figure 5.3.8 shows the field lines around some charged objects.

Equipotentials can be drawn for electric fields in the same way as for gravitational fields. Equipotentials run perpendicular to field lines, and we can imagine that if we moved some sort of contact connected to one terminal of a voltmeter along an equipotential, the voltmeter would show a constant reading. The box 'Measuring equipotentials and field strength' shows how this may be done.

LIGHTNING STRIKES

Lightning is produced as a result of an intense electric field within a thunder cloud, brought about as raindrops within the cloud travel up and down through the cloud in the intense air currents inside it. Although the exact way in which this happens is not fully understood, physicists think that as the drops are buffeted during their journey they become charged, the negatively charged drops falling to the lower parts of the cloud and the positively charged drops rising to the top. It is this charge separation that produces the electric field.

For dry air at atmospheric pressure to conduct electricity (that is, for sparks to be produced), an electric field of at least $3 \times 10^6 \, \text{V m}^{-1}$ is needed. However, the air in and around a thunderstorm is wet and at lower than normal atmospheric pressure, both of which conditions favour conduction at lower field strengths. A flash of lightning from a cloud down to the ground consists of a series of events which occur too quickly for the naked eye to resolve. Typically the flash begins when a column of electrons moves downwards from the base of the cloud as the air just below it becomes conducting in the intense electric field there. As these electrons flow downwards, they leave behind them a channel of ionised air, into which further negative charge can flow. The column is propelled downwards by the enormous concentration of electric charge near its tip. This generates an intense electric field which causes electrical breakdown of the air around it. The column is called a **stepped leader**, because it appears to move downwards in a series of luminous steps. Each of these is about 50 m long, and there is a pause of about $50 \, \mu s$ between them, during which the leader is not luminous. The path of the stepped leader is jagged, the apparently random changes of direction reflecting changes in electron density in the air around it. The leader's radius may be as large as 5 m, although only its centre is luminous.

When the tip of the stepped leader approaches the ground, the intense electric field produces an upward-moving discharge from the ground or an object on the ground. This discharge meets the stepped leader about 50 m above the ground. When the two tubes meet, a continuous conducting tube exists from the cloud to the ground. Electrons at the bottom of the tube drain out into the ground, followed by electrons from successively higher parts of the tube. In this way, an intense current flows from the ground up to the cloud (remember that the flow of current is in the opposite direction to the flow of electrons) at a speed up to one third of the speed of light. This is the **return stroke**, which has a typical peak value of 20 000 A lasting for less than $100 \, \mu s$.

Figure 5.3.9 The electrical storm is one of nature's greatest wonders, terrifying and yet inspiring humans since the earliest times.

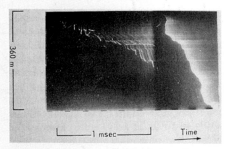

Figure 5.3.10 The film was moved horizontally behind the lens of the camera to obtain this photograph. It shows the stepped leader in the left-hand portion of the photograph, together with the return stroke in the right-hand portion.

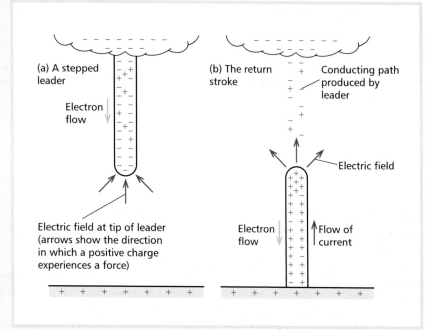

Figure 5.3.11 The propagation of a stepped leader and the subsequent return stroke

Measuring equipotentials and field strength

Several methods can be used to investigate electric fields. Conducting paper gives a method of obtaining equipotentials and hence field lines for electric fields in two dimensions and for a wide range of electrode shapes. Figure 5.3.12 shows the setup. The point of a needle connected to a voltmeter is moved over the surface of a sheet of conducting paper, keeping the reading on the voltmeter constant. Using moderate pressure, the path of the needle is traced out on the white paper by means of carbon paper underneath the conducting paper.

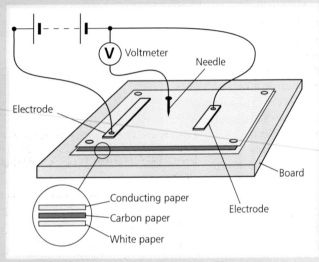

Figure 5.3.12 Measuring equipotentials using conducting paper. The voltmeter must have a high resistance so that the potential at a point is not affected by connecting the voltmeter into the circuit.

Alternatively, for investigations of electric fields in air, a small electroscope may be used. This is simply a piece of metal foil attached to the end of an insulating rod. The electroscope is placed between two charged metal plates as in figure 5.3.13. If it is touched to one of the plates, the foil becomes charged, experiences a

force and becomes deflected – the deflection is a measure of the strength of the field between the plates. If the charged electroscope is moved about in the space between the plates, the deflection is constant except at the very edge of the space, showing that the field in this region is uniform (see also figure 5.3.8(e)).

If the gap between the plates is made smaller, the deflection increases, showing that the field strength has increased. Similarly, increasing the potential difference across the plates can be shown to increase the field strength between the plates. Since the field between the plates is uniform, the potential gradient between them is uniform too, and so the magnitude of the field strength E between plates with separation d is given by:

$$E = \frac{V}{d}$$

The field is directed from the positively charged plate to the negatively charged plate.

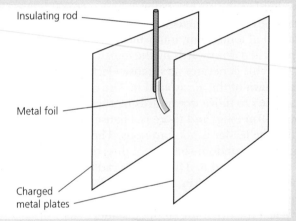

Figure 5.3.13 A simple electroscope may be used to investigate the field between the plates of a parallel plate capacitor.

Conservative fields

Using field lines and equipotentials we can show that electric fields (and gravitational fields too) have a very interesting property.

Consider a small charge q moving from A to B between two parallel plates, as in figure 5.3.14(a). Since the potential difference between A and B is V, our knowledge of electricity leads us to believe that the energy transferred in this process is given by qV. But does it matter what path the charge takes between A and B? Is the same energy transferred whether q goes from A to B in a straight line or goes via C?

This question can be answered by considering what happens if q takes the path shown in figure 5.3.14(b). This path consists of a series of movements

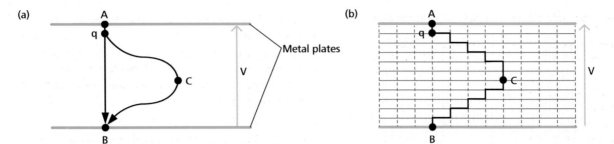

Figure 5.3.14 The energy transferred when a charge moves between two points in an electric field is independent of the path followed. This applies to gravitational fields too.

which lie either along a field line (dotted lines) or along an equipotential (solid lines). Since all points on an equipotential are at the same potential, q will have the same energy at all points along an equipotential, so energy is transferred only when q moves along a field line. The total distance travelled along the field lines is always the same (equal to the separation of the two plates), so when q starts at A and finishes at B the energy transferred is constant, no matter what path is followed. The same is true for gravitational fields.

The potential at any point in an electric field or in a gravitational field thus has a unique value which does not depend on the path taken to reach it. This means that when a charge or a mass moves from one point to another in an electric or gravitational field, the energy transferred is independent of the path taken, and depends only on the starting and finishing points. Fields that behave like this are said to be **conservative**.

Figure 5.3.15 Permittivity ε is a measure of how a medium affects electric fields – using a medium with a greater permittivity reduces the electric field strength in the medium.

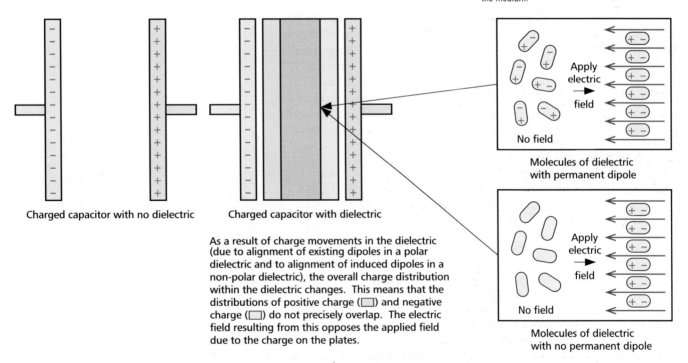

Charged capacitor with no dielectric

Charged capacitor with dielectric

As a result of charge movements in the dielectric (due to alignment of existing dipoles in a polar dielectric and to alignment of induced dipoles in a non-polar dielectric), the overall charge distribution within the dielectric changes. This means that the distributions of positive charge (□) and negative charge (□) do not precisely overlap. The electric field resulting from this opposes the applied field due to the charge on the plates.

Apply electric field

No field

Molecules of dielectric with permanent dipole

Apply electric field

No field

Molecules of dielectric with no permanent dipole

For given charges and separation, the force between these two charges depends on the permittivity of the medium they are in – using a medium with double the permittivity will halve the force between them.

Electric fields and electric flux – the relationship between k and ε_0

In section 4.3 we met the idea of permittivity and the effect of placing a dielectric between the plates of a capacitor. From our knowledge of the behaviour of electric fields, it should now be clear that the energy stored in a charged capacitor is stored in the electric field between its plates. A dielectric placed in this field reduces the potential difference between the plates for a given charge on them because a charge is induced on the molecules of the dielectric, which effectively reduces the electric field strength between the plates. The more the dielectric is capable of behaving in this way, the greater its permittivity ε, and the greater its effect on the capacitance of the capacitor. The permittivity of a medium also affects the force between two charges in that medium by the same mechanism – figure 5.3.15 illustrates this.

Because increasing the permittivity decreases the force between two charges, ε appears on the bottom of the right-hand side for Coulomb's law. We may write ε as:

$$\varepsilon = \varepsilon_0 \varepsilon_r$$

where ε_0 is the permittivity of free space (8.85×10^{-12} F m^{-1}) and ε_r is the relative permittivity of the medium ($\varepsilon_r = 1$ for a vacuum by definition).

Why $1/4\pi$?

The effect of the permittivity of a medium on electric fields within the medium explains the appearance of $1/\varepsilon$ in Coulomb's law – but why does $1/4\pi$ appear too? The answer lies in the way we have considered electric fields in two very different situations, one involving point charges, the other involving flat plates. The first of these two cases has spherical symmetry while the second does not. 4π is the factor involved in calculating how any quantity obeying an inverse square law is 'spread out' over the surface of a sphere (see box 'The inverse square law', section 3.1, page 212). We can think of electric field as a flow or **flux**, in exactly the same way as we considered light in section 3.

(a)

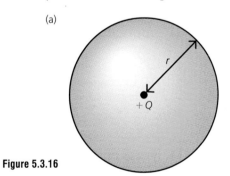

(b)

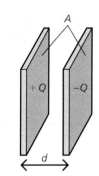

Figure 5.3.16

Consider the sphere shown in figure 5.3.16(a) with charge $+Q$ at its centre, and assume that the electric field behaves like light, since both obey an inverse square law. The total **electric flux** Ψ from $+Q$ at a distance r must be the **flux density** (which we are assuming is the same as the electric field strength E) at r multiplied by the surface area of the sphere:

$$\Psi = E \times 4\pi r^2$$

$$= \frac{kQ}{r^2} \times 4\pi r^2 \text{ (since we know that } E = \frac{kQ}{r^2}\text{, page 414)}$$

So:

$$\Psi = 4\pi kQ$$

Now the geometry of the shape chosen to calculate the electric flux should not affect the total electric flux from the charge $+Q$, any more than the total light flux from a lamp would be affected by the distance r at which we measure the flux density of the light from it. Thus it is reasonable to assume that in figure 5.3.16(b) the total electric flux between the plates of the capacitor is also $4\pi kQ$. This means that:

$$\text{Electric field between plates} = \text{flux density} = E = \frac{4\pi kQ}{A} = \frac{V}{d} \text{ (from page 418)}$$

Rearranging:

$$k = \frac{AV}{4\pi Qd}$$

Now:

$$C = \frac{\varepsilon_0 A}{d} = \frac{Q}{V}$$

so:

$$\frac{1}{\varepsilon_0} = \frac{AV}{Qd}$$

and therefore:

$$k = \frac{1}{4\pi\varepsilon_0}$$

In general in the SI system, relationships in electricity and magnetism concerning situations with spherical symmetry contain the factor 4π (for example, the field around a point charge). Those concerning cylindrical symmetry contain the factor 2π (for example, the magnetic field around a wire, as we shall see in section 5.4), and those with plane symmetry do not contain π (for example, the magnetic field inside a solenoid, also in section 5.4).

Applying electric fields – the cathode ray tube

The transfer of energy using an electric field is the principle behind the cathode ray tube, an application of physics which influences all our lives, at home and at work. As with many complex pieces of technology, the principles behind the operation of the cathode ray tube are simple, although there are many complex details. Figure 5.3.17 shows the most important elements of a tube.

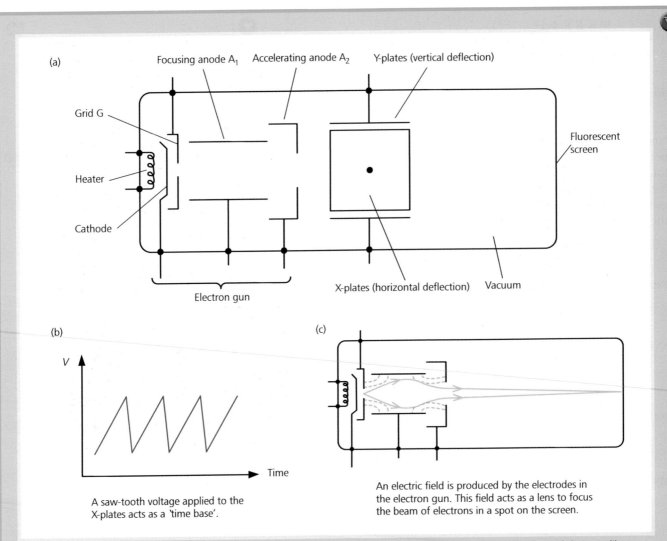

(a) Focusing anode A$_1$ Accelerating anode A$_2$ Y-plates (vertical deflection)

Grid G

Heater

Cathode

Fluorescent screen

Electron gun

X-plates (horizontal deflection)   Vacuum

(b)

V

Time

A saw-tooth voltage applied to the X-plates acts as a 'time base'.

(c)

An electric field is produced by the electrodes in the electron gun. This field acts as a lens to focus the beam of electrons in a spot on the screen.

Figure 5.3.17 The basic details of a simple cathode ray tube. Essentially the tube consists of an 'electron gun' that produces a narrow beam of electrons with a small range of energies. This beam is then deflected by means of electric fields produced by the X- and Y-plates. The fluorescent screen then produces a bright spot of light where the electrons hit it. (Section 6.1 explains why electrons are sometimes referred to as cathode rays.)

The cathode ray tube contains an electron gun. The gun produces electrons from the cathode by a process called **thermionic emission**, in which the heating effect of an electric current is used to 'boil off' electrons from a metal (a process similar to the evaporation of molecules from the surface of a liquid). The gun produces a narrow beam of electrons at the point where the beam hits the screen (see figure 5.3.17(c)). It does this by means of an electron lens which uses electric fields to guide the electrons produced from the cathode. A$_1$ is a cylindrical anode with a potential of around +1000 V relative to the cathode, while A$_2$ is a flat anode with a circular hole in its centre. The potential of A$_1$ may be adjusted in order to focus the beam at the screen – it is called the **focusing anode**. Varying the potential of the grid G

controls the number of electrons in the beam – the more negative G is made, the fewer electrons are available to form the beam, as more are repelled back towards the cathode. Thus the grid acts as a brightness control. The spot of light where electrons strike the screen is caused by a phosphor coating on the inside of the screen.

Having left the gun, the beam passes through two electric fields at right angles, causing deflection in the Y- and X-directions. If a potential difference varying with time like that shown in figure 5.3.17(b) is applied to the X-plates, the spot moves steadily across the screen from left to right and then flies back to its starting point rapidly and repeats its movement. An alternating voltage applied to the Y-plates causes the spot to trace out a path displaying the waveform of the alternating voltage, as we have already seen in section 4.4.

Colour televisions and computer screens use three electron guns, each one aimed at a separate array of dots producing red, blue or green light, and scanning the whole surface of the screen in a series of lines between 50 and 100 times a second.

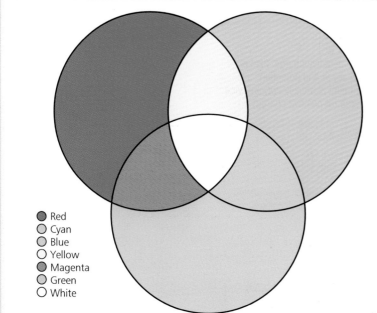

- ● Red
- ○ Cyan
- ○ Blue
- ○ Yellow
- ● Magenta
- ● Green
- ○ White

Figure 5.3.18 The range of colours in the visible spectrum can be produced using just three colours – the primary colours of light, red, blue and green. The human eye is so sensitive to variations in colour that when computers are used to produce digital images like these, each colour must be capable of having over 200 intensities, varying from black to saturation. This means that the intensity of each colour must be represented by an 8-bit number, from 0 to 255. Since three colours are involved, each part of the image requires $3 \times 8 = 24$ bits to describe it fully, giving over 16 million possible different colours.

Comparing gravitational and electric fields

Sections 5.1–5.3 have introduced a range of ideas about gravitational and electric fields. We have seen that there are many similarities in the relationships involved in both types of field, and these are summarised in table 5.3.1.

We should also remember that there are significant differences between these two types of field too. In particular, we have seen that the comparative strengths of the two types of field are very different, with electric fields being by far the stronger and by far the most important in our lives as far as friction, contact forces and so on are concerned. Also, since mass is always positive, gravitational force is only attractive and gravitational potential always zero or negative. By contrast, since the product Qq may be positive or negative depending on the signs of Q and q, the electrostatic force may be either attractive or repulsive, and electric potential may be zero, positive or negative. This has important consequences in the practical application of these fields – while it is possible to protect, say, delicate electronic components from electric fields using a shield of conducting material, it is impossible to do the same for gravitational fields.

Figure 5.3.19 Inside a hollow conductor, the electric field is zero even when there is a very strong electric field outside the conductor. The metal body of this plane forms a good shield against atmospheric electric fields, so that the occupants are quite safe from atmospheric electrical discharges (lightning!). Hollow conducting shields like this are called **Faraday cages**. They are effective because of the two types of electric charge – there is no equivalent of the Faraday cage for gravitational fields.

Quantity	Gravitational field	Electric field
Magnitude of force at distance r	$F = \dfrac{G\,Mm}{r^2}$ (Force is always attractive)	$F = \dfrac{1}{4\pi\varepsilon_0}\dfrac{|Qq|}{r^2}$ (Force may be attractive or repulsive)
Magnitude of field strength at distance r	$g = \dfrac{F}{m}$ $= \dfrac{G\,M}{r^2}$ $= \dfrac{dV}{dr}$ (Field is always radially *in*, potential gradient always radially *out*)	$E = \dfrac{F}{|q|}$ $= \dfrac{1}{4\pi\varepsilon_0}\dfrac{|Q|}{r^2}$ $= \left\lvert\dfrac{dV}{dr}\right\rvert$ (For negative charge, field is radially *in* and potential gradient is radially *out*, and vice versa for positive charge)
Potential energy at distance r	$E_p = -\dfrac{G\,Mm}{r}$	$E_p = \dfrac{1}{4\pi\varepsilon_0}\dfrac{Qq}{r}$
Potential at distance r	$V = -\dfrac{G\,M}{r}$	$V = \dfrac{1}{4\pi\varepsilon_0}\dfrac{Q}{r}$

Table 5.3.1 Comparing gravitational and electric fields. The vertical lines, e.g. $|q|$, mean 'take the magnitude of'. This is necessary since we are concerned here with the *magnitude* of the force or field strength, which is always positive.

SUMMARY

- An object can be **electrostatically charged** by friction with another material. Charge is **conserved** in this process – the total positive charge on one object equals the total negative charge on the other. A charged object can charge other bodies by **induction**.

- **Coulomb's law** says that the magnitude of the force F that two point charges q_1 and q_2 a distance r apart in a vacuum exert on each other is given by $F = (1/4\pi\varepsilon_0)(q_1 q_2/r^2)$, where ε_0 is the permittivity of free space. This force is attractive if q_1 and q_2 are oppositely charged, and repulsive if they are similarly charged.

- An **electric field** is a region in which an electric charge experiences a force. **Electric field strength** E is the force per unit positive charge, $E = F/q$.

- The magnitude of the electric field strength E a distance r from a charge Q is given by $E = (1/4\pi\varepsilon_0)(Q/r^2)$. If Q is a positive charge, the electric field is radially *out*; if Q is a negative charge, the electric field is radially *in*.

- The **electric potential energy** E_p of a charge q a distance r from a charge Q is given by $E_p = (1/4\pi\varepsilon_0)(Qq/r)$.

- **Electric potential** V at a point in an electric field is the electric potential energy per unit charge at that point.

- The electric potential V at a distance r from a charge Q is given by $V = (1/4\pi\varepsilon_0)(Q/r)$.

- Electric field strength $=$ –potential gradient. (Remember that both are vectors – the negative sign shows that electric field strength and potential gradient are in opposite directions.)

EXAMPLE

Figure 5.3.20 shows a simple model of the water molecule. In this model, the oxygen atom acts as a point negative charge of magnitude 1.1×10^{-19} C, and the hydrogen atoms act as point positive charges of magnitude 0.55×10^{-19} C. The distance between each hydrogen atom and the oxygen atom is 1.0×10^{-10} m.

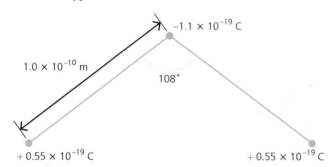

Figure 5.3.20

*Calculate **a** the magnitude of the force exerted by each hydrogen atom on the oxygen atom and **b** the total force due to the two hydrogen atoms (magnitude and direction) experienced by the oxygen atom. (Take ε_0 as 8.854×10^{-12} F m^{-1}.)*

a Using Coulomb's law, the magnitude of the force exerted on the oxygen atom by one hydrogen atom is:

$$F = \frac{1}{4\pi\varepsilon_0} \frac{1.1 \times 10^{-19} \text{ C} \times 0.55 \times 10^{-19} \text{ C}}{(1.0 \times 10^{-10} \text{ m})^2}$$

$$= \frac{1.1 \times 10^{-19} \text{ C} \times 0.55 \times 10^{-19} \text{ C}}{4 \times \pi \times 8.854 \times 10^{-12} \text{ F m}^{-1} \times 1.0 \times 10^{-20} \text{ m}^2}$$

$$= 5.44 \times 10^{-9} \text{ N}$$

b Figure 5.3.21 shows a free body diagram of the oxygen atom.

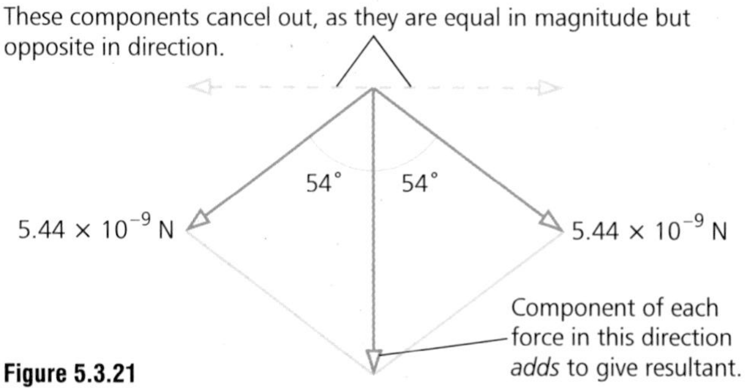

These components cancel out, as they are equal in magnitude but opposite in direction.

Component of each force in this direction *adds* to give resultant.

Figure 5.3.21

The two components of the forces shown as dotted lines cancel, leaving each with a component of 5.44×10^{-9} N $\times \cos 54°$ acting in the direction shown. The resultant force F_R thus has a magnitude:

$$F_R = 2 \times 5.44 \times 10^{-9} \text{ N} \times \cos 54°$$

$$= 6.4 \times 10^{-9} \text{ N}$$

This force makes an angle of 54° with each of the forces exerted by the two hydrogen atoms, as shown.

QUESTIONS

(Take ε_0 as 8.85×10^{-12} F m^{-1} and e as 1.6×10^{-19} C.)

1 The fairweather field of the Earth has a magnitude of around 100 V m^{-1}. A speck of dust carries a charge of $-e$ and has a mass of 10^{-17} g. Describe its motion.

2 The spark plug of a car engine has two electrodes a distance 0.64 mm apart. The electric field between the electrodes must reach 3×10^6 V m^{-1} if a spark is to be produced. What is the minimum potential required to do this?

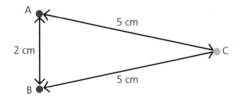

Figure 5.3.22

3 A small sphere carrying a charge of 8 nC hangs between two metal plates a distance 10 cm apart. The mass of the sphere is 0.05 g. What potential difference between the plates will cause the sphere to make an angle of 10° with the vertical?

4 Refer to figure 5.3.22. A charge of $+5 \times 10^{-6}$ C is placed at A, and one of $+1 \times 10^{-5}$ C at B. Calculate the magnitude and direction of the electric field at C.

5 A raindrop of mass 50 mg and a charge of -1×10^{-10} C falls from a raincloud. The electric field between the cloud and the ground is 300 V m^{-1}.
   a If the drop falls through a distance of 100 m, calculate the change in its:
      i gravitational potential energy
      ii electric potential energy.
   b What electric field strength would be necessary to prevent the drop from falling? Is this likely to occur?

6 In a linear accelerator, subatomic particles are accelerated to enormous speeds in an evacuated tube. In one such machine, protons are accelerated from rest and acquire a kinetic energy of 3.2×10^{-9} J. If this acceleration occurs in a distance of 1000 m, what electric field is required to produce this acceleration? (The charge on a proton is $+e$.)

7 An alpha particle with kinetic energy 5.1×10^{-13} J is fired at a uranium nucleus. Calculate how close the alpha particle gets to the uranium nucleus. The charge on the alpha particle is $+2e$, and that on the uranium nucleus is $+92e$. (Assume that the uranium nucleus remains stationary throughout, and treat both the alpha particle and the uranium nucleus as spheres of charge.)

8 A uranium nucleus may split into two equal fragments, each of which contains 46 protons (these are both nuclei of the element palladium). If the mass of each of these nuclei is 2.0×10^{-25} kg and the charge on each proton is $+e$, calculate:
  a the repulsive force between them when they are separated by a distance of 1.0×10^{-14} m
  b the acceleration of each nucleus at this point.

9 The subatomic particle known as the τ (tau) carries the same charge as the electron but is nearly 3500 times as massive. A tau is at rest a long distance away from a uranium nucleus, and is allowed to accelerate towards it. If the uranium nucleus is treated as a sphere of radius 7.4×10^{-15} m, calculate the speed at which the tau hits the uranium nucleus. (The charge on the uranium nucleus is $+92e$, and the mass of the tau can be taken as 3.2×10^{-27} kg.)

10 A pair of parallel flat metal plates are placed a distance of 10 mm apart. The plates are circular, with a radius of 10 cm. How much charge must be placed on each plate to produce an electric field of 500 V m^{-1} between them?

Developing Key Skills

Physicists estimate that a bolt of lightning involves an electric current of 20 000 A flowing for less than 100 μs, and that the potential difference between a thundercloud and the ground is about 10^8 V. At any one time there are roughly 2000 thunderstorms in progress around the Earth.

Produce a presentation on the topic of 'Atmospheric Electricity – could it provide all the energy required by humankind?'. Your presentation may be in the form of a poster, a series of slides produced by a computer presentation package, or a series of Web pages. You should use the information in the statement above, together with any other information you need – you may be able to find this in books or electronic reference sources, or you may be able to make sensible estimates. Present your arguments using any calculations necessary, making your points as clearly as you can for a non-technical audience.

[Key Skills opportunities: C, A, IT]

5.4 Magnetic fields

We are all familiar with magnetic fields as applied in the compass, and in the effect of a simple bar or horseshoe magnet on small nails or iron filings. The magnetic force is believed to have been used by the Chinese as early as the third century AD in a form of compass for finding direction, but it was only in the nineteenth century that physicists came to understand the magnetic force as another force acting between charges in motion. In studying the magnetic force in this section, we shall begin with the field around a simple bar magnet.

Introducing magnetic fields

The shapes of magnetic fields

Investigations of magnets show that the magnetic field around a magnet appears to come from two specific regions of the magnet, called the **poles**. Further investigations show that – like electric charges – magnetic poles are of two kinds, and that like poles repel one another while unlike poles attract each other. These poles appear to occur in equal and opposite pairs. One further observation shows that a freely suspended magnet swings and comes to rest so that its poles lie in a north–south direction. This suggests that the Earth itself acts as a large magnet, and gives the reason why the pole of a magnet that points towards the Earth's North Pole is called the **north pole** of the magnet, while the other is called the **south pole**.

The magnetic field around a bar magnet is easily investigated, using either a plotting compass or iron filings. Iron filings sprinkled on the surface of a piece of thin card held just above a bar magnet rapidly align themselves to produce a

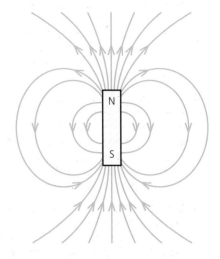

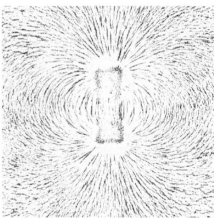

Figure 5.4.1 Iron filings sprinkled on card held above a bar magnet align themselves so that lines appear to join the two ends of the magnet in curved loops. These lines are shown drawn as field lines with arrows in the diagram.

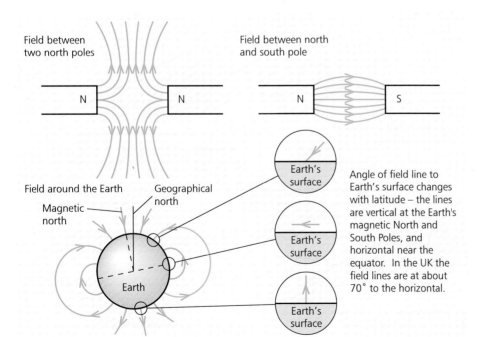

Field between two north poles

Field between north and south pole

Field around the Earth

Geographical north

Magnetic north

Earth

Earth's surface

Earth's surface

Earth's surface

Angle of field line to Earth's surface changes with latitude – the lines are vertical at the Earth's magnetic North and South Poles, and horizontal near the equator. In the UK the field lines are at about 70° to the horizontal.

Figure 5.4.2 Field lines in different situations. The cause and the behaviour of the Earth's magnetic field is far from understood – in fact, the field is thought to have reversed on many occasions in the distant past. Certainly the Earth's magnetic poles move over the centuries, causing due north and magnetic north to be several degrees apart at the moment.

pattern as shown in figure 5.4.1. This pattern can also be produced by using a plotting compass and tracing out the path of the needle as it is moved around the magnet.

In gravitational and electric fields, field lines are used to indicate the direction of the field, the closeness of the lines indicating the strength of the field. This is true for magnetic fields too, where the direction of the field lines indicates the direction of the force on a magnetic north pole in the field. Figure 5.4.2 shows the pattern of field lines between like and unlike poles and around the Earth.

The cause of magnetic fields

Permanent magnets are made from **ferromagnetic** materials – the best known example of such a material is probably steel. A ferromagnetic material effectively consists of a large number of tiny individual bar magnets. When the material is unmagnetised, these tiny magnets are aligned in such a way that their magnetic fields cancel each other out. When the material is subjected to a strong magnetic field, the tiny magnets line up. When the material is removed from the external magnetic field, the tiny magnets remain lined up, and the material is permanently magnetised. This simple model of ferromagnetism is shown in figure 5.4.3. (A fuller explanation is given in the box 'Magnetism and electrons' on page 429.)

Iron is another ferromagnetic material that behaves in the same way as steel when placed in a magnetic field. However, the tiny magnets in a piece of iron become aligned randomly once more when the iron is removed from the external magnetic field, and the iron is no longer magnetic. Materials that behave like this are sometimes said to be magnetically **soft**, while materials which retain their magnetism like steel are said to be magnetically **hard**.

Magnetic fields also exist around current-carrying wires. (Strictly speaking we should say around any moving charge – but we shall restrict ourselves to thinking about charges moving in a wire for the moment.) The magnetic field around some wires carrying a current is shown in figure 5.4.4. We shall look at the magnetic field around wires carrying a current more closely later on in this section, and in section 5.5.

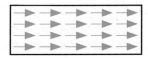

Externally applied magnetic field

External field removed

Figure 5.4.3 A simple model to explain how a piece of steel may be made into a permanent magnet.

Figure 5.4.4 The magnetic field around a current-carrying wire consists of a series of concentric field lines which may combine to produce more complex fields, as in the case of the coil and the solenoid shown here. (A solenoid is a cylindrical coil of wire carrying a current. We shall look at the magnetic field inside a solenoid in more detail later in this section.)

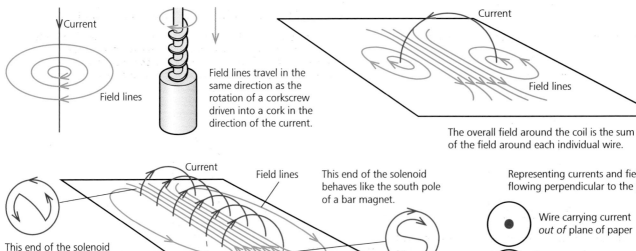

Current

Field lines

Field lines travel in the same direction as the rotation of a corkscrew driven into a cork in the direction of the current.

Current

Field lines

The overall field around the coil is the sum of the field around each individual wire.

Current

Field lines

This end of the solenoid behaves like the south pole of a bar magnet.

This end of the solenoid behaves like the north pole of a bar magnet.

The overall field around the solenoid is the sum of the field around each individual wire. The field around a solenoid resembles that around a bar magnet – a simple rule tells you which end of the solenoid is north and which is south from the direction of current flow looking into the solenoid.

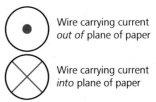

Representing currents and fields flowing perpendicular to the page

Wire carrying current *out of* plane of paper

Wire carrying current *into* plane of paper

The directions of fields may be represented in the same way.

Note that the magnetic field lines in these diagrams form closed loops and do not begin or end anywhere, unlike electric field lines which begin and end on positive and negative charges respectively. This results from the observation that magnetic poles come in pairs – there is no magnetic equivalent of electric charge that can act as a start or a finish for electromagnetic field lines.

Magnetism and electrons

It may seem puzzling that two such different situations – a permanent bar magnet and a solenoid – can give rise to identical magnetic fields. However, the two situations are in fact not so very different, as the following model shows.

The tiny bar magnets described as being responsible for the permanent magnetic behaviour of ferromagnetic materials are actually groups of atoms in which the electrons show magnetic behaviour because of their motion – each electron has a **magnetic moment**. Groups of these atoms form small **domains**, in which the magnetic moments of the electrons are aligned with each other. In non-magnetised material the domains are aligned at random so that their magnetic moments cancel each

other out. Subjected to an external magnetic field, the domains rearrange themselves so that they tend to align themselves with the external field. On removing the field, not all of the domains return to their original alignment, and the material remains magnetised. The alignment of the magnetic moments is effectively the same as a current running round the surface of the magnetised material. This surface current may amount to several hundred amperes around the circumference of a small bar magnet (see figure 5.4.5) and is related to the magnetic field in exactly the same way as the current flowing through a solenoid is related to magnetic field through the solenoid.

Random orientation of domains in unmagnetised material

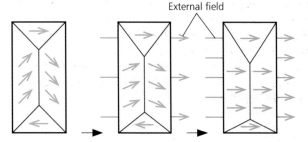

External field

In a weak externally applied field, the domain walls tend to realign themselves. Here, the top domain has increased in size at the expense of the bottom domain. As the strength of the field increases further, the direction of the magnetisation of the other domains tends to rotate to align with the field.

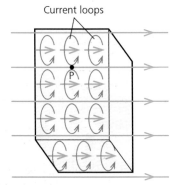

Current loops

The magnetic moment of each domain can be considered to be due to a current loop around it. The current cancels out between adjacent loops (for example at P) but not at the surface of the material.

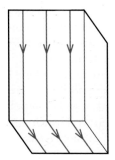

When the external field is removed, many of the domains remain aligned. The resulting magnetic field is effectively equivalent to a surface current running round the magnet.

Figure 5.4.5 The fields around a bar magnet and around a solenoid are similar – both fields effectively arise due to currents flowing in the same way.

LEVITATION – ALL DONE BY MAGNETS!

If you have ever tried to use a magnet to levitate another magnet or a magnetic object, you will have found how impossible this trick is. The fact that magnets cannot be used in this way has been known for many years, and was the subject of a theory published by Samuel Earnshaw in 1842 and known as **Earnshaw's Theorem**. This theory states that static levitation (that is, the stable suspension of an object in a gravitational field) cannot be achieved by using any combination of fixed magnets and electric charges. Although this theorem still holds good today, it is possible to levitate objects if we can get round the assumptions that form part of the theorem.

One way of doing this is to use a system of *feedback*. By using an electromagnet together with a sensing device, it is possible to increase the strength of the electromagnet if the levitating object starts to move away from it, so pulling the object back to its original position, and vice versa. This is how the angel in figure 5.4.6 has been levitated.

We have already seen how a magnet can be levitated above a superconducting surface in section 4.3. This levitation is due to the ability of the superconductor to produce a magnetic field which opposes the magnetic field due to the magnet, behaviour which is termed **diamagnetism**. Diamagnetism is not limited to superconductors – many common materials, including water, are also diamagnetic, repelling and being repelled by a magnetic field. In the case of superconductors, diamagnetism is due to the current that is induced to flow through the surface of the superconducting material by the magnetic field around the magnet. In non-superconducting materials, diamagnetism is the result of the electrons in the material rearranging their orbits slightly, creating small persistent currents which oppose the external magnetic field.

It is possible to levitate a magnet using diamagnetism if the correct arrangement is used. Figure 5.4.8 shows a small permanent magnet levitated between a person's finger and thumb. To do this, a very powerful electromagnet is placed about 2.5 m above the point at which the magnet is to be levitated. At this point the permanent magnet is stable in a horizontal plane but unstable in a vertical plane. The person's thumb and fingers are weakly diamagnetic – so if the magnet falls it will be repelled by the thumb, while if it rises it will be repelled by the finger.

If a more strongly diamagnetic substance (such as graphite) replaces the finger and thumb, the powerful electromagnet can be replaced by a strong permanent magnet. This means that the phenomenon is more than just spectacular. It is likely to find uses in producing virtually friction-free bearings, and can be used to simulate weightlessness for small objects without sending them into space.

Figure 5.4.6 Levitation by means of feedback is not included in the assumptions made in Earnshaw's theorem, so it does not violate it.

Figure 5.4.7 Although diamagnetic interactions of non-superconducting materials are very weak, levitation is possible using sufficiently large fields. Here, a live frog is levitated by a field of around 16 T. The diamagnetic repulsion between the frog and the magnet exactly balances the frog's weight.

Figure 5.4.8 The small permanent magnet is levitated between the thumb and finger of a person due to the diamagnetism of flesh and bone.

Forces on current-carrying wires in magnetic fields

A current-carrying wire in a magnetic field experiences a force. Figure 5.4.9(a) shows a simple investigation, in which a wire which is free to move passes through the magnetic field between the poles of a horseshoe magnet. Switching on the current causes the wire to move, since the magnetic field around the wire interacts with that of the permanent magnets and produces a distorted field. This distorted field then 'catapults' the wire. Figure 5.4.9(b) shows the directions of the force, current and magnetic field, and suggests a way to remember these, called **Fleming's left-hand rule**.

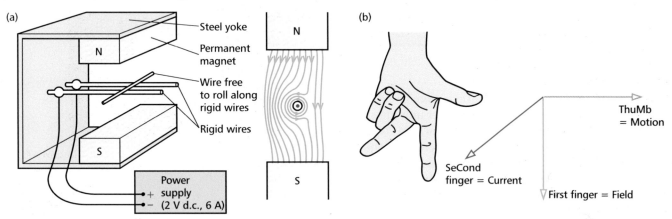

The field around the wire and the field between the poles combine to produce a field which looks a bit like streched rubber bands. This distortion of the field is responsible for the catapulting of the wire along the rigid wires.

Fleming's left-hand rule can be used to predict the relationship between the directions of the field, current and force.

Figure 5.4.9 The wire in this investigation will fly out from between the magnets if the current is large enough – the direction of travel can be predicted using Fleming's left-hand rule.

Further investigation of the force on a current-carrying wire perpendicular to a magnetic field shows that the *size* of the force is proportional to:

1   the current I through the wire

2   the length l of the wire in the field.

Investigating the force on a current-carrying wire in a magnetic field

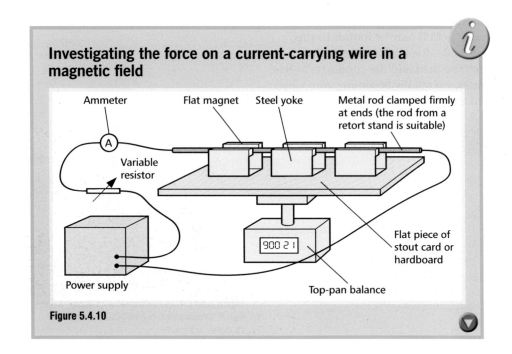

Figure 5.4.10

Figure 5.4.10 shows the experimental setup to investigate the dependence of the force on a current-carrying wire in a magnetic field on I and l. The reading of the top-pan balance changes when the current is on, and the difference in readings is a measure of the force on the magnets – which from Newton's third law we know must be equal in size to the force on the metal rod.

By using one pair of magnets and varying the current through the rod, the variation of force with current can be investigated. Adding more pairs of magnets next to the first pair increases the length of the rod in the field, and enables the relationship of force and length to be investigated while the current is kept constant.

Magnetic field strength

In sections 5.1–5.3 we have seen how gravitational field strength and electric field strength are defined in terms of force per unit mass and force per unit charge respectively. The situation for magnetic fields is not quite so straightforward, for the simple reason that there is no equivalent of mass and charge for magnetic fields, since a magnetic pole cannot exist in isolation. The definition of magnetic field strength used in the nineteenth century was based on the force on a single magnetic north pole, but the modern definition of magnetic field strength uses the force on a current-carrying conductor as its basis. The definition is based on the catapult effect – magnetic field, current and force all lying at right angles to each other.

Magnetic field strength B is defined as the force per unit length per unit current on a current-carrying conductor at right angles to the direction of the magnetic field, that is,

$$B = \frac{F}{Il}$$

The SI unit of magnetic field strength is the **tesla**, T.

The definition of magnetic field strength may be rearranged so that the force on a current-carrying conductor in a magnetic field B may be found. In this situation one further variable becomes important – the angle between the conductor and the field. If the angle between the field and the conductor is less than 90°, the force on the conductor decreases, eventually becoming zero when the field and the conductor are parallel (when the angle between them is zero).

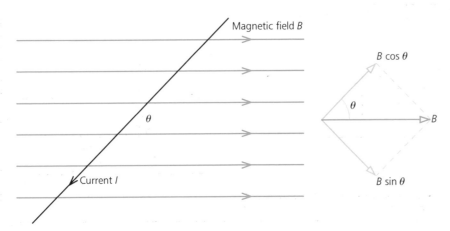

Figure 5.4.11 With a conductor at an angle θ to the field B, the component of B perpendicular to the conductor is $B \sin \theta$.

It is the component of the magnetic field *perpendicular* to the conductor that causes a force to be exerted on the conductor – figure 5.4.11 shows that this component is $B \sin \theta$. Thus:

$$F = (B \sin \theta) Il$$

$$= BIl \sin \theta$$

In this case the left-hand rule still applies, but the first finger now points in the direction of the component of the field perpendicular to the conductor. Strictly we should use vector techniques to manipulate these quantities – this is done later in the box 'Defining the magnetic field using vectors', on page 441.

Fleming's left-hand rule – worked example

A straight horizontal wire 2 m long carrying a current of 5 A makes an angle of 30° with the horizontal component of the Earth's magnetic field B_H, as shown in figure 5.4.12. If $B_H = 5 \times 10^{-5}$ T, what is the magnitude and direction of the force on the wire due to the horizontal component of the Earth's magnetic field?

$$F = BIl \sin \theta$$

$$= 5 \times 10^{-5} \text{ T} \times 5 \text{ A} \times 2 \text{ m} \times \sin 30°$$

$$= 2.5 \times 10^{-4} \text{ N}$$

Applying the left-hand rule shows that this force acts vertically upwards.

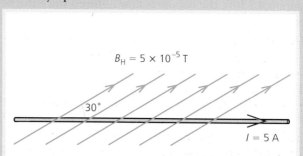

$B_H = 5 \times 10^{-5}$ T

30°

$I = 5$ A

Figure 5.4.12

A coil in a field – an important principle

Consider the rectangular loop of wire shown in figure 5.4.13. The loop is pivoted so that it can turn around the axis CD. It is placed in the magnetic field between the poles of a magnet. A current I flows into the loop, around it and out again along the path O → P → Q → R → S → T → U → V. If the distance PU is small, this is effectively equivalent to a loop QRST with a current *I* flowing round it.

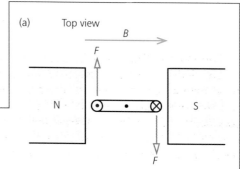

(a) Top view

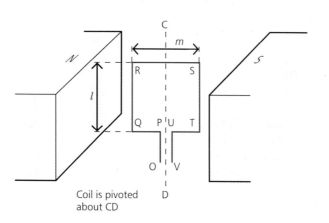

Coil is pivoted about CD

Figure 5.4.13 A rectangular coil pivoted in a magnetic field experiences a couple when a current flows through it. This tends to make the coil rotate – the basic principle behind electric motors.

If the coil is parallel to the field as in figure 5.4.13(a), sides QT and RS lie parallel to the field, and so there is no force on them. However, sides QR and ST each experience a force F in the directions shown (the left-hand rule can be used to find these directions). The size of this force is given by:

$$F = BIl$$

The two forces between them make up a couple which tends to make the coil rotate. The size of this couple C is given by:

$$C = F \times \text{perpendicular distance between forces}$$

$$= BIlm$$

$$= BIA, \text{ where } A \text{ is } l \times m, \text{ the cross-sectional area of the coil}$$

If the coil now rotates about CD so that it makes an angle θ with the field as in figure 5.4.13(b), the couple is now reduced since the two forces making up the couple are F'. Since $F' = F \cos \theta$, the magnitude of the couple C on the coil is given by:

$$C = BIA \cos \theta$$

(In this situation, although sides QT and RS are now no longer parallel to the field and therefore each experiences a force, these two forces are equal and opposite and do not form a couple – using the left-hand rule you should be able to show that they act only to stretch the coil up and down, not to turn it.)

In a coil with N turns, each turn has a couple of this size acting on it, so the total magnitude of the couple is given by:

$$C = BIAN \cos \theta$$

Using magnetic fields – meters and motors

Meters and motors both make use of the rotation of a coil in a magnetic field.

The **moving-coil galvanometer** makes use of a coil of many turns of fine wire suspended in a magnetic field. Current flows through the coil, causing a couple which tends to cause the coil to rotate. This rotation is opposed by a pair of springs in such a way that the angle through which the coil rotates is proportional to the current through it. Figure 5.4.14 shows how this works. The coil of the meter is constructed from fine copper wire to ensure that it is light. This makes the meter compact in size, as well as sensitive and responsive to small changes in current. However, it also means that the meter can carry only a small current, so a meter measuring currents in a circuit needs to be fitted with a **shunt**. This is simply a small-value resistor (much smaller in resistance than the resistance of the meter coil) which allows a known proportion of the current in the circuit to flow through the meter. The use of resistors to adapt the basic galvanometer to measure current or potential difference was discussed in section 4.2.

The principle of construction of the **motor** is similar to that of the galvanometer, except that the coil in the motor is arranged so that it rotates continuously, driving a shaft. To do this it is necessary to have some kind of arrangement to allow electrical contact with the rotating wires of the coil, and to provide a way of reversing the flow of current through the coil. As figure 5.4.14 shows, this is done by the **brushes** and **split-ring commutator** of the motor. Practical motors consist of several coils wound in slots on a core made of thin layers (laminations) of soft iron, known as an **armature**. This construction ensures that wherever the armature stops rotating when the current is switched off, a coil will be in a position to start it rotating again when the current is

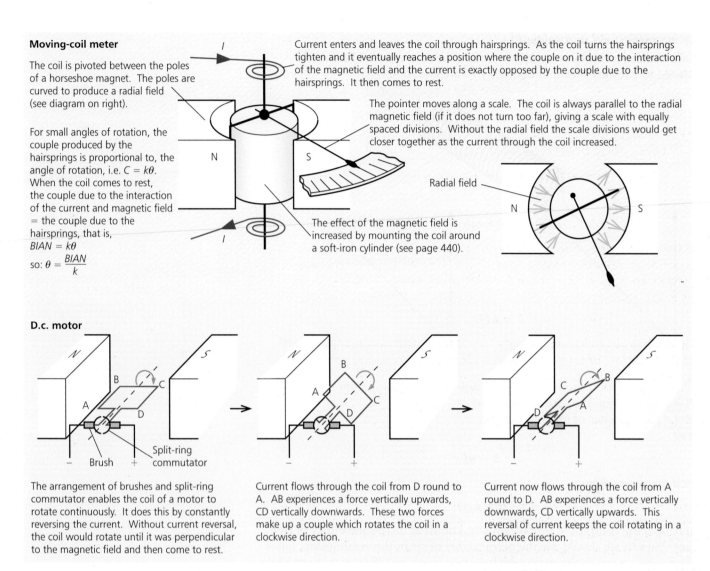

Moving-coil meter

The coil is pivoted between the poles of a horseshoe magnet. The poles are curved to produce a radial field (see diagram on right).

For small angles of rotation, the couple produced by the hairsprings is proportional to, the angle of rotation, i.e. $C = k\theta$. When the coil comes to rest, the couple due to the interaction of the current and magnetic field = the couple due to the hairsprings, that is,

$BIAN = k\theta$

so: $\theta = \dfrac{BIAN}{k}$

Current enters and leaves the coil through hairsprings. As the coil turns the hairsprings tighten and it eventually reaches a position where the couple on it due to the interaction of the magnetic field and the current is exactly opposed by the couple due to the hairsprings. It then comes to rest.

The pointer moves along a scale. The coil is always parallel to the radial magnetic field (if it does not turn too far), giving a scale with equally spaced divisions. Without the radial field the scale divisions would get closer together as the current through the coil increased.

Radial field

The effect of the magnetic field is increased by mounting the coil around a soft-iron cylinder (see page 440).

D.c. motor

The arrangement of brushes and split-ring commutator enables the coil of a motor to rotate continuously. It does this by constantly reversing the current. Without current reversal, the coil would rotate until it was perpendicular to the magnetic field and then come to rest.

Current flows through the coil from D round to A. AB experiences a force vertically upwards, CD vertically downwards. These two forces make up a couple which rotates the coil in a clockwise direction.

Current now flows through the coil from A round to D. AB experiences a force vertically downwards, CD vertically upwards. This reversal of current keeps the coil rotating in a clockwise direction.

Figure 5.4.14

restored. It also provides a more constant force on the shaft as it rotates (a single coil tends to produce short pulses of force which reach a maximum as the coil lies in the plane of the magnetic field).

Magnetic fields around current-carrying wires

We have already seen the shapes of the magnetic fields around some current-carrying wires in figure 5.4.4, and shall now look at how the size of the magnetic field is related to the current through the wire and to the position in relation to the wire.

Measurement of magnetic field strength is usually done by means of a **Hall probe**. The principles of this method of measurement are explored in the box 'The Hall effect' on pages 443–5.

The magnetic field in a solenoid

If one of these techniques is used to explore the magnetic field inside a solenoid, the results shown in figure 5.4.15 are obtained.

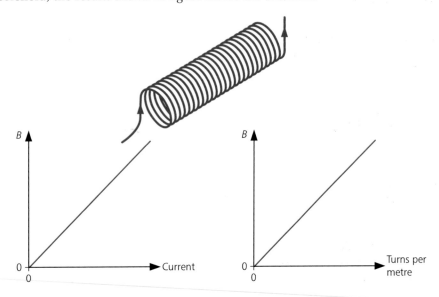

Figure 5.4.15

This investigation shows that inside a solenoid, well away from the ends:
- $B \propto I$, the current through the solenoid
- $B \propto n$, the number of turns per metre.

Thus:

$$B \propto nI$$

which may be written:

$$B = \mu_0 nI$$

where μ_0 is the constant of proportionality, known as the **permeability of free space**. (Strictly we should use the permeability of air in this relationship, but it is very nearly equal to the permeability of free space, just like permittivity.) Like permittivity, permeability concerns how magnetic fields are affected by matter, and we shall look at it in a little more detail shortly. For the moment we will simply note that μ_0 has an exact value of $4\pi \times 10^{-7}$ H m^{-1}.

The magnetic field in a solenoid – worked example

A solenoid is placed with its axis parallel to the Earth's magnetic field, as shown in figure 5.4.16.

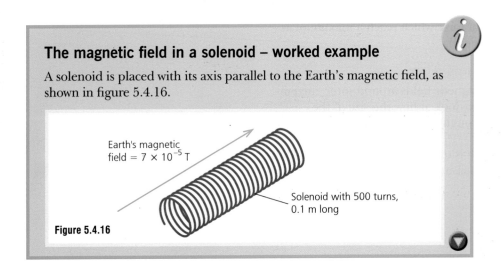

Earth's magnetic field = 7×10^{-5} T

Solenoid with 500 turns, 0.1 m long

Figure 5.4.16

Given the information in the diagram, what current must flow through the solenoid in order that the resultant magnetic field in the middle of the solenoid is zero?

If the resultant field at the centre of the solenoid is to be zero, the field due to the solenoid and the Earth's magnetic field must exactly cancel out. This means that the magnitude of $B_{solenoid} = 7 \times 10^{-5}$ T, so:

$$B = \mu_0 nI$$

$$7 \times 10^{-5} \text{ T} = 4\pi \times 10^{-7} \text{ H m}^{-1} \times \frac{500}{0.1 \text{ m}} \times I$$

Rearranging:

$$I = \frac{7 \times 10^{-5} \text{ T} \times 0.1 \text{ m}}{4\pi \times 10^{-7} \text{ H m}^{-1} \times 500}$$

$$= 1.1 \times 10^{-2} \text{ A}$$

This current must flow in such a way that the front end of the solenoid becomes a south pole, so the current must flow in a *clockwise* direction when the solenoid is viewed from this end (see figure 5.4.4).

The magnetic field around a straight wire

A similar exploration of the magnetic field near a long straight wire produces the result that $B \propto I$ and $B \propto 1/r$ (where r is the distance from the centre of the wire), as figure 5.4.17 shows.

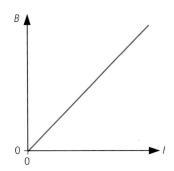 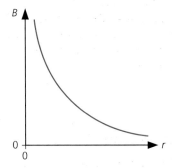

Figure 5.4.17

This means that around a wire carrying a current, the magnetic field lines are concentric rings centred on the wire, and the magnetic field strength at a distance r from the wire follows a relationship in which:

$$B \propto \frac{I}{r}$$

In this case, the constant of proportionality is $\mu_0/2\pi$ (see box 'Why $1/4\pi$?' on pages 420–1, section 5.3), so:

$$B = \frac{\mu_0}{2\pi} \frac{I}{r}$$

This relationship can be used to determine the force between two parallel wires carrying a current, which brings us back to the definition of the ampere.

The ampere

A simple demonstration like that described in figure 5.4.18 shows the interaction between two current-carrying wires.

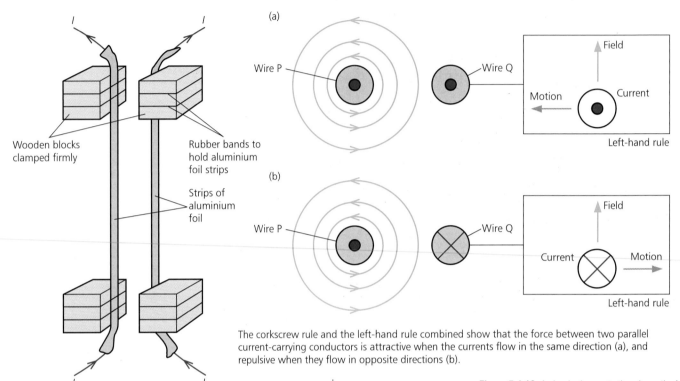

The corkscrew rule and the left-hand rule combined show that the force between two parallel current-carrying conductors is attractive when the currents flow in the same direction (a), and repulsive when they flow in opposite directions (b).

Figure 5.4.18 A simple demonstration shows the force between two conductors carrying currents, used to define the ampere. The two strips are pulled together when the currents through them are in the same direction, and forced apart when the currents are in opposite directions.

If we consider the magnetic field around wire P, at Q (a distance r from P) the magnitude of the field strength will be:

$$B = \frac{\mu_0 I_P}{2\pi r}$$

where I_P is the current in wire P. If I_Q is the current in Q, the magnitude of the force on a length l of wire Q is given by:

$$F = BI_Q l$$

$$= \frac{\mu_0 I_P I_Q l}{2\pi r}$$

The ampere is defined in terms of the force per unit length acting between two parallel conductors. This enables the definition to be in terms of the base units mass, length and time. Earlier definitions of the ampere were complex, and based on the amount of a substance deposited in electrolysis when a given current flowed for a certain length of time. Such definitions were abandoned for practical and theoretical reasons – they were hard to reproduce accurately, and were not in terms of the base quantities mass, length and time.

In this section we have obtained formulae in terms of I, l, μ_0 and so on for the magnetic field around current-carrying wires in various arrangements.

Although we obtained these formulae by investigation, they are in fact a result of the definition of the ampere, as the example in the box 'The effect of defining the ampere' shows.

The effect of defining the ampere

Since the ampere is defined in the way seen in section 4.1, page 278, its definition fixes the value of μ_0, since:

$$F = \mu_0 I_P I_Q l / 2\pi r$$

$$2 \times 10^{-7} \text{ N m}^{-1} = \frac{\mu_0}{2\pi} \frac{1 \text{ A} \times 1 \text{ A}}{1 \text{ m}}$$

that is,

$$\mu_0 = 4\pi \times 10^{-7} \text{ N A}^{-2}$$

This value for μ_0 is therefore *exact* – it is *not* determined by experiment.

The metre is defined by fixing the speed of light c in a vacuum as exactly 299 792 458 m s^{-1} (see section 3.3, page 242). We also saw in section 3.3 that μ_0, c and ε_0 are related by the expression:

$$c^2 = \frac{1}{\mu_0 \varepsilon_0}$$

(see box 'Maxwell's work on electromagnetic waves', page 240). It follows that ε_0 is an exactly defined quantity too, with a value given by:

$$\varepsilon_0 = \frac{1}{\mu_0 c^2}$$

$$\approx 8.854 \times 10^{-12} \text{ F m}^{-1}$$

Using electromagnetism

Electromagnetism plays an important part in our everyday lives, in a wide range of applications. The increasing importance of microelectronics has led to a large increase in the everyday applications of electromagnetism, due to the need for **relays**, required because electronic circuits are not generally capable of directly controlling large currents. Electronics also makes possible cheap, compact sources of sound and video reproduction (through compact disc players, radios, televisions and so on), in which electromagnetism plays an important role in the transfer of energy from the electrical circuit to sound waves via a **loudspeaker** or earpiece. Figure 5.4.19 shows the construction and simple principles of the relay and the loudspeaker.

The relay shown in figure 5.4.19 has a core inside its coil. This core increases the strength of the magnetic field due to the coil. It does this because the domains in the material of the core line up in the direction of the external magnetic field (see box 'Magnetism and electrons' on page 429). The relay needs to produce a strong field when current flows through the solenoid and no field when no current flows, so the core must be easy to magnetise and must demagnetise readily too. It must therefore be made of a material which is

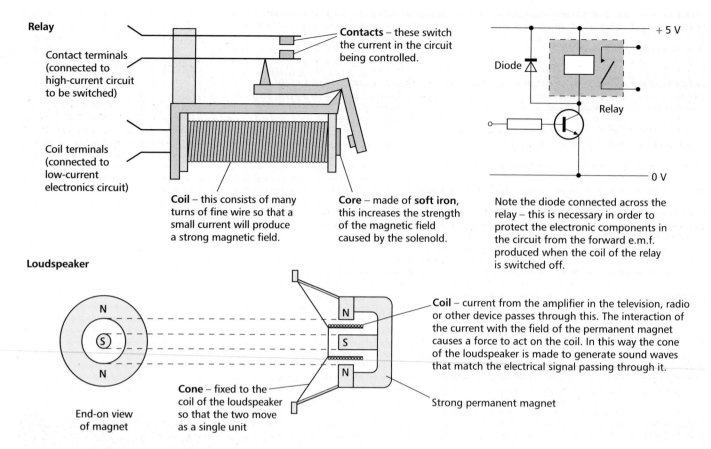

Relay

Contact terminals (connected to high-current circuit to be switched)

Coil terminals (connected to low-current electronics circuit)

Contacts – these switch the current in the circuit being controlled.

Coil – this consists of many turns of fine wire so that a small current will produce a strong magnetic field.

Core – made of **soft iron**, this increases the strength of the magnetic field caused by the solenold.

Diode

+ 5 V

Relay

0 V

Note the diode connected across the relay – this is necessary in order to protect the electronic components in the circuit from the forward e.m.f. produced when the coil of the relay is switched off.

Loudspeaker

N

S

N

End-on view of magnet

Cone – fixed to the coil of the loudspeaker so that the two move as a single unit

N

S

N

Coil – current from the amplifier in the television, radio or other device passes through this. The interaction of the current with the field of the permanent magnet causes a force to act on the coil. In this way the cone of the loudspeaker is made to generate sound waves that match the electrical signal passing through it.

Strong permanent magnet

Figure 5.4.19 Both relays and loudspeakers rely on the effects of electromagnetism and on the magnetic properties of materials.

magnetically soft, like iron. The strength of the magnetic field in the solenoid without a core is given by:

$$B_0 = \mu_0 nI$$

With a core, this becomes:

$$B = \mu_r \mu_0 nI$$

where μ_r and μ_0 are related in the same way as ε_r and ε_0 (see section 4.3, page 317). For iron which is very nearly pure, μ_r is about 5500, so the effect of putting an iron core in the solenoid is to increase the strength of the field in it by this factor. (Care must be taken in using μ_r to calculate magnetic fields in this way – once all the domains are lined up the material becomes **saturated** and no further increase in magnetic field is possible. There is thus a limit to the increase in magnetic field strength that can be produced by a core. In addition, this relationship is strictly true only for a toroidal (doughnut-shaped) core, which has no free poles. The free pole at each end of a cylindrical core produces a magnetic field that opposes the external field, and so reduces the overall field strength from its value calculated by this simple method.)

In contrast to the relay, the loudspeaker uses a permanent magnet. In order to retain its magnetism, the domains must remain lined up after the external field used in the manufacture of the magnet is removed. This requires a magnetically hard material like steel, which has a large **remanence** (this term describes the extent to which the material remains magnetised after an external field is switched off). The core material of an electromagnet must have a low remanence in order to ensure that little or no field remains when the current is zero.

Magnetic fields and moving charges

The relationship between charge, field and force

In this section so far we have considered the interaction of an electric current with a magnetic field. An electric current is no more than a flow of charge, and it is therefore appropriate that we should finish by looking at the interaction of moving charges and magnetic fields. Figure 5.4.20 shows a charge $+q$ moving with velocity v. Its displacement is l after time t.

As we have seen, a wire carrying a current in a magnetic field experiences a force according to the relationship:

$$F = BIl \sin \theta$$

We know that current is rate of flow of charge, and that the charge travels a length l in time t, where $l = vt$. Combining these relationships we get:

$$F = B\left(\frac{q}{t}\right)(vt) \sin \theta$$

or:

$$F = Bqv \sin \theta$$

In accordance with the left-hand rule, the force on the charge acts at right angles to its velocity and to the magnetic field. It is important to remember that this rule applies to the direction of flow of conventional current, and our calculations must take this into account.

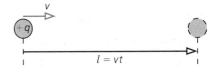

Figure 5.4.20 A moving charge can be considered to be the equivalent of an electric current. If the charge is positive, it moves in the same direction as conventional electric current, while if it is negative it moves in the opposite direction.

Defining the magnetic field using vectors

Force, magnetic field and velocity are all vector quantities. This enables us to use vectors in defining the magnetic field. If the velocity of the positive charge $+q$ is v, the charge experiences a force F when travelling in a magnetic field B such that:

$$F = qv \times B$$

The two vectors v and B are multiplied together using the **cross product** – figure 5.4.21 explains this further. This relationship then defines both the magnitude and direction of the magnetic field in terms of the velocity of a charge and the force on it.

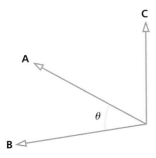

$$\mathbf{C} = \mathbf{A} \times \mathbf{B} = |\mathbf{A}|\ |\mathbf{B}| \sin \theta$$

The cross product of two vectors **A** and **B** produces a third vector **C**.

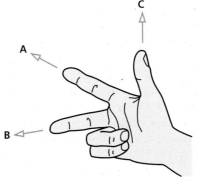

The right-hand rule is used to define the direction of **C**, which is shown by the direction of the thumb when the index finger points in the direction of **A** and the second finger in the direction of **B**. This means that

$$|\mathbf{A}| \times |\mathbf{B}| = -|\mathbf{B}| \times |\mathbf{A}|$$

Figure 5.4.21

The force on a moving charge in a magnetic field – worked example

An electron moves with a velocity of 10^5 m s^{-1} perpendicular to a magnetic field of 2×10^{-3} T. Calculate the force on the electron and show its direction on a diagram. How would the force be affected if the velocity of the electron made an angle of 30° with the magnetic field instead of being perpendicular to it? (The magnitude of the charge on an electron is 1.6×10^{-19} C.)

$$F = Bqv \sin \theta$$

In this case $\theta = 90°$, so $\sin \theta = 1$.
Therefore:

$$F = 2 \times 10^{-3} \text{ T} \times 1.6 \times 10^{-19} \text{ C} \times 10^5 \text{ m s}^{-1}$$

$$= 3.2 \times 10^{-17} \text{ N}$$

If $\theta = 30°$, $\sin \theta = 0.5$, so the force on the electron would be halved. Figure 5.4.22 shows the relative directions of the field, velocity and force.

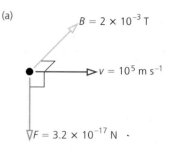

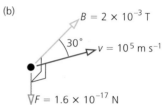

Figure 5.4.22 Changing the angle that the velocity of the charge makes with the field alters the *magnitude* of the force on it, but not its *direction*, that is, it is still perpendicular to both B and v.

The path of a charged particle in a magnetic field

A charge moving in a magnetic field experiences a force which acts at right angles to the velocity of the charge. If the magnetic field is uniform, the situation is one we met in section 1.6, where we saw that the motion of an object under these circumstances was circular. So when a moving charge enters a uniform magnetic field so that its velocity is perpendicular to the field direction, the charge travels along a circular path as shown in figure 5.4.23(a). If the charge enters the field at an angle, the path is slightly different – it is a **helix**, as shown in figure 5.4.23(b). A helical path results from circular motion and linear motion combined, as the worked example on page 446 shows.

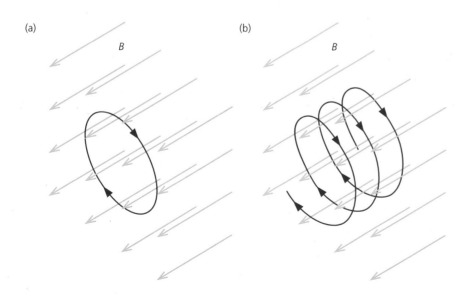

Figure 5.4.23 The pitch of the helix depends on the angle the charge makes with the field.

Charged particles and other types of field

The path of a charge in a uniform electric field is different from that in a uniform magnetic field. In a uniform electric field the force on the charge acts in the same direction, no matter what the direction of motion of the charge, in the same way as the force of gravity always acts in the same direction. Figure 5.4.24 shows the behaviour of a moving particle in a gravitational, an electric and a magnetic field.

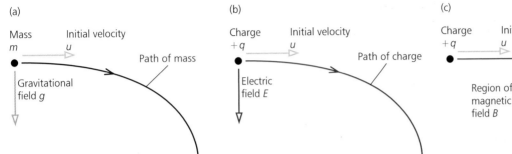

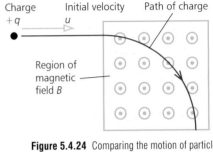

Figure 5.4.24 Comparing the motion of particles in gravitational, electric and magnetic fields.

The path followed by a particle with mass and charge in a uniform gravitational field is shown in figure 5.4.24(a). The same particle is shown moving in a uniform electric field in figure 5.4.24(b). These two diagrams show how both gravitational and electric fields produce parabolic paths. The mathematical tools used to investigate the motion of charges projected in electric fields are the same as those used in section 1.6 to investigate the motion of masses projected in gravitational fields, with charge and electric field strength substituted for mass and gravitational field strength respectively. Comparison of these two figures with figure 5.4.24(c) shows how the motion of the same particle in a uniform magnetic field differs, with the acceleration perpendicular to the field and the instantaneous motion, producing a circular rather than a parabolic path. The box on the mass spectrometer (page 483) shows how a combination of electric and magnetic fields may be used to select charged particles with a small range of velocities.

The Hall effect

The force on a charge moving through a magnetic field gives rise to a phenomenon called the **Hall effect**. Consider a stream of electrons moving through a magnetic field inside a conductor. The interaction between the moving charges and the field causes a force to act on the electrons, pushing them across the conductor and making one side of it positively charged and the other side negatively charged. This charge difference is observable as a potential difference, known as the **Hall voltage**, V_{H}.

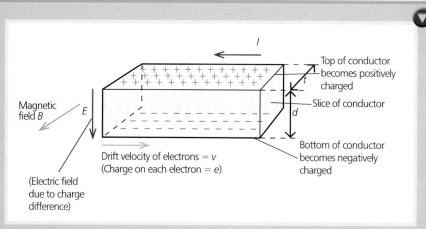

Figure 5.4.25

As electrons flow through the conductor, the magnetic field causes a charge difference to appear across it. This produces an electric field across the conductor perpendicular to the magnetic field. Once equilibrium is reached, the force on the electrons due to the electric field is equal in size and opposite in direction to the force on them due to the magnetic field.

We know from section 5.3 that:

$$E = V_H/d$$

Equating the expressions for force due to the electric field and force due to the magnetic field:

$$Eq = \frac{V_H q}{d} = Bqv$$

So:

$$V_H = Bvd$$

We know that for a conductor, $I = nAve$ (see section 4.2, page 308), so substituting for v:

$$V_H = \frac{BdI}{nAe}$$

$$= \frac{BI}{net} \text{ as } A = dt$$

(B = magnetic field strength, I = current, n = number of charge carriers per unit volume, e = charge on each charge carrier and t = thickness of the conductor.)

This expression shows that the Hall voltage is proportional to the strength of the magnetic field if all other variables are kept constant. It is also inversely proportional to the number of charge carriers per unit volume, so that a semiconductor slice in a magnetic field will produce a larger Hall voltage than a metal in the same field.

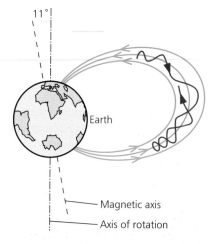

Figure 5.4.26 A highly spectacular example of the motion of particles in a magnetic field. Charged particles from space enter the Earth's magnetic field and become trapped. A detailed analysis of their motion shows that they spiral around the lines of the Earth's magnetic field, reversing direction at the poles (see diagram). The **Van Allen radiation belts** around the Earth consist of vast numbers of charged particles spiralling back and forth from pole to pole like this. When charged particles from these belts enter the Earth's atmosphere they produce the spectacular luminous glow known in the Northern Hemisphere as the **Aurora Borealis** or **Northern Lights.**

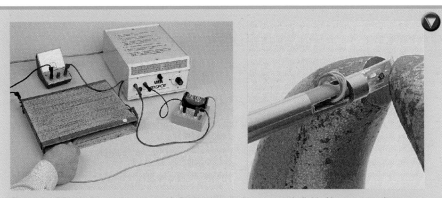

Figure 5.4.27 A Hall probe is calibrated before each use using a magnetic field of known strength – a solenoid carrying an accurately known current is suitable for this. The Hall voltage V_0 corresponding to this known field B_0 is recorded. The Hall voltage V for the unknown field B is then measured. In all cases it is most important to keep the slice of semiconductor in the probe perpendicular to the magnetic field. Since $B \propto V$ and $B_0 \propto V_0$, B can be calculated from the relationship:

$$B = \frac{B_0 V}{V_0}$$

SUMMARY

- **Ferromagnetic** materials are used to make permanent magnets. Once magnetised by a strong external magnetic field, **magnetically hard** materials remain magnetised. **Magnetically soft** materials are magnetic while in an external magnetic field, but lose their magnetism when removed from the external field.

- A wire carrying a current in a magnetic field experiences a force. **Fleming's left-hand rule** gives the relative directions of the force, the current and the field.

- **Magnetic field strength** B is the force per unit length per unit current in a current-carrying conductor at right-angles to the direction of the magnetic field, $B = F/Il$.

- The magnitude of the force F on a conductor of length l carrying a current I at an angle θ to the magnetic field B is given by $F = BIl \sin \theta$.

- For a coil of N turns carrying a current I at angle θ to a magnetic field B, the magnitude of the couple C experienced by the coil is given by $C = BIAN \cos \theta$, where A is the cross-sectional area of the coil.

- The magnitude of the magnetic field B inside a solenoid with n turns per metre is given by $B = \mu_0 nI$, where μ_0 is the permeability of free space.

- The magnitude of the magnetic field B at a distance r from a straight wire carrying a current I is given by $B = \mu_r \mu_0 / 2\pi r$.

- The magnitude of the force per unit length between two parallel conductors P and Q is given by $F = \mu_0 I_P I_Q / 2\pi r$. This relationship forms the basis of the definition of the ampere.

- The magnitude of the force on a charge q moving at velocity v at angle θ to a magnetic field is given by $F = Bqv \sin \theta$.

EXAMPLE

Consider the electron in the example on page 442 and describe its motion in each situation **a** and **b** below. (Take the mass of the electron m_e as 9.1×10^{-31} kg.)

a The electron travels in a circle.

$$F = \frac{mv^2}{r}, \text{ so } r = \frac{mv^2}{F}$$

Substituting:

$$r = \frac{9.1 \times 10^{-31} \text{ kg} \times (10^5 \text{ m s}^{-1})^2}{3.2 \times 10^{-17} \text{ N}}$$

$$= 2.84 \times 10^{-4} \text{ m}$$

The electron moves in a circle with a radius of 0.28 mm.

b The electron has an instantaneous velocity at an angle of 30° to the field.

The instantaneous velocity of the electron can be split into two components. The component parallel to the field is $v \cos 30°$. This component remains unchanged because the force on the electron acts perpendicular to it. The component perpendicular to the field is $v \sin 30°$. This is the tangential velocity of the electron as it travels in a circle.

In this case $F = 1.6 \times 10^{-17}$ N, so:

$$r = \frac{9.1 \times 10^{-31} \text{ kg} \times (10^5 \text{ m s}^{-1} \times \sin 30°)^2}{1.6 \times 10^{-17} \text{ N}}$$

$$= 1.42 \times 10^{-4} \text{ m}$$

The time taken for the electron to travel through 2π radians is $2\pi r/v$, so:

$$T = \frac{2\pi \times 1.42 \times 10^{-4} \text{ m}}{10^5 \text{ m s}^{-1} \times \sin 30°}$$

$$= 1.78 \times 10^{-8} \text{ s}$$

In this time the electron travels along parallel to the field a distance $d = (v \cos 30°)T$, so:

$$d = 10^5 \text{ m s}^{-1} \times \cos 30° \times 1.78 \times 10^{-8} \text{ s}$$

$$= 1.54 \times 10^{-3} \text{ m}$$

The electron travels around a helix with a radius of 1.42×10^{-4} m and a pitch of 1.54×10^{-3} m.

QUESTIONS

(Use $\mu_0 = 4\pi \times 10^{-7}$ H m^{-1}, $m_e = 9.1 \times 10^{-31}$ kg and take e as 1.6×10^{-19} C.)

1 An electron travels horizontally through a magnetic field without being deflected. What does this tell you about the magnetic field?

2 Cosmic rays (charged particles from space) enter the Earth's atmosphere more frequently at the poles than anywhere else. Why?

3 The vertical component of the Earth's magnetic field in the UK is around 5×10^{-5} T. Where round a horizontal wire carrying a current of 0.5 A will the total magnetic field strength be zero?

4 A compass is mounted 40 cm above a wire which runs horizontally in a direction joining magnetic north and magnetic south. The wire carries a direct current of 25 A. If the horizontal component of the Earth's magnetic field at this point is 2×10^{-5} T, by how many degrees will the compass be wrong?

5 What is the magnetic field 10 m from a lightning bolt carrying a current of 20 000 A?
(*Hint:* Treat the bolt as a straight wire carrying a current.)

6 A long solenoid is placed in a region where there is a horizontal magnetic field of 2×10^{-3} T parallel to the axis of the solenoid. The solenoid has 2000 turns per metre along its length.

Calculate:
a the current required to produce zero resultant magnetic field inside the solenoid
b the current required to produce a resultant field of 2×10^{-3} T inside the solenoid in a direction exactly opposite to the external field.
Draw diagrams in each case to explain the relationship between the direction of the current and the magnetic fields produced.

7 A rectangular coil with a mean height 5 cm and mean width 2 cm hangs vertically in a uniform horizontal magnetic field of 120 mT. The coil consists of 100 turns of wire and has a current of 200 mA flowing through it.
a What is the minimum couple that acts on the coil in this situation?
b What is the maximum couple that acts on the coil in this situation?
c Draw a diagram to show the orientation of the coil in the field for **a** and **b**.
d Calculate the forces (if any) that act on the top and bottom of the coil in **b**.
e If the coil is suspended by a torsion wire with a restoring couple of 1.0×10^{-4} N m degree^{-1}, calculate the current through the coil that will produce a rotation of 30°.

8 A slice of germanium with a cross-section 2 mm × 2 mm is placed in a magnetic field B of 0.5 T. A current of 0.1 A flows through the slice, as shown in figure 5.4.28. The apparatus is at room temperature.

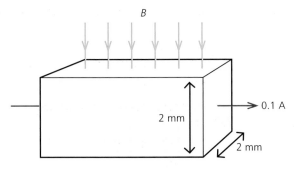

Figure 5.4.28

a If the number of electrons per unit volume in germanium at room temperature is 1.0×10^{23} m^{-3} and the charge on each of these electrons is -1.6×10^{-19} C, calculate the Hall voltage produced across the slice under these conditions.

b Why is it important to specify the temperature of the semiconductor?

9 In theory, a proton can be made to orbit the Earth under the influence of the Earth's magnetic field at the equator if the proton has the correct velocity. If the radius of the orbit is 6.6×10^4 km and the magnetic field at this radius is 2.0×10^{-5} T, calculate the velocity at which the proton must travel. (The charge on a proton is $+e$, and its mass can be taken as 1.67×10^{-27} kg.) Comment on your answer.

10 A beam of electrons enters a magnetic field of 5×10^{-3} T. What velocity must the electrons have if they are to travel in a circle of radius 10 cm?

11 Electrons travelling in a straight line at a speed of 3×10^7 m s^{-1} enter a region between two parallel plates 5 cm apart. The electrons are travelling initially along a path parallel to the two plates and equidistant from each of them. A potential difference of 500 V exists between the plates, the upper plate being positive.
a Sketch the path of the electrons between the two plates.
b Calculate the force on an electron between the two plates.
c Determine the final velocity of an electron leaving the region between plates if the plates are 15 cm long.

12 Electrons enter a region in which there is a magnetic field of 80 mT. If the speed of the electrons is 7.2×10^7 m s^{-1}, calculate the magnitude of the electric field required for the electrons to pass through undeviated. Draw a diagram showing the orientations of the velocity of the electrons, the magnetic field and the electric field.

Developing Key Skills

If you have not already done so, read the focus on page 430.

A well-known illusionist claims to be able to levitate people using magnets. Prepare a 'Science Snippet' for a popular national paper explaining the science behind using magnets in this way.

[Key Skills opportunities: C]

The discovery by Faraday and Henry that electricity could be generated using magnetism paved the way for the multitude of modern uses of electricity, providing ultimately the means for the generation and transmission of electricity. We shall now examine the physics behind the use of magnetic fields to produce electricity – a phenomenon called **electromagnetic induction**.

Introducing electromagnetic induction

Inducing e.m.f.s

Simple investigations like those shown in figure 5.5.1 using permanent magnets, insulated wire and a galvanometer show that it is possible to make a current flow through a conductor when the conductor and the magnet are moved relative to one another.

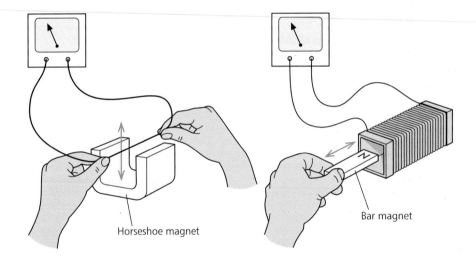

Bar magnet

Horseshoe magnet

Figure 5.5.1 Moving a magnet and a wire relative to one another produces a flow of current. This is sometimes called the **dynamo effect**.

Investigations like this show that:

1 A current flows when the wire is moved relative to the magnet.

2 A current flows when the magnet is moved relative to the wire.

3 No current flows when both wire and magnet are stationary relative to one another.

4 Reversing the direction of movement of the wire or the magnet reverses the direction of the current flow.

5 The magnitude of the current increases with the number of loops of wire in the field, the strength of the magnet and the speed of movement.

Although this investigation detects current, the current is caused by an e.m.f. across the ends of the wire moving in the field. This e.m.f. will be present even when there is no complete circuit. It is therefore usual to refer to the induced e.m.f. rather than the current.

It is also possible to induce an e.m.f. in a wire without physical movement. This can be done by the arrangement shown in figure 5.5.2.

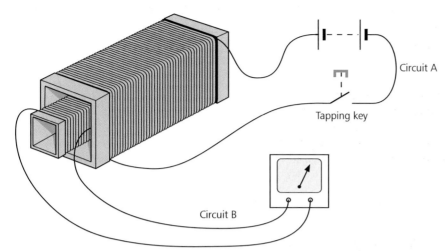

Circuit A

Tapping key

Circuit B

Figure 5.5.2 Changing the current flow in circuit A (by pressing and releasing the tapping key) causes a current to flow briefly in circuit B. This is sometimes called the **transformer effect**, and can be enhanced by inserting a soft-iron core in the smaller solenoid.

In this case an e.m.f. appears across the ends of circuit B (the **secondary circuit**) when a brief pulse of current is allowed to flow through circuit A (the **primary circuit**). This is an example of **mutual induction**, and is used widely in the distribution of electricity, as we shall see later in this section.

Magnetic flux and flux linkage

As with light and electric fields, magnetic fields can be considered using a flow model (see section 3.1, page 212 and section 5.3, box 'Why $1/4\pi$?' on pages 420–1). The term **magnetic flux** Φ describes the 'flow' of magnetism around a magnet or a wire carrying a current, in much the same way that we might measure the flow of light away from a lamp. As figure 5.5.3(a) shows, the **intensity** of a light source at a distance from it can be found by measuring the rate at which light energy passes through a given area, and dividing this rate by the area.

Figure 5.5.3(b) shows how this calculation can be done for magnetic fields. If we consider an area A with a uniform magnetic field B passing through it, the total magnetic flux passing through the area divided by the area tells us the **flux density** B at this point:

$$B = \frac{\Phi}{A}$$

The magnetic flux Φ through the area is measured in webers, Wb, while the magnetic flux density B is measured in tesla, T. These units are related, so that $1\,\text{T} = 1\,\text{Wb m}^{-2}$. Magnetic flux density B and magnetic field strength B are two different models for understanding the behaviour of magnetic fields and are entirely equivalent.

If the coil in figure 5.5.3(c) consists of N turns rather than just a single turn, each turn having a magnetic flux Φ passing through it. The total magnetic flux passing through the circuit in these circumstances is the product $N\Phi$, where $N\Phi$ is called the **flux linkage** through the circuit.

Magnetic flux and electromagnetic induction

The model for explaining electromagnetic induction uses the idea of magnetic flux. The investigations described in figures 5.5.1 and 5.5.2 show that a conductor moved through a magnetic field or placed in a changing magnetic field has an e.m.f. induced in it.

5

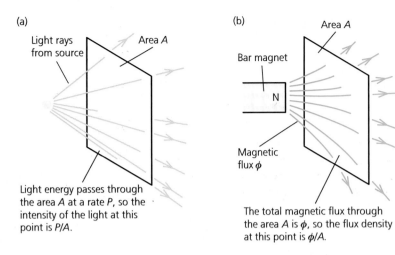

(a)

Light rays from source

Area A

Light energy passes through the area A at a rate P, so the intensity of the light at this point is P/A.

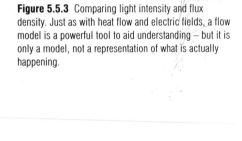

(b)

Area A

Bar magnet

N

Magnetic flux φ

The total magnetic flux through the area A is φ, so the flux density at this point is φ/A.

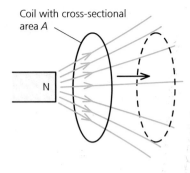

(c)

Coil with cross-sectional area A

N

If the coil of wire is moved relative to a bar magnet, there is a change in the magnetic flux passing through the coil.

Figure 5.5.3 Comparing light intensity and flux density. Just as with heat flow and electric fields, a flow model is a powerful tool to aid understanding – but it is only a model, not a representation of what is actually happening.

Using the idea of magnetic flux, we say that an e.m.f. is induced in a circuit if the flux linkage through the circuit changes. This may be made to happen:

1 by keeping the flux density constant and changing the area enclosed by the circuit, or

2 by changing the flux density and keeping the area enclosed by the circuit constant, or

3 by a combination of **1** and **2**.

Situation **1** is referred to as **flux cutting**, and describes the situation in which a conductor travels through a magnetic field, cutting the lines of flux much as a lawn mower moving through grass cuts the grass as it does so. Situation **2** is described as a **change of flux linkage** through the circuit, which occurs when, for example, a conductor experiences a changing magnetic field due to a changing current in a nearby wire. These situations are illustrated in figure 5.5.4. The e.m.f. induced in the conductor in each case is given by a statement which is known as **Faraday's law of electromagnetic induction**:

> **The e.m.f. induced in a circuit is directly proportional to the rate of flux cutting or to the change of flux linkage through the circuit.**

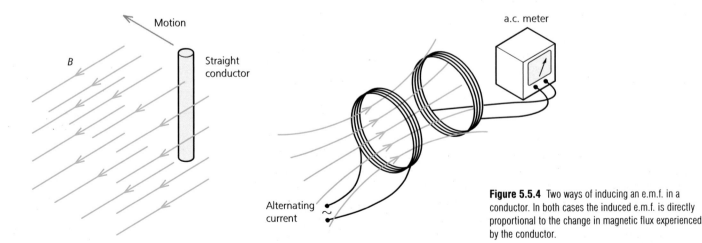

Figure 5.5.4 Two ways of inducing an e.m.f. in a conductor. In both cases the induced e.m.f. is directly proportional to the change in magnetic flux experienced by the conductor.

The magnitude of induced e.m.f. – Faraday's law

In section 4 we used E to represent e.m.f., and $\mathscr{E}$ for back e.m.f. We shall here represent induced e.m.f. by $\mathscr{E}$ to avoid confusion with electric field E.

Faraday's law may be written in mathematical terms using calculus notation:

$$\mathscr{E} \propto \frac{\mathrm{d}}{\mathrm{d}t}(N\varPhi)$$

where $\mathscr{E}$ is e.m.f. and the right-hand side of the relationship means 'the rate of change of flux linkage with time'. (The *direction* of the e.m.f. is given by another law, and will be considered shortly.) Before we can replace the $\propto$ sign with an equals sign, we need to know the constant of proportionality.

The constant of proportionality here can be made unity by choosing the units appropriately, as we did in the definition of the newton in section 1.4 (page 48) – this is in fact how the unit of flux density, the weber, is defined. Faraday's law can therefore be written as:

$$\mathscr{E} = \frac{\mathrm{d}}{\mathrm{d}t}(N\varPhi)$$

The following calculation of induced e.m.f. shows that the definition of the weber in this way is justified, since the relationship can be derived without using Faraday's law.

E.m.f. induced in a straight conductor

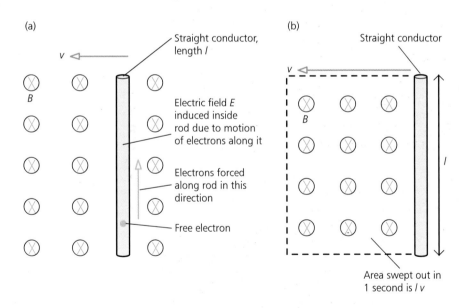

(a)

v

Straight conductor, length l

B

Electric field E induced inside rod due to motion of electrons along it

Electrons forced along rod in this direction

Free electron

(b)

Straight conductor

v

B

l

Area swept out in 1 second is $l\,v$

Figure 5.5.5

Consider a rod moving with a steady velocity v perpendicular to a magnetic field B as in figure 5.5.5(a). Due to the motion of the rod through the field, free electrons in the rod experience a force F and are pushed along the rod. (The direction in which the electrons are pushed can be found using Fleming's right-hand rule, pages 455–6.) This causes an electric field to be set up inside the rod. At equilibrium, the force on an electron due to the electric field and the force on it due to the motion of the rod through the magnetic field will be equal in magnitude and opposite in direction, and so we may write:

$$Ee = Bev$$

that is,

$$E = Bv$$

Now $E = \mathcal{E}/l$, so:

$$\mathcal{E} = Blv$$

Figure 5.5.5(b) shows that the area swept out by the rod each second is lv, so Blv is the area swept out by the rod each second multiplied by the flux density. Therefore:

$$\mathcal{E} = Blv$$

$$= \text{rate of flux cutting}$$

E.m.f. induced in a straight conductor – worked example

An aeroplane with a wingspan of 50 m flies horizontally with a velocity of 180 m s^{-1} at a location where the vertical component of the Earth's magnetic field is 3.5×10^{-5} T. What is the magnitude of the e.m.f. induced across the aeroplane's wingspan?

$$\mathcal{E} = Blv$$

$$= 3.5 \times 10^{-5}\,\text{T} \times 50\,\text{m} \times 180\,\text{m s}^{-1}$$

$$= 0.32\,\text{V (to 2 SF)}$$

E.m.f. induced in a rotating coil

The calculation of the e.m.f. induced in a rotating coil is more complex than that for a straight conductor since the e.m.f. varies with time. However, the calculation uses the same principle of calculating the rate of flux cutting.

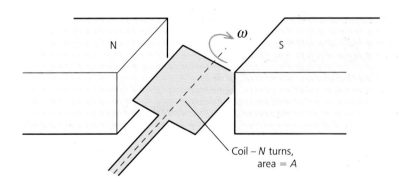

End-on view

Figure 5.5.6

Figure 5.5.6 shows a coil with cross-sectional area A rotating with angular velocity ω in a uniform magnetic field B. At the instant shown, the coil makes an angle θ with the magnetic field. The time at this point is t, which is measured from when $\theta = 0$.

At time t, the flux through each turn of the coil is Φ, given by the relationship:

$$\Phi = BA \sin \theta$$

Since $\theta = \omega t$, this means that:

$$\Phi = BA \sin \omega t$$

Faraday's law tells us that the magnitude of the e.m.f. induced in the coil is given by:

$$\mathscr{E} = \frac{\mathrm{d}}{\mathrm{d}t}(N\Phi)$$

$$= \frac{\mathrm{d}}{\mathrm{d}t}[N(BA \sin \omega t)]$$

$$= BAN \frac{\mathrm{d}}{\mathrm{d}t}(\sin \omega t)$$

$$= BAN\omega \cos \omega t$$

Now when the coil is parallel to the field, $\theta = 0$. This means that $\omega t = 0$, $\cos \omega t = 1$, and $\mathscr{E}$ has its maximum value of $\mathscr{E}_0$, where $\mathscr{E}_0 = BAN\omega$. The relationship for the magnitude of the e.m.f. induced in the coil can then be written as:

$$\mathscr{E} = \mathscr{E}_0 \cos \omega t$$

As we saw in section 1.7, page 94, the cosine variable in this relationship comes from our decision to take $t = 0$ when $\theta = 0$. If we had taken $t = 0$ when $\theta = 90°$, the relationship would have contained a sine variable in place of the cosine. Whichever variable we use, the e.m.f. generated in the coil varies sinusoidally with time, and will produce a similar sinusoidally varying current in any circuit connected to it.

E.m.f. induced in a rotating coil – worked example

A coil with 475 turns and a cross-sectional area of 20 cm^2 rotates at 600 revolutions per minute in a uniform magnetic field of 0.01 T. What are the peak e.m.f. $\mathscr{E}_0$ and the r.m.s. e.m.f. $\mathscr{E}_r$ induced in the coil? Show these values on a graph of the e.m.f. induced in the coil against time.

We know that $\mathscr{E}_0$, the peak e.m.f. induced in the coil, is given by:

$$\mathscr{E}_0 = BAN\omega$$

In this case, $B = 10^{-2}$ T, $A = 2 \times 10^{-3}$ m^2, $N = 475$ and $\omega = (600/60) \times 2\pi$ rad s^{-1} = 20π rad s^{-1}.

Therefore:

$$\mathscr{E}_0 = 10^{-2} \text{ T} \times 2 \times 10^{-3} \text{ m}^2 \times 475 \times 20\pi \text{ rad s}^{-1}$$

$$= 0.60 \text{ V (to 2 SF)}$$

From section 4.4, page 334, we know that $\mathscr{E}_{\text{r.m.s.}} = \mathscr{E}_0/\sqrt{2}$, so:

$$\mathscr{E}_{\text{r.m.s.}} = \frac{0.60 \text{ V}}{\sqrt{2}} = 0.42 \text{ V}$$

The graph showing these values is given in figure 5.5.7.

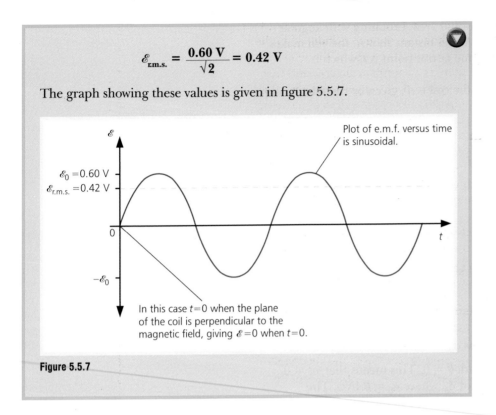

Plot of e.m.f. versus time is sinusoidal.

$\mathscr{E}_0 = 0.60$ V
$\mathscr{E}_{\text{r.m.s.}} = 0.42$ V

In this case $t=0$ when the plane of the coil is perpendicular to the magnetic field, giving $\mathscr{E}=0$ when $t=0$.

Figure 5.5.7

The direction of induced e.m.f. – Lenz's law

So far we have been concerned only with the magnitude of the induced e.m.f., and have said nothing about its direction – that is, the direction in which the induced e.m.f. will tend to make current flow if there is a complete circuit. This problem was considered around 1834 by the Russian physicist Emil Lenz, who formulated what is now known as **Lenz's law**:

> **The induced e.m.f. is always such as to oppose the change which is producing it.**

This statement becomes clearer if we think about the very simple situation shown in figure 5.5.8.

(a)   (b)

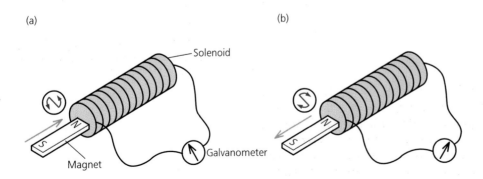

Solenoid

Magnet

Galvanometer

Figure 5.5.8

Figure 5.5.8(a) shows the north pole of a bar magnet approaching one end of a solenoid. Lenz's law tells us that in this situation, the e.m.f. induced in the solenoid causes a current to flow through the circuit (the ends of the solenoid are connected to a galvanometer, so that there is a complete circuit), and that the direction of this current is such that it opposes the change causing it. This means that the current through the solenoid must flow in the direction shown by the ⌇⌇(see figure 5.4.4, page 428, for an explanation of this), as the end of the solenoid will act as a magnetic north pole and produce a repulsive force between the magnet and the solenoid.

The opposite situation is shown in figure 5.5.8(b). Here the north pole of the magnet is moving away from the solenoid. The flow of current is such that the end of the solenoid now becomes a magnetic south pole, attracting the magnet towards the solenoid.

Why does this happen? Probably the simplest way to understand this behaviour is to think in terms of energy transfers. As the magnet is moved towards the solenoid, the current induced in the solenoid causes a magnetic field which repels the magnet. As a result, a force has to be exerted on the magnet to keep it moving towards the solenoid. In this way, energy is transferred from whatever system is pushing the magnet towards the solenoid (the arm muscles of the investigator, for example) to the electrical circuit, through the medium of the magnetic field. When the magnet is pulled away from the solenoid, the current flows in the opposite direction and the magnet experiences an attractive force, requiring a further energy transfer from the 'pulling system' to the electrical circuit. Figure 5.5.9 shows the result of contravening Lenz's law.

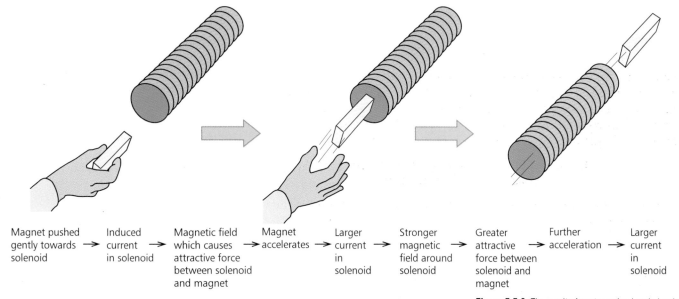

| Magnet pushed gently towards solenoid | → | Induced current in solenoid | → | Magnetic field which causes attractive force between solenoid and magnet | → | Magnet accelerates | → | Larger current in solenoid | → | Stronger magnetic field around solenoid | → | Greater attractive force between solenoid and magnet | → | Further acceleration | → | Larger current in solenoid |

Figure 5.5.9 The result of contravening Lenz's law is the production of energy out of nowhere, an event which runs counter to the laws of physics.

Fleming's right-hand rule

With straight conductors and uniform fields a version of Lenz's law known as **Fleming's right-hand rule** is useful. This rule is similar to the left-hand rule met in section 5.4, figure 5.4.9(b), except that while the left-hand rule relates the direction of the force on a conductor carrying a current in a magnetic field, the right-hand rule relates the direction of the current induced in a conductor moving through a magnetic field. Figure 5.5.10 shows how the right-hand rule is used.

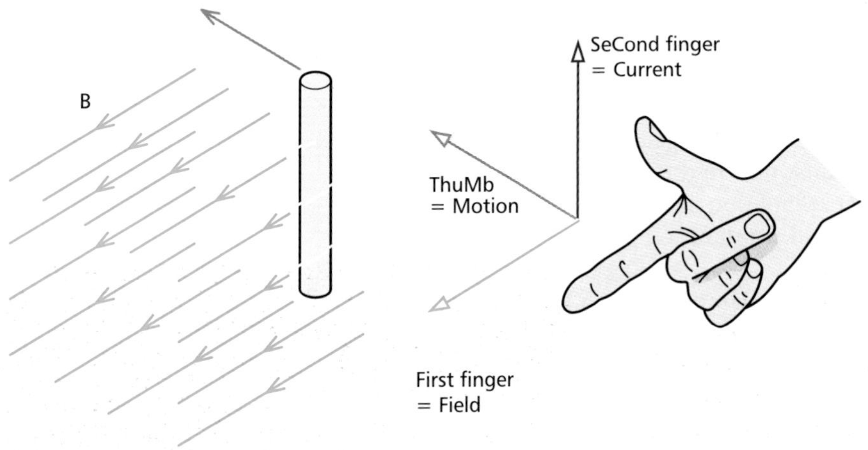

Figure 5.5.10 Fleming's right-hand rule can be used to predict the relationship between the directions of the field, induced current and motion for situations like this.

SeCond finger = Current

ThuMb = Motion

First finger = Field

B

The mathematical expression of Faraday's law of electromagnetic induction is modified to incorporate Lenz's law by placing a negative sign on the right-hand side of the expression:

$$\mathcal{E} = -\frac{d}{dt}(N\Phi)$$

This shows that the e.m.f. produced by the flux change acts to oppose the flux change.

Eddy currents

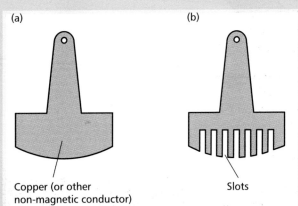

(a)

(b)

Copper (or other non-magnetic conductor)

Slots

Figure 5.5.11
A pendulum made from non-magnetic conducting material like that shown in figure 5.5.11(a) can be made to swing freely from a pivot. If the pendulum is then allowed to swing between the poles of a strong magnet, it comes quickly to rest – the oscillations are heavily damped. If this investigation is repeated with a pendulum with slots cut in it as shown in figure 5.5.11(b), the pendulum still swings quite freely between the poles of the magnet – the damping is much lighter.

The damping of the pendulum is due to **eddy currents** induced in it as it swings and cuts the magnetic flux. Lenz's law shows that the direction of these currents is such that they oppose the motion of the pendulum, and so damp its swing. The path taken by these currents can be found through the right-hand rule. Figure 5.5.12 shows their circular shape, which explains the term 'eddy' applied to them. Slots cut in the pendulum greatly reduce the flow of eddy currents, and so reduce the damping.

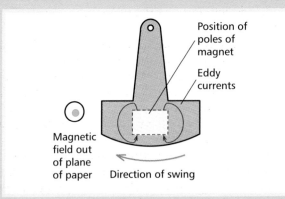

Position of poles of magnet

Eddy currents

Magnetic field out of plane of paper

Direction of swing

Figure 5.5.12

NIKOLA TESLA – THE MAN WHO GAVE THE WORLD ALTERNATING CURRENT

Born in 1856, Nikola Tesla grew up in a tiny village in what is now known as Croatia. Following a school career in which he excelled at mathematics, Tesla studied electrical engineering in Graz, Austria, and in Prague. A spell of work in Budapest on a project to introduce the telephone (recently invented by the American, Alexander Graham Bell) to the city then led to a position based in Paris and Strasbourg. This was with Continental Edison, a French company which manufactured dynamos and motors, and installed lighting systems under patents filed by the American inventor of the electric lamp, Thomas Edison.

Since his student days, Tesla had been critical of the design of direct current motors, with their clumsy commutators needed to reverse the current flow through the coil every half turn. Tesla was convinced that this system could be replaced by one in which alternating current was used to produce a rotating magnetic field that would lock the coil of a motor in its embrace, causing it to rotate without the need for any device to change constantly the direction of flow of current. With an uncanny gift for visualising the details of practical schemes like this so that they seemed absolutely real before his eyes, Tesla had already designed an alternator and motor before joining Continental Edison. Now, the workshops provided him with the facilities to realise his dream. Working without drawings, Tesla constructed his alternator and motor in a Strasbourg machine shop. With the assembly complete, he started up his alternator. Instantly the motor's armature turned, built up to full speed, and then continued to turn in almost complete silence.

Tesla could interest no-one in his ideas, and decided to emigrate to the USA in order to work with Edison, who was working on the production and distribution of electricity from electric power plants. Stepping off the boat in Manhattan in the summer of 1884, Tesla's worldly goods consisted of four cents, a book of his own poems, two technical articles he had written, some calculations for designing a flying machine, and some mathematics done in order to solve a particularly difficult integral.

In the USA it was a fellow electrical engineer called George Westinghouse who saw the possibilities of Tesla's ideas for alternating current – Edison was strongly wedded to the idea that the future lay in direct current. In a deal done with Westinghouse, Tesla became a rich man, and was able to spend much of the rest of his life working in his own laboratory on a variety of projects, including electromagnetic waves and the transmission of electrical energy through the Earth's atmosphere.

Tesla never married, and did not find personal relationships easy. He confided little in his assistants, and never took on the role of mentor to someone younger who could have carried on his work. With his phenomenal powers of memory, Tesla committed very few of his thoughts to paper in any formal way (with the exception of the many patents he held), and it is impossible to know how many of his ideas are lost forever. There seems little doubt that Tesla had the talent to influence the development of electrical engineering in even more ways than he did.

Figure 5.5.13 Tesla gave his name to the unit of magnetic field strength. He is seen here making notes in the midst of an electrical experiment in his laboratory.

Figure 5.5.14 Tesla's legacy is the system of alternating current generation and transmission used worldwide.

As we saw in section 5.4, an electric motor consists of a coil in a magnetic field. Current flowing through the coil makes it rotate, and it can then be used to do something useful. We have also seen in this section that an e.m.f. is induced in a coil rotating in a magnetic field – Lenz's law suggests that this e.m.f. will oppose the flow of current which is causing the coil to rotate. Investigations like that shown in figure 5.5.15 confirm that this induced e.m.f. exists. It is called a **back e.m.f.**, since it acts to oppose the flow of current through the motor.

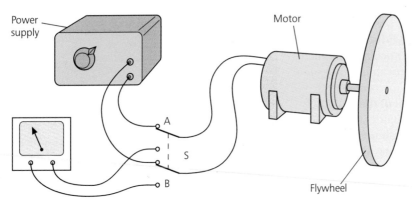

Figure 5.5.15 If switch S is moved from A to B while the motor is running, the voltmeter shows the presence of a back e.m.f., generated by the motion of the coil of the motor through the magnetic field.

If the motor is connected to a power supply with a negligible internal resistance and an e.m.f. V, the net e.m.f. across the motor will be $V - \mathscr{E}_{back}$. This net e.m.f. is responsible for the flow of current I through the resistance R of the windings of the motor, so we may write:

$$V - \mathscr{E}_{back} = IR$$

Rearranging this and multiplying both sides by I gives:

$$VI = \mathscr{E}_{back}I + I^2R$$

that is,

Power drawn from supply	=	**power used to move current against back e.m.f.**	+	**power dissipated in resistance of windings as thermal energy**

The power used to move current through the motor against the back e.m.f. represents the **useful power** supplied to the motor – it is the rate at which the motor transfers energy to the load (see question 7 on page 466). In a freely running motor, the back e.m.f. is almost equal to the e.m.f. of the power supply – the only energy input to the motor is that required to overcome the frictional and drag forces within it. However, once a load is connected to the motor, the speed of rotation drops. This causes a drop in $\mathscr{E}_{back}$, so that the current through the motor increases. This increase in current allows energy to be transferred to the load, at a rate equal to $\mathscr{E}_{back}I$. As a result of the increased current, energy is also dissipated in the coil of the motor, at a rate I^2R, so the increase in the rate of transfer of energy to the load is accompanied by a decrease in the efficiency of the motor.

Generators – a.c. and d.c.

Both a.c. and d.c. generators make use of a coil rotating in a magnetic field, as shown in figure 5.5.16. The basic arrangement is that shown in figure 5.5.6 on page 452. In the a.c. generator, the sinusoidally alternating current leaves the coil via brushes. These make contact with **slip rings** connected to each end of the coil. The d.c. generator uses a split-ring commutator like that used in the d.c. motor (figure 5.4.14, page 435). The connections to the coil change over when the plane of the coil is perpendicular to the magnetic field, so one brush is always positive while the other is always negative. As in the case of the motor, a single coil has been used in the diagrams here for clarity. Just like motors, practical generators use several coils wound on a laminated core.

The a.c. generator

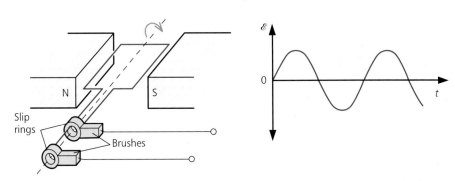

The d.c. generator

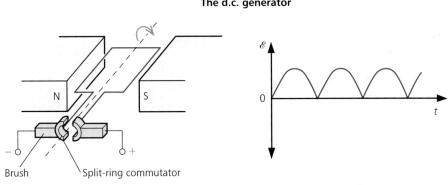

Figure 5.5.16

Transmission of electricity

National systems for transmitting electricity over long distances invariably use alternating current at high voltages, despite the fact that most domestic appliances require lower voltages and direct currents, especially if they use electronics in their control systems. The reason for this is concerned with energy losses. In the UK the National Grid uses voltages of 132 kV, 275 kV and 400 kV for transmission.

Transformers

Stepping up and stepping down

The 'stepping up' and 'stepping down' of voltages in the National Grid is carried out using **transformers**. These devices use the principle of mutual induction. The construction details of practical transformers vary, according to their particular function.

Power losses in cables

As with any other electrical circuit, the distribution of electricity relies on conductors to carry electricity, in this case from the power station to the consumer. A rough estimate of the resistance of the conductors used in the 132 kV part of the National Grid system gives a figure of about $0.2\ \Omega\ km^{-1}$. As an example, assume that a cable in this part of the grid supplies electricity to consumers such that the effective current through the cable is 500 A. The effective rate of energy supply to the cable is thus given by:

$$P = IV$$

$$= 500\ A \times 132\ 000\ V$$

$$= 6.6 \times 10^7\ W\ (66\ MW)$$

If the cable is 10 km long, the voltage drop V_{lost} along the length of the cable can also be calculated:

$$V_{lost} = IR = 500\ A \times (10\ km \times 0.2\ \Omega\ km^{-1})$$

$$= 1000\ V\ (or\ 1\ kV)$$

This represents a small voltage drop of $(1/132) \times 100\% \approx 0.8\%$. As a result of this voltage drop across the resistance of the cable, some of the energy supplied to the cable is dissipated as thermal energy along its length. This can be calculated too, from the resistance of the cable ($2\ \Omega$) and the current through it (500 A):

$$P_{lost} = I^2R$$

$$= (500\ A)^2 \times 2\ \Omega$$

$$= 5 \times 10^5\ W\ (or\ 0.5\ MW)$$

This represents the same loss in power as the drop in voltage across the cable – about 0.8% (0.76% to 2 SF). This is not surprising in view of the definition of the volt!

If the supply voltage was reduced by a factor of 10, to 13.2 kV instead of 132 kV, the current through the cable would have to be increased by a factor of 10 in order that the power input to the transmission line remained at 66 MW (since $P = IV$). Repeating the calculations for voltage drop and power lost along the cable in this case gives the following results:

$$V_{lost} = IR = 5000\ A \times (10\ km \times 0.2\ \Omega\ km^{-1})$$

$$= 10\ 000\ V\ (or\ 10\ kV)$$

$$P_{lost} = I^2R$$

$$= (5000\ A)^2 \times 2\ \Omega$$

$$= 5 \times 10^7\ W\ (or\ 50\ MW)$$

This time the voltage drop amounts to some 76% of the input voltage, and the power dissipated as thermal energy along the length of the cable is a similar proportion of the energy supplied to the cable. In both cases this represents an increase in losses by a factor of 100, because the energy dissipated in a resistance is proportional to (current)². Thus, increasing the current through the cable by a factor of 10 increases the energy dissipated in it by a factor of $10^2 = 100$, a good reason for transmitting electricity at high voltages.

A simple transformer consists of two coils, the **primary** and the **secondary**, wound over a **core** made of a magnetically soft material, as shown in figure 5.5.17. There is no electrical connection between the primary and secondary coils, but the soft-iron core provides a magnetic link between them.

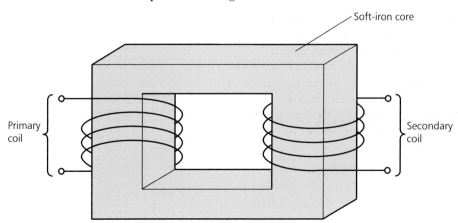

Figure 5.5.17 The principle of construction of the transformer

An alternating e.m.f. applied to the primary coil produces an alternating current through it, which produces an alternating magnetic flux in the core. This alternating flux passes through the secondary coil, in which it induces an alternating e.m.f. The e.m.f. induced in the secondary coil and the e.m.f. applied to the primary coil are related to the ratio of the numbers of turns in the two coils.

Transformer relationships

Investigations like those described in figure 5.5.19 overleaf show that, to a good approximation, transformers transform voltage in the same ratio as the ratio of turns on the primary and secondary coils:

$$\frac{V_s}{V_p} = \frac{N_s}{N_p}$$

where V_s = e.m.f. induced in secondary coil, N_s = number of turns on secondary coil, V_p = e.m.f. applied to primary coil, N_p = number of turns on primary coil.

Many practical transformers approach 100% efficiency, which means that virtually all the electrical energy supplied to the primary coil appears in the secondary coil. For an **ideal transformer** (one that is 100% efficient):

Figure 5.5.18 Maintenance work is carried out on a pole-mounted transformer.

Power supplied to primary = power appearing in secondary

Since $P = IV$, if I_p is the current through the primary and I_s the current through the secondary, then:

$$I_p V_p = I_s V_s$$

so:

$$\frac{V_s}{V_p} = \frac{N_s}{N_p} = \frac{I_p}{I_s}$$

The efficiency of a transformer

The overall efficiency of a transformer is governed by a number of factors:

- The resistance of the coils is important, especially if the current through them is high, since the energy losses are proportional to (current)² as we saw in the box 'Power losses in cables', page 460. The resistance of coils that carry large currents is minimised by the use of thick wire.
- The alternating magnetic flux induces eddy currents in the core. These cause the core to get hot, and can be a major source of energy loss. Eddy currents are minimised by using a core made of thin laminations separated by very thin insulating layers. These reduce eddy currents in the same way as the slots cut in the pendulum in figure 5.5.11, page 456.
- The magnetisation of the core is repeatedly changed from one direction to the other and back again. This requires energy, and causes the core to get hot. Suitable choice of material for the core reduces this effect, as figure 5.5.20 shows.
- If the core of the transformer is not well designed and made, some leakage of the flux may occur, reducing the e.m.f. induced in the secondary coil. An extreme example of this is in the investigation described in figure 5.5.19(a), where the core is incomplete – insertion of the remaining part of the core in this investigation increases the e.m.f. induced in the secondary coil quite dramatically.

Investigating transformers

The behaviour of transformers is easily investigated using some simple apparatus.

Figure 5.5.19(a) shows the effect of changing the number of turns on the secondary coil of a transformer while keeping the number of turns on the primary constant. As more and more coils are looped onto the core, the brightness of the lamp increases, showing that the potential difference across it rises as the number of coils increases.

Using coils with a known number of turns, the effect of varying the ratio of the number of turns on the primary and secondary coils can be investigated (figure 5.5.19(b)). One way of doing this is to connect a known supply voltage (for example 2 V a.c.) to the primary and to make measurements of the output from the secondary using a cathode ray oscilloscope as a voltmeter.

Finally, a spectacular demonstration of the large current that may be supplied by the secondary of a step-down transformer is shown in figure 5.5.19(c).

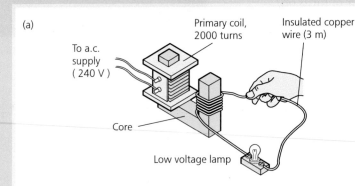

(a)

Primary coil, 2000 turns

Insulated copper wire (3 m)

To a.c. supply (240 V)

Core

Low voltage lamp

As wire is looped onto the core, forming the secondary coil of the transformer, the brightness of the lamp steadily increases. (Notice that the core of the transformer forms an incomplete magnetic loop – the effect of completing the loop is easily investigated with this apparatus.)

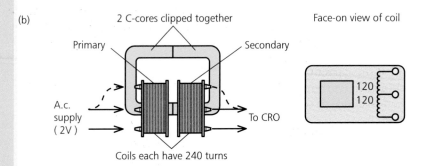

(b)

2 C-cores clipped together

Primary

Secondary

A.c. supply (2V)

To CRO

Coils each have 240 turns

Face-on view of coil

120
120

Each coil has a connection at either end of the wire, together with a third connection at its midpoint. This means that transformers with the following primary:secondary turns ratios can be made and studied – 120:120, 120:240, 240:120 and 240:240.

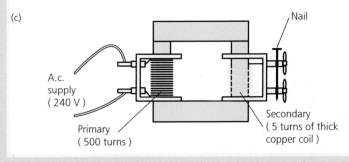

(c)

Nail

A.c. supply (240 V)

Primary (500 turns)

Secondary (5 turns of thick copper coil)

This demonstration shows clearly that when a transformer steps down the voltage, the current is stepped up, resulting in rapid melting of the iron nail.

Figure 5.5.19

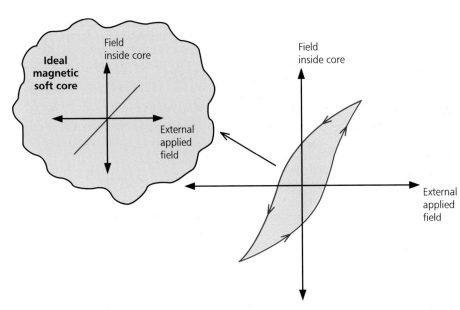

Figure 5.5.20 As the external field surrounding a piece of magnetic material is increased and decreased, the field inside the magnetic material varies like this – compare it with the stress–strain graph for rubber in figure 2.5.2, page 187. As with rubber, the work done in taking the material round the hysteresis loop depends on the area enclosed by the loop. An ideal core would have a hysteresis loop enclosing zero area.

Worked example

An ideal transformer has 40 turns on its secondary coil and 3200 turns on its primary. Calculate the current through a 15 Ω resistor connected to the secondary coil if a 240 V a.c. supply is connected to the primary coil. What current must flow through the primary coil?

We know that:

$$\frac{V_s}{V_p} = \frac{N_s}{N_p}$$

so substituting values we have:

$$\frac{V_s}{240\text{ V}} = \frac{40}{3200}$$

that is,

$$V_s = \frac{40 \times 240\text{ V}}{3200}$$

$$= 3\text{ V}$$

Applying Ohm's law to the resistor:

$$I = \frac{V}{R}$$

$$= \frac{3\text{ V}}{15\ \Omega}$$

$$= 0.2\text{ A}$$

The power dissipated in the resistor $= IV = 0.2\text{ A} \times 3\text{ V} = 0.6\text{ W}$. This power must have come originally from the primary, and as the transformer is ideal, the power supplied to the primary coil must equal the power dissipated in the resistor.

$$\textbf{Power in primary} = 0.6\text{ W} = V_p I_p = 240\text{ V} \times I_p$$

so:

$$0.6\text{ W} = 240\text{ V} \times I_p$$

that is,

$$I_p = \frac{0.6\text{ W}}{240\text{ V}}$$

$$= 2.5 \times 10^{-3}\text{ A}$$

Fields and telecommunications

Electromagnetic waves

Section 3.3 described how the physicist James Clerk Maxwell deduced that an oscillating electric field produced an oscillating magnetic field at right angles to it, and that these fields can be self sustaining if they travel through space with the velocity of light – in other words, they are electromagnetic waves. Telecommunications has always made great use of electromagnetic waves (even relatively simple methods of telecommunication like semaphore signalling and telegraphs). But the understanding of electromagnetic waves that came in the late nineteenth century paved the way for the communication technologies we know today, and the communications applications of the sophisticated electronic devices developed in the twentieth century.

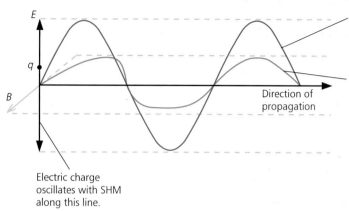

Motion of electric charge produces electric field which radiates out in this plane with amplitude that varies sinusoidally.

Motion of electric charge also produces magnetic field which radiates out in this plane with amplitude that varies sinusoidally.

Direction of propagation

Electric charge oscillates with SHM along this line.

Figure 5.5.21 The motion of an accelerated charge leading to the production of an electromagnetic wave that varies sinusoidally with time and position.

The first experimental evidence for the electromagnetic waves predicted by Maxwell was provided by Hertz, who showed that electric currents can be used to generate what we now call radio waves. The production of these waves requires a *changing* electric current, much as the induction of an electric current requires a changing magnetic field – it is charges with accelerated motion that are responsible for the production of electromagnetic fields. Figure 5.5.21 shows the motion of a charge moving with simple harmonic motion, and how this produces combined electric and magnetic fields.

We can understand how the two fields are related to the motion of the charge by using ideas met earlier. The charge in figure 5.5.21 moves with simple harmonic motion – its equation of motion can be written as:

$$x = A \sin 2\pi ft$$

as we saw in section 1.7. This expression explains the sinusoidal nature of the electric and magnetic fields. The relationship between moving charges and magnetic fields seen in section 5.4 shows why the electric field and the magnetic field are perpendicular to one another. Finally, just as the electromagnetic wave is produced by a charge moving with SHM, so the wave may cause a charge to move with SHM as the wave travels past it. This interaction of charges moving with accelerated motion and electromagnetic waves forms the basis of radio telecommunications, where charges move in the aerials used to broadcast and receive the radio signals. The plane of these aerials must be oriented in the same plane as the oscillation of the electric field in the radio wave, as was noted in figure 3.4.29, page 264.

SUMMARY

- **Magnetic flux** Φ describes the magnetic field around a magnet or current-carrying conductor in terms of a flow model. The magnetic flux through an area A in which the magnetic field strength is B is given by $\Phi = BA$. The **flux linkage** or total magnetic flux through a coil of N turns is given by $N\Phi$.

- The e.m.f. induced in a circuit $\mathcal{E}$ is given by **Faraday's law of electromagnetic induction** – the induced e.m.f. in a circuit is directly proportional to the rate of flux cutting or to the change in flux linkage through a circuit, $\mathcal{E} \propto \mathrm{d}(N\Phi)/\mathrm{d}t$.

- **Lenz's law** gives the direction of induced e.m.f. – the induced e.m.f. is always such as to oppose the change which is causing it. For a straight conductor in a uniform field, Fleming's right-hand rule gives the relative directions of the current induced, the direction of motion and the direction of the field. Combining Faraday's law and Lenz's law gives the relationship $\mathcal{E} = -\mathrm{d}(N\Phi)/\mathrm{d}t$.

- For a rod of length l moving with a velocity v through a magnetic field B, $\mathcal{E} = Blv$ when B, l and v are mutually perpendicular.

- For a coil with N turns and cross-sectional area A rotating with angular velocity ω in a uniform magnetic field B, $\mathcal{E} = BAN\omega \cos \omega t = \mathcal{E}_0 \cos \omega t$ where $\mathcal{E}_0$ is the maximum value of $\mathcal{E}$, when the coil is parallel to the field.

- A.c. and d.c. **generators** both generate a current by rotating a coil in an electric field. In the a.c. generator, the brushes make contact with slip rings, while the d.c. generator has a split-ring commutator.

- In the National Grid, electricity is transmitted at high voltages to avoid energy losses. The voltages are stepped up and down by **transformers**.

- The ratio of voltages in the **primary** and **secondary** coils of a transformer is equal to the ratio of the number of turns in each coil: $V_S/V_P = N_S/N_P$. An **ideal transformer** is 100% efficient, and $N_S/N_P = I_P/I_S$.

QUESTIONS

1 The north pole of a bar magnet is moved towards one end of a copper pipe. Describe and explain what happens.

2 The **magneto** used in old-fashioned car engines consisted of a magnet mounted on the flywheel of the engine and a coil fixed next to the flywheel. When the flywheel rotated, the magnet passed the coil and caused a spark to be produced at the spark plug. How did this work?

3 An aeroplane with a wingspan of 32 m is flying horizontally in a region where the vertical component of the Earth's magnetic field is 6.0×10^{-4} T. If the aeroplane's velocity is 800 km h^{-1}, what is the potential difference between the wing tips of the aeroplane? Could this potential difference be used to provide power for the aircraft's systems?

4 Figure 5.5.22 shows a rod of length $2l$ rotating in a magnetic field.
  a Write down an expression for the area swept out by one half of the rod in one revolution.
  b If the period of rotation of the rod is $2\pi/\omega$, write down an expression for the rate at which one half of the rod sweeps out area.
  c If the flux density in this region is B, write down an expression for the rate at which one half of the rod sweeps out magnetic flux.
  d Hence write down an expression for the e.m.f. between the centre of the rod and each end.
  e What is the p.d. between the two opposite ends of the rod?

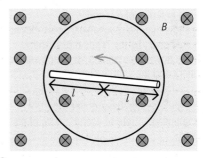

Figure 5.5.22

5 The device described in question 4 is a **homopolar generator** which can be used to generate a steady e.m.f. A practical version of this uses a copper disc rotating in a magnetic field. This reduces the internal e.m.f. of the device, and it is used in applications where a low d.c. voltage is required together with a high current – in electroplating, for example. One such generator consists of a metal disc 1.5 m in diameter, rotating in a vertical plane in a horizontal magnetic field of 80 mT. What speed of rotation is required to produce an e.m.f. of 5.0 V between the rim of the disc and its axis?

6 A conducting liquid flowing through a pipe in a magnetic field may cut lines of magnetic flux and so generate an e.m.f. across opposite sides of the liquid. This e.m.f. can be used to measure the flow rate of the liquid, which may be fruit juice, water, mercury or even sewage. In a brewery, beer flows through a 20 cm diameter horizontal plastic pipe at a rate of 0.5 m^3 s^{-1}. The pipe is in a vertical magnetic field of 5×10^{-3} T. What is the e.m.f. between opposite sides of the liquid?

7 Figure 5.5.23 shows a rod of length l carrying a current I in a magnetic field B.

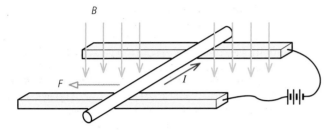

Figure 5.5.23

Because of the interaction of the current and the magnetic field, the rod experiences a force F, which causes it to move with a constant velocity v.

a Write down an expression for the force F in terms of B, I and l.

b Show that the force F does mechanical work at a rate given by $P_m = BIlv$.

c Write down an expression for the back e.m.f. $\mathcal{E}$ induced in the rod in terms of B, l and v.

d Hence show that the mechanical power developed in this situation is given by the product of $\mathcal{E}$ and I.

e Now write down expressions for the power supplied by the battery and the energy dissipated in the circuit as heat, assuming the total resistance of the circuit is R.

f Use the expressions that you have derived to show that:

Power supplied by battery	=	rate of useful (mechanical) work	+	rate of dissipation of heat in circuit

g Derive the same expression by applying Kirchhoff's laws to the circuit.

8 An electric motor is connected to a 15 V battery of negligible internal resistance and is allowed to spin freely at 40 r.p.m. A back e.m.f. of 14 V across the motor is measured.

a If the resistance of the coil is 5 Ω, what current flows through the motor?

b Calculate the mechanical power being developed by the motor when spinning freely – this power is being used to overcome friction within the motor itself.

c Calculate the power supplied by the battery.

d Calculate the power dissipated as heat in the motor.

e The motor is now connected to a load, and its speed drops to 30 r.p.m. Assuming that the mechanical power required to overcome friction is the same as before (that is, as calculated in your answer to **b**), what useful mechanical power does the motor now develop?

f Deduce the running speed that would produce the greatest mechanical power from this motor.

9 A factory is to be supplied with electricity at a rate of 15 MW using a high voltage distribution system. The resistance of the power line is 5 Ω. Calculate the power losses in the line if the supply voltage is **a** 100 kV **b** 10 kV. Which supply voltage would be more suitable?

10 An a.c. generator consists of a rectangular coil of 500 turns, with an area of 3.2×10^{-3} m^2. This coil rotates at a rate of 3000 r.p.m. in a horizontal magnetic field of 6.0×10^{-2} T.

a Calculate the peak e.m.f. produced by this generator.

b Sketch a graph of e.m.f. versus time for one complete cycle.

c Using sketches and text as necessary, add to your graph in **b** details of the orientation of the coil with respect to the field when the e.m.f. has its maximum, minimum and zero values.

d Show on your graph what would happen if the rate of rotation of the coil was reduced to 2000 r.p.m.

11 A.c. generators produce voltages that vary sinusoidally. This is convenient when we come to use transformers to step voltages up and down – why?

Developing Key Skills

Write and design an entry for an illustrated children's encyclopaedia explaining *either* gravity *or* static electricity *or* magnetism. The encyclopaedia is aimed at children between the ages of 9 and 14, and it is important that the entry describes and explains ideas at a level appropriate to this age group. Each entry can be up to one page in length, including necessary diagrams and photographs.

[Key Skills opportunities: C, IT]

5 | QUESTIONS

Where further data are required, consult the table on page 583.

1 a Define *gravitational field strength* at a point in a gravitational field. **(1 mark)**

b Tides vary in height with the relative positions of the Earth, the Sun and the Moon which change as the Earth and the Moon move in their orbits. Two possible configurations are shown in the figure.

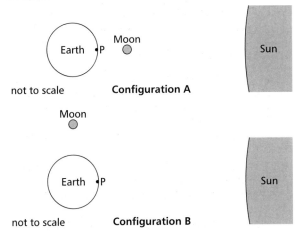

Consider a 1 kg mass of sea water at position **P**. This mass experiences forces F_E, F_M and F_S due to its position in the gravitational fields of the Earth, the Moon and the Sun respectively.

i Draw labelled arrows on copies of **both** diagrams in the figure to indicate the three forces experienced by the mass of sea water at **P**. **(3 marks)**

ii State and explain which configuration, **A** or **B**, of the Sun, the Moon and the Earth will produce the higher tide at position **P**. **(2 marks)**

c Calculate the magnitude of the gravitational force experienced by 1 kg of sea water on the Earth's surface at **P**, due to the **Sun's** gravitational field.

radius of the Earth's orbit $= 1.5 \times 10^{11}$ m
mass of the Sun $= 2.0 \times 10^{30}$ kg
universal gravitational constant, $G = 6.7 \times 10^{-11}$ N m² kg⁻²

(3 marks)
(Total 9 marks)

(AQA 1999)

2 Solar storms consist of protons and helium nuclei emitted from the sun. A particular solar storm hits the Earth's atmosphere at a speed of 1.2×10^6 m s⁻¹. The particles pass above the North magnetic pole moving parallel to the Earth's surface. In this region the Earth's magnetic field is directed vertically downwards and has a flux density of 5.8×10^{-5} T.

a Calculate the radius of the path of a proton from the storm as it passes directly above the Earth's North magnetic pole.

mass of a proton $= 1.7 \times 10^{-27}$ kg
charge on a proton $= 1.6 \times 10^{-19}$ C **(3 marks)**

b The figure shows the initial velocity of a proton and the direction of the Earth's magnetic field. Draw and label, on a copy of the figure, the path of the proton and that of a helium nucleus which has the same initial velocity as the proton. State on your copy of the diagram the radius of the path of each particle.

mass of a helium nucleus $= 6.8 \times 10^{-27}$ kg
charge on a helium nucleus $= 3.2 \times 10^{-19}$ C

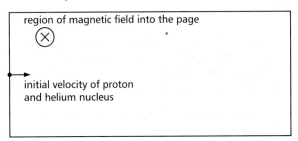

(3 marks)
(Total 6 marks)

(AQA 1999)

3 A uniform conducting bar has a length L and a mass M. The electrical resistance of a length L of the bar is R. It slides, with negligible friction, down two thin parallel metal rails inclined at angle θ as shown in the figure.

The rails are a distance $L/2$ apart and may be assumed to be perfectly conducting. They are connected together at the bottom of the incline with conducting wire that has negligible resistance. A uniform vertical magnetic field of flux density B exists everywhere along the track.

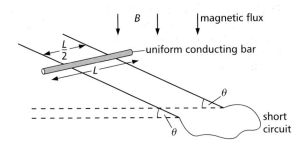

a Although there is no frictional force opposing motion, the bar reaches a terminal velocity. Explain why this occurs. **(4 marks)**

b i Write down an expression for the initial force acting on the bar along the slope. **(1 mark)**

ii The terminal velocity of the bar is v. Show that, at a speed v, the force opposing the motion of the bar is given by:
$$F = \frac{B^2L^2v\cos^2\theta}{2R}$$
(3 marks)

c The mass of one bar of length 0.55 m is 0.15 kg and its total resistance is 0.20 Ω. The magnetic flux density is 0.30 T. Calculate the terminal speed of the bar down the ramp when $\theta = 15°$.

acceleration of free fall, $g = 9.8$ m s^{-2} **(2 marks)**
(Total 10 marks)

(AQA 1999)

4 Figure A illustrates an isolated conducting sphere which has been charged positively.

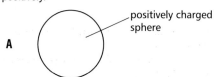

positively charged sphere

A

For points on the surface or outside the sphere, the charge on the sphere behaves as if it were concentrated at the centre.
a Copy figure A and on your diagram draw
  i the electric field lines (label these lines E),
  ii lines joining points of equal potential (label these lines V).
(4 marks)

b Measurements of the distance x from the centre of the sphere and the corresponding values of the potential V are given in the table.

x / cm	V / V
19	1.50×10^5
25	1.14×10^5
32	0.89×10^5
39	0.73×10^5

  i Without drawing a graph, use the data to verify that the potential V is inversely proportional to the distance x.
  ii The potential at the surface of the sphere is 1.9×10^5 V. Calculate the radius of the sphere. **(4 marks)**
c Using your answer to **b ii**, determine
  i the charge on the sphere,
  ii the capacitance of the sphere. **(4 marks)**
d A source of protons is situated inside a similar positively charged sphere and these protons accelerate to earth along an evacuated tube, as illustrated in figure B.

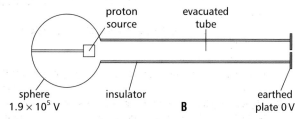

proton source   evacuated tube

sphere   insulator   earthed
1.9×10^5 V   **B**   plate 0 V

For a proton accelerated from rest through a potential difference of 1.9×10^5 V,
  i calculate the change in potential energy,
  ii show that its speed is 6.0×10^6 m s^{-1}. **(4 marks)**

e The protons emerge from the evacuated tube into a region of uniform magnetic field of flux density 0.18 T. The region is evacuated and the magnetic field is normal to the direction of motion of the protons.
  i Calculate the radius of the path of the protons in the magnetic field.
  ii Measurement of this radius can be used as a means of determining the kinetic energy of the protons. State and explain what happens to the radius if the kinetic energy of the protons were to be reduced. **(4 marks)**

(OCR 1998)

5 The gravitational field strength at the surface of a planet, X, is 19 N kg^{-1}.
a i Calculate the gravitational potential difference between the surface of X and a point 10 m above the surface, if the gravitational field can be considered to be uniform over such a small distance.
  ii Calculate the minimum amount of energy required to lift a 9.0 kg rock a vertical distance of 10 m from the surface of X.
  iii State whether the minimum amount of energy you have found in part **a ii** would be different if the 9.0 kg mass were lifted a vertical distance of 10 m from a point near the top of the highest mountain of planet X. Explain your answer. **(3 marks)**
b Calculate the gravitational field strength at the surface of another planet, Y, that has the same mass as planet X, but twice the diameter of X. **(2 marks)**

(AQA 1999)

6 a Figure A shows the magnetic field of a wire P carrying a steady current I perpendicular and into the plane of the paper.

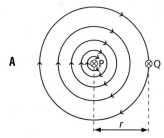

A

A second wire Q, parallel to P and at a distance r from P, carries an equal current I, also into the plane of the paper.
  i On a copy of figure A, mark and label with a letter N a point where the resultant magnetic flux density produced by the two currents is zero. **(2 marks)**
  ii Explain why the magnetic flux density at N is zero. **(2 marks)**
  iii On your copy of figure A, draw arrows to show the directions of the electromagnetic forces experienced by P and by Q. Label these forces F_P and F_Q. Name the rule used to determine the directions of the forces F_P and F_Q. **(3 marks)**

b Figure B shows an arrangement for measuring the magnetic flux density B between the poles of a magnet.

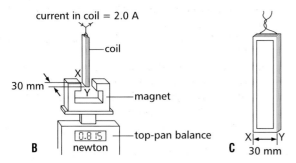

The coil shown in figures B and C has 50 turns. Its lower side XY is horizontal and has a mean length of 30 mm. Before the current is switched on, the balance reading is 0.850 N. With a current of 2.0 A in the coil, the balance reading becomes 0.815 N.

  i Determine the magnitude (newtons) and direction of the electromagnetic force acting in the magnet. **(2 marks)**

  ii Calculate the magnetic flux density B between the poles of the magnet. **(3 marks)**

(OCR specimen)

7 A planet P of mass m orbits the Sun S of mass M in a circular orbit of radius r as shown in the figure.

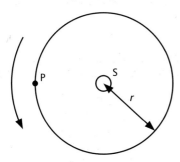

The speed of the planet in its orbit is v.

a On a copy of the figure, draw an arrow to represent the linear velocity of P. Label the arrow V. Draw a second arrow representing the direction of the force acting on P. Label this arrow F. **(2 marks)**

b **i** Write down an expression, in terms of r and v, for the magnitude of the centripetal acceleration of P.

  ii Write down an expression, in terms of m, r and v, for the magnitude of the force F acting on P.

  iii Write down an expression, in terms of m, M, r and G, for the magnitude of the gravitational force exerted by the Sun on the planet. **(4 marks)**

c From observations of the motions of the planets around the Sun, Kepler (1571–1630) found that T^2, the square of the period of revolution of a planet around the Sun, was proportional to r^3.

  i Write down an expression for T in terms of the speed v of the planet and the radius r of its orbit.

  ii Use your answers to **b ii**, **b iii** and **c i** to show Kepler's relation
$$T^2 \propto r^3$$
would be expected. **(3 marks)**

(OCR specimen)

8 **a** State two pieces of information that can be deduced from drawings of electric field lines. **(2 marks)**

  b The figure illustrates some of the electric charges in a thundercloud and on the surface of the Earth beneath it.

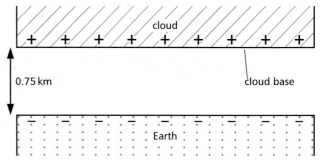

The base of the cloud and the surface of the Earth can be considered horizontal.

  i On a copy of the figure, sketch the electric field between the cloud and the Earth.

  ii The cloud base is 0.75 km above the Earth. A lightning flash occurs in air containing raindrops when the electric field strength exceeds 5.0×10^4 N C^{-1}. Calculate the minimum electric potential difference (in volts) between the cloud base and the Earth's surface for a lightning flash to occur. **(5 marks)**

(OCR specimen)

9 Figure A shows the front view of a pivoted square coil. The plane of the coil is at right angles to a uniform magnetic field directed into the paper. Figure B is a side view of the same coil.

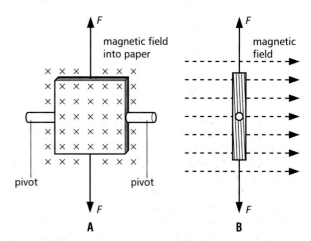

a The coil conducts a current causing electromagnetic forces to act on the coil. The directions of the forces F on the upper and lower sides are shown in both Figures.

On a copy of figure A, draw and label arrows to show the directions of

  i the current in the coil,

  ii the electromagnetic forces acting on the other sides of the coil. **(3 marks)**

b Suggest why the forces in **a ii** are not considered when calculating the torque produced by the coil. **(3 marks)**

(OCR specimen)

10 Figure A shows the magnetic field between the two pole pieces of a large U-shaped magnet, with the north pole vertically above the south pole. When the strength of the magnetic field is measured along the line AB, it is found to vary as shown in Figure B.

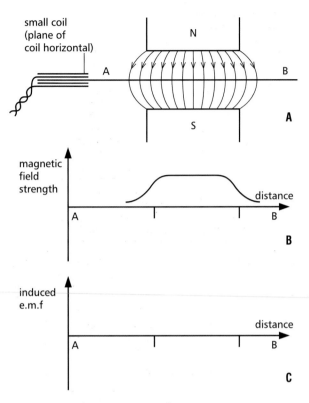

a Describe in words how the magnetic flux linkage in the coil changes as the coil in figure A moves from A to B. **(3 marks)**

b State Faraday's law of electromagnetic induction. **(2 marks)**

c Draw, on a copy of the axes provided in figure C, a graph to show how the e.m.f. induced in the coil varies as the coil moves from A to B. **(4 marks)**

(OCR specimen)

11 Ganymede is one of the moons of Jupiter. Ganymede has a mass M_G and orbits Jupiter, mass M_J. The radius of the orbit is r.
Write down Newton's law of gravitation as applied to the Jupiter–Ganymede system. **(2 marks)**
Write down an expression for the centripetal force F required to cause Ganymede to orbit Jupiter with an angular speed of ω.
Show that $r^3\omega^2 = GM_J$ where G is the universal gravitational constant. **(3 marks)**
Ganymede orbits Jupiter once every 7.16 days and the radius of its orbit is 1.07×10^9 m. Calculate the mass of Jupiter. **(3 marks)**
(Total 8 marks)

(Edexcel 1999)

12 Magnetic flux density B varies with distance beyond one end of a large bar magnet as shown on the graph below.

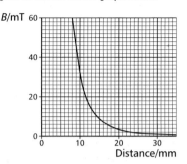

A circular loop of wire of cross-sectional area $16\,cm^2$ is placed a few centimetres beyond the end of the bar magnet. The axis of the loop is aligned with the axis of the magnet.
Calculate the *total* magnetic flux through the loop when it is 30 mm from the end of the magnet.
Calculate the total magnetic flux through the loop when it is 10 mm from the end of the magnet. **(3 marks)**
The loop of wire is moved towards the magnet from the 30 mm position to the 10 mm position so that a steady e.m.f. of $15\,\mu$V is induced in it. Calculate the average speed of movement of the loop. **(3 marks)**
In what way would the speed of the loop have to be changed while moving towards the magnet between these two positions in order to maintain a steady e.m.f.? **(1 mark)**
(Total 7 marks)

(Edexcel 1999)

13 The diagram shows a rectangular coil PQRS which can rotate about an axis which is perpendicular to the magnetic field between two magnetic poles.

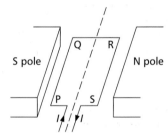

Explain why the coil begins to rotate when the direct current I is switched on.
Add to a copy of the diagram an arrow showing the direction of the force on PQ.
State *three* factors which would affect the magnitude of this force. **(7 marks)**
A student notices that as the coil rotates faster the current in it reduces. Explain this observation. **(2 marks)**
(Total 9 marks)

(Edexcel 1999)

FIELDS CONCEPT MAP

How to use the map

The map is a way of representing the structure of the knowledge contained in this section. It is designed to be used as you get towards the end of the section, when you should begin to see a pattern in the key concepts you have met. The map shows how one area of knowledge builds on another, so that more complex ideas develop as you go through the section.

As you study, try to think about how you learn best. Do you prefer to have understood one idea completely before going on to another? Or do you like to meet several related new ideas and then put these together rather like you might put together several pieces of a jigsaw at once?

The concept map will help you to see how ideas are related. You can use it to help you to put your knowledge and understanding in some sort of order so that you can organise your learning. You can also use it to organise your revision at the end of the section and before your examinations. Alternatively, try drawing up your own concept map as you revise.

Notes on the map

The key ideas in the section are contained in the green boxes. Solid lines with arrows between these boxes show how ideas in the section develop. Where parts of this section relate to other sections, dashed lines with arrows indicate this – the links are described in yellow boxes. Finally, some sections introduce and apply key mathematical skills – this is indicated by purple boxes, with double arrows indicating areas where the skill is applied.

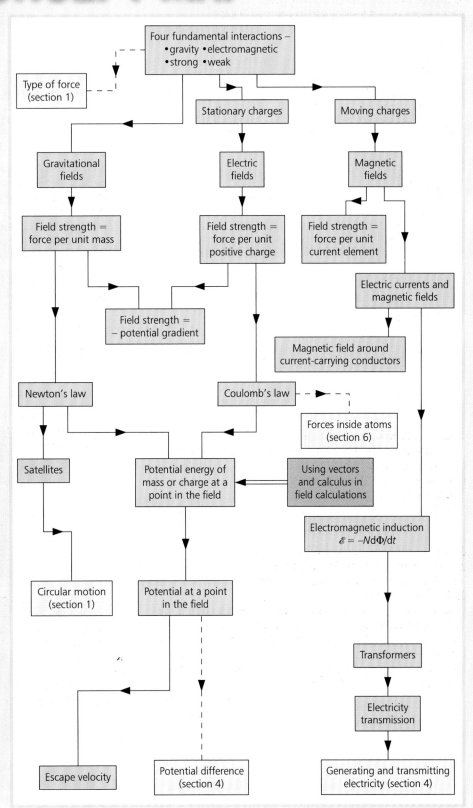

6 ATOMIC & NUCLEAR PHYSICS

Introduction

In section 2 we looked at some of the properties of matter, and described the kinetic theory, a model through which these properties can be understood, and which also explains some of the ways in which matter and energy interact. In this section we shall now explore the behaviour and interaction of energy and matter in more detail, in particular at a scale below that of whole atoms – the **subatomic** level. In doing this, we move into the physics of the twentieth century, a period that was as momentous in the advancement of the subject as was the period of Newton.

We begin by looking at a simple model for the atom, examining the evidence that was first produced in the early part of the twentieth century that led scientists to think in terms of an atom consisting of very light, negatively charged particles, called **electrons**, orbiting around a massive, positively charged **nucleus**. We shall then look at **radioactivity**, developing some simple tools to help us understand it, and looking at what radioactivity itself tells us about what goes on inside the nucleus.

Having examined the nucleus in detail, our attention then turns to the electrons in the atom. We shall look at these both in terms of particles and as waves – and we shall see too that we need to think of electromagnetic waves like light (which we studied in section 3) as particles if we are to understand fully the way in which light and matter interact.

Our final look in this section will be at 'work in progress' – an introduction to the study of the family of subatomic particles that the twentieth century began to unravel, and to which the twenty-first century may provide the final answers.

Figure 6.1 A computer-simulated picture of the tracks produced when two protons collide, producing a particle called the Higgs boson.

 **FOCUS** ## UNRAVELLING THE STRUCTURE OF THE ATOM

Sir William Crookes (1855) uses some of the first vacuum tubes to produce cathode rays from negatively charged metals in a vacuum.

Jean-Baptiste Perrin (1895) deflects cathode rays using a magnetic field, showing that negative charge collects wherever the rays hit.

Joseph John Thomson (1897) measures the mass:charge ratio of cathode rays using magnetic and electric fields, showing that they are in fact negatively charged particles – electrons.

Albert Einstein (1905) proposes that light may behave as a particle as well as a wave. This explanation enables scientists to understand fully the **photoelectric effect** for the first time.

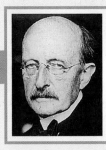

Max Planck (1900) announces that atoms can emit light only at certain frequencies, the first step towards quantum theory.

Hans Geiger (left) and **Ernst Marsden (1909)** obtain evidence for a model of the atom in which there is a massive, positively charged nucleus, by firing beams of alpha particles at thin metal foils. They work under the supervision of Rutherford.

Ernest Rutherford (1911) presents a paper to the Manchester Literary and Philosophical Society in which he describes the nuclear model of the atom.

Niels Bohr (1913) proposes a model for the electrons in the atom in which electrons are found in **orbits** centring on the nucleus.

Louis-Victor de Broglie (1923) suggests that electrons may have wave-like properties as well as behaving like particles – this becomes known as **wave–particle duality**.

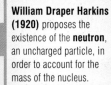

William Draper Harkins (1920) proposes the existence of the **neutron**, an uncharged particle, in order to account for the mass of the nucleus.

Erwin Schrödinger (1926) publishes the first paper on **wave mechanics** in which the electron is modelled as a wave rather than a particle.

Werner Heisenberg (1927) outlines his **uncertainty principle** – there are inevitable uncertainties introduced in measuring any variable in a system on an atomic scale.

James Chadwick (1932) obtains the first evidence for the existence of the neutron.

6.1 Atomic structure

Classical and modern physics

The establishment of the physics of the twentieth century saw the overthrow of many ideas established in the 200 years from around 1700 to 1900. The physics of this time is now known as **classical physics**. It is characterised by the idea that the Universe functions according to a set of straightforward laws which, once discovered, lead to a complete understanding of the behaviour of the Universe in the past, present and future – as if the Universe were a giant piece of clockwork. Newton's laws of motion and his law of gravitation are an example of such a **deterministic** view of the Universe. In contrast to this, **modern physics** is much less certain. It recognises that the Universe is a complex and sometimes quite unpredictable place (although it may still be governed by simple rules), and that the observer in an experiment may influence its outcome. Most physicists would probably name Albert Einstein as Newton's successor in the age of modern physics – but even he had problems in coming to terms with the implications of the upheaval of physics in the early twentieth century.

Figure 6.1.1 Albert Einstein (1879–1955). As well as his famous work on relativity, Einstein made fundamental contributions to the other cornerstone of twentieth century physics, quantum theory. Grappling with some of the implications of quantum physics, in particular the apparently totally random behaviour of some aspects of the Universe, he made his now famous remark, 'God does not play dice with the Universe.'

The building blocks of matter

Evidence for the particulate nature of matter

Our understanding of the behaviour of matter is based on the assumption that matter is made up of particles, as we saw in section 2.1. Brownian motion provided the best evidence for the particulate nature of matter at the end of the nineteenth century, although modern technology enables us to obtain much more direct evidence, as figure 6.1.2 shows.

Even though there is powerful evidence that matter is made up in this way, our everyday observations do not confirm it – after all, a piece of steel (say) appears smooth and continuous. This appearance of the smoothness and solidity of matter is an illusion, caused by the sheer number of particles in a small volume of matter. We shall see shortly how the names **atom**, **molecule** and **ion** are given to these building blocks of matter – each has a very specific meaning.

The size of particles of matter

Two approaches enable us to obtain some idea of the size of the particles of matter. Both of these rely on the measurement of physical quantities, one using solids, the other liquids.

Using molar mass and density

The molar mass of a substance and its density can be used to obtain an estimate for the size of its particles. For example, the molar mass of iron M_{Fe} is 0.056 kg mol^{-1} (that is, 1 mol of iron atoms has a mass of 0.056 kg). The density of iron ρ_{Fe} is 7900 kg m^{-3}. This means that the molar volume of iron $V_{m(Fe)}$ (the volume occupied by 1 mol of iron atoms) is given by:

Figure 6.1.2 This photograph of the tip of an iridium needle was taken using an ion microscope. This instrument uses helium ions instead of light, which makes it possible to obtain much higher magnifications. The pattern in the photograph shows that the needle consists of layers of iridium atoms, arranged in a highly symmetrical crystal lattice.

$$V_{m(Fe)} = M_{Fe} / \rho_{Fe}$$

$$= \frac{0.056 \text{ kg mol}^{-1}}{7900 \text{ kg m}^{-3}}$$

$$= 7.1 \times 10^{-6} \text{ m}^3 \text{ mol}^{-1}$$

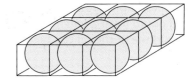

Figure 6.1.3

This is the volume occupied by N_A atoms of iron, so the volume V occupied by 1 atom of iron is given by:

$$V = \frac{7.1 \times 10^{-6} \text{ m}^3 \text{ mol}^{-1}}{6.0 \times 10^{23} \text{ mol}^{-1}}$$

$$= 1.2 \times 10^{-29} \text{ m}^3$$

If each iron atom is assumed to be a sphere of diameter d, it will occupy a cube of volume d^3, as shown in figure 6.1.3. The value of V obtained above gives the approximate diameter of an iron atom as $\sqrt[3]{(1.2 \times 10^{-29} \text{ m}^3)} = 2.3 \times 10^{-10}$ m.

The oil drop experiment

When oil is dropped onto the surface of clean water, given sufficient surface area, it spreads out to form a patch one molecule thick. By measuring the volume of the oil drop used and the diameter of the patch formed, an estimate for the thickness of the film (and hence the size of the oil molecule) can be made. Figure 6.1.4 shows the principles of this experiment.

If the diameter of the oil drop is d, its volume is $\frac{4}{3}\pi(d/2)^3$. This is equal to the volume of the patch formed on the surface of the water, $\pi(D/2)^2 t$, where D is the diameter of the patch and t its thickness. Thus we can write:

$$\frac{4}{3}\pi \frac{d^3}{8} = \pi \frac{D^2}{4} t$$

Rearranging this gives:

$$t = \frac{2d^3}{3D^2}$$

Figure 6.1.4

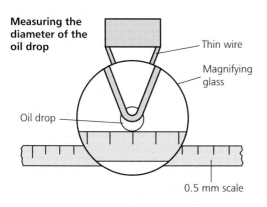

Measuring the diameter of the oil drop

Thin wire

Magnifying glass

Oil drop

0.5 mm scale

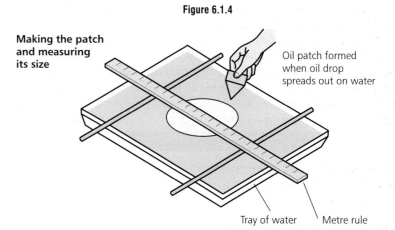

Making the patch and measuring its size

Oil patch formed when oil drop spreads out on water

Tray of water   Metre rule

As an example, a drop of oil approximately 0.3 mm in diameter might spread out to form a patch 20 cm across. From this information, the diameter of a molecule of the oil can be estimated:

$$t = \frac{2d^3}{3D^2}$$

$$= \frac{2 \times (0.3 \times 10^{-3} \text{ m})^3}{3 \times (20 \times 10^{-2} \text{ m})^2}$$

$$= 4.5 \times 10^{-10} \text{ m}$$

So the diameter of the oil molecule is approximately 5×10^{-10} m.

Uncertainties in the oil drop experiment

Even if the diameter of the oil patch in the example above can be measured to within 2 mm, representing an uncertainty of 1% in the diameter and thus an uncertainty of 2% in the area, the patch is unlikely to be exactly circular in shape, which will introduce further uncertainty. Photographing the patch against a grid and measuring the area by counting grid squares might overcome this. However, there is a more fundamental problem – measuring the drop size.

Using a lens and estimating the size of the drop against a 0.5 mm rule introduces a large uncertainty. This could be as much as ± 0.1 mm, an uncertainty in the diameter above of 33%. The diameter is cubed in order to calculate the thickness of the oil film, making the uncertainty ($3 \times 33\%$), that is, 100%!

Further uncertainty is introduced by the shape of the drop, which is unlikely (except in conditions of zero gravitational field strength) to be precisely spherical.

Two conclusions can be drawn from this:
(1) The experiment produces a value for the size of the oil molecule which is an order of magnitude estimate, but no more. This means that the precision of the result obtained makes quoting the result to more than one significant figure completely meaningless.
(2) It is completely inappropriate to try to find ways to measure the area of the oil patch with less uncertainty, since the uncertainties in other measurements far outweigh those in the measurement of the area of the patch. Any improvement in the accuracy of the experiment needs to come from an improvement in the measurement of the volume of the oil drop.

Using molar mass and density and the oil drop experiment are two quite different methods that give very similar results. This is a good basis for concluding that the building blocks of matter have a size of around 10^{-10} m. We shall now consider evidence showing that these blocks of matter are not in fact indivisible (remember the meaning of the word 'atom'), but are themselves composed of smaller blocks.

The structure of the atom

Cathode rays and the structure of the atom

In section 4.1 we saw how an electron gun can produce electrons travelling at high speed, and in section 5.3 how the cathode ray oscilloscope makes use of such a gun. The first investigations of the behaviour of metals heated in a vacuum was carried out by Sir William Crookes in 1855. The experiments of Crookes and others showed that a heated cathode produced a stream of radiation of some sort which could cause gases at low pressure to glow, and which could cause other substances to emit light too. The radiation emitted from the cathode was given the name **cathode rays**. By the mid-1890s it was known that these rays could be bent by a magnetic field, and that they carried a negative charge, as shown in figure 6.1.5.

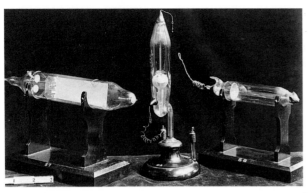

Some of the tubes used by Crookes in his work on the behaviour of metals heated in gases at very low pressures. Modern tubes use electric heaters to heat the cathode. By contrast, the cathodes in these tubes were heated as they were struck by positive ions accelerated by the large potential difference across the tubes.

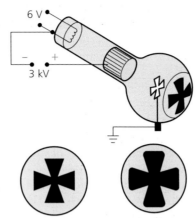

A metal object (in this case in the shape of a Maltese cross) placed in the path of a beam of cathode rays casts a shadow on the screen, showing the rectilinear propagation of the rays, just like light.

If the cross is not earthed, a larger shadow with rounded corners results. This is because charge carried by the cathode rays collects on the cross, repelling the rays as they pass it.

Applying a uniform magnetic field results in the rays being deflected, which is shown by the movement of the cross on the screen.

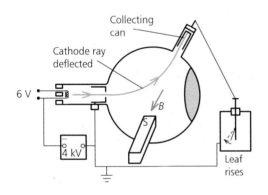

The negative charge on cathode rays was first demonstrated by the French physicist Jean-Baptiste Perrin in 1895, using a form of the apparatus represented here, now known as a 'Perrin tube'. The beam of rays is deflected into the collecting can using a magnetic field. The electroscope leaf then deflects, showing that a charge has been collected. Isolating the electroscope from the collecting can and then testing the charge shows it to be negative.

Figure 6.1.5 Investigating the behaviour of cathode rays using different types of vacuum tube. The tubes have a screen consisting of a layer of material that glows when struck by the radiation from the cathode.

Throughout the latter part of the nineteenth century, physicists debated the nature of cathode rays, and many theories were advanced. Some physicists felt that the rays were waves, similar in properties to electromagnetic waves, while others were more inclined to think that the rays were particles. The Irish physicist George Stoney even went so far as to name the particle – the electron. In 1897 J. J. Thomson, an English physicist, showed that the rays were indeed streams of electrons, since the rays could be deflected by an electric field. Thomson used the size of the deflection to calculate the charge:mass ratio of an electron, which he found to be about 2000 times larger than the charge:mass ratio of a hydrogen atom.

The discovery of the electron led to a flurry of speculation about the structure of the atom. In 1898, Thomson proposed the 'plum pudding' model for the atom, in which negative electrons are embedded in a sphere of positive charge. Directly opposing this idea, the Japanese physicist Hantaro Nagaoka proposed a model resembling the planet Saturn, in which a positive nucleus was surrounded by a ring of thousands of circling electrons. This idea was supported by experimental evidence obtained by Philipp von Lenard, who proposed a model in which an atom consisted of a number of electrons, each paired with a small positive charge, in a region which was mostly empty space.

These models were based on the assumption that the mass of an atom was contained in its electrons. The mass of one electron was assumed to be about 0.0005 times that of a hydrogen atom in order to account for the difference in charge:mass ratios, and it followed that a hydrogen atom must contain around 2000 electrons.

The nuclear atom

The model of the nuclear atom was first proposed by Ernest Rutherford and his colleagues in 1911, from work carried out at Cambridge University, England. This work depended upon the use of a product of radioactive decay, the alpha particle, which Rutherford and Frederick Soddy had shown to be a helium ion in 1909. (Radioactive decay and the radiations resulting from it are discussed in section 6.2.) Under the direction of Rutherford, Hans Geiger and Ernst Marsden subjected thin metal foils to a beam of alpha particles. The majority of alpha particles passed straight through the foils with very little deflection, even when the thickness of the foil was as great as 10^4 atoms. In a very few cases (as few as one in 1800), alpha particles showed some deflection, while in fewer cases still the alpha particles were deflected through an angle greater than 90°.

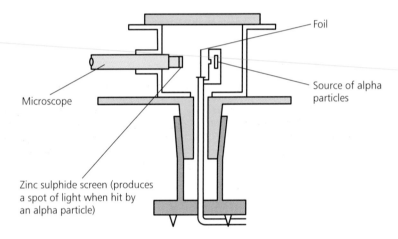

Foil

Source of alpha particles

Microscope

Zinc sulphide screen (produces a spot of light when hit by an alpha particle)

Figure 6.1.6 Geiger and Marsden's apparatus. The microscope and screen can be rotated around the foil so as to detect alpha particles deflected through different angles.

This large angle of scattering for a very small number of particles led Rutherford to propose that the majority of the mass of the atom was concentrated in a minute positively charged region, around which the electrons circulated. When an alpha particle came close to the nucleus, Rutherford reasoned, the electrostatic repulsion between the two would be sufficient to repel the alpha particle and so produce the large angle of scattering. Since the nucleus was small, this scattering would occur for only the few particles which approached the nucleus sufficiently closely.

Rutherford calculated the fraction of alpha particles that should be deflected through particular angles on the basis of this model, and showed that their trajectories would be hyperbolas. Figure 6.1.7 shows some trajectories. The perpendicular distance between the original, undeflected, trajectory and the centre of the nucleus is called the **impact parameter** p. Rutherford showed that if the nucleus is considered to have a radius b, then for the case where $p = b$, the angle of deflection = 53°. The angle of deflection decreases rapidly as p increases, as figure 6.1.7 shows.

Using his model, Rutherford was able to show that the nucleus of an atom is of the order of 10^{-14} m across. Comparing this with the size of atoms calculated on pages 475–6, of the order of 10^{-10} m, the diameter of the nucleus is about

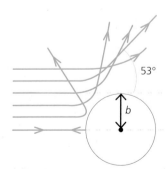

53°

b

Figure 6.1.7 The trajectories of alpha particles with different impact parameters p, deflected by a positively charged nucleus with radius b. The trajectories are all hyperbolas.

0.0001 times the diameter of the atom itself. It is therefore unsurprising that most of the alpha particles in Geiger and Marsden's experiments passed through the foil with no deflection – although it is difficult to imagine that virtually all the mass of the atom is concentrated in the tiny volume of the nucleus.

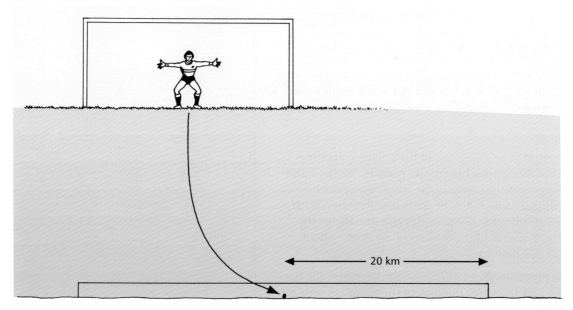

20 km

Rutherford's model pictured the atom as a miniature Solar System, in which electrons orbited the nucleus much as planets orbit the Sun. Because matter is electrically neutral, the positive charge in the nucleus of each atom would be balanced by the negative charge on the orbiting electrons. The model says no more about the distribution of the electrons outside the nucleus, other than that they move in a space far larger than that occupied by the nucleus. In section 6.5 we shall examine in some detail the behaviour of electrons in atoms, and look at some further models of the atom that physicists have developed in an attempt to understand its behaviour.

Figure 6.1.8 To get some idea of the scale of the atom, imagine a goalkeeper standing with arms outstretched in the centre of a goal. If the goalkeeper represents the nucleus of an atom, and a football kicked at the goal represents an alpha particle, the goalposts would need to be 20 km either side of the keeper to represent the scale of the atom.

Rutherford's calculations

Using the principle of conservation of energy, it is possible to calculate the closest an alpha particle could approach to a nucleus if it were to collide with it head-on – that is, a collision for which the impact parameter $p = 0$.

Initially the alpha particle has kinetic energy $\frac{1}{2}mu^2$. At the point of closest approach, the centre of the alpha particle is separated from the centre of the nucleus by a distance b, and the alpha particle is at rest. All the initial kinetic energy of the alpha particle has been transferred to electrical potential energy. Assuming that an inverse square law can be applied to the electrical forces between the alpha particle and the nucleus (see section 5.3, page 411), we may write:

$$\tfrac{1}{2}mu^2 = \frac{1}{4\pi\varepsilon_0}\frac{q_1q_2}{b}$$

Rearranging:

$$b = \frac{1}{4\pi\varepsilon_0} \frac{q_1 q_2}{\frac{1}{2}mu^2}$$

For an alpha particle, $m = 6.7 \times 10^{-27}$ kg, $q_1 = 2 \times (1.6 \times 10^{-19}$ C) and u is around 2×10^{-7} m s^{-1}. If the foil at which the alpha particles are fired is made of gold, then q_2 is $79 \times (1.6 \times 10^{-19}$ C). These figures can then be used to give a value for b:

$$b = \frac{1}{4\pi \times 8.854 \times 10^{-12} \text{ F m}^{-1}} \times \frac{(2 \times 1.6 \times 10^{-19} \text{ C}) \times (79 \times 1.6 \times 10^{-19} \text{ C})}{\frac{1}{2} \times 6.7 \times 10^{-27} \text{ kg} \times (2 \times 10^7 \text{ m s}^{-1})^2}$$

$$= 2.7 \times 10^{-14} \text{ m}$$

This value of b cannot be said to be the radius of the nucleus, since it is dependent on the speed of the approaching alpha particle. We have also made an assumption about the law governing the force between the particles at this minute distance which may be quite unwarranted. What can be said, however, is that this value of b provides an estimate for the order of magnitude of the diameter of the nucleus of an atom – about 0.0001 of the diameter of the atom itself.

With the information we now have about the properties of atoms, the data for such calculations are easily found. At the turn of the twentieth century, this was far from the case, and Rutherford had to make estimates for the quantities involved. To do this Rutherford had to use his abilities as a scientist, and also drew on the work of others (for example, that of the fellow Englishman Charles Glover Barkla, who in 1911 had suggested a relationship between the mass of an atom and the number of electrons in it). Although the quantities involved were not known precisely, it was the principle of the calculation that was important, together with the order of magnitude of the result it gave – showing how the nucleus must be considerably smaller than the atom as a whole, yet containing almost all the mass.

Rutherford clearly saw the importance of this work. He could discern how physics had been influential since the time of Newton and before, and would remain so for the foreseeable future. His view of the centrality of physics in understanding and explaining the world around us is summed up by his statement: 'There is only physics – the rest is merely stamp collecting.'

Describing the atom

Our current understanding of the atom is based on the work of many scientists, and is a superb example of the way in which scientific knowledge forms a complex, interlocking web of theories each of which depends on other theories. We shall develop and extend our ideas of the structure of the atom in sections 6.4 to 6.6, having first looked at the nucleus and its properties.

A simple model of the nucleus

The nuclei of atoms are made up of protons and neutrons. These two components of the nucleus are usually referred to as **nucleons**. The number of protons in the nucleus of an atom is exactly equal to the number of electrons. This number is called the **proton number** (or sometimes the **atomic number**) of the element, given the symbol Z. All atoms of a particular element have the same proton number, since it is the number of electrons in the atom that determines its chemical properties. Atoms may have different numbers of neutrons, however, giving atoms of the same element different masses. Atoms with the same proton number but with different numbers of neutrons are called **isotopes**.

The number of protons plus the number of neutrons in the nucleus is called the **nucleon number** (or sometimes the **mass number**) of the element, given the symbol A. The average distance between the protons in the nucleus is very small, which means that there is a very large repulsive electric force between them. At these small separations, the strong force (see section 5.1) provides an even larger attractive force which keeps the nucleons together. Nevertheless, in large atoms the repulsive electric force is significant, and can lead to the breaking up of the nucleus, as we shall see in sections 6.2 and 6.3. Figure 6.1.10 shows how the data for a nucleus are written alongside its chemical symbol, and table 6.1.1 overleaf gives some examples.

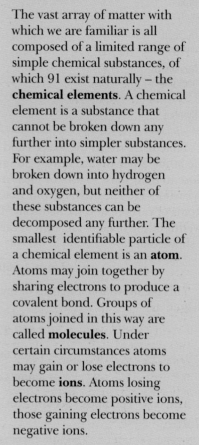

● Proton

Neutron

Electron

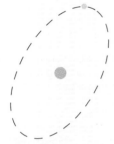
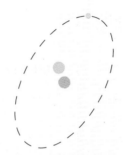
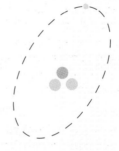

The most common isotope of hydrogen has a single proton in its nucleus, with a single electron outside the nucleus.

This is the isotope of hydrogen called **deuterium**. With a neutron in its nucleus as well as a proton, this atom is about twice as massive as the atom containing no neutron.

This isotope of hydrogen is called **tritium**. Its atom contains two neutrons, and is therefore about three times as massive as the atom containing no neutron.

Figure 6.1.9 The three isotopes of hydrogen. Around 99.985% of the atoms in a container of hydrogen will have only a single proton in the nucleus, while about 0.015% will have a proton and a single neutron. The number of atoms with two neutrons in the nucleus will be variable – these nuclei are **unstable**, and undergo radioactive decay, a process we shall examine in section 6.2. Although their physical properties differ, all three isotopes have identical chemical properties, since each consists of atoms with only a single electron. 'Shorthand' notation for representing the elements and their isotopes is explained in figure 6.1.10.

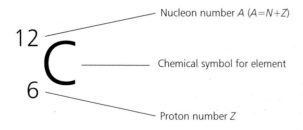

Nucleon number A ($A=N+Z$)

$^{12}_{6}\text{C}$

Chemical symbol for element

Proton number Z

Figure 6.1.10 An atom with Z protons and N neutrons is represented like this. In text, elements may be referred to by their name followed by their nucleon number, for example, carbon-12, uranium-235.

	Lithium-7	Silicon-28	Copper-65	Dysprosium-164	Uranium-238
Proton number Z	3	14	29	66	92
Nucleon number A	7	28	65	164	238
Number of neutrons N (= A − Z)	4	14	36	98	146
Symbol	$^{7}_{3}\text{Li}$	$^{28}_{14}\text{Si}$	$^{65}_{29}\text{Cu}$	$^{164}_{66}\text{Dy}$	$^{238}_{92}\text{U}$

Table 6.1.1 How protons and neutrons are combined to make up the nuclei of different atoms

Table 6.1.2 shows the masses and charges for the three particles making up the atom. Since the masses are so small, it is convenient to have a unit of mass close to their mass to use for measurements. Like the mole, this unit is related to carbon-12. The atoms of this isotope of carbon have six protons, just like all atoms of carbon, and six neutrons. The **atomic mass unit** u is defined as one-twelfth of the mass of an atom of carbon-12. The experimental measurement of u shows that:

$$1 \text{ u} = 1.660\ 540 \times 10^{-27} \text{ kg}$$

This means that the masses of the proton, neutron and electron can be written as:

$$\left.\begin{array}{l} m_{\text{proton}} = 1.007\ 276 \text{ u} \\ m_{\text{neutron}} = 1.008\ 665 \text{ u} \end{array}\right\} \text{ (that is, about 1 u)}$$

$$m_{\text{electron}} = 0.000\ 549 \text{ u} \quad \text{(that is, about u/1800)}$$

The box 'The mass spectrometer' gives details of the measurement of the masses of atoms.

	Proton	Neutron	Electron
Mass/kg	$1.672\ 623 \times 10^{-27}$	$1.674\ 929 \times 10^{-27}$	$9.109\ 390 \times 10^{-31}$
Mass/u	1.007 276	1.008 665	0.000 548 580
Charge/C	$+1.602\ 177 \times 10^{-19}$	0	$-1.602\ 177 \times 10^{-19}$

Table 6.1.2 The proton, neutron and electron – their masses and charges. These data are given to seven significant figures, although they have in fact been measured with even greater precision than this. For most purposes, values to two or three significant figures suffice, but the calculations of nuclear stability in the following sections will require more precision than this.

The mass spectrometer

The first direct investigation of the mass of an atom was made possible by the development of the **mass spectrometer** by Aston in 1918. This machine uses the interaction of charged particles with electric and magnetic fields to measure the masses of atoms and to find their relative abundances. Figure 6.1.11 shows how the mass spectrometer works.

Ions are produced in the mass spectrometer by bombarding atoms with a stream of energetic electrons (see section 6.4). These ions are accelerated and then selected, so that the beam of ions produced at point A

consists of ions which all have the same velocity. These ions then travel through a uniform magnetic field. This causes the ions to move in a circular path with radius r, which depends on the mass:charge ratio of the ion. For ions with mass m and charge q travelling with velocity v through the magnetic field B_2:

Centripetal force = force due to magnetic field B_2

so:

$$\frac{mv^2}{r} = B_2 q v$$

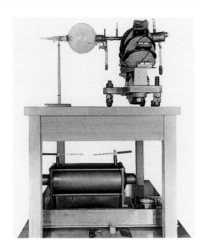

The first mass spectrometer was built in 1918 by Francis William Aston, a student of J. J. Thomson. Ions of the element being studied were produced in the glass bulb. An electric field then accelerated them towards a magnetic field produced by the large coils on the right of the apparatus. The high voltages needed were produced by means of the induction coil at the bottom of the apparatus. When a steady current flowing through this coil is suddenly stopped, the rapid collapse of the magnetic field around it induces a large e.m.f. in another coil wound around the induction coil.

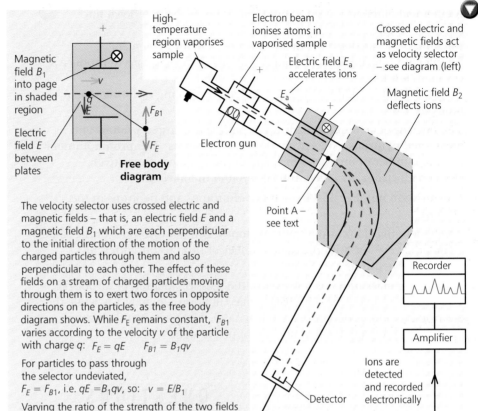

Free body diagram

The velocity selector uses crossed electric and magnetic fields – that is, an electric field E and a magnetic field B_1 which are each perpendicular to the initial direction of the motion of the charged particles through them and also perpendicular to each other. The effect of these fields on a stream of charged particles moving through them is to exert two forces in opposite directions on the particles, as the free body diagram shows. While F_E remains constant, F_{B1} varies according to the velocity v of the particle with charge q: $F_E = qE$ $F_{B1} = B_1qv$

For particles to pass through the selector undeviated,
$F_E = F_{B1}$, i.e. $qE = B_1qv$, so: $v = E/B_1$

Varying the ratio of the strength of the two fields enables the selected velocity to be varied.

Figure 6.1.11

that is,

$$r = \frac{v}{B_2}\frac{m}{q}$$

But for the velocity selector:

$$v = E/B_1$$

so:

$$r = \frac{E}{B_1B_2}\frac{m}{q}$$

that is, the radius of the circular path described by the particle depends on its mass:charge ratio for given values of E, B_1 and B_2.

By varying E/B_1B_2, the mass of the ions arriving at the detector may be varied, and the relative abundance of different masses of ions in a sample can be measured, together with the masses of the ions themselves.

SUMMARY

- The model of the **nuclear atom**, with a tiny positive nucleus containing most of the mass of the atom, was suggested by Rutherford as a result of experiments with metal foils and alpha particles.

- A **chemical element** is a substance that cannot be broken down into anything simpler.
  An **atom** is the smallest identifiable part of a chemical element.
  A **molecule** is formed when groups of atoms share electrons to produce a covalent bond.
  An **ion** is an atom that has become charged by gaining or losing one or more electrons.
- The nucleus of an atom is made up of positively charged **protons** and uncharged **neutrons**, collectively known as **nucleons**. The **proton number** Z is the number of protons, which equals the number of negatively charged **electrons** arranged in space around the nucleus.
- The **nucleon number** A is the number of protons and neutrons in the nucleus.
- An element may have two or more **isotopes**. Different isotopes of the same element have atoms with the same number of protons but different numbers of neutrons.
- The **atomic mass unit** u is one-twelfth the mass of an atom of carbon-12. The proton and neutron both have a mass of approximately 1 u, while the electron has a mass of approximately u/1800. The proton and electron carry charges of equal magnitude but opposite sign.

QUESTIONS

(Take N_A as 6.0×10^{23} mol^{-1}, e as 1.6×10^{-19} C and ε_0 as 8.85×10^{-12} F m^{-1}.)

1 The molar mass of sodium is 0.023 kg and its density is 970 kg m^{-3}. Calculate the approximate size of a sodium atom. Repeat your calculation for magnesium (0.024 kg mol^{-1} and 1740 kg m^{-3}). Compare your answers. Can you suggest (electrostatic) reasons for the difference?

2 If the radius of a nucleus is taken to be the distance from the centre of the nucleus to a point where the density of the nuclear material has fallen to half, the radius of a nucleus is given approximately by the relationship:

$$r = 1.4 \times 10^{-15} \text{ m} \times A^{\frac{1}{3}}$$

where A is the nucleon number of the nucleus.
Starting with this relationship, calculate:
  a the radius of a gold nucleus ($A = 197$)
  b the volume of the gold nucleus.
  c The molar mass of gold is 0.197 kg mol^{-1} and its density is 18 880 kg m^{-3}. Calculate the approximate volume of a gold atom. Compare this with your answer to **b**.

3 Use your answers to question 2 to estimate what volume of **a** your body and **b** the Earth is filled with nuclear material. The radius of the Earth is approximately 6400 km.

4 Neutron stars are composed almost entirely of neutrons, and have a density approximately equal to that of nuclear material. The mass of the Sun is approximately 2×10^{30} kg. Use your answers

to question 2 to calculate **a** the approximate density of nuclear material and **b** the diameter of a neutron star with the same mass as the Sun.

5 **a** Calculate the ratio:

$$\frac{\text{electrostatic force}}{\text{gravitational force}}$$

for an alpha particle 1×10^{-13} m from a gold nucleus. The charge on an alpha particle is $+2e$ and its mass is 6.64×10^{-27} kg. The charge on a gold nucleus is $+79e$ and its mass is 3.27×10^{-25} kg.
  b Show that this ratio is constant for all separations. (Take G as 6.67×10^{-11} N m^2 kg^{-2}.)

6 An alpha particle and a proton are each travelling directly towards the centre of a stationary uranium nucleus at a speed of 2.0×10^7 m s^{-1}. Calculate the closest distance of approach of each particle to the uranium nucleus, given that the charge on the proton is $+e$, that on the alpha particle is $+2e$ and that on the uranium nucleus is $+92e$. Take the mass of the proton as 1.67×10^{-27} kg and that of the alpha particle as 6.64×10^{-27} kg.

7 In a mass spectrometer helium atoms become ionised (lose electrons) and enter a magnetic field of 1.0 T acting vertically downwards. If the velocity selector is adjusted so that the velocity of the helium ions entering the field is 5.0×10^7 m s^{-1}, calculate the possible trajectories of the helium ions.

6.2 Radioactivity

In section 6.1 we saw that there is overwhelming evidence for a model of atomic structure in which the mass and positive charge in an atom reside in a tiny central nucleus. Before going on to examine the arrangement of electrons in such a model (which we shall do in section 6.4), we shall look at the nucleus in a little more detail, in particular at what makes some nuclei stable while others break apart – the phenomenon of **radioactivity**.

Describing radioactivity

The properties of radioactivity

Alpha, beta and gamma radiation

Figure 6.2.2 describes the investigations of Becquerel, the Curies, Rutherford and others at the turn of the twentieth century which showed that radioactive substances may emit one or more of three kinds of radiations – **alpha particles**, **beta particles** and **gamma rays**. Alpha (α) particles consist of two protons and two neutrons and are therefore helium nuclei. They are the least penetrating of the three radiations, being stopped by a thin sheet of paper or even by 5 cm of air at atmospheric pressure. Beta (β) particles are more penetrating, and can travel through a 3 mm sheet of aluminium or up to 1 m of air at atmospheric pressure. They consist of streams of high-energy electrons. Gamma (γ) rays are the most penetrating of the three radiations, passing through several centimetres of lead or more than a metre of concrete. They consist of electromagnetic waves, with wavelengths much shorter than that of light.

Penetrating powers and ionisation

The relative penetrating powers of the radiations are due to the way they interact with matter. When alpha, beta or gamma radiation passes through matter, it tends to knock electrons out of atoms, **ionising** them. (Radiation that behaves in this way is called **ionising radiation**, and includes X-rays – see section 6.5.) Because alpha particles are large, relatively slow moving and carry two positive charges, they are strongly ionising. In contrast to this, gamma rays are weakly ionising as they are electromagnetic waves and carry no charge. Beta particles fall between alpha particles and gamma radiation in ionising power. Ionisation involves a transfer of energy from the radiation passing through the matter to the matter itself. This transfer happens most rapidly in the case of alpha particles since they are most strongly ionising, and this is why alpha particles are the least penetrating of the three radiations. Gamma rays transfer energy less rapidly, and are therefore the most penetrating. Question 3 on page 501 concerns the range of the radiations in matter.

The effect of a magnetic field

When alpha, beta and gamma radiations pass through a magnetic field, gamma rays are undeflected, while alpha and beta particles are deflected in opposite directions, as shown in figure 6.2.3. This is consistent with alpha particles having a positive charge and beta particles being negative. Gamma rays are undeflected since they are electromagnetic waves.

Figure 6.2.1 Many people fear radioactivity without really understanding it. Is leaking radiation the danger here, or is the escape of radioactive substances the real hazard?

Antoine-Henri Becquerel 1896 Working just after Röntgen had discovered X-rays, Becquerel thinks that X-rays might be produced by certain materials after exposure to sunlight. He calls these materials 'phosphorescent'. Working with a uranium salt, he covers a photographic plate with thick black paper to exclude light, places a piece of the salt on top of the paper and exposes it to sunlight. Developing the plate produces an image of the salt on the negative. Having prepared another experiment, the weather is cloudy for several days. Becquerel places the plate and the salt in a drawer for several days, developing the plate even though the salt has not been exposed to sunlight. He observes an image of the salt on the plate 'with great intensity'.

Marie and Pierre Curie 1898 The Curies find that the element thorium gives off 'uranium rays', which they rename **radioactivity**.

Ernest Rutherford 1899 Rutherford shows that the radioactivity from uranium has at least two different components, which he calls alpha and beta rays.

Frederick Soddy 1902 Rutherford and Soddy publish their paper 'The cause and nature of radioactivity'.

1900 Becquerel shows that beta rays are electrons.

1908 Rutherford and T. D. Royds show that alpha particles are helium nuclei.

1911 Soddy observes that an atom emitting an alpha particle moves two places down in the Periodic Table.

1913 Soddy and others observe that emission of a beta particle causes an atom to move one place up in the Periodic Table.

Figure 6.2.2

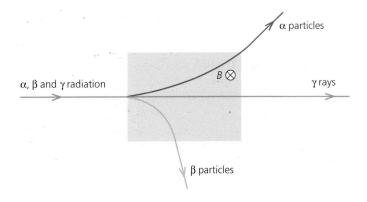

Figure 6.2.3 The deflection of the three types of radiation by a magnetic field shows that alpha particles are positively charged, beta particles are negatively charged and gamma rays are uncharged. Note that the deflections are not shown to scale.

THE UNRAVELLING OF RADIOACTIVITY

When Marie Curie had finished her first degree and was looking for something interesting for her research, her imagination was caught by the findings of Henri Becquerel on the rays produced by uranium. This work was so new that the field was wide open – ideal for work on a doctoral thesis.

First Marie showed that the quantity of radiation produced by uranium depended only on the amount of uranium present. The relationship between the amount of uranium and the quantity of radiation was constant, and was unaffected by light, temperature or the chemical state of the uranium. This showed that the radiation discovered by Becquerel was a new and unique phenomenon, probably of the atoms themselves.

Then Marie moved on – was uranium the only element to possess this new property, or did other elements produce these strange rays as well? She started to examine all the known chemical elements of the time, soon finding that compounds of the element thorium also emitted rays like those of uranium. The phenomenon was clearly not unique to uranium and needed its own name. Marie suggested 'radioactivity'.

Not content with her work so far, she then began to examine different ores and minerals. As she expected, only the ores of uranium and thorium showed radioactivity. However, when she studied these minerals in detail her results showed more radiation being given off than expected from the amount of uranium or thorium present. Her first assumption was that her results were wrong, and with painstaking care she checked all of her measurements a further 20 times – but the results were consistently the same. Marie had already tested all the known elements for radioactivity. This new source of radioactivity, far more powerful than uranium or thorium, could mean only one thing – she had discovered a new element. Her husband Pierre left his own research on crystals to join his wife in her search for the new element.

Figure 6.2.4 Once Marie Sklodovska left her Polish homeland and moved to Paris to begin her university studies, she showed the most remarkable focus on her work, although she did find time to fall deeply in love with and marry Pierre Curie.

Figure 6.2.5 The damp and draughty storeroom of the School of Physics where Marie Curie carried out her initial work on radioactivity. The humidity and temperature changed all the time, making careful scientific measurements almost impossible, but it was all that was available and Marie certainly made the best of it.

Bit by bit Marie and Pierre separated pitchblende (uranium ore) and looked for radioactivity in each of the fractions. To their astonishment, after eliminating the uranium, they had not one but two sources of radioactivity – they had discovered two new elements. The first Marie christened polonium after Poland, her beloved birthplace. The second they named radium – and this was the more stable, radioactive and useful of the two. In 1903 Marie and Pierre, along with Becquerel, were awarded the Nobel prize for physics for their work on radioactivity.

It was the supreme tragedy of Marie's life that Pierre was killed in a road accident while they were still relatively young. Although she continued her work on radioactivity and was awarded a second Nobel prize in 1911 (this time for chemistry), she was always affected by his loss.

The stature of Marie Curie's work on radioactivity can be measured by the fact that she was awarded not one but two Nobel prizes – and this at a time when women were rarely liberated from their roles as housewives and mothers. She died in 1934, aged 67, while still engaged in her research, her body destroyed by the radiation with which she had spent so much of her life.

Hazards of radioactivity

Ionising radiation passing through a living cell may damage the complex chemicals responsible for the functioning of the cell. If this damage is sufficiently great that natural repair processes cannot quickly regenerate the damaged cell components, the cell will die.

Ionising radiation may also damage the DNA (deoxyribonucleic acid) of a cell. This substance acts as the blueprint for the production of the proteins that make up a cell. Damage to the DNA may cause changes to the chemicals produced by a cell, and this can lead to changes in the way the cell functions. These changes may be lethal, or the cell may begin to grow and divide uncontrollably. Uncontrolled growth leads to the development of a **cancer**, a clump of cells growing and dividing in an abnormal way. Since cancer cells are themselves sensitive to ionising radiation, one way of treating a cancer is to expose the cancerous cells to ionising radiation.

Personal danger from ionising radiation may come from sources outside or inside the body. With a source *outside* the body (say a radioactive fuel rod from a nuclear reactor), gamma radiation is likely to be the most hazardous, since it is the most penetrating radiation and therefore most likely to reach the interior of the body. By contrast, any alpha particles reaching the body will be stopped by the surface layer of (dead) skin cells, and will do little or no damage to the living cells beneath. However, the opposite is true for sources *inside* the body (say from a radioactive substance that has been swallowed or inhaled as dust). In this case the weakly ionising gamma radiation will cause less damage than strongly ionising alpha particles.

There are strict rules concerning the exposure to ionising radiation of workers in the nuclear industry and members of the public. The units used to measure radiation and doses received are examined later in this section, on page 491.

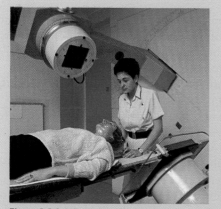 

Figure 6.2.6 Left – treating a group of cancerous cells using radiotherapy. Cancers have a wide variety of causes, including ionising radiation, and a range of treatments is used besides radiotherapy. Right – in this situation the main radiation hazard is likely to be from the radiation source outside the worker's body.

Detection and measurement of radioactivity

Detecting radioactivity

Detectors of ionising radiation make use of the ionising properties of the radiation to cause changes that may be observed and measured. Early experimenters used screens coated with zinc sulphide. Such screens emit **scintillations** (tiny pulses of light) when ionising radiation falls on them. The rate at which radiation strikes the screen can be observed by direct measurement of the number of scintillations, as we saw in Geiger and Marsden's apparatus in figure 6.1.6.

A **cloud chamber** provides a similar method of direct observation of ionising events. Ethanol vapour condenses on the ions formed along the path of the ionising radiation, as shown in figure 6.2.7. Observation of cloud chamber tracks provides further evidence for the nature of alpha, beta and gamma radiations:

1 The tracks of alpha particles are well defined and straight, suggesting that they are strongly ionising and massive, being little deflected from their path by air molecules.

2 The tracks of beta particles are less defined, and tend not to be straight near the end of the path. This suggests that beta particles are less strongly ionising than alpha particles, and that as they lose energy by colliding with air molecules they become easier to deflect.

3 Gamma radiation leaves virtually no trace at all in a cloud chamber, showing that it is very weakly ionising.

An electric field directed vertically down may be applied to the cloud chamber. This ensures that the positive ions produced by ionising radiation travelling slightly upwards are pulled down into the region of supersaturated ethanol vapour, producing a sharp trace. In a simple cloud chamber like that shown here, this field may be produced by rubbing the perspex lid of the chamber with a cloth.

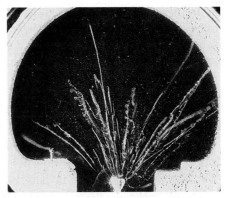

Alpha particle tracks from a single source.

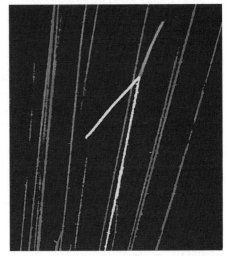

The tracks of alpha particles travelling through nitrogen. One alpha particle has collided with a nitrogen nucleus – the tracks of the alpha particle and the nitrogen nucleus after the collision are clearly visible.

Figure 6.2.7 The diffusion cloud chamber makes use of solid carbon dioxide (temperature around −78 °C) to produce a layer of supersaturated ethanol vapour. The smallest local increase in concentration of vapour will cause the vapour to condense, forming droplets which can be seen. Ionising radiation travelling through this layer leaves a trail of ionised air molecules on which ethanol vapour condenses, rather like the vapour trail left by a high-flying aeroplane. The photographs show the tracks of ionising radiations in such cloud chambers.

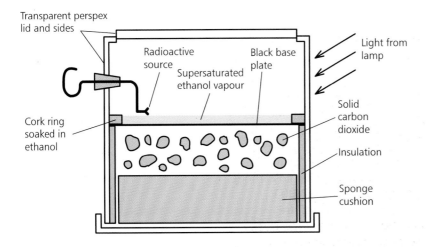

Early experiments by Rutherford used another type of chamber called an **ionisation chamber**. This is effectively a conducting box containing an electrode. An electric field is set up inside the box, the box itself forming the other electrode, as shown in figure 6.2.8. The source to be studied is placed in the chamber. As ionising radiation is emitted it ionises some of the air molecules in its path, and the ions so formed move in the electric field. This causes a tiny current to flow, of the order of 10^{-9} A, which can be measured using a d.c. amplifier as figure 6.2.8 shows. Investigations show that the ions produced have charges of the same order as the charge on the electron. The number of ions produced per second by the source of ionising radiation can therefore be estimated from the current flowing. This estimate is dependent on several conditions:

1 The ionisation chamber must be sufficiently large to enable the ionising radiation to travel its full range so that it generates the maximum number of ions it is capable of producing.

2 The electric field must be large enough to ensure that all the ions formed travel to the electrode before recombining with free electrons.

In practice, these conditions generally limit the use of ionisation chambers to alpha sources.

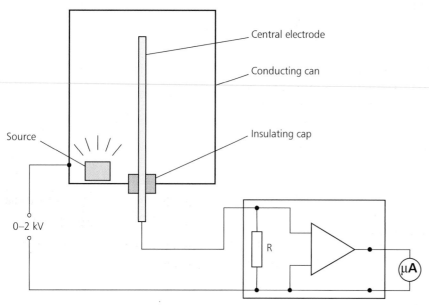

D.c. amplifier with input resistance of around 10^9 Ω. This amplifies the current and so enables it to be measured using a moving-coil microammeter.

Figure 6.2.8

A development of the ionisation chamber is the **Geiger-Müller (GM) tube**, shown in figure 6.2.9. The tube consists of a metal cylinder, sealed at one end with a thin mica window (this window is very delicate and is protected with a plastic grid). The tube is filled with air or argon at low pressure. The cylinder itself forms the cathode, while a metal rod running along the tube forms the anode. An electric field is applied to the region between the anode and cathode by making the anode positive with respect to the cathode by about 400 V.

When ionising radiation enters the tube, ions and free electrons are produced. The electrons are accelerated rapidly towards the anode by the electric field. As they travel, they produce more ions and free electrons by collisions with gas molecules (or atoms in the case of argon). These free electrons are also accelerated towards the anode, and in turn produce even more ions and free electrons. This effect is referred to as an **avalanche**. The avalanche of electrons causes a pulse of current to flow through the tube, producing a potential difference across the resistor R. This p.d. is detected by an electronic circuit, which triggers a counting circuit to count the pulse.

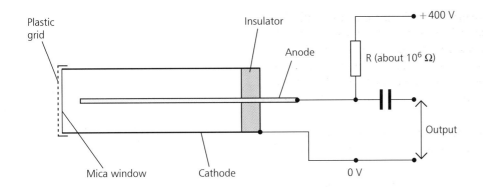

Figure 6.2.9 The Geiger-Müller (GM) tube. This detector is used quite widely for teaching purposes, although it is unsuitable for high count rates due to its substantial 'dead time' (see text). For high count rates **solid state** detectors are preferred, which make use of the production of electron–hole pairs in semiconductors by ionising radiation.

The tube contains a trace of bromine to act as a **quenching agent**. This helps to ensure that the electrons and ions produced in the avalanche lose their energy quickly and recombine, allowing the tube to detect another ionising event. The time during which the tube is unable to detect a second ionising event due to the presence of an avalanche from a previous event is known as the tube's **dead time**. A typical dead time for a GM tube is around 100 μs, so count rates in excess of 10^4 s^{-1} are impossible using this type of detector.

Modern research laboratories use **scintillation counters** to detect ionising radiations. These devices make use of the ejection of electrons from the surface of metals when light falls on them, thus employing electronics to 'count' the pulses of light produced by ionising radiation rather than a human experimenter. Figure 6.4.12 (page 533) shows how the principle of the scintillation counter can be adapted to produce a camera capable of intensifying images taken in very poor light.

Measuring radioactivity

Radioactivity is produced by the decay of the nuclei of atoms, as we shall see in section 6.3. The **activity** of a radioactive source describes the rate at which nuclei are disintegrating within it. A rate of one disintegration per second may also be described as a rate of one becquerel (1 Bq) in SI units. The higher the activity of a source, the greater the rate of emission of ionising radiation from it and the more rapid the decay of the unstable nuclei within it.

Ionising radiation carries energy capable of damaging living tissue. The SI unit used to measure the amount of energy absorbed by matter when ionising radiation passes through it is the gray (Gy), where 1 Gy = 1 J kg^{-1}. This energy absorbed from radiation is described as the **dose**.

The damage done to living tissue by ionising radiation depends on the energy carried by the radiation, and also on the ionising power of the radiation. The **dose equivalent** is a measure of the potential of radiation to damage living tissue, and is measured in SI units called sieverts (Sv). The dose equivalent is found by multiplying the dose by a **quality factor** (1 for X-rays, gamma rays and electrons, 20 for alpha particles) which depends on the type of radiation. Like dose, dose equivalent is also a measure of energy absorbed per unit mass, so 1 Sv = 1 J kg^{-1}.

Older units called the curie (Ci), the rad and the rem are still often encountered. Table 6.2.1 shows how these relate to their equivalent SI units.

Activity	1 Ci = 3.7×10^7 Bq
Dose	100 rad = 1 Gy
Dose equivalent	100 rem = 1 Sv

Table 6.2.1

Background radiation

We are surrounded by radioactive substances, our food contains traces of isotopes which are radioactive (particularly an isotope of potassium), and the matter of our own bodies is naturally radioactive. In addition we are constantly bombarded by streams of high-energy charged particles from outer space, and we also make use of ionising radiation for medical benefits (in particular X-rays). It is therefore important to appreciate that we are all exposed to ionising radiation from quite natural sources, and we must take this into account when considering the personal risks from exposure to sources of ionising radiation.

On a practical note, this background radioactivity makes it necessary to correct any experiment in which radioactivity is measured by first carrying out a **background count**. This background count must be carried out using the detector to be used in the experiment, in the location where the experiment is to be done. The background count rate must then be deducted from subsequent measurements made.

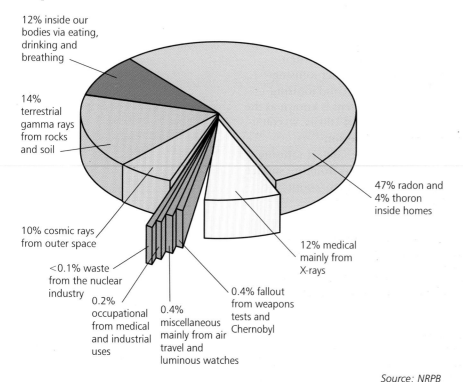

12% inside our bodies via eating, drinking and breathing

14% terrestrial gamma rays from rocks and soil

10% cosmic rays from outer space

<0.1% waste from the nuclear industry

0.2% occupational from medical and industrial uses

0.4% miscellaneous mainly from air travel and luminous watches

0.4% fallout from weapons tests and Chernobyl

12% medical mainly from X-rays

47% radon and 4% thoron inside homes

Source: NRPB

Figure 6.2.10 We are all exposed to background radiation, no matter where we live. A typical inhabitant of Britain receives an average annual dose equivalent of about 2.16 mSv, about 87% of which comes from natural sources. In certain regions of Britain, natural radiation from rocks is several times greater than elsewhere, increasing the exposure to radiation further.

Investigating radioactivity – the attenuation of gamma rays

The inverse square law for gamma rays

Gamma rays are absorbed very little by air, and their intensity in air therefore obeys an inverse square relationship like other electromagnetic radiation (see section 3.1, page 212). The investigation of this is straightforward, although it requires correction to allow for errors at small distances between source and detector (usually a GM tube).

The count rate recorded by the counter connected to the GM tube is C (after correction to allow for the background count rate). If the inverse square law for intensity is obeyed, it follows that:

$$C = \frac{k}{(D + d)^2}$$

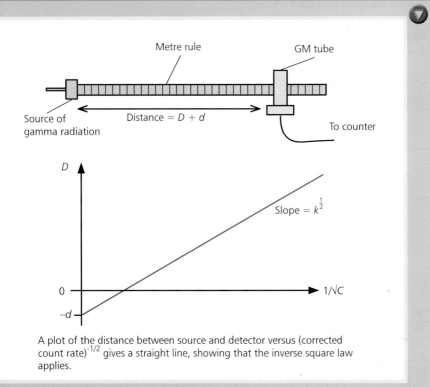

Distance = D + d

Source of gamma radiation

Metre rule

GM tube

To counter

$$\text{Slope} = k^{\frac{1}{2}}$$

A plot of the distance between source and detector versus (corrected count rate)$^{-1/2}$ gives a straight line, showing that the inverse square law applies.

Figure 6.2.11 Measuring the intensity of gamma radiation at various distances from a source. The GM tube is placed so that the radiation enters the tube through the side wall. This minimises the uncertainty about the exact point of detection of the gamma ray (and hence the uncertainty about the exact distance from the source to the detector). D is the distance from the face of the source to the side of the GM tube, and d is the unknown distance from the side of the tube to the point of detection of the gamma ray within the tube.

Rearranging this:

$$D + d = \sqrt{\left(\frac{k}{C}\right)}$$

so:

$$D = \sqrt{\left(\frac{k}{C}\right)} - d$$

Plotting D versus $C^{-1/2}$ gives a graph with slope $k^{1/2}$ and intercept $-d$ on the y-axis as in figure 6.2.11, showing that the intensity of gamma rays travelling through air obeys an inverse square law.

The rate of radioactive decay

Random events

The emission of radioactivity by an atom occurs spontaneously and quite unpredictably – it is impossible to predict, for example, when a particular thorium-228 atom will emit an alpha particle and decay to radium-224. Not only is the decay unpredictable, it also appears to be unaffected by external conditions like chemical reactions, pressure and temperature. Nevertheless, in a sample containing many thorium atoms, there is one factor that does appear to govern the overall rate of decay of thorium nuclei – the number of nuclei left undecayed.

We shall examine the processes by which atoms decay to produce ionising radiation in section 6.3. In what follows here we shall be concerned only with developing a simple model to understand the rate at which radioactive decay occurs.

Investigating radioactive decay

Figure 6.2.12 This apparatus enables the activity of radon-220 gas (sometimes called thoron gas) to be measured as it decays.

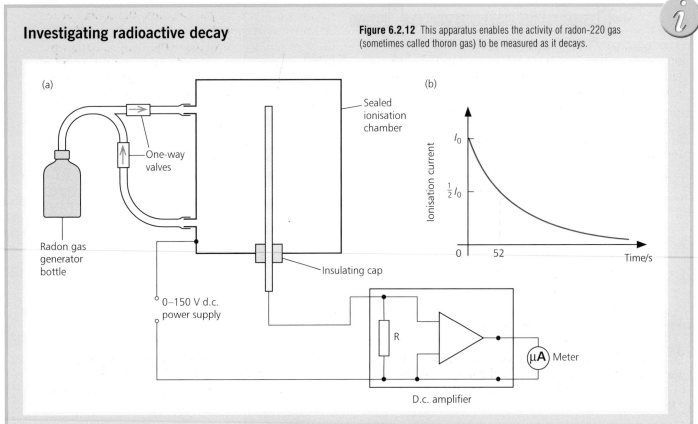

The measurement of the activity of radon-220 gas is straightforward using the ionisation chamber shown in figure 6.2.12(a). The generator bottle contains a compound of thorium-232 which undergoes a series of decays to produce, among other things, radon-220 – the actual series is shown on page 503 of section 6.3. The concentration of each element in the decay series remains constant, since although radium-224 atoms are constantly decaying into radon-220, they are constantly replaced by the decay of thorium-228.

The same argument applies to radon-220 itself, so the concentration of radon-220 gas in the bottle remains constant.

Radon-220 gas is squeezed out of the bottle into the ionisation chamber. This results in a large ionisation current, which can be read on the meter connected to the d.c. amplifier. Recording this current and plotting it against time gives the characteristic graph of figure 6.2.12(b).

Exponential decay

The graph shown in figure 6.2.12(b) is similar to the graph we saw for the decay of charge on a capacitor (figure 4.3.16). In the study of the capacitor, we noted that the rate of flow of charge off the plates of the capacitor was proportional to the charge remaining on the plates. This relationship resulted in decay of a type known as exponential decay, in which the decaying quantity has a constant half-life. Radioactive decay is also an example of exponential decay – the rate of decay of nuclei in a sample of radioactive material at a particular time is proportional to the number of nuclei remaining undecayed at that time.

Modelling radioactive decay

Radioactive decay can be modelled very easily using a type of sweet with lettering on one side, as shown in figure 6.2.13(a). If a known number of these sweets is tipped out of a container, some will land with the lettering on the upper face, others with the lettering on the lower face. The probability of a particular sweet landing 'letters up' is obviously 1/2. This provides us with a simple model for the decay of radioactive atoms, if we say that the collection of sweets represents a sample of radioactive material and that a sweet landing 'letters up' represents an atom that has just decayed.

After the sweets have been tipped out of the container, the 'letters up' sweets are removed. The remaining sweets are put back into the container to be tipped out again. This process represents the decay of radioactive atoms in the sample, each 'tip' being equivalent to a period of time (in this case 1 s). The process of tipping out sweets and removing those which are 'letters up' is repeated a number of times. Table 6.2.2 shows some results for this investigation. It was carried out with 50 sweets and repeated four times further (B to E). The results were then totalled, providing data for 250 sweets.

Time/s	0	1	2	3	4	5	6
A	50	30	14	7	3	2	0
B	50	28	14	5	4	3	1
C	50	28	12	8	3	1	0
D	50	24	10	5	2	0	0
E	50	25	15	8	3	1	0
Total	250	135	65	33	15	7	1

Table 6.2.2

Figure 6.2.13(b) shows the number of sweets remaining after each tip. The curve is approximately exponential, with a 'half-life' $t_{\frac{1}{2}}$ of a little over 1 s. In other words, there is a pattern to the behaviour of the group of sweets as a whole, even though the behaviour of a particular sweet is subject to the laws of probability.

(a)

Figure 6.2.13 Investigating radioactive decay using a very simple model

This simple investigation provides some justification for treating radioactive decay using statistical techniques that describe the behaviour of a group of atoms as a whole, even though this behaviour arises as a result of the random decay of individual atoms.

(b)

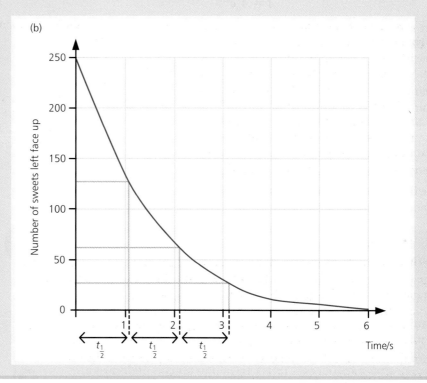

Radioactive decay and half-life

If we have N unstable atoms at a particular time t, we can write the rate of change of the number of unstable atoms with time as dN/dt. This is the **activity** A of the source, measured in becquerels (Bq) – see page 491.

This rate of change is proportional to the number of unstable atoms N, so we may write:

$$\frac{dN}{dt} \propto N$$

or:

$$\frac{dN}{dt} = -\lambda N$$

where λ is a constant called the **decay constant**. (The negative sign is included because N is a decreasing quantity and therefore dN/dt is negative, while N itself is positive.)

Once again we require some simple calculus to explore the use of this relationship in full (see the box 'The mathematics of radioactive decay' below). The most important points to note about this decay are:

- Radioactive decay follows an equation which can be written as

$$N = N_0 e^{-\lambda t}$$

This relationship expresses the number of undecayed nuclei N at time t in terms of the number of undecayed (unstable) nuclei N_0 at $t = 0$ and the decay constant λ – the larger the value of λ, the more rapid the radioactive decay. Representing this relationship on a graph of N versus t produces a curve like that in figure 6.2.12(b), that is, exponential decay.

- Because the activity A of a sample is directly proportional to the number of undecayed atoms in it, we can also write:

$$A = A_0 e^{-\lambda t}$$

where A is the activity at time t and A_0 is the activity at $t = 0$.

- The **half-life** is the time for half of the radioactive atoms to decay, so that when $t = t_{\frac{1}{2}}$, half of the atoms remain undecayed. When $t = 2t_{\frac{1}{2}}$, $(\frac{1}{2})^2 = \frac{1}{4}$ of the atoms remain undecayed, when $t = 3t_{\frac{1}{2}}$, $(\frac{1}{2})^3 = \frac{1}{8}$ of the atoms remain undecayed, and so on. In general, after n half-lives, $(\frac{1}{2})^n$ atoms remain undecayed. This relationship also applies to the activity of a sample.

- Half-life $t_{\frac{1}{2}}$ and activity constant λ are related:

$$t_{\frac{1}{2}} = \frac{\log_e 2}{\lambda} \approx \frac{0.693}{\lambda}$$

If the decay constant has units s^{-1}, this expression will give the half-life in seconds. Notice that if the activity is large, the half-life is small, and vice versa.

Radioactive decay – worked example

Antimony-124 has a half-life of 60 days. If a sample of antimony-124 has an initial activity of 6.5×10^6 Bq, what will its activity be after one year?

In any sample of radioactive material, the decay follows a simple pattern. After one half-life half the atoms in the sample remain undecayed, after two half-lives $1/(2^2)$ of the atoms remain undecayed, and so on. In general, after n half-lives, $1/(2^n)$ of the atoms remain undecayed.

In this case, one year represents:

$$\frac{365}{60} \text{ half-lives} = 6.083 \, t_{\frac{1}{2}}$$

The proportion of the antimony-124 atoms left after one year is thus:

$$\frac{1}{2^{6.083}} = \frac{1}{67.80}$$

The activity of the sample is directly proportional to the number of undecayed atoms, so after one year the activity of the sample will have fallen to a value of:

$$6.5 \times 10^6 \text{ Bq} \times \frac{1}{67.80} = 9.6 \times 10^4 \text{ Bq}$$

The mathematics of radioactive decay

1 Simple statistics

In the 'radioactive sweets' investigation, the laws of probability predict that 50% of the sweets tipped out of the container will land 'letters up'. The data in table 6.2.2 show that the actual results often deviate from this figure – there are **statistical fluctuations**. In this type of investigation, the distribution of the results about the expected value x is described by a curve like that shown in figure 6.2.14. This is similar to the distribution of a set of readings subject to random errors seen earlier (see box 'Uncertainties and errors' on pages 299–300).

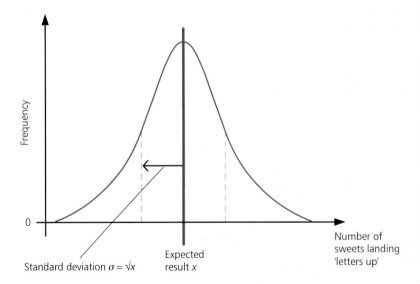

Figure 6.2.14 This distribution, called the **Poisson distribution**, can be used to describe the distribution of outcomes in any experiment that involves counting random events with two possible results (for example, 'letters up' or 'letters down').

For any process like radioactive decay, the distribution of observations is found to be described by the Poisson distribution. Using this distribution, if the expected result is x it is found that a little over two-thirds of the observations (68%) lie within $\sqrt{x}$ of the expected value, that is, between $(x - \sqrt{x})$ and $(x + \sqrt{x})$, while 95% lie in the range $(x \pm 2\sqrt{x})$. The quantity $\sqrt{x}$ is called the **standard deviation** of the distribution, and is a measure of the spread of the results.

The importance of this in making measurements of radioactivity lies in the number of readings taken. Consider an investigation in which a radioactive source which emits 100 counts per minute is monitored. If 100 counts are recorded we can be confident that there is a 68% chance of the expected value lying between 90 and 110 (plus or minus one standard deviation, $\sqrt{100} = 10$), that is, within 10% of the observed value. If 10 000 counts are recorded, then there is a 68% chance that the expected value lies between 9900 and 10 100 ($\sqrt{10\ 000} = 100$), that is, within 1% of the observed value.

2 Solving the equation for radioactive decay

We know that for the radioactive decay process we can write:

$$\frac{dN}{dt} = -\lambda N$$

This equation may be rearranged and solved in the same way as the equation for the decay of charge on the capacitor, choosing the limits of integration so that the number of undecayed nuclei is N_0 when $t = 0$.

$$\int_{N_0}^{N} \frac{dN}{N} = -\int_{0}^{t} \lambda\, dt$$

The solution to this is:

$$\log_e\left(\frac{N}{N_0}\right) = -\lambda t$$

This may be rewritten as:

$$\frac{N}{N_0} = e^{-\lambda t} \quad \text{or} \quad N = N_0 e^{-\lambda t}$$

After one half-life the number of undecayed nuclei will have fallen to $N_0/2$, so:

$$\log_e\left(\frac{\frac{1}{2}N_0}{N_0}\right) = -\lambda t_{\frac{1}{2}}$$

that is,

$$\log_e \tfrac{1}{2} = -\lambda t_{\frac{1}{2}}$$

or:

$$\log_e 2 = \lambda t_{\frac{1}{2}} \quad (\text{since } \log_e \tfrac{1}{2} = -\log_e 2)$$

This rearranges to give:

$$t_{\frac{1}{2}} = \frac{\log_e 2}{\lambda}$$

Determination of half-life from radioactive decay

The model of radioactive decay using sweets can be used to demonstrate how the equations for radioactive decay can be rearranged to plot a straight-line graph to find $t_{\frac{1}{2}}$.

We have:

$$\log_e\left(\frac{N}{N_0}\right) = -\lambda t$$

This expression can be rearranged to give:

$$\log_e N - \log_e N_0 = -\lambda t$$

or:

$$\log_e N = \log_e N_0 - \lambda t$$

A plot of $\log_e N$ versus t will give a straight-line graph with y-intercept $\log_e N_0$ and slope $-\lambda$. If λ is found, then $t_{\frac{1}{2}}$ is easily calculated from $t_{\frac{1}{2}} = (\log_e 2)/\lambda$.

Figure 6.2.15 shows the graph of $\log_e N$ versus t for the sweet experiment. From the slope of the graph, $t_{\frac{1}{2}}$ can be calculated as 1.07 s. This agrees quite well with the half-life marked on the graph in figure 6.2.13. The value of $t_{\frac{1}{2}}$ is slightly larger than the expected value of 1 s – can you suggest why this might be?

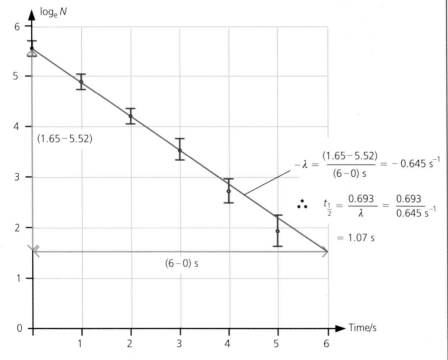

Figure 6.2.15 A plot of $\log_e N$ versus t enables a straight line to be plotted to find λ and hence $t_{\frac{1}{2}}$. Note the error bars on the graph, representing the recorded value ±1 standard deviation. (The true value of the quantity being measured may be expected to fall within these limits with a probability of 68%.) The uncertainty in the readings increases as the number of counts recorded falls, and so the error bars get larger. The final reading of 1, recorded after 6 s, has been ignored.

SUMMARY

- **Radioactive** substances emit radiations as their nuclei break up. There are three types of such radiations – **alpha particles**, **beta particles** and **gamma rays**. Alpha particles are helium nuclei and are positively charged. Beta particles are high-energy electrons and are negatively charged. Gamma rays are electromagnetic radiation. Alpha and beta particles are deflected in opposite directions when passed through a magnetic field.

- Of the three types of radiation, alpha particles are the least **penetrating** and gamma rays the most. The radiations **ionise** matter as they pass through it, alpha particles being the most strongly ionising and gamma rays the least.

- Ionising radiations may be detected by:

  a **scintillation screen** that emits a pulse of light when ionising radiation falls on it

  a **cloud chamber** containing supersaturated ethanol vapour in which ionising radiations leave a trail of droplets

  an **ionisation chamber** in which air molecules ionised by the radiation cause a tiny current to flow between the outer case and a central electrode, which can be amplified and measured

  a **Geiger-Müller tube**, an ionisation chamber containing a gas in which an **avalanche effect** occurs, resulting in a p.d. being set up by one ionisation that can be detected and counted

  scintillation counters, which make use of the ejection of electrons from the surface of metals when light falls on them.

- The **activity** of a radioactive source is the rate of disintegration of nuclei in the source with time. One disintegration per second is one becquerel (Bq). The energy absorbed from radiation is the **dose**, measured in grays (Gy). The **dose equivalent** represents the potential damage to living tissues by radiation, and is measured in sieverts (Sv).

- Investigations to measure radioactivity must take account of the **background radiation**, ionising radiation from natural and artificial sources that is always present.

- Radioactive decay is an example of an exponential process. The decay of radioactivity may be expressed as $dN/dt = -\lambda N$, where λ is the decay constant and N the number of undecayed atoms at time t.

- The equation for radioactive decay has the solution $N = N_0 e^{-\lambda t}$, where N_0 is the number of undecayed atoms at $t = 0$.

- The **half-life** $t_{\frac{1}{2}}$ of a radioactive decay is the time taken for half the atoms to decay. This is constant for a given decay. $t_{\frac{1}{2}} = (\log_e 2)/\lambda \approx 0.693/\lambda$.

EXAMPLE

0.25 kg of radium-226 emits alpha particles at a measured rate of 9.0×10^{12} s^{-1}. What is the half-life of radium-226? (Take N_A as 6.0×10^{23} mol^{-1}.)

We have:

$$t_{\frac{1}{2}} = \frac{\log_e 2}{\lambda}$$

and:

$$\frac{dN}{dt} = -\lambda N$$

226 g of radium-226 contains 6.0×10^{23} atoms, so:

$$N = \frac{250}{226} \times 6.0 \times 10^{23} \text{ atoms}$$

$$= 6.64 \times 10^{23} \text{ atoms}$$

We know that the rate of decay of this sample is 9.0×10^{12} s^{-1}, so:

$$-9.0 \times 10^{12} \text{ s}^{-1} = -\lambda \times 6.64 \times 10^{23}$$

which gives:

$$\lambda = \frac{9.0 \times 10^{12} \text{ s}^{-1}}{6.64 \times 10^{23}}$$

$$= 1.36 \times 10^{-11} \text{ s}^{-1}$$

Therefore, substituting values into the expression above relating $t_{\frac{1}{2}}$ to λ, we get:

$$t_{\frac{1}{2}} = \frac{0.693}{1.36 \times 10^{-11} \text{ s}^{-1}}$$

$$= 5.1 \times 10^{10} \text{ s}$$

$$\approx 1620 \text{ years}$$

QUESTIONS

1 Alpha particles are stopped much more easily than beta particles with the same energy, yet alpha particles are much more massive than beta particles. Explain this.

2 Why does ionising radiation travel further in air if the pressure is reduced?

3 Alpha and beta particles lose about 5×10^{-18} J of kinetic energy in each collision they make with an air molecule. An alpha particle travelling through air at STP undergoes around 10^5 ionising collisions with air molecules for each centimetre of travel, while a beta particle undergoes only around 10^3 such collisions. Calculate the range of **a** an alpha particle and **b** a beta particle in air at STP if both particles start with an energy of 4.8×10^{-13} J.

4 Radon-220 is a naturally occurring radioactive gas with a half-life of 54 s. What fraction of a sample of this gas remains after:
a 54 s
b 108 s
c 540 s?

5 Radioactive ^{238}U found on Earth was originally produced in nuclear reactions which occurred thousands of millions of years ago in outer space – explosions then scattered this material throughout the Universe, and some of it became incorporated into the Earth when it was formed. The half-life of ^{238}U is 4.5×10^9 years. If the Earth was formed 4.6×10^9 years ago, how much of the original ^{238}U remains?

6 Cobalt-60 is used in many applications where gamma radiation is required. The half-life of cobalt-60 is 5.26 years. If a cobalt-60 source has an initial activity of 2×10^{15} Bq, what activity will it have after 3 years?

7 Cosmic rays high up in the atmosphere result in the production of $^{14}CO_2$ from $^{12}CO_2$. Carbon-14 is unstable, with a half-life of 5730 years. Living things take up $^{14}CO_2$ as well as $^{12}CO_2$, so that the proportion of carbon-14 to carbon-12 in living matter is the same as that in air. When the organism dies, the uptake of CO_2 ceases, and the decay of the carbon-14 provides a way of measuring the age of the organism – this is the basis of **radiocarbon dating**.

Living matter has an activity due to carbon-14 of 260 Bq kg^{-1}. In a sample of wood from a recently discovered burial site, the activity was 155 Bq kg^{-1}. Estimate the age of the burial site.

Developing Key Skills

In 1903, Marie and Pierre Curie were awarded the Nobel prize for physics, along with Henri Becquerel. Write a short article for a broadsheet newspaper (*Times*, *Guardian*, *Telegraph*, etc.) entitled 'One hundred years of radioactivity'. Your article should enable readers with little or no scientific background to grasp the importance of the discovery of radioactivity, both at the time and for life at the start of the twenty-first century.

[Key Skills opportunities: C]

6.3 The decay of the nucleus

Sections 6.1 and 6.2 have examined the structure of the nucleus, the radioactive rays emitted by atoms and the laws governing radioactive decay. In this section we shall be concerned with the process of radioactivity within the atom itself. This concerns the structure of the nucleus, and requires an understanding of the forces acting within the nucleus to see why some nuclei decay and emit radioactivity and others do not. We shall conclude by examining the energetics of the nucleus and what makes nuclear power possible.

Radioactive decay

Nuclear equations

Radioactive decay occurs when an unstable nucleus emits alpha, beta or gamma radiation in order to become more stable. In this process the radiation carries away energy as it is emitted from the nucleus, resulting in a reduction of the energy of the nucleus.

An alpha particle consists of two protons and two neutrons – it is a helium nucleus. Emission of an alpha particle occurs when a nucleus ejects two protons and two neutrons, reducing its nucleon number by four and its proton number by two. In this process a new chemical element is produced – this is called **transmutation**. For example, the decay of uranium-238 into thorium-234 by the emission of an alpha particle is written as:

$$^{238}_{92}\text{U} \rightarrow {}^{234}_{90}\text{Th} + {}^{4}_{2}\text{He}$$

Just as with chemical equations, nuclear equations must balance. In this case we start with 238 nucleons in the uranium atom (146 neutrons and 92 protons) and finish with 234 nucleons in the thorium atom (144 neutrons and 90 protons) and 4 nucleons in the helium nucleus (2 neutrons and 2 protons).

A beta particle is a high-energy electron, emitted when a neutron in the nucleus decays to form a proton and an electron. The electron is then ejected from the nucleus at high speed (as much as $0.99 \times$ the speed of light, or $0.99c$). When this happens, the proton number of the nucleus increases by one, leaving the nucleon number unchanged. The decay of carbon-14 by beta emission can be represented as shown here. Note that the beta particle has a nucleon number of zero and a proton number of -1, showing that it has a negative charge.

$$^{14}_{6}\text{C} \rightarrow {}^{14}_{7}\text{N} + {}^{0}_{-1}\beta$$

Once again, this equation is balanced, although this time the decay process results in an increase in the proton number of the nucleus, not a decrease as in the case of alpha emission.

When a nucleus emits alpha or beta particles it is often left in an **excited state**, that is, a state in which it has excess energy. In order to lose this energy and so become more stable, the nucleus may emit a gamma ray, an electromagnetic wave of very short wavelength. Gamma emission is thus often part of a two-stage process, with alpha or beta emission preceding the gamma emission. Because the composition of the nucleus is unchanged in this process, the element itself remains unchanged. An example of gamma decay is the decay of cobalt-60, often used in producing gamma radiation for industrial and medical purposes. As the equation shows, the actual emitter of the gamma rays is nickel, produced when cobalt undergoes beta decay.

$$^{60}_{27}\text{Co} \rightarrow {}^{60}_{28}\text{Ni} + {}^{0}_{-1}\beta$$
$$\downarrow$$
$$^{60}_{28}\text{Ni} + \gamma$$

In the example of the decay of cobalt-60, the product of the first disintegration, the **daughter nuclide**, was itself unstable and underwent further changes. It is possible for a nucleus to undergo a whole series of changes, resulting in a **radioactive decay series** as shown here.

$$^{232}_{90}\text{Th} \xrightarrow{\alpha} {}^{228}_{88}\text{Ra} \xrightarrow{\beta} {}^{228}_{89}\text{Ac} \xrightarrow{\beta} {}^{228}_{90}\text{Th} \xrightarrow{\alpha} {}^{224}_{88}\text{Ra} \xrightarrow{\alpha} {}^{220}_{86}\text{Rn} \xrightarrow{\alpha} {}^{216}_{84}\text{Po} \rightarrow$$

Holding the nucleus together

Within the nucleus there is a delicate balance between the electromagnetic force (pushing the protons apart) and the strong force (keeping the nucleons together). Neutrons are an advantage in achieving this balance, since their presence in the nucleus increases its size and so increases the distance between the protons. However, since the strong force acts over a limited range while the electromagnetic force acts over all distances, very large nuclei are unstable, since any individual proton is repelled by *all* of the other protons in the nucleus (due to the electromagnetic force) while it is attracted only by the nucleons closest to it (due to the strong force). All stable nuclei (except $^{1}_{1}\text{H}$) contain at least as many neutrons as protons, while heavy nuclei contain substantially more neutrons than protons, as figure 6.3.1 shows.

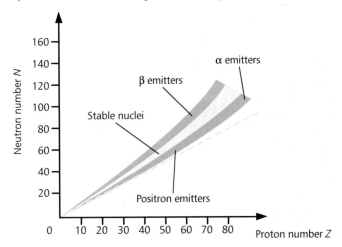

Figure 6.3.1 A plot of the number of neutrons N versus the proton number Z for the stable elements. The dotted blue line on the graph represents the points for which $N = Z$.
Notice several features of the graph:
1 For stable isotopes of small mass, the numbers of protons and neutrons are almost equal ($N \approx Z$).
2 Alpha emitters are large nuclei lying below the band of stable nuclei. Alpha decay increases the N:Z ratio slightly, and also produces a nucleus that is lighter, and therefore more stable.
3 Beta emitters convert a neutron into a proton, thereby reducing their N:Z ratio.
4 A nucleus lying below the stable band may increase its N:Z ratio by emitting a **positron** or **antielectron** (effectively a positively charged beta particle), or by **electron capture**.

A model called the 'liquid drop' model for the nucleus provides a simple way of visualising how the nucleus behaves, regarding it as being composed of a sort of 'nuclear fluid'. The strong force between nucleons has very similar characteristics to the intermolecular forces between molecules in a liquid, as shown in figure 6.3.2, with a repulsive component making the nuclear fluid almost incompressible (just like a real liquid), and an attractive component keeping the nucleons from flying apart. Using this model we should expect the nucleus to adopt a shape which is basically spherical, like a water droplet. Experimental observations suggest that this is reasonably close to the truth, and this model provides a simple, graphic explanation for many aspects of the behaviour of the nucleus (figure 6.3.3).

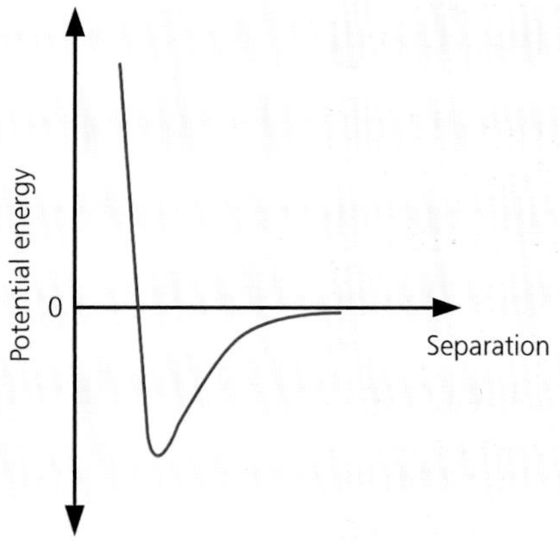

Figure 6.3.2 A graph of the potential due to the strong force between two nucleons. The equilibrium separation is at the minimum of the curve. Compare the shape of this graph with that in figure 2.1.8 on page 119.

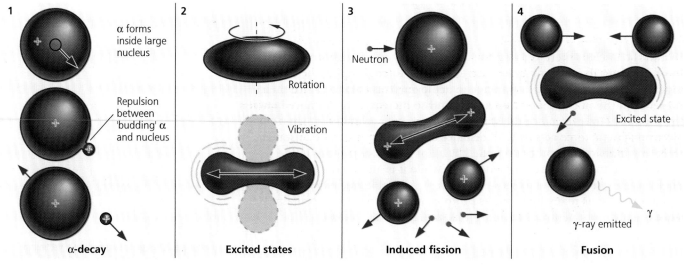

Figure 6.3.3 The liquid drop model of the nucleus – simple, but powerful.

Energy and atoms – the electronvolt

When considering energy and subatomic particles it is convenient to use a unit of energy called the **electronvolt** (eV). 1 eV is the energy transferred when an electron travels through a potential difference of 1 volt. Since the size of the charge on the electron is 1.6×10^{-19} C, and energy transferred = charge × p.d.,

$$1\text{ eV} = 1.6 \times 10^{-19}\text{ J}$$

The usefulness of the electronvolt is twofold. First, it is a small unit of energy, so that large negative powers of ten do not have to appear in energies relating to subatomic particles. Second, if we know the charge on a particle in terms of a multiple of the charge on the electron, that is, $1e$, $2e$, $3e$, etc. (and we shall see in section 6.4 that charges always do occur in such multiples), then it is a simple matter to calculate the energy transfers that occur as the particle travels through known potential differences.

Worked example

An alpha particle is just brought to rest as it travels through a potential difference of magnitude 2×10^6 V. What was its initial kinetic energy?

Magnitude of charge on alpha particle = $2e$. Alpha particle is just brought to rest by p.d. of 2×10^6 V, so:

$$E_k(\textbf{initial}) = \textbf{change in kinetic energy} = QV$$

$$= 2e \times 2 \times 10^6 \textbf{ V}$$

$$= 4 \times 10^6 \textbf{ eV or 4 MeV}$$

Binding energy

If we consider what would happen if we were to assemble a nucleus from its constituent nucleons brought together from infinity, it is clear that in order to produce a nucleus which is stable, energy must be *released* as the nucleons are brought together. (Compare this with the repulsive and attractive forces between atoms as two atoms approach to produce a simple molecule, in section 2.1.) The energy that would be released in this process is called the **binding energy** of the nucleus. Figure 6.3.4 shows a graph of binding energy per nucleon plotted against nucleon number.

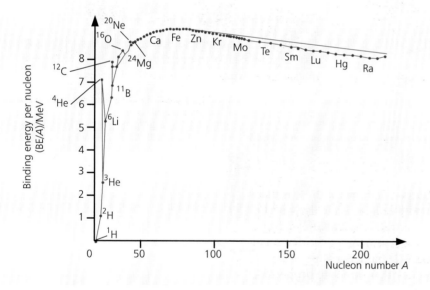

Figure 6.3.4 Binding energy per nucleon (BE/A) plotted against nucleon number A. Since it consists of only a single proton, the nucleus ^{1}H has zero binding energy. All other nuclei have non-zero binding energies.

Our everyday experience suggests that the mass of a nucleus should be equal to the masses of the individual nucleons making it up. This comparison is quickly done for the helium nucleus using data from table 6.1.2 (page 482).

Mass of 2 protons = $2 \times 1.007\ 276$ u	= 2.014 552 u
Mass of 2 neutrons = $2 \times 1.008\ 665$ u	= 2.017 330 u
Total mass	= 4.031 882 u
Measured mass of helium nucleus	= 4.001 504 u
Difference	= 0.030 378 u

This difference in mass is called the **mass defect** of the nucleus, and arises because as the nucleons combine to form the nucleus, there is a reduction in the energy of the system. As we have just seen, this reduction in energy is the binding energy of the nucleus, and results in a reduction in the measured mass. The equivalence of mass and energy was first pointed out by Albert Einstein in the relationship:

$$E = mc^2$$

where E is the amount of energy, m the mass and c the speed of light.

Using this relationship, the mass defect of the helium nucleus represents an amount of energy given by:

$$E = 0.030\ 378 \times 1.660\ 540 \times 10^{-27}\ \text{kg} \times (2.998 \times 10^8\ \text{m s}^{-1})^2$$

$$= 4.533\ 898 \times 10^{-12}\ \text{J}$$

$$= (4.533\ 898 \times 10^{-12})/(1.602 \times 10^{-19})\ \text{eV}$$

$$= 2.830 \times 10^7\ \text{eV}$$

that is, 28.3 MeV, or a little over 7 MeV per nucleon. This value is shown on the graph in figure 6.3.4 – the graph is plotted from calculations using mass defects.

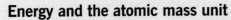

Energy and the atomic mass unit

Using the relationship $E = mc^2$, we can calculate the energy in one atomic mass unit.

$$1\ \text{u} = 1.660\ 540 \times 10^{-27}\ \text{kg}$$

Therefore:

$$E = 1.660\ 540 \times 10^{-27}\ \text{kg} \times (2.997\ 924 \times 10^8\ \text{m s}^{-1})^2$$

$$= 1.492\ 418 \times 10^{-10}\ \text{J}$$

$$= (1.492\ 418 \times 10^{-10})/(1.602\ 177 \times 10^{-19})\ \text{eV}$$

$$= 9.315 \times 10^8\ \text{eV or } 931.5\ \text{MeV}$$

This is a useful quantity to know, since it enables us to use the mass defect to calculate the energy changes in nuclear transformations, as we shall see later.

The equivalence of mass and energy

The relationship $E = mc^2$ has two interpretations. The first of these is that *mass is a form of energy*. This can be demonstrated quite spectacularly in the collision of matter and antimatter. When an electron and an antielectron collide, they annihilate each other to produce electromagnetic radiation of energy given by $E = mc^2$. (Each subatomic particle has a corresponding antiparticle, with the opposite charge and some other opposite properties, although both particle and antiparticle have the same mass. When matter and antimatter meet, the result is the annihilation described here.) According to this relationship, the annihilation of only 3 kg of matter (1.50 kg of matter and 1.50 kg of antimatter) would produce an amount of energy E given by:

$$E = 3.0\ \text{kg} \times (3 \times 10^8\ \text{m s}^{-1})^2 = 2.7 \times 10^{17}\ \text{J}$$

This is about enough energy to satisfy the demands of Europe for one day. Unfortunately, antimatter is not available in large quantities (at least on Earth), being produced only by particle accelerators like that found at CERN. (You can find out more about these topics in section 6.6.)

The second interpretation of the relationship is that *energy has mass*. The change in mass that accompanies a change in energy is $\Delta m = E/c^2$. Thus a tennis ball increases in mass when it is hit! This increase is very small for speeds not close to that of light, so that the change in mass is simply not discernible. For speeds close to that of light, the mass increment becomes large. For example, an electron accelerated in a particle accelerator may reach a velocity of around 0.999 999 999 7 c, increasing its mass by a factor of nearly 45 000.

In effect, mass and energy must be regarded as the same thing. Therefore the laws of conservation of mass and conservation of energy are not separate laws but part of the same law. When nucleons combine to form a nucleus the mass of the nucleus is less than the sum of the masses of its constituent nucleons. The energy escaping from the nucleons as they come together carries with it the energy represented by the mass defect – in other words, the mass/energy account balances exactly. The same applies to a discharging battery or a cooling cup of coffee – both lose mass as their energy decreases, although in both cases the decrease in mass is imperceptible (about 10^{-13} kg for the cup of coffee).

The energetics of atomic changes

The rearrangement of a nucleus in a nuclear reaction is accompanied by a change in mass and a change in energy. These changes must balance according to the relationship $E = mc^2$. The changes occurring in radioactive decay are **spontaneous changes** – the decay occurs without any interaction from outside the nucleus. The energetics of these changes are quite simple to consider for alpha and beta radiations.

Alpha decay

$$^{228}_{90}\text{Th} \rightarrow {}^{224}_{88}\text{Ra} + {}^{4}_{2}\text{He}$$

In this reaction a thorium-228 nucleus decays to form a radium-224 nucleus by alpha emission. The masses of each of the **atoms**, that is, the nuclei plus the electrons around them, can be obtained easily from tables of data compiled from mass spectrometer studies. (Strictly we should use the mass of each nucleus, obtained by subtracting the mass of the electrons in each atom from its total mass, but the electrons on each side of the equation 'cancel out' as we shall see.)

Mass of thorium-228 atom = 228.028 73 u

Mass of radium-224 atom = 224.020 20 u

Mass of helium atom = 4.002 60 u

So:

Mass of nucleus before disintegration = 228.028 73 u – 90 m_e

and:

Mass of nuclei after disintegration = (224.020 20 u – 88 m_e) + (4.002 60 u – 2 m_e) + mass defect

The mass defect is therefore given by:

Mass defect = (228.028 73 u – 90 m_e) – [(224.020 20 u – 88 m_e) +
(4.002 60 u – 2 m_e)]

= 228.028 73 u – (224.020 20 u + 4.002 60 u)

= 0.005 930 u

As we saw in the box 'Energy and the atomic mass unit', this mass defect is equivalent to an amount of energy E given by:

E = 0.005 930 × 931.5 MeV

= 5.5 MeV

This energy is almost all carried away by the alpha particle as kinetic energy, since the nucleus is so massive (see section 1.4 on momentum and recoil – this is like a massive cannon firing a very small shell, where the kinetic energy in the recoil of the cannon will be negligible).

In general, alpha particles emitted from a given type of nucleus are **monoenergetic**, with an energy characteristic of the type of nucleus.

Beta decay

$$^{228}_{89}\text{Ac} \rightarrow \, ^{228}_{90}\text{Th} + \, ^{0}_{-1}\beta$$

This example of beta decay involves the production of a thorium-228 nucleus from an actinium-228 nucleus. The thorium nucleus then decays by alpha emission as we saw in the example above. Once again, the calculations can be done on the basis of the atomic masses:

Mass of actinium-228 atom = 228.031 10 u

Mass of thorium-228 atom = 228.028 73 u

Mass of beta particle   = 0.000 55 u (= m_e)

So:

Mass before disintegration = 228.031 10 u – 89 m_e

and:

Mass after disintegration = (228.028 73 u – 90 m_e) +
m_e + mass defect

The mass defect is therefore given by:

Mass defect = (228.031 10 u – 89 m_e) – [(228.028 73 u – 90 m_e) + m_e]

= 228.031 10 u – 228.028 73 u

= 0.002 37 u

This mass defect is equivalent to an amount of energy E given by:

E = 0.002 37 × 931.5 MeV

= 2.2 MeV

This is the energy released by the transformation of the nucleus in this beta emission.

Gamma emission

When a nucleus has emitted an alpha particle or beta particle it is usually left with its nucleons arranged in a way that leaves it with some excess energy (this is sometimes called an 'excited state'). In order to release this energy, the nucleus emits radiation in the form of a gamma ray, high-energy electromagnetic radiation. The emission of this energy returns the nucleus to its normal 'ground state'. For example, cobalt-60 decays by beta emission:

$$^{60}_{27}\text{Co} \rightarrow {}^{60}_{28}\text{Ni} + {}^{0}_{-1}\beta + \gamma$$

The initial beta decay of cobalt-60 leaves the nickel-60 nucleus in an excited state, from which it decays by emitting two gamma rays, with energies of 1.33 MeV and 1.17 MeV.

Other modes of decay

While the emission of a beta particle from the nucleus reduces the number of neutrons in the nucleus, some unstable nuclei have too few neutrons in the nucleus to be stable. These nuclei may decay by one of two routes – by β^+ emission or by electron capture.

Both of these routes result in the conversion of a proton into a neutron. β^+ decay involves the emission of a positively charged electron or **positron**, a particle we shall meet again later in this section:

$$^{8}_{5}\text{B} \rightarrow {}^{8}_{4}\text{Be} + {}^{0}_{1}\beta$$

In electron capture a proton in the nucleus captures one of the electrons in the inner shells of the atom, becoming a neutron in the process. The gap in the inner shell is filled by one of the outer electrons, producing X-ray radiation.

The puzzle of beta emission

Calculations using the masses of nuclei suggest that beta particles from a source should be monoenergetic in a similar way to alpha particles. Observation shows that this is not so – the *maximum* energy of beta particles is characteristic of their source, but the particles are emitted over a continuous range of energies, from zero up to the maximum.

This observation was first made in 1928, and puzzled physicists for some time. It appeared that energy and momentum might not be conserved in this process. In an attempt to avoid rewriting two laws of physics which had been proved fundamentally sound in every other area of physics then known, the Austrian physicist Wolfgang Pauli suggested that another particle was also involved in beta decay. This particle would have to be uncharged, have little or no mass, and be able to carry away the energy not carried away by the beta particle. It was christened the **neutrino** ('little neutral one') by the Italian physicist Enrico Fermi. Because of its properties, the neutrino interacts only very weakly with matter, and it was not until 1955 that evidence for its existence was obtained.

$$^{228}_{89}\text{Ac} \rightarrow {}^{228}_{90}\text{Th} + {}^{0}_{-1}\beta + \bar{\nu}_e$$

Pauli's suggestion that beta decay also involved another particle meant that the equation for beta decay needed to be modified to look like the example given (this shows the rewritten equation for the decay of actinium-228). The new particle (actually an **antineutrino**, the antimatter particle corresponding to the neutrino) carries away the energy not carried away by the beta particle.

Figure 6.3.5 The existence of the neutrino was believed without absolute evidence for it – an example of the power of the structure of physics and the faith of physicists!

Wolfgang Pauli

Splitting the atom

Nuclear reactions that are not spontaneous may occur, in which an incoming particle (an alpha particle, a neutron or a proton) causes the change to occur. The first example of this type of reaction was observed by Rutherford in 1919, in an experiment which has come to be known as 'splitting the atom'.

Rutherford fired alpha particles through nitrogen gas. As expected, most of the particles simply caused ionisation of the gas, but occasionally one alpha particle was absorbed by a nitrogen nucleus and caused a nuclear reaction – figure 6.3.6 shows such an event happening in a cloud chamber. The equation for this reaction is:

$$\ce{^4_2He + ^{14}_7N -> ^{17}_8O + ^1_1H}$$

Calculations like those earlier in this section show that the mass of the products of this reaction is greater than the mass of the reactants – in other words, energy needs to be supplied in order to make this reaction happen. This energy is supplied by the incoming alpha particle. Reactions of this sort, requiring the input of energy to make them feasible, are called **induced reactions**. Such a reaction led to the discovery of the neutron, as figure 6.3.7 illustrates.

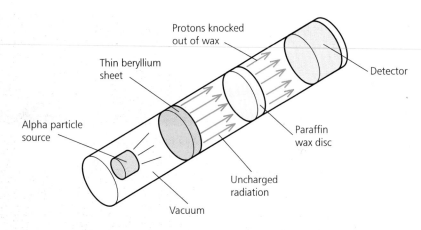

Fission and fusion – bombs and nuclear energy

Nuclear fission

The **fission** of a nucleus involves splitting it into two more or less equal fragments. This process was first observed in the element uranium, which fissions when bombarded by neutrons to produce a great variety of products. One of the possible fission reactions is:

$$\ce{^{235}_{92}U + ^1_0n -> ^{144}_{56}Ba + ^{90}_{36}Kr + 2^1_0n}$$

This transformation results in the liberation of about 200 MeV per uranium atom fissioned – that is, 1 kg of uranium-235 could produce an amount of energy E given by:

$$E = 2.0 \times 10^8 \text{ eV} \times 1.6 \times 10^{-19} \text{ J eV}^{-1} \times 6.0 \times 10^{23} \text{ mol}^{-1} \times \frac{1.0 \text{ kg}}{0.235 \text{ kg mol}^{-1}}$$

$$\approx 8 \times 10^{13} \text{ J}$$

By way of comparison, 1 kg of coal produces about 3×10^7 J when burnt – almost a million times less energy than the same mass of uranium-235 when fissioned.

Figure 6.3.6 The collision of an alpha particle with a nitrogen nucleus resulting in the ejection of a proton and the production of an atom of oxygen-17 (left). Knowledge of the energy of the alpha particles (a source was used that emitted alpha particles of known energy) and measurement of the angles of the tracks makes it possible to calculate the masses of the particles concerned, using conservation of momentum.

Figure 6.3.7 An induced nuclear reaction led to Chadwick's discovery of the neutron in 1932. Bombarding a beryllium sheet with alpha particles produced a mysterious uncharged radiation on the opposite side of the sheet. Placing a solid material containing many hydrogen atoms (paraffin wax) in the path of this radiation caused protons to be knocked out of the wax. Chadwick showed that the unknown radiation must consist of uncharged particles with a mass close to that of the proton. The equation for the nuclear reaction is:

$$\ce{^4_2He + ^9_4Be -> ^1_0n + ^{12}_6C}$$

The photograph shows a part of Chadwick's original apparatus.

Fission and the liquid drop model

Using the liquid drop model (figure 6.3.3, page 504), fission can be understood in terms of the incoming neutron distorting the nucleus in such a way that some parts of the nucleus move far enough apart for the repulsion caused by the electromagnetic force between the protons to overcome the attraction caused by the strong force acting between all the nucleons. This imbalance in repulsive and attractive forces causes the nucleus to split apart.

Figure 6.3.8 The explosion of a nuclear bomb, in which the uranium nucleus splits into two parts, is a spectacular example of the triumph of the electromagnetic force over the strong force. The energy liberated from the splitting of the atoms carries away with it an amount of mass exactly equivalent to the mass 'lost' in the disintegration process.

The fission reaction needs neutrons to cause it. Fission also produces neutrons, so that there is the possibility of the reaction being self-sustaining – that is, a neutron from the fission of one atom can cause the fission of another. In principle it is possible for both neutrons from the fission reaction described above to cause fission, and for the neutrons from these fission reactions to cause fission in further atoms, leading to a **chain reaction**, as in figure 6.3.11. This chain reaction will be self-sustaining if the mass of the fissionable material exceeds the **critical mass**.

The production of energy from nuclear fission can be understood in terms of the curve of binding energy in figure 6.3.4. A heavy atom of uranium-235 splits apart to produce two lighter atoms. In doing so the binding energy per nucleon increases from about 7.5 MeV to a little under 8.5 MeV. As there are over 200 nucleons involved in the reaction, this represents the release of approximately 200 MeV of energy per uranium-235 atom fissioned, as quoted earlier.

Figure 6.3.9 Working on the fission of uranium with Otto Hahn, Lise Meitner gave the name 'fission' to the process in which a heavy atom splits into two lighter atoms. Hahn did not acknowledge her contribution when publishing the results and he was subsequently awarded a Nobel prize for discovering nuclear fission.

Factors affecting the critical mass

Critical mass varies with the particular substance being fissioned, and also with the shape into which that substance is formed. Shape (or 'geometry') is important, since sustaining the chain reaction will depend upon retaining the fission neutrons within the material to be fissioned.

The rate at which neutrons are produced by spontaneous fission within the material depends on its volume, while the rate at which neutrons are lost through the surface of the material depends on its surface area. The lowest critical mass for which fission will occur with any particular material will therefore be with a geometry which minimises the ratio of surface area to volume – i.e. a sphere. A sphere of uranium-235 has a critical mass of a few kilograms.

The nuclear fission reactor

In a nuclear reactor, atoms of uranium undergo fission and in doing so liberate a large amount of energy. The purpose of the equipment in a nuclear power station as shown in figure 6.3.10 is to capture this energy and use it to generate electricity.

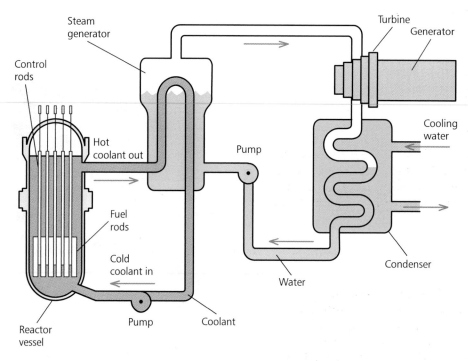

Figure 6.3.10 A schematic diagram of a nuclear reactor. The exact nature of the uranium fuel used in the reactor varies according to the reactor type, as does the coolant. All reactors used in electricity production make use of water in the form of steam to drive the turbines which turn the generators, producing electricity.

Uranium-235 is usually used in fission processes, since its nucleus is less stable than that of uranium-238, and so only a small disturbance is needed to fission it. This disturbance is provided by a neutron. Neutrons are always present in small numbers in uranium, produced by a very low rate of spontaneous fission of uranium atoms. The trick that the nuclear physicist must accomplish is to ensure that the rate of production of neutrons in the uranium is sufficient for fission to be self-sustaining, while not allowing it to become a runaway process, a delicate balancing act shown in figure 6.3.11.

The need for a moderator

The neutrons produced by the fission of uranium-235 have a good deal of kinetic energy, and are referred to as 'fast' neutrons for this reason. Fast neutrons are not very efficient at causing the fission of uranium-235, and so the core of a reactor contains a substance to slow the neutrons down in order to make self-sustaining fission possible. This is the job of the **moderator** in the reactor. In collisions with the moderator nuclei, fast neutrons lose a proportion

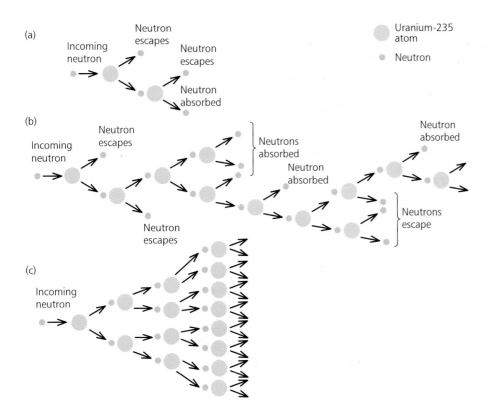

Figure 6.3.11 The process of fission. Each atom requires one neutron to cause it to fission. In (a), the fission reaction is not self-sustaining since more neutrons are absorbed or escape from the fissionable material than are required to keep the fission process going. The fissionable material is said to be **subcritical** under these conditions. For the fissionable material to be **critical**, the number of neutrons produced by each fission that themselves cause fission must be unity. The fission reaction then proceeds at a constant rate, as (b) shows. In the **supercritical** case shown in (c), the number of neutrons increases with each fission, causing the fission reaction to proceed ever faster and faster. This leads to a **chain reaction**, which produces a nuclear explosion. This type of reaction produces a result that is literally awesome, as figure 6.3.8 shows.

of their kinetic energy so that after a few collisions they have a kinetic energy of $\frac{3}{2}kT$, where T is the absolute temperature of the moderator. These neutrons are referred to as 'thermal' neutrons. Thermal neutrons are very efficient at causing the fission of uranium-235, and with such neutrons the continuous fission of uranium-235 becomes viable.

Choosing a moderator

The moderator must be chosen so as not to absorb neutrons strongly, and it must have a low atomic mass number. This ensures that much of the energy of a neutron which collides with the nucleus of an atom in the moderator is transferred to the nucleus, rather than the neutron simply bouncing off it. (Think about what happens when one table tennis ball bounces off a massive ball bearing compared to when it bounces off another table tennis ball.) Materials used as moderators include graphite, carbon dioxide and water; the latter two are also employed as coolants (see below) in certain types of reactors.

Controlling the reaction

Control over the rate of fission in a nuclear reactor is achieved by the use of **control rods**, made of boron or cadmium, both of which have nuclei which absorb neutrons strongly. These rods may be moved in and out of the core between the fuel rods. When the control rods are fully inserted into the core (for example, when a reactor is freshly loaded with new fuel) neutrons are absorbed and the reactor is **subcritical**. The production of neutrons in the core is then increased by progressively withdrawing the control rods from the core, bringing the reactor to its **critical state** in which the fission reaction becomes

Reactor type	Fuel	Coolant	Moderator
Magnox (gas-cooled reactor)	Uranium metal encased in a magnesium alloy can	Carbon dioxide, operating at a temperature of around 400 °C	Graphite
AGR (advanced gas-cooled reactor)	Uranium dioxide pellets encased in a stainless steel can	Carbon dioxide, operating at around 660 °C	Graphite
PWR (pressurised water reactor)	Uranium dioxide pellets encased in a zirconium can	Water under pressure (to prevent it boiling at the operating temperature of 320 °C)	Water acts as the moderator as well as the coolant

Table 6.3.1 The most common type of reactor worldwide is the PWR – the AGR is unique to the UK.

self-sustaining. Further withdrawal of the rods at this point would result in the reactor becoming **supercritical** – brief instants during which the reactor is in this state are referred to as **excursions**. As fission products build up in the fuel, species such as ^{135}Xe slow down the nuclear reactions by absorbing neutrons. Together with the gradual depletion of the fuel, this means that there are insufficient neutrons available for criticality, so the control rods must be withdrawn further. Eventually the control rods can be withdrawn no further, and the reactor must be refuelled.

Table 6.3.1 gives some details of different types of reactors.

Fuel

The principal fuel used in most nuclear electricity generating plants is uranium oxide, the fissionable nuclei being ^{235}U. Uranium oxide has a higher melting point than pure uranium, allowing the reactor to operate at a higher temperature. (The properties of the nucleus of an atom are not affected by chemical combination with other elements.) Naturally occurring uranium is only slightly radioactive, but its decay products such as thorium, radium and radon (a gas) present a considerable radiation hazard to miners. The risks to miners are reduced by ventilating mines, and by the use of respirators to prevent inhalation of dust to which radionuclides are attached.

After mining, the uranium ore is crushed to the texture of fine sand. The uranium is concentrated by treatment which produces uranium oxides, a process called **milling**. The **tailings** that are left after milling comprise the vast bulk of the material that has been mined, and contain considerable quantities of ^{230}Th, ^{226}Ra and ^{210}Po which must be prevented from entering the atmosphere and groundwater from the tailing piles. The uranium oxides produced in milling are purified further by conversion to uranium hexafluoride. Above 58 °C this is a gas, which allows diffusion to be used to increase the concentration of ^{235}U to between 2% and 4% from its natural concentration of around 0.7%. (Molecules containing the lighter ^{235}U diffuse more rapidly than molecules containing ^{238}U.)

The manufacture of fuel elements involves ensuring that criticality cannot occur. Strict limits on the amount of fuel that can be stored are observed, and water must not be allowed to enter areas where it might act as a moderator and so allow fission to occur. Fuel elements must be manufactured to fine tolerances so that their shape and size change in predictable ways in the reactor, when they are subjected to high temperatures and irradiation. The fuel is encased in metals such as stainless steel, magnesium alloy or zirconium alloy.

Figure 6.3.12 The core of a research reactor, in which nuclear fuel rods are being tested by subjecting them to temperatures that melt them. The blue glow is due to Čerenkov radiation, emitted when energetic charged particles travel through the water surrounding the core faster than light.

Coolant

To transfer the heat produced in the core to the steam generator, a fluid is pumped through the core at a rate sufficient to remove heat at the same rate as it is produced. This may be a gas (in AGRs), although PWRs (the most common type of reactor) use water under pressure, as their name implies. Some 'fast' reactors, used to manufacture plutonium, have liquid sodium as a coolant. Backup systems are installed as part of the cooling system to ensure that it remains possible to cool the reactor even if the primary cooling system fails.

Shielding

Even in the event of a serious accident, a nuclear reactor cannot explode like a nuclear weapon, so this is not an issue when designing the building that will house it. However, *chemical* explosions are possible, and there is a danger that the reactor housing will be breached in such a situation, leading to the loss of radioactive materials and radiation to the outside world, as happened at Chernobyl in 1986.

Reactors contain many in-built safety features which are designed to ensure that the reactor is shut down quickly if anything does go wrong. However, a steel pressure vessel surrounds the reactor core to provide containment of its contents if even these systems fail, and this in turn is surrounded by thick concrete to act as shielding from the neutrons and gamma radiation produced by the core.

Dealing with waste

Nuclear power generation produces solid, liquid and gaseous waste products, both directly from the power plant itself and from fuel reprocessing, in which fission products are removed from 'spent' fuel rods.

The gases released from nuclear power plants include ^{41}Ar, ^{85}Kr and ^{133}Xe, ^{129}I and ^{131}I, ^{3}H and ^{13}N. Most of these are of little environmental significance either because they are released in very small quantities or because they have very short half-lives. Radioactive iodine is released from fuel elements. The main hazard to humans is ^{131}I, with a half-life of 8 days. Iodine can get into the body either by direct inhalation or through cow's milk, and it is then concentrated in the thyroid gland, which is then irradiated. A similar range of gases is also released from fuel reprocessing. As with nuclear power plants, the gases produced in reprocessing are carefully monitored before being released into the atmosphere.

Liquid waste from nuclear power plants comes mainly from the cooling ponds. These contain water in which the spent fuel rods are stored to allow short-lived fission products to decay before reprocessing. The intense neutron fluxes in the reactor produce radioactive nuclides such as ^{55}Fe and ^{51}Cr – the corrosion products from the fuel cladding are therefore present in these cooling ponds. Fuel reprocessing produces liquid waste which comprises about 99% of the long-lived radioactive material involved in nuclear power production. It is the disposal of this waste that poses the most acute problems, being an acid solution which contains large numbers of radionuclides. These include elements in the periodic table between arsenic and europium together with other elements, the most important of which are plutonium, americium and curium. High-level liquid wastes are stored in double-skinned stainless steel and concrete tanks, each of which has several independent cooling systems to remove the heat produced by radioactive decay. Without this the liquids would boil, concentrating the radioactive materials within them. High-level liquid wastes will need to be stored for many thousands of years in order to allow their radioactivity to decay.

Figure 6.3.13 The wrecked containment building at Chernobyl. The chemical explosion (which occurred when an experiment being carried out on the reactor went wrong) lifted the lid off the building and tipped it on its side.

FOCUS NUCLEAR ACCIDENTS AND HUMAN ERROR

Three Mile Island, USA

At the Three Mile Island power plant in Harrisburg, Pennsylvania, in the early hours of the morning of 28 March 1979, failure of a valve led to a loss of water in the primary cooling circuit – the system that removes heat from the core of the reactor itself – and a large bubble of steam mixed with hydrogen and oxygen in the cooling system formed inside the reactor core. In addition, coolant was forced out of the primary circuit and overflowed into the reactor building, despite emergency cooling systems that should have prevented this. A series of operating errors meant that precious time was lost before the plant's operators fully understood the crisis they were dealing with and got the situation under control. To do so the operators had to vent the hydrogen gas formed in the core out to the atmosphere, even though there was no way of doing this without venting other, radioactive, gases with it.

While the immediate problems were solved within a few days of the initial incident, the final major release of radioactive gas from the core was in 1981, and further cleanup operations went on for some considerable time. During the incident, every one of the 36,000 fuel rods in the core had ruptured, releasing highly radioactive fission products into the primary coolant.

Chernobyl, Russia

While the Three Mile Island accident resulted in the release of radioactive gases into the atmosphere, the accident at Chernobyl on 26 April 1986 was much more serious. The plant's operators wanted to test whether one of the plant's turbine generators had sufficient kinetic energy after disconnection from both the steam supply and the grid to drive the pumps of the emergency core cooling system for a minute or so, to provide backup in the event of a power failure. In order to conduct this experiment, for which the reactor was required to be operating at 25% of its designed output, the operators had to disable one of the reactor's automatic control systems.

Figure 6.3.14 The nuclear plant at Three Mile Island. During the accident it was necessary to release water containing many different radionuclides into the Susquehanna river to prevent it overflowing from the sumps where it had collected in the reactor building.

NUCLEAR ACCIDENTS AND HUMAN ERROR
(continued)

As the experiment got underway, reactor power dipped uncontrollably to about 1.5% of designed output as the core of the reactor was poisoned by xenon-135. The operators managed to bring the reactor output up to 10% of full power, but only by overriding five of the reactor's built-in safety systems. Problems arose with the circulation of water through the core, and the amount of steam produced in the core rose. The reactor became supercritical, and the rise in power output led to further steam production, which led to increased power output and still further steam production. At this point the temperature in the reactor is estimated to have been rising at around 250 °C per second. Less than a minute after the start of the experiment, the operators heard two loud explosions, one after the other, caused by the explosive reaction of fuel with the steam at very high temperature, followed by the explosion of hydrogen and carbon monoxide (formed by reactions in the core) reacting with oxygen as the reactor vessel ruptured.

The explosions blew the reactor roof off (figure 6.3.13), and 6–7 tonnes of radioactive materials were ejected into the outside atmosphere. After the initial dumping of tonnes of dolomite, boron, sand and lead over the reactor, it is now entombed in concrete. Many thousands of people have had to leave the area, which will remain uninhabitable for the foreseeable future.

Tokaimura, Japan

While the Three Mile Island and Chernobyl accidents both involved nuclear power plants, the accident at Tokaimura occurred at a factory producing nuclear fuel, at 10:35 am on 30 September 1999.

The accident occurred when three workers were dissolving uranium oxide (U_3O_8) in nitric acid in the final stages of making uranium dioxide (UO_2) fuel. On the morning of the accident, they poured the last of seven batches of uranium oxide/nitric acid solution into a tank. The approved procedure for this operation involved the use of a special tank and buffer columns, to prevent a critical mass of uranium accumulating. However, in November 1996 the procedure for this process had been changed by the company operating the plant, so the workers were mixing the materials in stainless steel buckets and pouring them directly into the tank. No approval for these changes had been obtained from the appropriate nuclear authorities.

As the last of the solution was poured into the tank criticality occurred, and the workers reported seeing blue-white flashes of light. All three were taken to hospital suffering from acute exposure to high levels of neutron and gamma radiation. Despite the criticality, only trace amounts of radioactive noble gases and iodine were released from the plant itself into the atmosphere, as the plant was undamaged. High levels of neutron and gamma radiation were measured around the factory, and people living within 350 m of the factory were evacuated for 48 hours. The criticality was brought under control after about 20 hours by draining water from the cooling jacket of the tank containing the solution. (The water had been sustaining criticality by reflecting neutrons back into the solution.) Samples of water, soil and plants were taken after the accident from a 10 km radius around the site; only trace levels of radionuclides with very short half-lives were found.

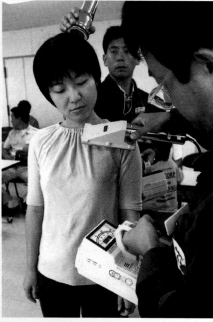

Figure 6.3.15 During the incident at Tokaimura, all local residents were checked for evidence of exposure to radiation.

Solid waste is also produced in nuclear power generation. This waste includes worn-out parts of the reactors which have been irradiated by the intense neutron flux, together with other parts of the plant in which radionuclides have accumulated, such as filters and ion-exchange resins. This waste is stored on-site in concrete vaults.

Producing artificial radionuclides

Many different radionuclides can be produced artificially by bombarding various stable nuclei with high-energy particles such as neutrons, protons and α-particles. One of the most convenient ways of producing radionuclides is by making use of the neutron flux inside a nuclear reactor. The lack of charge on the neutron makes it particularly easy for it to penetrate the nucleus of target atoms.

To obtain a sample of radionuclide, some pure nuclide is placed into the core of a nuclear reactor, using a remote handling device. Of the possible nuclear reactions that may take place in the core, neutron capture followed by γ-ray emission is the most common:

$$^{34}_{16}S + ^{1}_{0}n \rightarrow ^{35}_{16}S + \gamma$$

This can be shortened to:

$$^{34}_{16}S(n, \gamma) \rightarrow ^{35}_{16}S$$

In this case, the radionuclide produced is chemically identical to the starting substance. This means that the product will have a substantial amount of the original target substance in it. Separation is possible if the product undergoes radioactive decay (this is likely to be by β-emission, since the nuclide is neutron-rich). The product from such a decay is a further radionuclide, which is chemically different from the original substance, from which it can be separated. Iodine-131 is produced from tellurium in this way:

$$^{130}_{52}Te + ^{1}_{0}n \rightarrow ^{131}_{52}Te + \gamma$$

$$^{131}_{52}Te \rightarrow ^{131}_{53}I + ^{0}_{-1}\beta$$

Nuclear fusion

Just as producing lighter nuclei from a heavier nucleus can result in the liberation of energy, so the joining of two light nuclei to form a heavier nucleus can also produce energy. This process is called **fusion**. Once again, the production of energy results from the increase in binding energy of the product of the reaction over the reactants.

As an example, consider the fusion of two deuterium ('heavy hydrogen') nuclei to form a helium nucleus and a neutron. The energy released in this process is some 3.3 MeV.

$$^{2}_{1}H + ^{2}_{1}H \rightarrow ^{3}_{2}He + ^{1}_{0}n$$

Mass of reacting nuclei = $(2.014\ 102\ u - m_e) \times 2$

Mass of products = $3.016\ 030\ u - 2m_e + 1.008\ 665\ u$ + mass defect

The mass defect is therefore given by:

Mass defect = $(2.014\ 102\ u - m_e) \times 2 - (3.016\ 030\ u - 2m_e + 1.008\ 665\ u)$

$= 2.014\ 102\ u \times 2 - 3.016\ 030\ u - 1.008\ 665\ u$

$= 0.003\ 509\ u$

Figure 6.3.16 Barrels containing radioactive waste from the Savannah River Nuclear Plant, South Carolina, USA, stacked prior to burial.

Figure 6.3.17 Remote handling equipment like this makes it possible for an operator to carry out intricate operations on highly radioactive material without danger of contamination by ionising radiation or by the radioactive material itself.

This mass defect is equivalent to an amount of energy E given by:

$$E = 0.003\ 509 \times 931.5 \text{ MeV}$$
$$= 3.27 \text{ MeV}$$

Although this seems small compared with the 200 MeV or so produced by the fission of one uranium-235 nucleus, it is not small when considering the mass of material involved.

Nuclear fusion has been achieved in an uncontrolled way in thermonuclear explosions (the 'hydrogen bomb'). The difficulty in harnessing it for more peaceful purposes comes in providing the energy to enable two positively charged nuclei to overcome the potential barrier caused by the electric force so that they can come close enough for the strong force to cause them to fuse. Each nucleus has to be given a large kinetic energy, which can be achieved most practically through the use of extremely high temperatures, between 10^8 and 10^{10} K.

The temperature required for fusion

Using high temperatures to supply nuclei with the energy required to fuse is called **thermonuclear fusion**. To calculate the temperatures required for two deuterium nuclei to fuse, assume that each nucleus requires energy of around 1 MeV to overcome the potential barrier due to the electric force. (Remember that the binding energy per nucleon is around 1 MeV, so this is probably not an unreasonable assumption.)

What temperature is required for the nuclei to travel at this speed? If we assume that the collection of nuclei behaves as an ideal gas we can write:

$$E_k = \frac{3}{2} kT \text{ (see section 2.2, page 145)}$$

where k is the Boltzmann constant and T is the absolute temperature. To use this expression we need E_k expressed in joules. We know that 1 MeV $= 1.6 \times 10^{-13}$ J, so substituting this value for E_k gives:

$$1.6 \times 10^{-13} \text{ J} = \frac{3}{2} \times 1.38 \times 10^{-23} \text{ J K}^{-1} \times T$$

that is,

$$T = \frac{2 \times 1.6 \times 10^{-13} \text{ J}}{3 \times 1.38 \times 10^{-23} \text{ J K}^{-1}}$$

$$= 7.7 \times 10^9 \text{ K}$$

In other words, a temperature of the order of 10^{10} K will be needed – probably 10–100 times hotter than the centre of the Sun, which is of course itself fuelled by nuclear fusion.

Figure 6.3.18 Inside the Sun, nuclear fusion generates vast quantities of energy by creating heavier elements from lighter ones. At present, hydrogen nuclei (protons) are being fused to form helium nuclei, yielding about 28 MeV of energy per fusion. (The rate of conversion of hydrogen into helium is estimated to be about 6×10^{11} kg s^{-1}.) As the Sun gets older and runs out of hydrogen nuclei to fuse, it will eventually begin to fuse helium nuclei into still heavier nuclei. At this point the Sun will increase in size dramatically to become a 'red giant', swallowing up the inner planets (including Earth) in the Solar System. Estimates put the age of the Sun at about 5×10^9 years. It is thought that the Sun has so far converted about 5% of its hydrogen into helium – the red giant stage of its life is therefore a long way off.

SUMMARY

- An unstable nucleus emits radiation which carries energy away from the nucleus, thus making the nucleus more stable.
- **Alpha decay** is the emission of an alpha particle and results in **transmutation**, the production of a new element with a nucleon number four smaller and a proton number two smaller than those of the original atom.
- **Beta decay** results when a neutron forms a proton and emits an electron, and also results in transmutation. The nucleon number is unchanged, but the proton number is increased by one.
- Atoms that have emitted an alpha or beta particle may be in an **excited state**. Further energy may then be lost by the emission of a gamma ray.
- A nucleus may undergo a **series of radioactive decays**, producing a series of different elements by the emission of alpha, beta and gamma radiations.
- The **binding energy** of a nucleus is the energy that would be released if the nucleons were brought together from infinity to form the nucleus. The binding energy is carried away by a reduction in mass called the **mass defect**.
- Mass and energy are related by the equation $E = mc^2$.
- **Fission** is the splitting of a nucleus into two roughly equal fragments. Uranium splits when bombarded with neutrons. Very large quantities of energy are given out as the reaction involves an increase in binding energy per nucleon. The fission of uranium itself produces more neutrons,

which can cause subsequent fission reactions, leading to a **chain reaction**. ▼

- **Fusion** is the joining of two smaller nuclei to form a larger one. Energy is given out, due to an overall increase in binding energy per nucleon.

- The **liquid drop model** of the nucleus provides a simple explanation for radioactive decay, fission and fusion.

- In a nuclear fission reactor the fuel (usually uranium-235 in the form of uranium dioxide) is maintained in a critical state by means of a **moderator** and **control rods**. Heat is removed from the reactor by the primary coolant (water in the PWR, carbon dioxide in the AGR), which then produces steam to drive the turbines connected to the electricity generator.

QUESTIONS

1 What isotopes are formed by the alpha decay of:
a ^{240}Pu   **b** ^{230}Th   **c** ^{212}Po   **d** ^{241}Am?

2 What isotopes are formed by the beta (β^-) decay of:
a ^{14}C   **b** ^{8}Li   **c** ^{32}P   **d** ^{19}O?

3 What isotopes are formed by the positron (β^+) decay of:
a ^{22}Na   **b** ^{56}Co?

4 ^{210}Po decays to form ^{206}Pb by alpha emission. If the mass of the polonium atom is 209.982 870 u, the mass of the lead atom is 205.974 470 u and the mass of a helium atom is 4.002 603 u, calculate the energy of the alpha particle.

5 Nuclei containing 2, 8, 14, 20, 28, 50, 82 or 126 protons or neutrons are exceptionally stable. Because of this, they are sometimes called **magic nuclei**.
  a Why is the ^{16}O nucleus a magic nucleus?
  b Calculate the binding energy per nucleon of the ^{16}O nucleus if the mass of the atom (including electrons) is 15.994 915 u. (You will need to use the data in table 6.1.2 on page 482.)
  c Calculate the binding energy per nucleon of the ^{16}N nucleus. The mass of the ^{16}N atom including electrons is 16.006 103 u.
  d Compare your answers to **b** and **c**.

6 The Sun produces thermal energy by means of the following series of reactions:
  (1) ^{1}H + ^{1}H → ^{2}H + e$^+$ + ν
  (2) ^{1}H + ^{2}H → ^{3}He + γ
  (3) ^{3}He + ^{3}He → ^{4}He + ^{1}H + ^{1}H
  (e$^+$ is a positron, with the same mass as an electron but opposite charge, and ν is a neutrino.)
  Reactions 1 and 2 both happen twice for each time reaction 3 happens. This results in the net consumption of four protons and the net production of one helium-4 nucleus.
  a Calculate the energy produced in each reaction. The mass of the ^{2}H nucleus is 2.013 005 u, that of the ^{3}He nucleus is 3.014 933 u, and that of the ^{4}He nucleus is 4.001 504 u. (You will also need to use the data in table 6.1.2 on page 482.) Note that the neutrino and the gamma ray produced have no mass, and can be regarded as part of the energy production.

  b Calculate the energy produced per proton consumed.
  c The Sun produces thermal energy at a rate of about 4×10^{26} W. At what rate (in kg s^{-1}) is the Sun consuming protons?

Developing Key Skills

A nuclear power station is to be built a few kilometres away from a small town. An article in the local newspaper about this development includes a table showing the possible numbers of deaths from the Chernobyl disaster (Table 6.3.2). The article quotes a supporter of nuclear power as saying: 'The Chernobyl disaster has shown us that the virtually undetectable number of extra deaths caused by a large-scale nuclear accident is a price worth paying for nuclear power.'

In the same article, an opponent of nuclear power says: 'Even one extra death caused by the use of nuclear power is one death too many, and makes nuclear power unacceptable.'

Write a letter for publication in the local paper in response to one or both of these statements.

Population	Western Russia 75 000 000	Europe 400 000 000	UK 56 000 000
Deaths 1986–2026	30 000 000	160 000 000	26 000 000
Cancer deaths 1986–2026	6 000 000	35 000 000	6 000 000
Cancer deaths due to background radiation 1986–2026	78 000	416 000	40 000
Deaths due to Chernobyl	8000–34 000	2000	40

Table 6.3.2 Projected deaths from the Chernobyl nuclear accident (based on estimates made approximately six months after the accident).

[Key Skills opportunities: C, A]

6.4 The nature of the electron

Section 6.1 examined evidence for the structure of matter and considered some of the general properties of the particles of which matter is composed. In sections 6.2–6.3 we were then concerned with the nucleus, particularly its stability (or lack of it), leading to the phenomenon of radioactivity, and also the energetics of nuclear reactions as applied to the possibilities of nuclear fission and fusion.

The final two sections of the book take a closer look at the other constituent of matter, the electron. We shall begin by considering the properties of the electron and its interaction with matter.

The properties of the electron

Specific charge

At the end of the nineteenth century physicists were searching for clues that would provide some idea about the structure of atoms, as we saw in figure 6.1.9. One of the most important early pieces of evidence came from work done by J. J. Thomson, with the discovery that cathode rays, known since the 1850s, consisted of streams of charged particles called electrons.

The ratio of a particle's charge to its mass (e/m) is called its **specific charge**. The first measurement of the specific charge of the electron was made by J. J. Thomson in 1897, as mentioned on page 477. Thomson used a method employing crossed electric and magnetic fields for this measurement, similar to the velocity selector in the mass spectrometer. A modern version of this method for finding e/m_e is described in the box 'Measuring the specific charge of the electron', together with an alternative method.

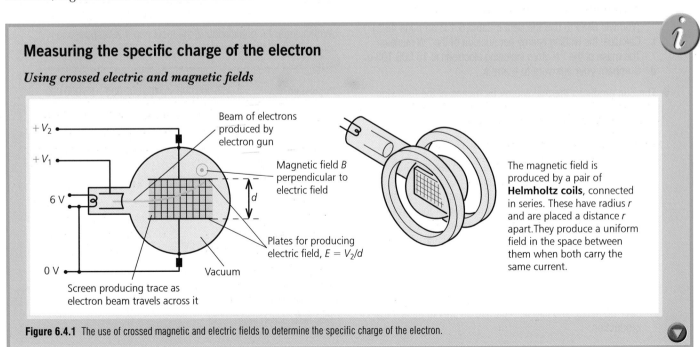

Measuring the specific charge of the electron

Using crossed electric and magnetic fields

+V_2
+V_1

Beam of electrons produced by electron gun

6 V

Magnetic field B perpendicular to electric field

Plates for producing electric field, $E = V_2/d$

0 V

Vacuum

Screen producing trace as electron beam travels across it

The magnetic field is produced by a pair of **Helmholtz coils**, connected in series. These have radius r and are placed a distance r apart. They produce a uniform field in the space between them when both carry the same current.

Figure 6.4.1 The use of crossed magnetic and electric fields to determine the specific charge of the electron.

A beam of electrons is produced by an electron gun with an accelerating voltage V_1, as shown in figure 6.4.1. The beam travels across a screen which produces a luminous trace of the electrons' path. This screen is arranged in such a way that the electrons travelling across it may be influenced by an electric field and a magnetic field. These are positioned so that the initial velocity of the electron, the electric field and the magnetic field are all mutually perpendicular.

If the apparatus is set up so that an electron from the gun is undeflected as it travels across the screen, the force on the electron due to the electric field must be exactly opposed by the force on it due to the magnetic field (as we saw in the case of the velocity selector). Therefore, if the electron has velocity v,

$$eE = Bev$$

Now as we saw on page 281, the kinetic energy of the electron is given by:

$$\tfrac{1}{2}m_e v^2 = eV_1$$

These two equations may be combined to eliminate v:

$$\frac{e}{m_e} = \frac{E^2}{2B^2 V_1}$$

But the electric field strength $E = V_2/d$, so:

$$\frac{e}{m_e} = \frac{V_2^2}{2B^2\, d^2 V_1}$$

This relationship may be used to obtain a value for e/m_e from single measurements of V_1, V_2, B and d. However, a preferable method is to rearrange the relationship to give:

$$V_2^2 = 2d^2 V_1 \frac{e\,B^2}{m_e}$$

A plot of $V_2{}^2$ against B^2 then gives a straight-line graph passing through the origin with slope $2d^2 V_1 e/m_e$.

B may be obtained either from measurements with a Hall probe or by calculation from the relationship:

$$B = 0.716\,\mu_0 NI/r$$

where N is the number of turns on one coil, I is the current through the coils and r is their radius.

This experiment assumes that the two fields are constant in strength along the entire length of the electron beam, which is not usually the case. As a result, values for e/m_e obtained using this method are usually only correct in their order of magnitude.

The fine beam tube

An alternative method for measuring e/m_e uses a **fine beam tube**. This tube contains a gas (usually hydrogen) at a low pressure, about 10^{-5} atmospheres, together with an electron gun that produces a beam of electrons in a direction perpendicular to the axis of the tube, as shown in figure 6.4.2.

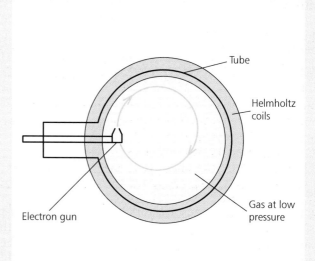

Tube

Helmholtz coils

Gas at low pressure

Electron gun

Figure 6.4.2 The fine beam tube.

Electrons from the gun collide with molecules of the gas and ionise them. This results in a 'trail' of positive ions along the path of the electron beam, which serves to focus the electrons into a very fine beam. In addition, a molecule or atom that has lost an electron can emit light when it regains another electron, so the path of the electron beam is revealed by gas molecules emitting light. (This phenomenon is explained further in section 6.5.)

The Helmholtz coils produce a uniform field in the tube, perpendicular to the axis of the tube and the velocity of the electrons emerging from the electron gun. This field causes the electrons to travel in a circular path.

We know that the force on an electron with velocity v in this situation is given by:

$$F = Bev$$

and that this force provides the centripetal acceleration for the electron's circular motion. Hence we can write:

$$\frac{m_e v^2}{r} = Bev$$

from which:

$$v = \frac{Ber}{m_e}$$

If the accelerating potential of the electron gun is V, the kinetic energy of the electrons will be given by:

$$\tfrac{1}{2}m_e v^2 = eV$$

Substituting the previous expression for v into this gives:

$$\tfrac{1}{2}m_e \left(\frac{Ber}{m_e}\right)^2 = eV$$

from which:

$$\frac{e}{m_e} = \frac{2V}{B^2 r^2}$$

Once again, this relationship may be used to calculate e/m_e directly. Alternatively, a plot of B (calculated or measured as for the crossed fields experiment above) versus $1/r$ gives a straight-line graph through the origin, with slope $\sqrt{(2Vm_e/e)}$.

The currently accepted value of e/m_e is $-1.758\,820 \times 10^{11}$ C kg^{-1}.

The charge on the electron

The importance of Thomson's work lay in the evidence it provided for the existence of the electron as a particle. By showing that cathode rays were streams of electrons, Thomson showed that all electrons behave identically when subjected to electric and magnetic fields, and was able to relate the electron's specific charge to that of the hydrogen ion.

The specific charge of the hydrogen ion had been calculated from electrolysis experiments prior to Thomson's work on the electron. The specific charge of the hydrogen ion was known to be 9.65×10^7 C kg^{-1}, about 1850 times smaller than that of the electron. Thomson believed that the correct interpretation of this was that the electron carried a charge equal in size to that on the hydrogen ion, but had a mass 1850 times smaller. This interpretation came to be accepted in the early years of the twentieth century, but it was not until 1909 that conclusive evidence for it was obtained.

Robert Millikan investigated the charge on the electron in an experiment usually referred to as **Millikan's oil drop experiment**. Like many of the finest experiments, it is simple in design but has complex finer points, with many details which require attention. The box on pages 525–6 sets out the basic details of Millikan's work.

Millikan's results from hundreds of measurements showed that no matter what the charge on an oil drop, it was always a multiple of the same basic charge: 1.6×10^{-19} C. Charge is thus a quantity which is *not* continuous, but comes in fixed amounts or quanta, just as we saw for energy in section 2.4. We shall see how important the quantisation of physical quantities is in the remainder of this section and in the next. For the moment we shall leave the story of the investigation of the properties of the electron, but shall pick it up again later.

Measuring the charge on the electron – Millikan's oil drop experiment

Essentially, Millikan measured the charge on a great number of tiny oil drops which had been charged by friction as they were sprayed out of a nozzle. He was then able to show that each drop carried a charge that was a multiple of a basic unit of charge. Figure 6.4.3 outlines his apparatus.

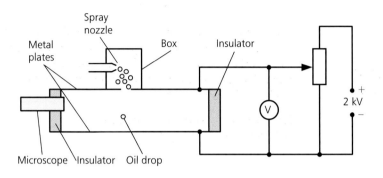

Figure 6.4.3 The principle of Millikan's experiment. The light source illuminating the drops between the plates has been omitted for clarity.

A small number of the oil drops sprayed into the box make their way through the hole in the top plate and are seen through the microscope. With no electric field between the plates the drops fall slowly with a steady terminal velocity. An individual drop of mass m and carrying charge q may be brought to rest by applying a p.d. across the plates such that:

$$Eq = mg$$

where E is the electric field strength between the plates. The problem is thus to measure the mass m of the drop.

This is carried out by measurement of the drop's terminal velocity. If the drop falls slowly it is approximately spherical in shape, and the aerodynamic drag force F on it is given by the relationship:

$$F = 6\pi\eta rv$$

where r is the radius of the drop, η the viscosity of air and v the drop's terminal velocity. (This relationship is called **Stokes' law**, and applies to any sphere travelling with velocity v through a fluid of viscosity η.)

Since the drop is moving with a steady velocity, the drag force is equal to the weight of the drop, so:

$$mg = 6\pi\eta rv$$

But the mass of the drop is equal to its volume multiplied by the density of the oil, so:

$$\frac{4\pi r^3 \rho g}{3} = 6\pi\eta rv$$

that is,

$$r^2 = \frac{9\eta v}{2\rho g}$$

The radius of the oil drop is thus calculated from its terminal velocity, and this is then used to calculate the mass of the drop, using the density of the oil.

In practice a single drop is used for several sets of measurements, the drop being charged by ionising the air between the plates using ionising radiation.

Several refinements are necessary to ensure the highest accuracy:
(1) Allowance must be made for the upthrust on the drop, due to the weight of air it displaces.
(2) An oil that does not readily evaporate must be used so that the mass of the oil drop does not change appreciably while in use for long periods.
(3) Any change in viscosity of air with temperature (as much as 4% for a 10 K rise) must be allowed for.

Worked example

Given the following data from an experiment using apparatus similar to Millikan's, calculate the magnitude of the charge on the oil drop:

Density of oil = 900 kg m^{-3}   **Plate separation = 10 mm**
P.d. across plates = 613 V   **Viscosity of air = 1.8 × 10^{-5} N s m^{-2}**

The droplet is observed to fall steadily through a distance of 2.50 mm in 22.0 s when there is no field between the plates. Take g as 9.8 m s^{-2}.

The droplet radius can be calculated from:

$$r^2 = \frac{9\,\eta v}{2\,\rho g}$$

From the data given, $v = 2.50 \times 10^{-3}$ m/22.0 s $= 1.14 \times 10^{-4}$ m s^{-1}, so:

$$r^2 = \frac{9 \times 1.8 \times 10^{-5} \text{ N s m}^{-2} \times 1.14 \times 10^{-4} \text{ m s}^{-1}}{2 \times 900 \text{ kg m}^{-3} \times 9.8 \text{ m s}^{-2}}$$

$$= 1.05 \times 10^{-12} \text{ m}^2$$

which gives $r = 1.02 \times 10^{-6}$ m.

The mass of the drop is thus:

$$\tfrac{4}{3}\pi r^3 \rho = \tfrac{4}{3}\pi \times (1.02 \times 10^{-6} \text{ m})^3 \times 900 \text{ kg m}^{-3} = 4.00 \times 10^{-15} \text{ kg}$$

We know that when the drop is stationary, $Eq = mg$, and we also know that $E = V/d$, so:

$$q = \frac{mg}{E} = \frac{mgd}{V}$$

$$= \frac{4.00 \times 10^{-15} \text{ kg} \times 9.81 \text{ m s}^{-2} \times 10 \times 10^{-3} \text{ m}}{613 \text{ V}}$$

$$= 6.4 \times 10^{-19} \text{ C}$$

This is a charge of magnitude $4e$ ($e = -1.6 \times 10^{-19}$ C).

Robert Millikan was awarded the Nobel prize for physics in 1923 for his work on electronic charge, only the second American to be so honoured. The story of his work makes interesting reading, not least because it provides us with some insight into the way in which scientists work.

Millikan wrote up his results in a series of papers, one of which was published in 1913. As we have already seen, these results indicated that the charges on the droplets were always multiples of the same number – the charge on the electron. So convinced was he of his results that he wrote in his autobiography 'he who has seen that experiment, and hundreds of observers have observed it, [has] in effect SEEN the electron.'

Millikan's records and laboratory notebooks show that he was careful about the results that he chose to publish, choosing results from some drops and rejecting those from others. In addition, his notebook records how results later on in the series of experiments are 'beautiful' – as Millikan and his technician refined their technique so as to produce the results which they knew they were looking for.

Another physicist, Felix Ehrenhaft of Vienna, contested Millikan's results, claiming that he had evidence for the existence of 'subelectrons' and that some of Millikan's own published data supported him. The subsequent 'battle of the electron' lasted for some years. Writing about the dispute between the two men some 60 years after Millikan's Nobel prize, Gerald Holton wrote: 'If Ehrenhaft had had access to Millikan's notebook, he would have found precisely those [results] most valuable for his purposes, which, for Millikan, were failed.'

Something that has caused particular concern among scientists and scholars who have examined Millikan's notebooks and papers is the way in which Millikan refers to his results. In a paper on some earlier work on water drops, published in 1910, Millikan writes quite openly 'Although all of these observations gave values of e within 2 percent of the final mean, the uncertainties of the observations were such that I would have discarded them had they not agreed with the results of the other observations, and consequently I felt obliged to discard them as it was.'

But Millikan was not open about the process of selection of results in his 1913 paper. In this he states (writing in italics for special emphasis) '*It is to be remarked that this is not a selected group of drops but represents all of the drops experimented upon during 60 consecutive days.*' Millikan's notebook fails to provide support for this assertion, since only 140 results are included in the paper, while his notebook shows that 189 observations were made during the period in question.

Some people have said that Millikan was guilty of doing 'bad science' when he treated and presented his data. They argue that the statement published in his 1913 paper cannot be reconciled with an unbiased interpretation of his laboratory notebooks. Other people have pointed to the honest (if slightly strange) statement in his 1910 paper as evidence that he was far from attempting to deceive anyone. For some others, Millikan can be allowed a considerable degree of freedom to exercise his 'scientific intuition' in deciding which results to include and which to leave out – a pragmatic view that may be based on the notion that any scientist who is able to obtain consistent results that turn out to be correct must be doing 'good science'.

Figure 6.4.4 Robert Millikan (1868–1953).

Figure 6.4.5 The reliability of the results in a paper in a scientific journal depends upon the honesty of the scientist submitting the work, and upon the other scientists who review the work before it is accepted for publication.

Wave or particle?

The nature of light

At around the same time as Thomson was investigating the behaviour of cathode rays and coming to the conclusion that they were particles, a German physicist called Max Planck was trying to obtain a theoretical model to understand the way a **black body** emits electromagnetic radiation. A black body is a perfect emitter and absorber of electromagnetic radiation, capable of absorbing and radiating all wavelengths. This is explained further in the box 'Black body radiation'. Planck found that he could not develop a model for this unless he made an assumption that ran completely contrary to the laws of physics known at the time – he had to assume that energy could be absorbed or radiated by a body only in discrete quantities, not in continuous amounts.

Based on thermodynamics, Planck showed that the emission of thermal radiation by a black body could be modelled using a reasonably simple relationship which included a new constant h, now known as **Planck's constant**. (Planck's constant has a value of 6.63×10^{-34} J s.) This model pictured the black body as a series of oscillators, rather like the 'marbles on a spring' model we saw in section 2.1. Planck envisaged that the oscillators vibrated in such a way that they could only absorb or lose specific amounts of energy, although the radiation they absorbed or emitted remained a continuous distribution of energies as demanded by classical physics.

Although Planck's work was not fully understood at the time, it was later taken up by Einstein. In 1905 Einstein showed that the radiation from a black body could be understood more simply if it was assumed that the radiation

Figure 6.4.6 Max Planck, discoverer of the quantisation of energy. Planck invented the idea of quantisation in 'an act of desperation' because 'a theoretical explanation had to be found at any cost, whatever the price.' He received a Nobel prize for this work in 1918.

Black body radiation

A black body is a perfect absorber of radiation, able to absorb completely radiation of any wavelength which falls on it. Figure 6.4.7 shows the simplest possible type of black body – a hole in a box painted black inside.

A black body not only absorbs all wavelengths of radiation falling on it, but also radiates all wavelengths too. The exact spectrum of the radiation from the black body depends on its temperature, as the graph shows. Classical physics can predict this pattern of emission at long wavelengths but not at short wavelengths, leading to a disagreement christened the **ultraviolet catastrophe**.

Figure 6.4.7 A cavity (box) with a small hole in it behaves like a black body. The most probable wavelength of the radiation radiated from it is proportional to the temperature of the black body, a relationship known as **Wein's displacement law**. An understanding of this relationship is important to astronomers, since stars behave as black body radiators. Knowledge of the wavelengths of the radiation from a star enables astronomers to make estimates of its temperature.

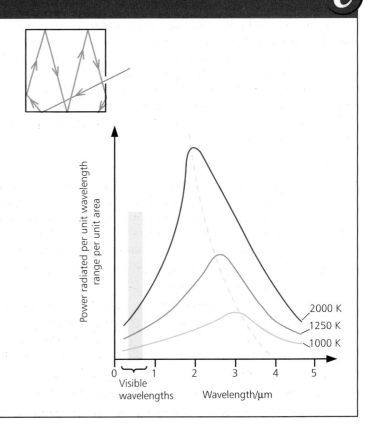

itself was quantised, consisting of particle-like packets of energy. Each packet is called a **photon**. If the frequency of a wave is f, the energy of the photons in it is given by the relationship:

$$E = hf$$

where h is Planck's constant.

The quantisation of radiation – worked example

Energy from the Sun strikes the Earth's surface at a rate of about 1000 W m^{-2}. What rate of arrival of photons is this, assuming that the average wavelength of sunlight is 500 nm? Take Planck's constant as 6.63×10^{-34} J s and the velocity of light as 3×10^8 m s^{-1}.

$$c = f\lambda$$

so we can write the energy E of one photon as:

$$E = \frac{hc}{\lambda}$$

Substituting:

$$E = \frac{6.63 \times 10^{-34}\ \text{J s} \times 3 \times 10^8\ \text{m s}^{-1}}{5 \times 10^{-7}\ \text{m}}$$

$$= 4 \times 10^{-19}\ \text{J}$$

The number of photons n arriving per square metre per second is given by the energy incident per square metre per second divided by the photon energy, so:

$$n = \frac{1000\ \text{W m}^{-2}}{4 \times 10^{-19}\ \text{J}}$$

$$= 2.5 \times 10^{21}\ \text{photons per m}^2\ \text{per second}$$

The 'particle nature' of light is therefore not likely to be evident in our macroscopic world, because of the vast numbers of photons involved.

The fact that light behaves like a wave under some circumstances and like a particle under others demonstrates that neither the wave model nor the particle model of classical physics is adequate for understanding the behaviour of light. For a full understanding of light we have to regard it as a **wavicle**, a wave–particle object that behaves sometimes like a classical wave and sometimes like a classical particle, and at other times like a mixture of the two! This is clear if we examine another puzzle from physics at the turn of the twentieth century, the **photoelectric effect**.

The photoelectric effect

Metals are capable of losing electrons if given enough energy, as shown by the production of electrons by thermionic emission in the electron gun. The electron gun uses heat to supply energy to the electrons, but it is possible to use light too, as the demonstration illustrated in figure 6.4.8 shows.

An investigation like this shows a number of interesting features.

1 With no light falling on the zinc plate, the leaf falls only very slowly if at all (due to charge leaking away through the air).

2 If ultraviolet light is shone onto the plate the leaf falls rapidly. This fall is stopped if a sheet of glass is placed between the zinc plate and the ultraviolet lamp (glass absorbs ultraviolet light strongly).

3 The rate of fall of the leaf depends on the distance of the lamp from the plate – the closer the lamp, the more rapid the fall.

4 Visible light has no effect on the behaviour of the leaf.

5 A positively charged electroscope is unaffected by ultraviolet light.

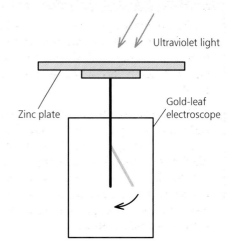

Figure 6.4.8 The leaf on a negatively charged gold-leaf electroscope slowly falls if a zinc plate resting on the cap of the electroscope is irradiated with ultraviolet light.

Prior to Einstein's work, scientists had already interpreted results like this as showing that ultraviolet light was capable of transferring energy to electrons in a metal, giving them sufficient energy to escape from the metal surface. Electrons liberated in this way were given the name **photoelectrons**. The leaf of the negatively charged electroscope thus falls as electrons are ejected from the zinc plate, decreasing the overall negative charge on the plate. The leaf does not fall if the electroscope is positively charged, as the ultraviolet light cannot transfer sufficient energy to the electrons to enable them to escape from the much deeper potential well. For a given surface there is a minimum frequency of light (the **threshold frequency**) below which no emission of photoelectrons occurs. This accounts for visible light having no effect on the electroscope in figure 6.4.8, and explains why a sheet of glass stops the leaf falling. The number of photoelectrons emitted from the metal surface depends only on the intensity of the light falling on it. Moving the ultraviolet lamp closer to the electroscope therefore increases the rate at which photoelectrons are ejected from the plate as the intensity of the incident radiation increases.

Even though physicists could agree on the general interpretation of the photoelectric effect, using classical physics no model could be constructed which could explain:

- why there was a threshold frequency below which no photoelectrons were emitted, and why this threshold frequency was different for different metals
- why the number of photoelectrons emitted per second depended on the intensity of the light incident on the metal surface but not on its frequency.

Einstein was able to show that a complete explanation of the photoelectric emission of electrons is possible if light is assumed to be quantised. If we consider a free electron close to the surface of a piece of metal, the electron will require a certain amount of energy in order to escape completely from the metal and reach infinity. (This is rather like the calculation in section 5.2 of the energy needed for a spacecraft to escape to infinity from the surface of the Earth. Both the electron and the spacecraft are in a potential well – to escape from the potential well requires the transfer of energy.) When photons of light strike the surface of the metal, one may strike the electron. As a result of this collision the photon's energy may be transferred to the electron, and it may now have sufficient energy to escape from the metal. Figure 6.4.9 shows a metal surface being bombarded by photons with three different energies.

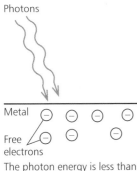

The photon energy is less than the minimum energy required to eject an electron from the metal – no photoelectrons are produced.

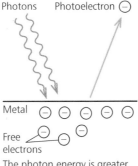

The photon energy is greater than the minimum energy required to eject an electron from the metal. Photoelectrons are produced which have a range of kinetic energies up to a maximum value.

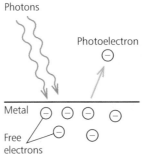

The photon energy is just large enough to cause emission. Photoelectrons with zero kinetic energy are produced.

Figure 6.4.9 The emission of photoelectrons from a metal surface and their subsequent kinetic energy both depend on the frequency of the incident light. An electron absorbs energy from an incident photon in order to escape from the metal. Any energy remaining after the electron has done the work necessary to escape from the metal remains as the electron's kinetic energy.

Note that absorption of the energy required to escape from the metal surface must happen in a single interaction with a photon – no multiple collisions to acquire this energy are allowed.

Einstein's photoelectric equation expresses these ideas mathematically:

$$hf = \phi + \tfrac{1}{2}mv_{max}^2$$

The photon energy is given by hf as we have already seen, and $\tfrac{1}{2}mv_{max}^2$ is the maximum kinetic energy of the photoelectron. The quantity ϕ is the **work function** of the metal surface under consideration, which is the energy required to completely remove an electron from the metal. Figure 6.4.10 shows how the maximum kinetic energy of electrons varies with the frequency of incident light for sodium.

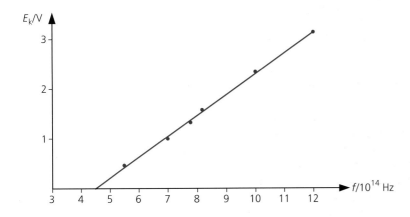

Figure 6.4.10 Graph showing the maximum kinetic energy for photoelectrons emitted from sodium by light of different frequencies.

The photoelectric effect – worked example

(a) Use the graph in figure 6.4.10 to obtain an estimate for the work function of sodium.

(b) Light of wavelength 300 nm is incident on a sodium surface. Calculate the maximum kinetic energy of the photoelectrons emitted from the surface. ($c = 3.0 \times 10^8$ m s^{-1}, $h = 6.63 \times 10^{-34}$ J s.) Express your answers to an appropriate degree of accuracy.

(a) An electron emerging from the metal with zero kinetic energy will have absorbed just enough energy to have escaped from the metal, so:

$$hf = \phi + 0$$

The work function is thus obtained from the graph in figure 6.4.10 as the intercept on the x-axis, where $\tfrac{1}{2}mv_{max}^2 = 0$.

Intercept on x-axis = 4.5×10^{14} Hz, so:

$$\phi = 6.63 \times 10^{-34} \text{ J s} \times 4.5 \times 10^{14} \text{ Hz}$$

$$= 3.0 \times 10^{-19} \text{ J}$$

This answer is given to two significant figures, since it is impossible to read the graph with any greater accuracy.

(b) For light of incident wavelength 300 nm:

$$hf = \frac{hc}{\lambda} = \phi + \tfrac{1}{2}mv_{max}^2$$

Rearranging and substituting:

$$\tfrac{1}{2}mv_{max}^2 = \frac{6.63 \times 10^{-34} \text{ J s} \times 3.0 \times 10^8 \text{ m s}^{-1}}{3.0 \times 10^{-7} \text{ m}} - 3.0 \times 10^{-19} \text{ J}$$

$$= 3.7 \times 10^{-19} \text{ J (again to 2 SF)}$$

So the work function for sodium as calculated from the graph is 3.0×10^{-19} J, and the maximum kinetic energy of the photoelectrons is 3.7×10^{-19} J.

Note: It is common to express both work function and the kinetic energy of photoelectrons in electronvolts. These answers may be converted to electronvolts by dividing them by 1.6×10^{-19} J eV^{-1}, which gives:

$$\phi = 1.9 \text{ eV} \qquad \tfrac{1}{2}mv_{max}^2 = 2.3 \text{ eV}$$

Investigating the photoelectric effect

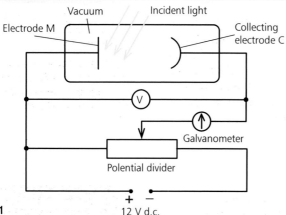

Figure 6.4.11

The investigation of the photoelectric effect may be carried out using the apparatus shown in figure 6.4.11. Light of a known frequency is shone onto a metal electrode M. Photoelectrons from M travel towards a collecting electrode C and then flow round the external circuit through the galvanometer.

The maximum kinetic energy of the ejected electrons can be found by applying a potential difference across C and M, making C negative with respect to M. As this potential difference is increased (by means of the potential divider), the number of electrons reaching C from M will decrease as fewer and fewer electrons have sufficient energy to overcome the potential barrier. Eventually the potential difference will be such that even the most energetic electrons will just fail to reach C. This potential is called the **stopping potential**, V_{stop}. The measured value of this stopping potential gives the maximum kinetic energy of the electrons:

$$\tfrac{1}{2}mv_{max}^2 = eV_{stop}$$

Using apparatus like this, the frequency of the incident light may be varied (a spectrometer may be used as a source of incident light, or alternatively filters admitting a narrow range of frequencies may be used) and the maximum kinetic energy of the electrons found from the stopping potential. This is the method used to obtain the graph shown in figure 6.4.10.

Applications of the photoelectric effect

The photoelectric effect has practical applications in a number of areas concerned with the detection of light. In the **photomultiplier tube**, a single incident photon produces a pulse of current through an external circuit as a result of a series of electron avalanches, as shown in figure 6.4.12. This tube may find use in an image intensifying camera used to obtain pictures in extremely low light levels or in a scintillation counter used to detect ionising events. In the case of the scintillation counter the photon of light comes from a crystal of sodium iodide which emits a weak flash of light when ionising radiation passes through it.

Electrons as waves

Following the work on the particle nature of electromagnetic waves, Louis de Broglie suggested that it was possible that particles like electrons might have wave properties. As we shall see in section 6.5, the wave-like nature of electrons is fundamental to our present understanding of the behaviour of electrons in atoms, as well as the behaviour of all the other 'particles' found in nature – protons, neutrons, neutrinos and so on. de Broglie stated that the wavelength associated with a particle (called the **de Broglie wavelength**) is inversely proportional to its momentum p:

$$\lambda = \frac{h}{p}$$

The wave properties of the electron were subsequently confirmed independently by the American Clinton Davisson and by George Thomson in England in 1927, showing the diffraction of electrons by crystals.

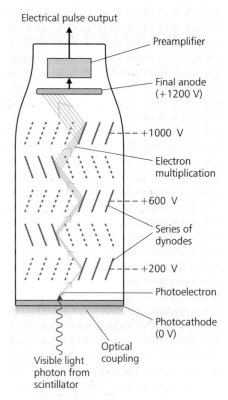

Figure 6.4.12 The photomultiplier tube is a powerful tool to increase the intensity of images taken in poor light. A high-gain tube may produce as many as 10^9 electrons from a single photon.

Wavelength and energy

Since we know that

$$E = \frac{1}{2}mv^2 = \frac{(mv)^2}{2m} = \frac{p^2}{2m}$$

it follows that

$$p^2 = 2mE$$

and so

$$p = \sqrt{2mE}$$

Now

$$\lambda = \frac{h}{p}$$

so

$$\lambda = \frac{h}{\sqrt{2mE}}$$

i.e. the wavelength of a particle is inversely proportional to the square root of its energy.

The wavelength of particles – worked examples

(1) An electron produced by an electron gun has a velocity of 7×10^6 m s^{-1}. What is its wavelength?

$$p = m_e v$$

$$= 9.11 \times 10^{-31} \text{ kg} \times 7 \times 10^6 \text{ m s}^{-1}$$

$$= 6.38 \times 10^{-24} \text{ kg m s}^{-1}$$

$$\lambda = h/p$$

$$= 6.63 \times 10^{-34} \text{ J s}/6.38 \times 10^{-24} \text{ kg m s}^{-1}$$

$$\approx 10^{-10} \text{ m}$$

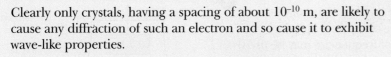

Clearly only crystals, having a spacing of about 10^{-10} m, are likely to cause any diffraction of such an electron and so cause it to exhibit wave-like properties.

(2) What is the wavelength of a tennis ball, travelling at a velocity of 10^2 m s^{-1}? (The mass of a tennis ball is 0.058 kg.)

$$\boldsymbol{p} = \boldsymbol{mv}$$
$$= 0.058 \text{ kg} \times 10^2 \text{ m s}^{-1}$$
$$= 5.8 \text{ kg m s}^{-1}$$
$$\boldsymbol{\lambda} = \boldsymbol{h/p}$$
$$= 6.63 \times 10^{-34} \text{ J s}/5.8 \text{ kg m s}^{-1}$$
$$\approx 10^{-34} \text{ m}$$

To exhibit wave-like properties a tennis ball would need to interact with something with dimensions of the order of 10^{-34} m (over one million million million times smaller than the nucleus of an atom). A tennis ball therefore does not exhibit wave-like properties.

Uncertainty

The mysterious world of quantum physics has many surprises in store. It is very different in some ways from the everyday world around us, which is largely governed by the laws of classical physics. We have already noted in earlier sections that the measurement of any physical quantity involves the interaction of the observer with the experiment, and that this will affect the quantity being measured (for example, the change in temperature of a liquid when a thermometer is put into it in order to measure the temperature of the liquid). In our macroscopic world these limitations are usually unimportant, or can at least be minimised, but in the world of subatomic particles this is not so.

Consider making a measurement of the speed and position of a particle – a single electron in a beam of electrons, for example, as shown in figure 6.4.13. In order to pinpoint the electron we might fire a photon at it which might then rebound into a photomultiplier tube. But when the photon hits the electron there will be a transfer of energy, making the precise measurement of the electron's speed and position impossible.

It was the German physicist Werner Heisenberg who first pointed out these problems, formulating a set of relationships called **Heisenberg's uncertainty relations**. For the measurement of position the relation can be written as:

$$\Delta s \Delta p \geq \frac{h}{4\pi}$$

where h is Planck's constant, Δs is the uncertainty in position and Δp is the uncertainty in momentum.

A rapidly moving electron has a momentum of around 10^{-23} kg m s^{-1}, which leads to an uncertainty in position of around 10^{-11} m, about one-tenth of the diameter of an atom. It follows that the more accurately we know the speed of the electron (the smaller Δp), the less we know about where it is (the larger Δs), and this uncertainty is significant.

These quantum uncertainties are not noticed in everyday life. For example, a car moving at 25 m s^{-1} (just over 50 m.p.h.) has a momentum of approximately

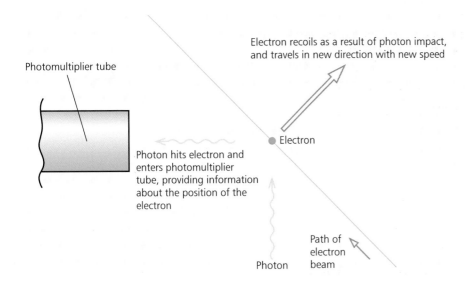

Electron recoils as a result of photon impact, and travels in new direction with new speed

Photomultiplier tube

Photon hits electron and enters photomultiplier tube, providing information about the position of the electron

Electron

Path of electron beam

Photon

Figure 6.4.13 In measuring the speed and position of an electron we alter these quantities, introducing uncertainties into the measurements.

2.5×10^4 kg m s^{-1}. However, the car driver will be unable to use the uncertainty principle to convince the magistrates that the police were mistaken in believing the car to be in a 30 m.p.h. limit. This is because the quantum uncertainty in the car's position is of the order of 10^{-30} m – hardly sufficient to place it elsewhere!

SUMMARY

- The **specific charge** on the electron e/m_e may be measured using crossed electric and magnetic fields, or by using a fine beam tube.
- As shown by Millikan's oil drop experiment, charge is **quantised**, each quantum corresponding to the charge on the electron.
- Energy is also quantised.
- Light and other electromagnetic radiations can be thought of as **wavicles**, which combine wave and particle behaviour. A 'particle' of electromagnetic radiation is called a **photon**.
- The energy E of a photon is given by $E = hf$, where h is Planck's constant and f the frequency of the electromagnetic wave.
- Metals can lose electrons (**photoelectrons**) when irradiated by electromagnetic radiation. This is called the **photoelectric effect**. The energy required to remove an electron from the metal surface is called the **work function** ϕ of the metal.
- Einstein's photoelectric equation relates the frequency f of electromagnetic radiation irradiating a metal, the work function of the metal and the maximum kinetic energy of the electron produced, $\frac{1}{2}mv^2_{max} = hf - \phi$.
- The photoelectric effect is applied in the **photomultiplier tube**, in which a photon of light brings about a series of electron avalanches and produces a pulse of current through an external circuit.
- Electrons have wave properties in addition to their particle properties. The wavelength λ of an electron is given by de Broglie's relationship $\lambda = h/p$, where h is Planck's constant and p the momentum of the electron.

EXAMPLE

A metal surface with a work function of 2.86 eV is illuminated with light of wavelength 400 nm. What will be the measured stopping potential for the photoelectrons?
($h = 6.63 \times 10^{-34}$ J s, $c = 3 \times 10^8$ m s^{-1}, $e = -1.6 \times 10^{-19}$ C.)

The work function ϕ expressed in joules is given by:

$$\phi = 2.86 \text{ eV} \times 1.6 \times 10^{-19} \text{ J eV}^{-1}$$

$$= 4.58 \times 10^{-19} \text{ J}$$

Now:

$$hf = \frac{hc}{\lambda} = \phi + \tfrac{1}{2}mv^2_{max}$$

$$= \phi + eV_{stop}$$

Rearranging and substituting:

$$V_{stop} = \left(\frac{6.63 \times 10^{-34} \text{ J s} \times 3 \times 10^8 \text{ m s}^{-1}}{4.0 \times 10^{-7} \text{ m}} - 4.58 \times 10^{-19} \text{ J} \right)$$

$$\times \frac{1}{1.6 \times 10^{-19} \text{ C}}$$

$$= 0.25 \text{ V}$$

QUESTIONS

(Take e as 1.6×10^{-19} C, h as 6.63×10^{-34} J s, c as 3.0×10^8 m s^{-1} and m_e as 9.1×10^{-31} kg.)

1 An electron is accelerated from a hot cathode towards a metal plate at a potential of +2.5 kV with respect to the cathode.
   a What is the kinetic energy of the electron just before it hits the plate **i** in eV and **ii** in joules?
   b What is the speed of the electron just before it hits the plate?

2 Electrons in a cathode ray tube are accelerated through a potential difference of 3000 V between the cathode and the screen.
   a Calculate the velocity of the electrons just before they hit the screen.
   b If all the energy of the electrons is lost as they hit the screen and 10^{13} electrons strike the screen each second, calculate the power dissipated at the screen.

3 Two horizontal conducting plates are 5.0 mm apart. A small oil drop of mass 1.62×10^{-13} kg is held stationary between the two plates by applying a potential difference of 2500 V across them, the upper plate positive with respect to the lower plate. How many excess electrons are on the drop?

4 The visible spectrum runs from about 400 nm to 700 nm. Calculate the range of energies present in visible photons.

5 The wavelength of green light is 550 nm.
   a What is the momentum of a photon of green light?
   b Using the calculation carried out in the worked example on page 529, estimate the force on a person lying flat on the ground due to the photon flux from the Sun. Is this detectable?

6 The work function of zinc is 4.24 eV. What is the maximum wavelength of light that will cause electrons to be emitted from a zinc surface?

7 A metal surface with a work function of 4.0 eV is illuminated by light of wavelength 200 nm. What is the maximum velocity of the photoelectrons produced?

8 The work function of caesium is 1.35 eV. A photocell contains a caesium surface that is illuminated with light of 400 nm. What potential difference must be applied to the cell to just prevent a current passing through it?

9 How would our world be affected if Planck's constant were 10^{34} times larger?

In section 6.1 we examined the evidence for the atomic model consisting of a tiny nucleus containing virtually all the mass of the atom. The electrons in such an atom lie outside the nucleus, although we noted at the time that the model says nothing more about the electrons. Most people's idea of the model of the atom is of a 'mini Solar System' – a collection of electrons orbiting the nucleus in much the same way as planets orbit the Sun. This model is quite effective for explaining some simple phenomena, and also has the merit that it is easy to imagine. However, we saw in section 6.4 that the electron cannot really be imagined as a simple particle (in just the same way as light cannot be imagined as a simple wave) – just as classical physics breaks down when trying to fully understand light, so it breaks down when trying to understand the behaviour of electrons in atoms.

To begin this final section, we shall look at spectra, the patterns of emission and absorption of light which first led to the simple model of the electrons in an atom.

Spectra

Types of spectra

In section 3.4, page 250, we saw how a spectrometer can be used to separate different wavelengths of light to form a spectrum. Two different types of spectra may be seen through a spectrometer – one consisting of lines, the other of a continuous range of colours. These two types of spectra are called **line spectra** and **continuous spectra** respectively, and result from the way electrons in matter are able to radiate energy. Because these spectra result from the emission of energy they are called **emission spectra**.

Seen through a spectrometer, line emission spectra consist of a set of coloured lines against a dark background, each line being a particular wavelength of light emitted by the source. These lines also extend beyond the visible spectrum in many cases, to include lines in the infra-red and ultraviolet regions. Convenient sources of line spectra to use in the laboratory include gases contained at low pressure in electric discharge tubes, and substances heated in a blue Bunsen flame. Figure 6.5.1 shows a gas discharge tube and some spectra resulting from different gases in such tubes. The line spectrum from a sample of an element is peculiar to that element, and can be used for identification purposes.

The continuous range of colours seen in continuous spectra can be observed in light from a tungsten filament lamp. This type of spectrum was first produced by artificial means (as opposed to by raindrops falling through air) by Newton, using a prism. Unlike line spectra, continuous spectra cannot be used to identify their source, although the wavelength of maximum intensity of the spectrum is linked to the temperature of the source, as figure 6.4.7 showed.

The spectra of molecules differ slightly from those of atoms, as a comparison of the nitrogen monoxide spectrum in figure 6.5.1 with the other line spectra shows. This is an example of a **band spectrum**. The chemical bonds in a molecule vibrate, leading to a fine structure of lines appearing in association with those lines caused by the emission of energy by the molecule's electrons.

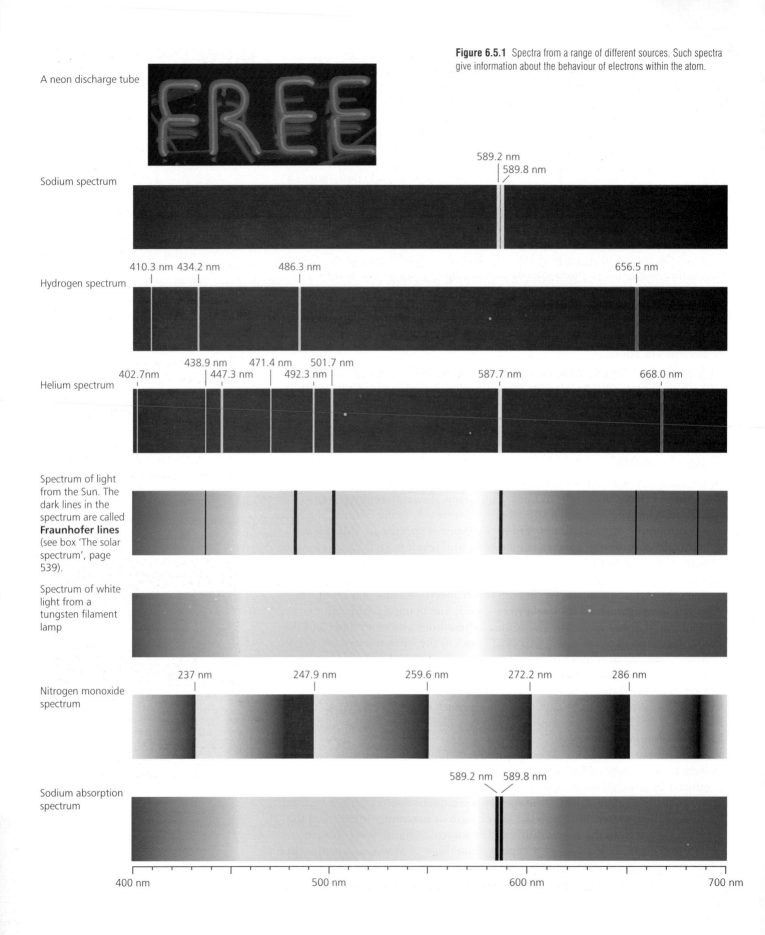

A neon discharge tube

Sodium spectrum

Figure 6.5.1 Spectra from a range of different sources. Such spectra give information about the behaviour of electrons within the atom.

589.2 nm
589.8 nm

Hydrogen spectrum

410.3 nm   434.2 nm   486.3 nm   656.5 nm

Helium spectrum

402.7nm   438.9 nm   471.4 nm   501.7 nm
             447.3 nm   492.3 nm   587.7 nm   668.0 nm

Spectrum of light from the Sun. The dark lines in the spectrum are called **Fraunhofer lines** (see box 'The solar spectrum', page 539).

Spectrum of white light from a tungsten filament lamp

Nitrogen monoxide spectrum

237 nm   247.9 nm   259.6 nm   272.2 nm   286 nm

Sodium absorption spectrum

589.2 nm   589.8 nm

400 nm   500 nm   600 nm   700 nm

The final spectrum in figure 6.5.1 is due to the absorption of light by a sample, and is therefore an example of an **absorption spectrum**. In this case, light from a tungsten filament source has been passed through sodium atoms in the vapour phase. In place of the two strong lines of yellow light in the sodium emission spectrum, there appear two black lines due to the absorption of light by sodium atoms at exactly the same wavelengths.

The explanations for the appearance of all these spectra are based on an understanding of the behaviour of electrons in atoms. Before considering this, however, it is worth looking in a little more detail at the appearance of the hydrogen spectrum, on which the first model of the electrons in the atom was founded.

The hydrogen spectrum

If we examine the emission spectrum of hydrogen in the visible and the near ultraviolet regions, we see the series of converging lines shown in figure 6.5.3(a). Examining these lines in 1885, the Swiss physicist Johann Balmer deduced that the frequency of each line was given by the formula:

$$f = \text{constant} \times \left(\frac{1}{2^2} - \frac{1}{n^2} \right)$$

Balmer proposed that other series like this might exist, and indeed these series were discovered subsequently. They are shown in figure 6.5.3(b).

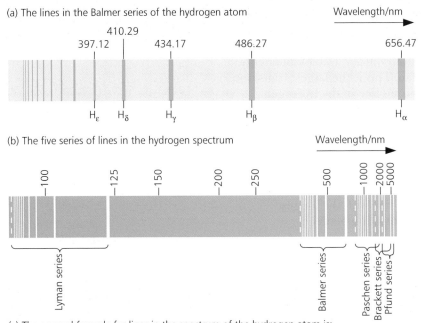

(a) The lines in the Balmer series of the hydrogen atom

(b) The five series of lines in the hydrogen spectrum

(c) The general formula for lines in the spectrum of the hydrogen atom is:

$$f = \text{constant} \times \left(\frac{1}{m^2} - \frac{1}{n^2} \right)$$

The solar spectrum

The presence of dark lines in the spectrum of sunlight was first recorded by William Hyde Wollaston in 1802, but it was Joseph von Fraunhofer who realised their significance, in his 1815 map of the solar spectrum (containing 324 lines).

The solar spectrum in figure 6.5.1 is a simplified one, with only the main Fraunhofer (dark) lines, but there is clearly strong absorption at wavelengths corresponding to the lines in the emission spectra of hydrogen and helium. This shows the presence of these elements in the mantle of hot gas around the Sun. The careful analysis of these lines led to the discovery of helium by Joseph Lockyer some 50 years later. (The name 'helium' comes from the Greek name for the Sun, Helios.) Figure 6.5.2 is a photograph of the solar spectrum showing the full range of Fraunhofer lines.

Figure 6.5.2 The solar spectrum.

Figure 6.5.3 Each series in the line emission spectrum of the hydrogen atom follows a simple formula, first deduced by Johann Balmer.

Despite Balmer's insight about the pattern of these lines in his series and the possible existence of other series, line spectra could not be fully understood until Einstein developed his theory of the photon, some 20 years later. Linking energy to the frequency of radiation, it was this theory that at last made possible a theory about the detailed behaviour of the electron in the hydrogen atom.

Energy levels and electrons in atoms

An energy level model for hydrogen

On the basis of what we know about line emission spectra and Einstein's photon theory, it seems reasonable to think of an atom emitting a photon of light when the atom moves from a state of high energy to one of low energy. The frequency f of the photon emitted will be given by:

$$\Delta E = hf$$

where ΔE is the difference between the two energy states or **levels**. Using this idea, it is possible to obtain a series of energy differences for the hydrogen atom, converting the wavelengths in figure 6.5.3(b) into energy differences.

Obtaining the energy levels of the hydrogen atom

The shortest wavelength line in the hydrogen spectrum (in the Lyman series) has a wavelength of 9.17×10^{-8} m. This corresponds to an energy transition ΔE given by:

$$\Delta E = \frac{6.63 \times 10^{-34}\,\text{J s} \times 3 \times 10^{8}\,\text{m s}^{-1}}{9.17 \times 10^{-8}\,\text{m}}$$

$$= 2.17 \times 10^{-18}\,\text{J}$$

$$= 13.6\,\text{eV}$$

Using this technique we end up with a series of values of ΔE. What do they mean? Assume that the transition with greatest energy difference ($\Delta E = 13.6$ eV) represents a transition from a level for which $E = 0$ to one for which $E = -13.6$ eV. In this transition the hydrogen atom will *lose* 13.6 eV of energy, emitting a photon with wavelength 9.17×10^{-8} m. This is the largest transition possible for the hydrogen atom (because there is no line in the hydrogen emission spectrum with a shorter wavelength). This must represent a transition from the highest energy level to the lowest energy level, that is, from $n = \infty$ to $n = 1$ in Balmer's general formula. This is illustrated in figure 6.5.4(a). The level for which $n = 1$ is the lowest possible energy state for the atom and is called its **ground state**. Other lines in the Lyman series have longer wavelengths and can be fitted onto the same diagram, with transitions between levels below $n = \infty$ down to the ground state. The line with the longest wavelength in the Lyman series is thus due to a transition between $n = 2$ and $n = 1$.

Having constructed the energy level diagram in this way using the Lyman series, calculations show that the lines in the Balmer series are associated with transitions from higher levels to $n = 2$. In exactly the same way, lines in the Paschen series are associated with transitions down to $n = 3$, and so on – figure 6.5.4(b) shows the energy levels and transitions for these series.

This approach can explain the most important aspects of the hydrogen atom spectrum:

1   The production of lines is due to the existence of distinct energy levels within the atom.

2   The pattern of energy levels is consistent with Balmer's formula for the spectral lines, with n in the formula corresponding to the starting level and m to the finishing level.

3   The absorption spectrum of hydrogen (seen, for example, in the spectrum of light from the Sun) is due to the absorption of light and the transition of the atom from a lower energy level to a higher one.

(a) The transition between energy levels associated with the line with shortest wavelength in the spectrum of the hydrogen atom. In going from $n = \infty$ to $n = 1$ the atom loses 13.6 eV of energy and releases a photon with 13.6 eV of energy.

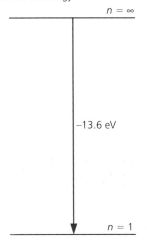

(b) Transitions from higher energy levels to lower ones are responsible for the emission of light with wavelengths corresponding to the lines in the known series for the hydrogen atom.

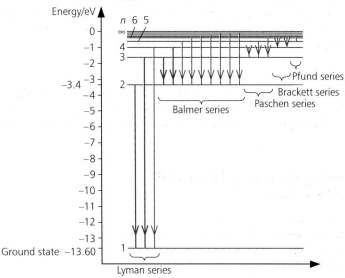

Figure 6.5.4 Energy levels in the hydrogen atom and the production of spectral lines.

It can also explain the structure of the spectra of other atoms, although for these no simple formula corresponding to Balmer's formula is available.

What is an energy level?

Although the model we have just seen explains the spectrum of the hydrogen atom quite neatly, we have not so far discussed exactly what an energy level is or what a transition between two levels means.

The existence of a negatively charged electron outside the nucleus of a hydrogen atom suggests that the removal of that electron is associated with an input of energy to the atom – in other words, the further away the electron gets from the nucleus, the higher the potential energy of the atom. Emission and absorption of light can then be explained in terms of electrons moving between different energy levels in the atom.

These electron transitions are called **excitation** when an electron moves from a lower level to a higher one, and **ionisation** when an electron is removed from an atom completely. Ionisation of a hydrogen atom in its ground state involves a transition from $n = 1$ to $n = \infty$, which corresponds to an energy change of 13.6 eV – this is the **ionisation energy** of hydrogen.

Experiments on absorption and emission of radiation by atoms were carried out by Franck and Hertz in 1913.

Franck and Hertz's experiment

In this experiment, a triode (three-electrode) valve was used. Electrons from the cathode were accelerated towards the grid. These electrons then continued towards the anode, from which they could flow back to the power supply via a galvanometer. A small stopping potential of about 2 V was applied between the grid and the anode – that is, the anode had a potential of about 2 V less than the grid.

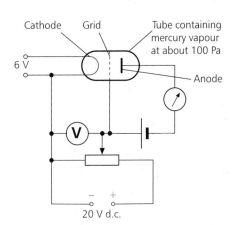

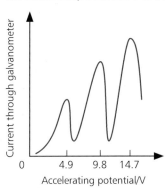

The relationship between _V_ and _I_

Current through galvanometer

0   4.9   9.8   14.7

Accelerating potential/V

Figure 6.5.5 Franck and Hertz's experiment used a tube containing low-pressure mercury vapour. Triode valves of this type used to be commonly found in radio sets until the advent of the transistor.

The graph shows the results of the experiment. As the accelerating potential (the potential _V_ across the cathode and the grid) was increased, the current through the tube increased, reaching an initial maximum at 4.9 V and then decreasing sharply. Further increasing the accelerating potential caused the current to rise again, when it peaked again at 9.8 V and then fell. Another peak at 14.7 V was also seen. At these peaks of current, the mercury vapour glowed.

Franck and Hertz explained these observations in terms of the energy levels of electrons in the mercury atom. With an accelerating potential below 4.9 V, electrons collided elastically with mercury atoms in their path. However, electrons accelerated by a potential of 4.9 V underwent inelastic collisions with mercury atoms, having just enough energy to excite an electron in the mercury atom to a higher energy level and in the process lose all their own energy. As the accelerating potential was increased above 4.9 V, electrons had some energy remaining after an inelastic collision, so could overcome the stopping potential between the grid and anode. The subsequent peaks at 9.8 V and 14.7 V corresponded to electrons having sufficient energy to excite two and three mercury atoms respectively. A similar arrangement can be used to measure the ionisation energy of an atom.

The electrons in the atom – Bohr's model

Working at around the same time as Franck and Hertz, the Danish physicist Niels Bohr developed a model of the hydrogen atom, supplementing the laws of classical mechanics and electromagnetism with ideas of his own, since the classical laws did not appear to provide consistent insight to the behaviour of electrons in atoms. Figure 6.5.8 shows the problems in applying classical physics to the hydrogen atom, and table 6.5.1 outlines how Bohr overcame them.

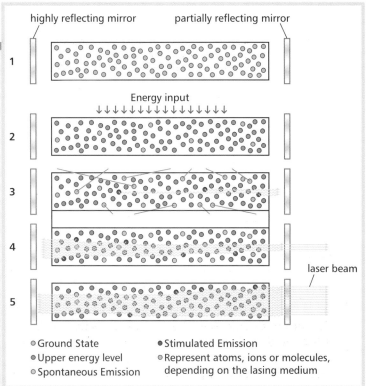

Figure 6.5.6 A simplified model showing the sequence of events in laser operation.

From checking out the shopping at the supermarket to precision hospital surgery, from printing your homework to communicating along thin strands of glass – **laser** light is all around us. Our many uses of lasers today make it hard to credit that the laser was once a scientific curiosity in search of a solution.

The output of a modern laser can be in pulses or a continuous beam, the light emitted can be in the visible, IR, or UV parts of the spectrum, and its output power may be anywhere between a fraction of a watt to millions of watts. However, most lasers share the following components:

- a **lasing medium** (a solid, a liquid or a gas);
- a way of pumping energy into the lasing medium;
- a **resonator** in which light can bounce backwards and forwards through the lasing medium.

A schematic diagram of laser operation is shown in figure 6.5.6. The following description is based on a lasing medium consisting of a mixture of helium and neon gases, as found in lasers used at the supermarket checkout and in school science laboratories. Diagram 1 represents the lasing medium before energy has been pumped into it, when all the atoms in the gas are in their ground state. Once enough energy has been pumped into the gas (in this case by applying a high voltage across the ends of the tube containing the gas, causing an electric current to flow through it), the situation in diagram 2 exists. Due to the excitation of electrons into higher energy levels by the electric current, more atoms are now in an excited state than are in the ground state – a situation described as a **population inversion**.

If one of the excited atoms now decays to the ground state, as an electron falls from an upper energy level back down to a lower level, it will emit a photon of light – this is **spontaneous emission**, which is not in itself of much interest to us. However, if this photon of light then meets another excited atom, it may cause that one to drop back to the ground state, emitting another photon of light. Many years before the first laser was built, Einstein had shown that this second photon – produced by **stimulated emission** – would have some very useful properties compared to the first photon, in that it would:

- have the same wavelength;
- have the same phase;
- be emitted in exactly the same direction as the first photon was travelling.

If a photon is emitted along the axis of the tube, diagrams 3 and 4 show how it can bounce back and forth down the tube, stimulating other excited atoms to produce photons as it does so. This avalanche effect produces more and more photons until a beam of laser light emerges through the partial mirror at the end of the tube (diagram 5). This intense beam is almost completely monochromatic (almost entirely a single wavelength of light), coherent (all the wavefronts are in step) and almost completely parallel – all properies that the applications of lasers exploit to the full.

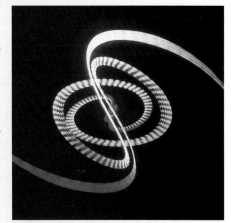

Figure 6.5.7 Laser light of many colours combines to make spectacular shows.

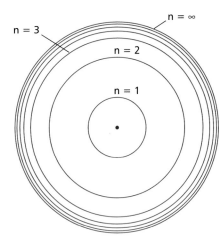

n = 3
n = ∞
n = 2
n = 1

The energy level diagram of figure 6.5.4(b) results in a model for the hydrogen atom in which possible electron orbits are arranged like this. Moving out from the centre of the atom, the difference in radii between successive orbits decreases in the same way as the gap between energy levels decreases.

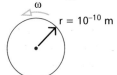

ω

$r = 10^{-10}$ m

An electron moving in an orbit with a radius of 10^{-10} m has a centripetal acceleration of about 10^{23} m s^{-2}, according to classical mechanics. The electron should thus spiral into the nucleus, emitting light of constantly increasing frequency and amplitude.

Figure 6.5.8 Classical physics suggests that the hydrogen atom cannot exist – it is unstable. The irreconcilable differences between the predictions of classical physics and the observed properties of atoms led Bohr to propose his four postulates.

Bohr's postulates

1 Only certain discrete orbits and energies are allowed for the electrons in an atom – these are called **stationary states**. An electron may make a **quantum jump** from one state to another.

2 The laws of classical mechanics apply to an electron in a stationary state but not to an electron making a quantum jump.

3 During a quantum jump energy is transferred according to the relationship $E = hf$.

4 Permitted orbits have fixed values of angular momentum which is always a multiple of $h/2\pi$ – in other words, **angular momentum is quantised**.

Table 6.5.1 Bohr's postulates. The fourth postulate uses the idea of angular momentum – the product of linear momentum and radius for a particle moving in a circle.

Using these ideas, Bohr's model was a striking success. The equations derived from it could successfully be used to calculate values for the radius of the hydrogen atom and its energy levels (particularly its ionisation energy), and they could be combined to produce a relationship resembling Balmer's formula. Yet it could not successfully explain the behaviour of atoms with more than one electron (even helium) – a new type of physics was needed. This new physics is called **quantum mechanics**.

Beyond Bohr's atom – quantum mechanics

Bohr's work, together with that of others, led to the development of quantum mechanics, in which the wave properties of electrons play a vital part, and where the positions of electrons within atoms are described in terms of probabilities. (The uncertainty principle discussed in section 6.4 gives the background to why it is necessary to think in terms of probabilities, since it is impossible to have precise information about an electron's energy and its position, for example.)

A simple model for the electron in a hydrogen atom which takes account of the electron's wave-like properties is shown in figure 6.5.9. Here the electron is represented as a wave travelling round the nucleus, although in calculations it is still treated as having some particle-like properties – the model uses the idea of wavicles described in section 6.4. A whole number of wavelengths must fit round the circumference of the orbit. This is so that the wave has the same amplitude at a given point on the circumference during each orbit, otherwise destructive interference would occur. It follows then that:

$$2\pi r = n\lambda$$

where n = 1, 2, 3 ....

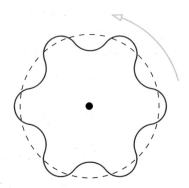

Figure 6.5.9 An electron wave around a nucleus. This diagram shows six complete wavelengths fitting round the circumference of the orbit.

Since we know that $\lambda = h/p$, we can write:

$$2\pi r = nh/p$$

which rearranges to:

$$pr = nh/2\pi$$

Now pr is the angular momentum of the electron. This means that this equation is in agreement with Bohr's fourth postulate, since it says that angular momentum (pr) varies in multiples of $h/2\pi$, that is, it is quantised.

The stability of an atom using the wavicle model

What does our wavicle model say about the stability of the atom?
We have that:

$$pr = nh/2\pi$$

so:

$$p = \frac{nh}{2\pi r}$$

The kinetic energy of the electron is $\frac{1}{2}m_e v^2 = \frac{1}{2}m_e(p/m_e)^2 = p^2/2m_e$, so:

$$E_k = \frac{\left(\dfrac{nh}{2\pi r}\right)^2}{2m_e}$$

Substituting values into this:

$n = 1$ for the lowest energy level (that is, the most stable state of the atom)

$h = 6.6 \times 10^{-34}$ J s

$r = 1 \times 10^{-10}$ m, the order of magnitude of the radius of an atom

$m_e = 9.11 \times 10^{-31}$ kg

$$E_k = \frac{(1 \times 6.6 \times 10^{-34} \text{ J s})^2}{(2\pi \times 1 \times 10^{-10} \text{ m})^2} \times \frac{1}{2 \times 9.11 \times 10^{-31} \text{ kg}}$$

$$= 6.1 \times 10^{-19} \text{ J}$$

$$= 3.8 \text{ eV}$$

From section 5.3 we know that the potential energy of an electron a distance r from a proton is given by:

$$E_p = \frac{-e^2}{4\pi\varepsilon_0 r}$$

Substituting into this we get:

$$E_p = \frac{-(1.6 \times 10^{-19} \text{ C})^2}{4 \times \pi \times 8.85 \times 10^{-12} \text{ F m}^{-1} \times 1 \times 10^{-10} \text{ m}}$$

$$= -2.3 \times 10^{-18} \text{ J}$$

$$= -14.4 \text{ eV}$$

The total energy E_T of the electron is thus given by:

$$E_T = E_k + E_p$$
$$= 3.8 \text{ eV} + (-14.4 \text{ eV})$$
$$= -10.6 \text{ eV}$$

This shows that the atom's total energy is negative – so it is at least feasible that the atom can exist.

It is surprising that our simple version of the quantum mechanical model, with its odd mixture of classical and new physics, works at all, and we should not attempt to push it or its use too far. The model can suggest why atoms are the size they are, but it is extremely limited in its scope. A more complex treatment is needed to understand the atom better, and this is beyond any physics course at this level.

The new physics

One of the new models describing the behaviour of electrons within atoms takes the form of a wave equation, describing the motion of an electron in terms of standing waves like those we saw in section 3.1. **Schrödinger's wave equation** deals with the electron's motion in terms of a **wave function** ψ (psi). It is impossible to know for sure where an electron actually is, but ψ (or strictly ψ^2) at a given point tells us the probability of finding the electron there. This idea of a wave function determining the probability of an event (of finding an electron at a point or not finding an electron at a point) can be extended to cover the

emission of radioactivity too. It was the interpretation of this probability aspect of the wave function that led to the paradox known as Schrödinger's cat.

The apparatus is set up and the detector is switched on for just long enough to ensure that there is a 50:50 chance of a radioactive particle having been emitted. The state of affairs inside the box is described by a wave function which provides information about the emission of a radioactive particle. This wave function describes *both* the possible outcomes of the experiment:

No radioactive particle = live cat
Radioactive particle = dead cat

There is no way of knowing what has happened in the experiment until the box is opened, when the wave function is said to 'collapse' to describe only one of the two states. Therefore in the unopened box we have a cat that is both dead and alive (or neither alive nor dead, if you prefer).

Schrödinger invented the cat paradox in an attempt to show that it was nonsense to think of an electron behaving as both a particle and a wave at the same time. Debate about this has raged on for over 50 years, with variations including the replacement of the cat in the box by other forms of life (from insects to humans) and by computers too. This problem serves to underline the strange nature of the world of quantum mechanics and the atom – in the words of Bohr himself, 'Anyone who is not shocked by quantum theory has not understood it'.

Figure 6.5.10 Schrödinger's cat paradox. The closed box contains a live cat, a radioactive source, a detector and a phial of poison (say cyanide). These are arranged in such a way that if radioactive decay occurs the detector records it, the glass bottle of poison breaks and the cat dies.

The production of X-rays

As mentioned in section 6.1, X-rays were discovered accidentally by Röntgen in 1895 while working on gas discharge tubes. Their penetrating power and their ability to blacken photographic emulsions and cause fluorescence led to their rapid adoption by doctors for examining suspected internal injuries, especially broken bones. The damage done to the body by their strongly ionising properties was not recognised or thought significant for many years, with the result that some people exposed to them over long periods developed illnesses induced by the ionising radiation.

X-rays are generated when high-energy electrons hit a solid target, whereupon they decelerate rapidly and transfer some of their kinetic energy to electromagnetic waves as X-rays. Only about 0.5% of the kinetic energy of the electrons is transferred in this way, the rest heating the target, which may be the anode of an X-ray tube or the glass of a television screen. The accelerating potential required to produce X-rays varies from about 25 kV to about 400 kV. Due to the enormous heating effect, the anode must be of a material with a high melting point and an efficient cooling system is required for it. Figure 6.5.12 shows a typical X-ray tube.

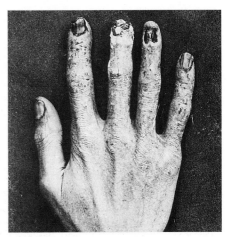

Figure 6.5.11 Using X-rays over long periods with little or no radiological protection led to some doctors suffering severe damage to their hands.

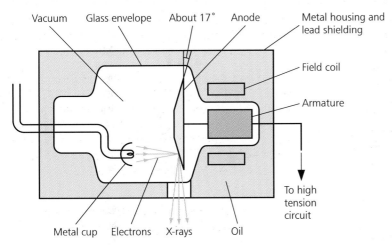

The anode in a typical X-ray tube is made of tungsten, which has a melting point of about 3700 K. The anode is inclined at a sharp angle to the beam, as shown in the figure. This ensures that a narrow beam of X-rays leaves the tube, producing a sharp image.

Figure 6.5.12 The X-ray tube is surrounded by cooling oil, which is constantly circulated. In order to minimise the heating effect on any particular part of the anode, most X-ray tubes employ a rotating anode. This is set into rotation as the X-ray tube is energised – if you listen carefully when you have an X-ray you may hear the high-pitched 'whizz' of the motor driving the rotating anode as the radiographer takes the X-ray.

X-ray spectra

X-rays have a minimum wavelength governed by the energy of the electrons producing them, as figure 6.5.14(a) shows. A typical X-ray spectrum consists of a series of sharp peaks superimposed on a continuous spectrum. These peaks occur at wavelengths independent of the tube voltage, depending only on the material of the target anode.

The continuous part of the X-ray spectrum is caused by the transfer of part or all of an electron's kinetic energy to X-ray photons. This emission of radiation as a result of a rapid reduction in kinetic energy is given the name **bremsstrahlung**, meaning 'braking radiation'.

The characteristic lines in the spectrum result from rapidly moving electrons knocking electrons out of the inner shells of the target atoms. These spaces are then filled by electrons dropping down from higher energy levels in the atom,

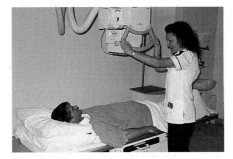

Figure 6.5.13 A typical X-ray examination.

emitting X-ray photons as they do so. The K-series of peaks (see figure 6.5.14(b)) results from spaces in the innermost shell – called the 'K-shell' – being refilled in this way, while the L-series of peaks results from a similar set of transitions down to the L-shell. A third set of peaks is seen in anodes of materials of extremely high atomic number, associated with transitions down to the third shell. In all cases there is a series of lines, the exact wavelength of the line depending on the higher energy level from which the electron falls.

In medical use the X-ray beam is filtered or **hardened** to remove the long wavelength or 'soft' X-rays. These are readily absorbed by the soft tissues, and so increase the patient's exposure to X-rays while not contributing in any way to the production of a clear picture. In addition, a grid is placed in front of the photographic plate to absorb X-rays that have been scattered by the patient's body, which would otherwise blur the photograph, as shown in figure 6.5.15.

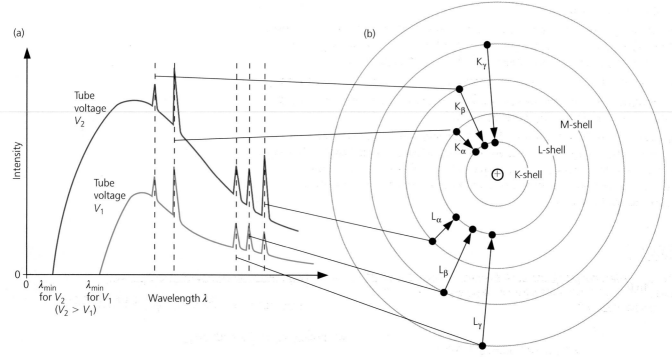

Figure 6.5.14 The spectra of X-rays produced by a particular tube is a function of the tube voltage (accelerating potential) and the proton number of the anode material.

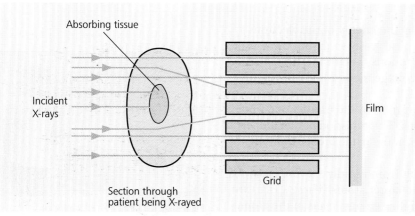

Figure 6.5.15 A grid prevents scattered X-rays from the patient's body reaching the photographic plate as they would reduce the contrast. In some types of equipment this grid is made to oscillate rapidly in the plane of the film as the photographic plate is exposed to the X-rays. This prevents the grid's shadow being recorded on the plate.

SUMMARY

- An **emission spectrum** is produced when matter emits electromagnetic radiation.
- An **absorption spectrum** is produced when electromagnetic radiation travelling through matter is absorbed.
- Spectra can be interpreted in terms of the transition of electrons in atoms between different energy levels.
- Atoms in the gas phase produce **line spectra** – the line spectrum of an element is characteristic of that element.
- Molecules produce **band spectra**, due to a combination of electronic transitions and bond vibrations.
- **Continuous spectra** consist of a continuous range of wavelengths – sunlight and the light from a tungsten filament lamp both produce continuous spectra.
- A simple model of the hydrogen atom consists of a series of energy levels that the electron may occupy. Transitions between these energy levels produce the characteristic spectrum of the hydrogen atom.
- Complete removal of an electron from an atom is known as **ionisation**.
- **Excitation** involves the absorption of energy by an electron associated with a transition to a higher energy level.
- **X-rays** are produced when high-energy electrons hit an anode, most of their kinetic energy being converted to heating of the anode, and a small percentage to X-rays. An X-ray spectrum consists of sharp peaks superimposed on a continuous spectrum. The peaks are specific to the material of the anode.

EXAMPLE

What is the kinetic energy in joules of an electron accelerated through a potential of 50 kV? What is the minimum wavelength of X-rays this electron could produce?

$$E_k = eV$$
$$= 1.6 \times 10^{-19} \text{ C} \times 50\,000 \text{ V}$$
$$= 8.0 \times 10^{-15} \text{ J}$$

For the X-ray wavelength we have $E = hc/\lambda_{min}$, so:

$$8.0 \times 10^{-15} \text{ J} = \frac{6.63 \times 10^{-34} \text{ J s} \times 3 \times 10^8 \text{ m s}^{-1}}{\lambda_{min}}$$

which gives $\lambda_{min} = 2.5 \times 10^{-11}$ m.

QUESTIONS

(Take e as 1.6×10^{-19} C, h as 6.63×10^{-34} J s, c as 3.0×10^8 m s^{-1} and m_e as 9.1×10^{-31} kg.)

Energy/eV
0.0
−1.6
−3.7
−5.5
−10.4

Figure 6.5.16

1 Figure 6.5.16 shows some of the energy levels of the mercury atom.
   a What wavelengths of electromagnetic radiation can be produced by electronic transitions between these levels?
   b Which of the wavelengths in **a** is in the visible region of the spectrum?
   c Light from a tungsten filament lamp is passed through mercury vapour and then through a spectrometer. Describe the appearance of the spectrum produced.

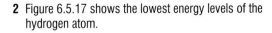

2 Figure 6.5.17 shows the lowest energy levels of the hydrogen atom.

n	Energy/eV
6	−0.38
5	−0.54
4	−0.85
3	−1.51
2	−3.39
1	−13.58

Figure 6.5.17

  a What is the ionisation energy of hydrogen **i** in eV and **ii** in joules?

  b An electron with kinetic energy 13 eV collides with a hydrogen atom in the ground state. What are the possible kinetic energies of the electron after the collision?

3 A photon with a wavelength of 82 nm strikes a hydrogen atom in its ground state.
Using the information in figure 6.5.17, calculate the maximum velocity of the ejected electron.

4 Calculate the minimum wavelength of X-rays that can be produced by an X-ray tube with an accelerating voltage of:

  a 10 kV   **b** 25 kV   **c** 80 kV.

  d Why is a *range* of wavelengths produced by an X-ray tube rather than just a single wavelength?

  e What implication does the production of a range of wavelengths have for:

    i the design of X-ray tubes

    ii the use of X-rays in medical diagnosis?

5 Explain how a grid placed in front of the X-ray plate helps to produce a sharper image on the plate.

6 An X-ray tube operates at 25 kV, and a current of 3 mA flows through the tube.
Calculate:

  a the number of electrons striking the anode each second

  b the power of the resulting X-ray beam if the tube has an efficiency of 1%.

7 Show that the shortest possible wavelength of X-rays that can be produced in an X-ray tube is given by:

$$\lambda_{min} = hc/E_k$$

where E_k is the kinetic energy of the incident electrons. How is λ_{min} related to V, the accelerating potential applied to the tube?

Developing Key Skills

A company which produces spectacular displays of laser light requires a poster to explain to people how the light is produced.

Produce a poster suitable for people with no knowledge of science, which explains ideas in simple, entertaining language and diagrams.

[Key Skills opportunities: C, IT]

6.6 Probing the structure of matter

Scattering experiments

At the beginning of this section we saw how Rutherford and his fellow physicists found evidence for the structure of the atom by bombarding gold foil with alpha particles and recording how the alpha particles were scattered by the gold atoms. Although the techniques used by today's physicists are far more sophisticated than those available to physicists nearly 100 years ago, the principal means of finding out about the structure of matter still remains the **scattering experiment**.

In the early years of particle physics, the particles used in scattering experiments were those readily available as a result of radioactive decay, with energies of a few MeV. In addition to evidence for the existence of the nucleus, the use of such particles also led to the splitting of the atom (in 1919) and the discovery of the neutron (in 1932). However, physicists soon came to realise that obtaining particles with higher energies was crucial to the development of further ideas in particle physics research.

Physicists therefore turned their attention to **cosmic rays**, high-energy particles that arrive from space. These particles have energies as high as 10^{11} GeV and create a myriad of new particles as they collide with atoms in the Earth's upper atmosphere. The study of cosmic rays yielded many surprises during the 1930s and 1940s, including the discovery of particles such as the **positron** and the **muon**. Eventually physicists found evidence for the existence of a great variety of subatomic particles, and the challenge was to make some sense of the way in which each particle was related to all the others. Alongside these studies of cosmic rays, **particle accelerators** capable of producing high-energy particles in the laboratory were under development. It was these machines that enabled physicists to untangle the complex relationships between particles, so the story of particle physics since the mid-twentieth century has been concerned almost entirely with *artificially* accelerated particles.

Particle accelerators

Particle accelerators use electric and magnetic fields to accelerate charged particles, based on the principles we met in section 5. The simplest type is the **electron gun** (page 422). Such a device accelerates charged particles by means of a potential difference between two plates (figure 6.6.2), which makes it simple to build and use. Robert Jemison van de Graaff built one of the earliest accelerators in 1932, using a moving belt to transport electric charge to build up a large potential difference. Modern **van de Graaff generators** can accelerate particles to energies of up to 25 MeV, but energies greater than this require enormous potential differences which are impractical owing to problems of insulation.

The linear accelerator

The design for the **linear accelerator** was proposed in the late 1920s. Such a machine would enable particles with GeV energies to be produced. It consists

Figure 6.6.1 While Rutherford's original scattering experiment was carried out in a physics laboratory not much larger than a school science laboratory, modern scattering experiments require huge facilities, like those available at CERN in Switzerland. The circular dotted line shows the 27 km underground path of the large-electron-positron (LEP) collider (see page 554). This section of the book will help you to understand why we need such enormous machines to find out more about minute particles of matter.

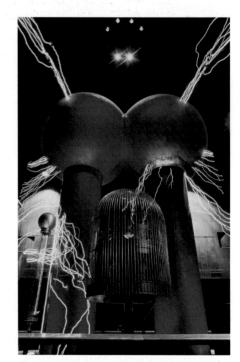

Figure 6.6.2 This Van de Graaff generator was built by Robert Van de Graaff in 1932. Now in the Boston Museum of Science, it can produce potential differences of up to 2.5 million volts.

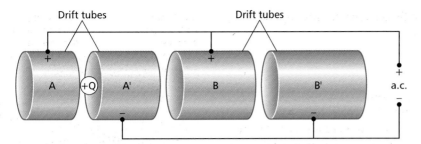

Drift tubes   Drift tubes

A   +Q   A'   B   B'   a.c.

Figure 6.6.3 The linear accelerator or LINAC. Because the velocity of the particle increases as it travels through the LINAC, the length of the drift tubes must increase.

In this schematic diagram of a LINAC, a particle with a charge $+Q$ is moving from left to right. As the particle reaches the end of drift tube A, the potential difference between A and A' makes A' negative relative to A. This produces a force F on the particle, so it accelerates.

As the particle travels through tube A' it is in a region of constant potential difference. It does not experience a force, so its velocity remains constant.

The alternating voltage across the tubes is arranged in such a way that by the time the particle has reached the end of A', the alternating supply has passed through half a cycle, making B negative with respect to A'. Once again the particle experiences a force and accelerates.

This process is repeated all the way down the tubes, accelerating the particle in a series of steps.

of a series of **drift tubes** arranged in a straight line, an alternating voltage being used to accelerate the charged particle as it moves in the gaps between the tubes. Figure 6.6.3 explains how this works.

The longer, the better?

At first sight it might appear that the longer the LINAC, the greater the particle's final velocity, but this is not actually the case.

Once a particle has reached a speed very close to that of light, it is impossible to increase its speed much further no matter how much energy is supplied to it. This agrees with Einstein's theory of relativity, which asserts that no mass can move at or above the speed of light. This means that we can look on a particle accelerator as a machine designed to increase the *energy* of particles. But the theory of relativity also tells us that energy and mass are related by the relationship $E = mc^2$ that we met on pages 506–7. So we can also take the view that a particle accelerator increases the *mass* of particles that it accelerates. Both of these views are entirely equivalent.

Figure 6.6.4 At 3.2 km, the Stanford Linear Accelerator (SLAC) is the longest LINAC in the world. It can accelerate electrons up to 30 GeV.

The cyclotron

Linear accelerators have the disadvantage that they have to be very long in order to produce high energies, and the idea of the **cyclotron** was proposed very shortly after the LINAC. Essentially the cyclotron is a kind of 'circular LINAC', inside which charged particles travel in a spiral path as their energy increases. This enables the replacement of the series of drift tubes with a single pair of hollow electrodes each shaped like the letter D, as figure 6.6.5 shows.

The magnetic field surrounding the cyclotron electrodes keeps the charged particles moving in a curved path, while an alternating potential is applied across the electrodes. This has exactly the right frequency to ensure that the particles experience a force which accelerates them as they reach the gap between the electrodes. The frequency, f, at which the potential between the electrodes must vary in order to accelerate a particular particle is called the cyclotron resonance. For a particular magnetic field strength, this depends only on the charge:mass ratio of the particle:

$$f = \frac{Bq}{2\pi m}$$

As the particles gain energy in the cyclotron, they spiral outwards with increasing radius. Eventually, above about 25 MeV, the increase in mass of the particles due to relativity affects the charge:mass ratio sufficiently to make the calculated cyclotron resonance larger than it needs to be. The particles then arrive at the gap between the electrodes out of step with the accelerating voltage, and further increases in energy are impossible.

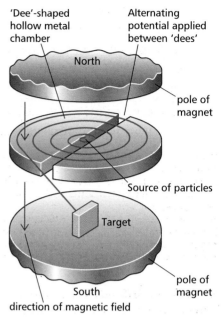

In a cyclotron the charged particles from a source at the centre follow a spiral path until they emerge to strike a target. The magnetic field bends the tracks of the particles, while the alternating field between the 'dees' accelerates them.

Figure 6.6.5 The first cyclotron was designed by Ernest O Lawrence in 1929. Ten years later, Lawrence received the Nobel prize for physics in recognition of his work. Cyclotrons require a magnetic field over the whole of the area of the D-shaped electrodes, which effectively limits their size. The largest cyclotron in the world is the 600-cm 'phasotron' at the Dubna Joint Institute for Nuclear Research in Russia, which accelerates protons to more than 700 MeV and has magnets weighing almost 7000 tonnes.

Charged particles in the cyclotron

From earlier work in section 1.6, we know that for a particle moving in a circle

$$F = \frac{mv^2}{r}$$

and, from section 5.4, for a charged particle moving in a magnetic field

$$F = Bqv$$

This means that we can write

$$Bqv = \frac{mv^2}{r}$$

so

$$r = \frac{mv}{Bq}$$

The time taken for the particle to travel through one complete circle is therefore

$$T = \frac{2\pi r}{v} = \frac{2\pi mv}{Bqv} = \frac{2\pi m}{Bq}$$

The frequency of the alternating potential (the cyclotron resonance) is therefore

$$f = \frac{1}{T} = \frac{Bq}{2\pi m}$$

Notice how this does not depend on the velocity of the particle, although it does depend on the particle's charge:mass ratio.

One way to overcome the problems caused by the relativistic increase in the mass of particles as they accelerate is to change the frequency of the accelerating potential used in the cyclotron. This can be slowly decreased as the kinetic energy of the particles rises, producing a machine that is called a *synchro-cyclotron*, or **synchrotron**.

The synchrotron

The disadvantage of cyclotrons is the need for a large area over which a uniform magnetic field must be applied in order to allow the charged particles to spiral outwards as their energy increases. This is avoided in the synchrotron by using a variable magnetic field to keep the particles moving in a path with a constant radius. Since the field can be applied over a much smaller area, this enables the construction of much larger machines that can accelerate particles to much greater energies.

The largest synchrotrons are huge – for example, the large-electron-positron (LEP) collider at CERN has a circumference of 27 km. In operation, a LINAC accelerates particles to high energies before injecting them into the synchrotron, where supercooled magnets keep the particles moving in a closed path while radio frequency cavities accelerate them to high energies. A synchrotron has several points at which accelerated particles may be deflected for scattering experiments to be performed.

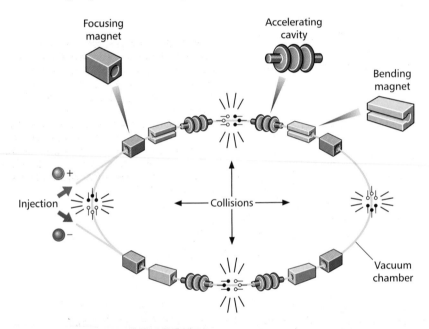

Figure 6.6.6 The basic principles of operation of a synchrotron.

LINACs and accelerating electrons

Although the synchrotron may seem to be the best choice of accelerator for all purposes, LINACs remain particularly useful for accelerating electrons, at which they are very efficient.

This is because a charged particle moving in a circle is accelerating, and accelerating charges radiate energy, as we saw in section 5.5. Electrons moving rapidly in a circle therefore radiate large amounts of energy as electromagnetic waves (this is called **synchrotron radiation**). This is particularly problematic, since the high charge:mass ratio of electrons means that they dissipate a large proportion of their kinetic energy in this way; the effect is much less noticeable for more massive particles such as protons.

Moving targets and energy

While colliding fast-moving charged particles with a stationary target (as Rutherford did nearly 100 years ago) has the virtue of being relatively simple, much of the energy of the particles merely causes the target to recoil and is of

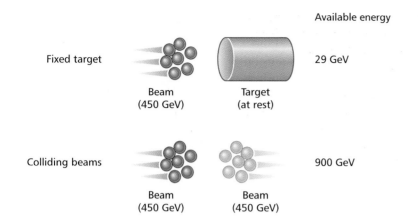

	Available energy
Fixed target	29 GeV
Beam (450 GeV) — Target (at rest)	
Colliding beams	900 GeV
Beam (450 GeV) — Beam (450 GeV)	

Figure 6.6.7 Colliding two 450 GeV beams of particles increases the energy available to make new particles by a factor of 30 compared to colliding one 450 GeV beam with a stationary target. Energy and momentum must be conserved in collisions. If two particles with similar masses and energies travel in opposite directions, their total momentum is zero. The momentum of the particles formed after these two particles have collided must also be zero – so all of the energy is available to produce new matter. But when one particle simply collides with another stationary particle, any new particles formed must carry away the momentum of the incoming particle – and much less energy is available to produce new matter.

no use to particle physicists. By colliding two beams of high-energy particles travelling in opposite directions, much better use is made of the energy available (figure 6.6.7). This 'excess' energy then appears after the collision as mass (remember that $E = mc^2$!), producing a flux of particles that can be detected and studied.

Figure 6.6.8 In the large-electron-positron (LEP) collider at CERN a beam of electrons and a beam of positrons are accelerated to almost 100 GeV before the two beams are made to cross so that electrons and positrons collide. It is possible to accelerate and focus beams of electrons and positrons in the same ring, since electrons and positrons have the same mass but opposite charges – so electric and magnetic fields have exactly opposite effects on them. This diagram shows a cross-section through the LEP installation, with the Alps in the background and underground experimental areas in the foreground.

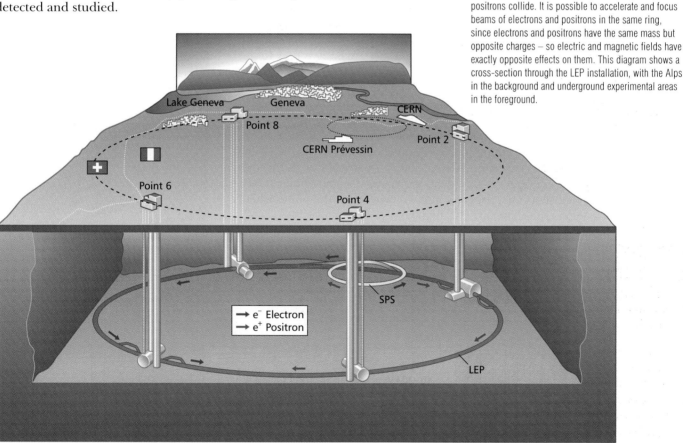

Detectors

Having looked at ways of accelerating particles in order to collide them with fixed or moving targets, we now consider the problem of finding out what has happened to the particles after collision – a problem of *detection*.

Techniques for detecting particles rely on electromagnetic interactions between the particles and matter. Possible instruments include the

spinthariscope, in which an experimenter sits in a darkened room counting the tiny flashes of light produced when charged particles hit a layer of zinc sulphide (not an easy task, nor a particularly pleasant one!), and the **cloud chamber**, in which charged particles travelling through the air form ions on which ethanol vapour condenses, producing visible tracks. These and other simple detectors were discussed in section 6.2.

Modern experiments that involve particles with energies measured in GeV cannot make use of such simple detectors, which are limited to providing information about particles with energies measured in MeV. The **bubble chamber** (figure 6.6.9), which was developed from the cloud chamber, uses very pure liquid hydrogen instead of ethanol vapour. The hydrogen is cooled to about 20 K (−253 °C) and kept under pressure to stop it boiling. A few milliseconds before a pulse of particles from an accelerator is due to arrive at the chamber, the pressure in the chamber is lowered suddenly so that the boiling point of the hydrogen falls. Because it is very pure, the hydrogen does not boil but becomes *superheated* (still liquid at a temperature above its boiling point). As charged particles travel through the superheated liquid hydrogen they create ions around which bubbles of hydrogen gas rapidly grow. These bubbles form the characteristic tracks of particles seen in bubble chamber experiments (figure 6.6.10), which are recorded for analysis using photography.

Bubble chambers have the disadvantage that the arrival of particles and the triggering of the detector have to be closely coordinated, making it easy to miss a particle of interest. **Spark chambers** were designed to overcome this problem, as well as to deal with the inconvenience of the long cycling time of bubble chambers (it takes around a second to restore the chamber to a bubble-free state). Figure 6.6.11 shows the design of the basic spark chamber, together with the **wire spark chamber**, a development devised at CERN.

The basic spark chamber contains a set of thin metal plates arranged closely together in an inert gas such as neon. When a charged particle travels through the chamber, it produces a trail of ionised gas molecules. Geiger-Müller (GM) tubes, or other similar detectors, trigger a high voltage across the plates when a charged particle enters the chamber. This high voltage causes a visible discharge of light that reveals the path of the particle through the chamber (figure 6.6.12).

Figure 6.6.9 The construction of the bubble chamber at CERN (Conseil Européen pour la Recherche Nucléaire), Geneva. The tank holds 38 m³ of liquid hydrogen.

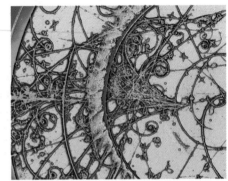

Figure 6.6.10 Tracks of subatomic particles in a bubble chamber.

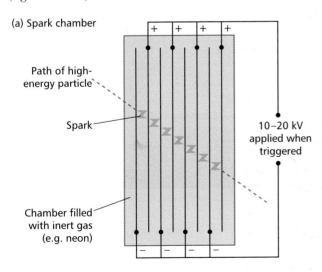

(a) Spark chamber

Path of high-energy particle

Spark

Chamber filled with inert gas (e.g. neon)

10–20 kV applied when triggered

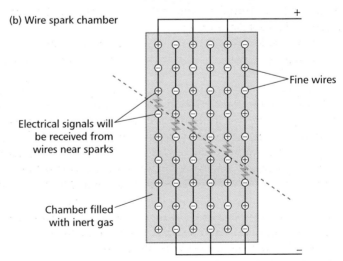

(b) Wire spark chamber

Fine wires

Electrical signals will be received from wires near sparks

Chamber filled with inert gas

N.B. (i) Supply connections only shown at edges of chamber although *all* wires are connected to supply.
(ii) Signal leads only shown for responding wires above although all wires do have signal leads attached.

Figure 6.6.11 Spark chambers.

In the wire spark chamber a set of fine wires replaces the metal plates. Sparks produced between two wires cause a tiny current to flow. The electrical signals that result from these sparks can then be analysed to calculate the path taken by the particle as it travels through the chamber.

Instead of responding to the current produced when a spark jumps between two wires, the wire spark chamber can be adapted so that it responds to the cascade of electrons produced by a charged particle, using the same principle as the Geiger-Müller (GM) tube (pages 490–1). Such a detector is known as a **multiwire proportional chamber** and can track the path of a particle to within a millimetre.

More sophisticated still is the **drift chamber**, which records the *time* at which individual wires respond to ionising events in the chamber. This allows much more accurate measurement of the position of the track between the wires, in principle down to uncertainties of about 50 μm.

Figure 6.6.12 A spark chamber at CERN showing the tracks of ionising particles as red lines.

Interpreting the results

Identification of the particles involved in producing tracks requires some detective work, bringing together a number of features and thinking carefully about the possible connections between two or more tracks in the chamber. Some of the clues used to deduce the properties of a particle from its track include the following.

- **The length of the track**. The more energetic the particle, the longer the track. This is because a particle will lose a certain amount of energy each time it collides with an atom. The more energy it has, the more collisions it will make before its energy expires, so the further it will travel. Since different particles lose different amounts of energy when they collide with atoms, track length also depends on particle type.
- **The thickness of the track**. The greater the charge on the particle, the thicker the track it makes. Track thickness is also affected by a particle's energy – the faster the particle moves, the thinner the track, since the particle has less time to interact with atoms as it passes them.
- **The curvature of the track**. A magnetic field perpendicular to the path of the particles as they enter the chamber causes them to travel in a curve. The charge and momentum of a particle can be deduced from the direction of this curve and from its radius, which decreases as the particle's energy is absorbed and it slows down.
- **Missing tracks**. Two tracks may appear to be connected, even if no track can be seen joining them. This may be evidence for a neutral particle.

The structure of matter

Following the work of Rutherford and Bohr in the first two decades of the twentieth century, a model of the atom emerged in which a massive central nucleus containing neutrons and positively charged protons was surrounded by very light, negatively charged electrons arranged in orbits – a model with more than a passing resemblance to the solar system. The following years saw a rapid development of this model of matter, with evidence emerging for the existence of more and more particles. We have already seen in section 6.3 how the need for energy conservation in beta decay led to the idea of an uncharged particle with little or no mass, dubbed the **neutrino**.

At about the same time as the existence of the neutrino was being proposed, the British physicist Paul Dirac concluded that an equation he had derived to describe the behaviour of the electron implied that any charged particle had a matching **antiparticle** with the same mass but opposite charge. While direct experimental evidence for the existence of the neutrino took nearly 30 years to emerge, evidence of an anti-electron (the **positron**) came quickly, through the observation of tracks in a cloud chamber.

The discovery of the positron

In 1932 the American physicist Carl Anderson was using a cloud chamber to investigate cosmic rays, and noticed that a pair of tracks in a magnetic field provided strong evidence for the production of a pair of particles with opposite charge (figure 6.6.13). Physicists were already fairly confident that the negatively charged tracks caused by cosmic rays were due to the electrons knocked out of atoms by the rays. Since the tracks produced by the positively charged particles were so similar to those thought to be produced by electrons, Anderson wondered if it was possible that he was seeing tracks due to a positively charged particle with the same mass as an electron – the positron predicted by Dirac. A simple experiment in which Anderson measured the path of the positively charged particles before and after passing through a lead plate proved beyond doubt that he had found the positron.

Figure 6.6.13 In this false colour photograph, a gamma ray travelling from left to right has created an electron–positron pair, the electron travelling in a downward spiral, the positron in an upward one. The track continuing from left to right is an electron knocked out of an atom by the same gamma ray.

While the production of matter–antimatter pairs (called **pair production**) provided the first experimental evidence for the existence of antimatter, matter–antimatter pairs can also annihilate, their mass-energy producing more matter and/or electromagnetic radiation. We can write the following equations for these processes.

Pair production (occurs only near other particles, such as a nucleus):

$$_0^0\gamma \rightarrow \,_{-1}^{0}e^- + \,_1^0e^+$$

Pair annihilation (producing two gamma rays):

$$_{-1}^{0}e^- + \,_1^0e^+ \rightarrow 2\,_0^0\gamma$$

Notice that both mass-energy and charge are conserved in these interactions. We shall examine the need for conservation in more detail later in this section.

Antiparticles can be represented in two ways. Where the original particle is charged, the antiparticle is simply given the opposite charge. The particle and the antiparticle both have the same mass. For example, a proton and an antiproton are represented as follows:

proton: p^+
antiproton: p^-

Where the original particle is uncharged, the antiparticle is represented with a bar over it:

neutron: n
antineutron: $\bar{n}$

Conservation and pair annihilation/production

Figure 6.6.14 shows how the production of two gamma rays rather than just one in pair annihilation is due to the need to conserve energy and momentum. Before the electron and positron collide, their total momentum is zero. If only one gamma ray is produced, momentum cannot be conserved. However, two gamma rays travelling in opposite directions *do* have zero total momentum – so energy and momentum are conserved.

For similar reasons, pair production happens only when there is another particle whose momentum can be changed in the interaction in order to conserve both energy and momentum.

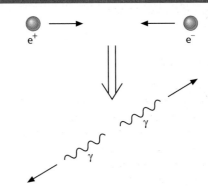

Figure 6.6.14 Production of two gamma rays from e⁺/e⁻ pair.

Classifying the 'particle zoo'

The middle years of the twentieth century revealed more and more particles as physicists carried out experiments using accelerators and cosmic rays. At first, these ever-growing numbers of particles were classified on the basis of mass, and three groups of particles were proposed: the **leptons** (light particles), **baryons** (heavy particles) and **mesons** (those with masses between leptons and baryons). However, properties such as mass and charge proved to be an unsatisfactory basis for classification, and physicists needed to look to other theories in order to understand the relationships between the particles.

Wanted – a *scientific* theory for classifying particles

As they sought to understand the particles of matter by classifying them, the problem facing physicists was the need to develop a theory on which to base their classification. This may not be too difficult when you have found all the things you are trying to classify, and when you know that you have all the necessary information about them, but it is a different proposition when you are uncertain about both aspects.

For this reason, particle physicists in the middle of the twentieth century were in a very similar position to chemists in the mid-nineteenth century – both were trying to use the incomplete information available in order to create a pattern into which experimental results would fit. In chemistry, it was not until the development of the electronic structure of the atom that the pattern of the Periodic Table could be fully understood. Particle physics needed a number of new ideas to emerge before sense could begin to be made of the plethora of apparently unrelated particles of matter.

A classification of objects based on a *scientific* theory highlights important *scientific* relationships between

the objects, rather than any other type of relationships. Because of this, scientific classifications are more likely to increase our scientific understanding of the world around us than are other kinds of explanations.

Figure 6.6.15 The scientific classification of a whale as a mammal highlights its relationships with other animals that breathe air, are warm-blooded and give birth to live young – humans, for example. An alternative way of classifying living things might group whales and fish together, based on the fact that both live in water. But this would tell us very little about the really important similarities and differences between, say, a blue whale, a goldfish and a human.

In section 5.1 we met the idea of the *four fundamental interactions* that describe how particles of matter interact with each other. It turns out that the way particles 'feel' these four forces provides an important means of classifying them. While the leptons are not affected by the strong force, the baryons and mesons are affected – they comprise a group called the **hadrons**.

The four fundamental interactions

Force	Acts on	Range	F
Gravitational	mass	infinity	10^{-34} N
Electromagnetic	electric charge	infinity	10^2 N
Strong	nuclear particles	10^{-15} m	10^4 N
Weak	most elementary particles	$<10^{-17}$ m	10^{-2} N

Table 6.6.1 The strength of each interaction is given in terms of the force acting between two protons separated by a distance equal to their diameter (2×10^{-15} m).

The leptons form a distinct group of particles that are described as being **fundamental** – that is, they are not themselves made up of simpler particles, unlike baryons and mesons, as we shall see shortly. The electron, positron, neutrino and antineutrino make up one 'generation' of particles within the leptons. Two heavier generations are known to exist: the muons (with a mass slightly more than 200 times that of an electron) and the taus (about 3500 times as massive as an electron, making the tau more than twice the mass of a proton!). While the electron generation is stable, the heavier generations can undergo various decay reactions – for example, muons decay into electrons and neutrinos, with a half-life of around 2 μs.

The properties of leptons are described by a set of **lepton numbers**. In any allowed reaction of leptons, these lepton numbers must be conserved – just like the nucleon number and proton number in the radioactive decays we have met previously. Table 6.6.2 shows the various leptons and their lepton numbers:

- L – total lepton number
- L_e – electron-lepton number
- L_μ – muon-lepton number
- L_τ – tau-lepton number

Particle	Symbol	Relative mass	Relative charge	L	L_e	L_μ	L_τ
electron	e^-	1	−1	1	1	0	0
electron-neutrino	ν_e	0?*	0	1	1	0	0
positron	e^+	1	+1	−1	−1	0	0
antielectron-neutrino	$\bar{\nu}_e$	0?	0	−1	−1	0	0
muon	μ^-	207	−1	1	0	1	0
muon-neutrino	ν_μ	0?*	0	1	0	1	0
antimuon	μ^+	207	+1	−1	0	−1	0
antimuon-neutrino	$\bar{\nu}_\mu$	0?	0	−1	0	−1	0
tau	τ^-	3490	−1	1	0	0	1
tau-neutrino	ν_τ	0?*	0	1	0	0	1
antitau	τ^+	3490	+1	−1	0	0	−1
antitau-neutrino	$\bar{\nu}_\tau$	0?	0	−1	0	0	−1

Table 6.6.2 Summary of lepton properties.

* Neutrinos have little or no mass.

The hadrons

By contrast with leptons, hadrons do experience the strong force. Another contrast with leptons is that hadrons have a *substructure* – that is, they are made up of even smaller particles called **quarks**. As with leptons, laws of conservation played an important part in the development of particle physicists' understanding of the hadrons.

Remember that the hadrons consist of two groups: baryons and mesons. At first, physicists separated these two groups purely on the basis of their mass. However, some very massive mesons do exist, so a better way of grouping them is based on how they relate to other particles, and especially how they decay. As an example, consider a neutron outside the nucleus of an atom. In this situation a neutron is unstable and decays to form a proton, an electron and an antielectron-neutrino:

$$_{0}^{1}n \rightarrow {}_{1}^{1}p^+ + {}_{-1}^{0}e^- + {}_{0}^{0}\bar{\nu}_e$$

This decay does not violate any laws of conservation – the mass of the neutron is greater than the mass of the particles into which it decays, leaving some mass to appear as kinetic energy of the products of the decay, and mass, momentum and charge are also conserved. You should also be able to show that the lepton number is conserved, too.

Although interactions like those on the previous page can be fully explained in terms of conservation of charge, mass, lepton number and so on, other interactions do not occur in nature, and the conservation laws we have seen so far do not manage to explain this. In order to get over this problem, all hadrons are assigned another quantity called the **baryon number**, B, which must also be conserved in any process. Mesons have $B = 0$, while baryons have $B = 1$ and antibaryons have $B = -1$. Conservation of baryon number explains why decays in which protons form **pions** (mesons with about one-seventh of the mass of a proton) cannot occur. The equations for such decays include

$$\mathbf{p^+ \rightarrow e^+ + \pi^0}$$

and

$$\mathbf{p^+ \rightarrow \pi^+ + \gamma}$$

neither of which conserves baryon number (see question 10 at the end of this chapter).

Reactions that appeared to be allowed but were never observed provided physicists with an important tool for developing the theoretical basis for classifying the growing numbers of particles. One such puzzle led to the introduction of yet another property that appeared to be conserved under certain circumstances. The idea of this new property came about in order to explain the behaviour of some particles which interact with one another by the strong interaction. An example of this is the reaction of a pion, the π^- (pi-minus), with a proton. It turns out that in order fully to explain the reaction of the π^- with a proton (which produces a type of meson called a **kaon**, K^+ or K^-), a new quantity called **strangeness**, S, must be involved. Except under certain very specific circumstances, strangeness must be conserved. Particles can have values of S from -3 to $+3$.

Stranger and stranger

One reaction that creates kaons from pions and protons has the equation

$$\mathbf{\pi^- + p^+ \rightarrow K^- + \Sigma^+}$$

Since the Σ^+ particle is a baryon, this reaction conserves all the quantities we have already met. However, other reactions of pions and protons also conserve these quantities, yet they are never observed. This is why it is necessary to incorporate the idea of strangeness into the classification scheme.

Starting by assigning the K^- particle a value of $S = -1$ (and its corresponding K^+ particle a value of $S = +1$), it is possible to assign a value of S to all known particles in such a way that the values agree with every known reaction and particle decay. This agreement is the evidence that, no matter how strange it seems, strangeness really is a property of particles.

By the early 1960s around 20 hadrons were known. Physicists were aware that it was no longer satisfactory to classify these particles on the basis of their mass, but were at a loss to suggest a better way of creating order among them, especially since such order must satisfy a complex set of conservation laws, including the idea of strangeness. It was at this point that Murray Gell-Mann and George Zweig had the idea of grouping the known hadrons as being made

Figure 6.6.16 Murray Gell-Mann and George Zweig, as drawn by Iutta Waloschek.

up of just three different particles and their associated antiparticles, called *quarks*.

This model describes the structure of baryons as consisting of three quarks (sometimes called 'quark triplets'), while mesons consist of a quark–antiquark pair. Combining the quarks of different types (or 'flavours', as they are known) in this way accounts nicely for the properties of all the hadrons, including their observed properties.

Quark flavour	Charge/e	Strangeness	Baryon number
up (u)	$+\frac{2}{3}$	0	$+\frac{1}{3}$
down (d)	$-\frac{1}{3}$	0	$+\frac{1}{3}$
strange (s)	$-\frac{1}{3}$	-1	$+\frac{1}{3}$
anti-up ($\bar{u}$)	$-\frac{2}{3}$	0	$-\frac{1}{3}$
anti-down ($\bar{d}$)	$+\frac{1}{3}$	0	$-\frac{1}{3}$
anti-strange ($\bar{s}$)	$+\frac{1}{3}$	$+1$	$-\frac{1}{3}$

Table 6.6.3 The properties of the up, down and strange quarks.

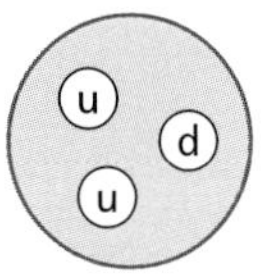

Figure 6.6.17 The quark structures of some hadrons.

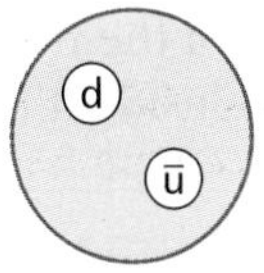

Proton		u	u	d
Charge	$+1$	$+\frac{2}{3}$	$+\frac{2}{3}$	$-\frac{1}{3}$
Baryon no.	$+1$	$+\frac{1}{3}$	$+\frac{1}{3}$	$+\frac{1}{3}$
Strangeness	0	0	0	0

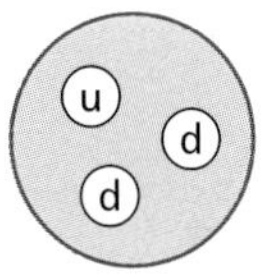

Neutron		u	d	d
Charge	0	$+\frac{2}{3}$	$-\frac{1}{3}$	$-\frac{1}{3}$
Baryon no.	$+1$	$+\frac{1}{3}$	$+\frac{1}{3}$	$+\frac{1}{3}$
Strangeness	0	0	0	0

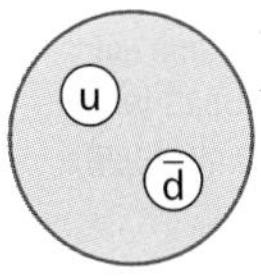

Pion (π^{+})		u	$\bar{d}$
Charge	$+1$	$+\frac{2}{3}$	$+\frac{1}{3}$
Baryon no.	0	$+\frac{1}{3}$	$-\frac{1}{3}$
Strangeness	0	0	0

Pion (π^{-})		d	$\bar{u}$
Charge	-1	$-\frac{1}{3}$	$-\frac{2}{3}$
Baryon no.	0	$+\frac{1}{3}$	$-\frac{1}{3}$
Strangeness	0	0	0

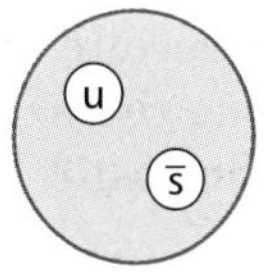

Kaon (K^{+})		u	$\bar{s}$
Charge	$+1$	$+\frac{2}{3}$	$+\frac{1}{3}$
Baryon no.	0	$+\frac{1}{3}$	$-\frac{1}{3}$
Strangeness	1	0	$+1$

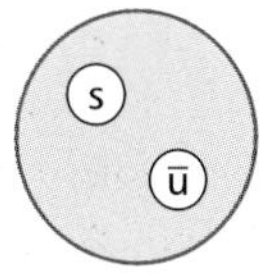

Kaon (K^{-})		s	$\bar{u}$
Charge	-1	$-\frac{1}{3}$	$-\frac{2}{3}$
Baryon no.	0	$+\frac{1}{3}$	$-\frac{1}{3}$
Strangeness	-1	-1	0

More quarks …

Although the three quarks described here can account for the properties of some hadrons quite adequately, three further quarks are necessary in order fully to describe the properties of all known hadrons. These have the flavours *charmed*, *bottom* and *top* – and each has its corresponding antiquark. Their relative masses are shown in table 6.6.4.

Quark	Relative mass
up	1
down	2
strange	20
charmed	300
bottom	about 1000
top	about 35000

Table 6.6.4 The six quarks. The enormously massive top quark required protons to be collided with antiprotons in a powerful synchrotron in order to provide enough energy to produce such a large mass. Evidence for the top quark eventually came from the collider at Fermilab, Chicago, in 1995.

Evidence for quarks – deep inelastic scattering

The evidence for the existence of quarks comes, unsurprisingly, from scattering experiments. However, in order to 'see' inside the nucleus, the particles used for scattering cannot be remotely like those used by Rutherford and his colleagues – instead we must use incident beams of high-energy electrons. The reason why these enable us to probe *inside* the nucleus and see its fine structure is down to wave–particle duality. As the wavelength of electrons is a function of their energy (see page 533), with a high enough energy the de Broglie wavelength of the electrons is shorter than the diameter of the nucleus, and makes it possible to resolve detail inside it (see page 265).

Electrons penetrating the nucleus collide with the quarks in it, and are scattered in a way that is reminiscent of the alpha-particle scattering experiments which first revealed the structure of the atom. The collisions are inelastic, giving rise to the description of this technique as **deep inelastic scattering**.

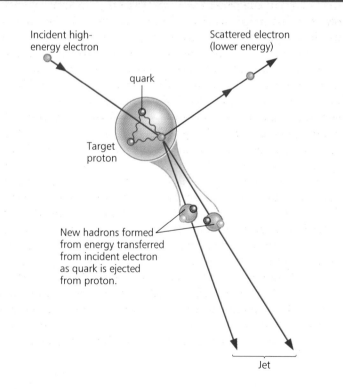

Figure 6.6.18 Deep inelastic scattering. Quarks knocked out of a hadron are never seen individually, since the energy involved in pulling quarks apart is sufficient to create more quarks – so all we see is more hadrons, which emerge from the nucleus in something called a jet.

FOCUS RICHARD FEYNMAN – UNIQUE PHYSICIST, UNIQUE DIAGRAMS

Gathered to watch the detonation of the first atomic bomb in New Mexico at dawn on 16 July 1945, all the observers – military staff, government officials, scientists – wore thick goggles intended to protect their eyes from the glare of the bomb's blast. All except one: Richard Feynman, the brilliant 27-year-old physicist who had been an integral member of the team that had performed the complex series of calculations needed to construct the first fission bomb. Always the rebel, Feynman reckoned that the thick glass of a military truck would be sufficient to screen his eyes from the blast of ultraviolet light from the bomb – and, as ever in matters relating to physics, he was right.

Feynman was curious about the world from a very early age, delighting in asking difficult questions and in seeking explanations to them. Such curiosity was to fuel Feynman's whole career during which he excelled in his research into the structure of matter, and in his teaching. One student even described watching the professor, with his animated arms and body, his thick Brooklyn accent (Feynman delighted in speaking in a down-to-earth way) and his inspired explanations, as being 'like watching a Broadway play'.

A Nobel prizewinner, one of Feynman's great contributions to physics was the **Feynman diagram**, a way of describing the interactions of particles with his own elegant simplicity. Modern physics explains the forces that act between particles as being carried by other particles called **gauge bosons** (table 6.6.5). Feynman diagrams take this idea and show how these **exchange processes** work, describing attraction or repulsion between a pair of particles as being due to the pair exchanging a virtual gauge boson. In this way the repulsive force between two electrons is described as being due to the exchange of a virtual photon, while the attractive force between two quarks can be explained as being due to the exchange of a virtual *gluon* (figure 6.6.20).

Feynman was called to serve on the Rogers Commission into the *Challenger* space shuttle disaster of 1986. Not content with interviewing senior managers at NASA, he insisted on talking directly to technical staff who had designed and built the shuttle. It was through such meetings that he became convinced that the disaster had been caused by faulty rubber O-rings, responsible for sealing joints in the solid rocket boosters used to launch the shuttle. At a subsequent press briefing, Feynman used iced water to give a brilliant demonstration of the effect of cold weather on the faulty seals, showing graphically for a non-technical audience how the seals had been to blame for the accident.

Richard Feynman died in 1988 at the age of 69. In memory of him, his students hung a banner from the library at Caltech, where he had taught and researched for the last 37 years. It read simply 'We love you, Dick' – a fitting tribute to a great physicist, and a great physics teacher.

Figure 6.6.19 Feynman revelled in life outside physics too – juggling was just one of the many activities which he enjoyed, and at which he excelled.

Interaction	Exchange particle (gauge boson)
weak	W, Z bosons
strong	gluon
electromagnetic	photon
gravity	graviton (not yet detected)

Table 6.6.5 The gauge bosons.

Figure 6.6.20 Feynman diagrams do not literally represent the track of particles through space and time – they are simply a model for understanding interactions, and help us to think about the conservation laws that apply in these interactions.

SUMMARY

- In the original form of **scattering experiment**, particles with energies in the MeV range are directed at various materials in order to investigate their atomic structure.

- More advanced experiments require particles with energies measured in GeV which are produced from **particle accelerators**.

- The **linear accelerator** (LINAC) uses a series of **drift tubes** with alternating voltages to accelerate charged particles.

- The **cyclotron** is a circular accelerator with an alternating potential across the electrodes which are surrounded by a magnetic field to keep the charged particles moving in a circular spiral path.

- The **synchrotron** was developed from the cyclotron. Instead of a uniform magnetic field through which the charged particles spiral outwards as their energy increases, it uses a variable magnetic field to keep the particles moving in a path with a constant radius. This **ring** structure allows huge machines to be built, the largest, at CERN in Switzerland, having a circumference of 27 km.

- The most efficient use of particle energy is made by colliding two beams of particles travelling in **opposite directions**.

- Particles produced by collisions leave **tracks** that are detected in various kinds of sealed chamber. **Cloud chambers** use condensing ethanol vapour in air, **bubble chambers** use bubbles of hydrogen gas in superheated liquid hydrogen, and **spark** and **drift chambers** use an inert gas such as neon.

- The properties of a particle in a detector can be deduced largely from the **length**, **thickness** and **curvature** of its track.

- Particles have **antiparticles** (forming **antimatter**) with the same mass but opposite charge.

- All particles are classified in three groups with increasing mass – **leptons**, **mesons** and **baryons**, the latter two comprising the **hadrons**. More modern scientific theories classify hadrons as being made from combinations of six simpler particles called **quarks**, with their respective **antiquarks**.

- **Conservation** of particle properties during interactions between particles explains why certain reactions are never seen. Properties conserved include **energy**, **momentum**, **lepton number** L, **baryon number** B, and **strangeness** S.

QUESTIONS

(For the electron, take the charge, e, as -1.6×10^{-19} C, and the rest mass as 9.1×10^{-31} kg.)

1 Explain why it is not possible to use a particle accelerator to accelerate neutrons.

2 Explain why
   a the electronvolt is a unit of *energy*
   b the units MeV/c^2 and GeV/c^2 are units of *mass*.

3 a What do particle physicists mean by the term *rest mass*?
   b Calculate your rest mass in units of **i** MeV/c^2, **ii** GeV/c^2.

4 An electron is accelerated through a potential difference of 15 000 V.
   a What is the kinetic energy of the electron **i** in eV, **ii** in keV, **iii** in J?
   b What is the electron's velocity?
   c Would it be fair to calculate the velocity of an electron accelerated through a potential difference of 10^6 V in the same way? Justify your answer.

5 Some physicists suggest that radio waves with a frequency of 10^9 Hz reaching us from Jupiter are caused by electrons orbiting in the planet's magnetic field, as if they were in a cyclotron. Calculate the strength of the magnetic field.

6 Why are neutral particles hard to detect?

7 A proton in a bubble chamber travels in a circular path with a radius of 3.5 m. If the bubble chamber is between the poles of an electromagnet that produce a magnetic field of 20 T, calculate the momentum of the proton.

8 A particle that lives for only 10^{-23} s cannot be detected in a bubble chamber. Why?

9 Why is there an upper limit to the size of nuclei?

10 Suggest whether each of the following particle reactions is possible, and give your reasons:
   a $\pi^- + p^+ \rightarrow n + \pi^+$
   b $p^+ \rightarrow \pi^+ + \gamma$
   c $n \rightarrow p^+ + e^- + \bar{\nu}_e$
   d $\mu^+ \rightarrow e^+ + \nu_e + \bar{\nu}_\mu$

11 Draw Feynman diagrams for the following interactions/reactions:
   a two protons repelling each other
   b two masses attracting each other
   c an electron and a positron colliding and producing a gamma ray photon
   d an electron and a positron colliding and producing a gamma ray photon, which then produces another electron and positron.

Developing Key Skills

In order to find out more and more about the tiny building blocks of matter, we need to build bigger and bigger machines, costing more and more money. Some people argue that money spent on this kind of research, which appears to have no kind of practical benefit, is money that could be better spent on other things. Others argue that so-called 'blue-sky' research is important since it satisfies our curiosity about the world around us, and might one day lead to important applications anyway.

Write a letter that you could send to your Member of Parliament setting out your views about the way in which the Government should spend money on blue-sky research.

[Key Skills opportunities: C]

6 QUESTIONS

Where further data are required, consult the table on page 583.

1 In the photoelectric effect, electrons are emitted from a metal surface when it is irradiated with electromagnetic radiation. The graph shows the variation of the maximum photoelectron kinetic energy with the frequency of the radiation incident on the emitting surface.

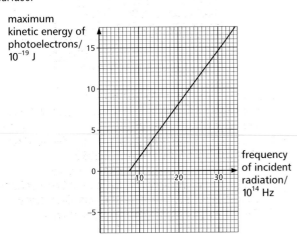

a Use the data from the graph to calculate the Planck constant.
(3 marks)

b Determine the minimum energy required to remove an electron from the target metal. **(2 marks)**

c Explain how the photoelectric effect produces evidence which illustrates the particulate nature of light. **(3 marks)**

(AQA 1999)

2 Deuterium ($_1^2$H) and tritium ($_1^3$H) nuclei will fuse together, as illustrated in the equation below.

$$_1^2\text{H} + _1^3\text{H} \rightarrow _Z^A\text{X} + \text{neutron}$$

a State the nucleon number and the proton number for the product of the reaction which has been written as X in the equation.
(2 marks)

b The masses of the particles involved in the reaction are:

mass of $_1^2$H $= 3.34250 \times 10^{-27}$ kg
mass of $_1^3$H $= 5.00573 \times 10^{-27}$ kg
mass of $_Z^A$X $= 6.62609 \times 10^{-27}$ kg
mass of neutron $= 1.67438 \times 10^{-27}$ kg

i Explain why energy is released during this reaction. **(2 marks)**
ii Calculate the amount of energy released when a deuterium nucleus fuses with a tritium nucleus.
The speed of electromagnetic radiation, $c = 3.0 \times 10^8 \text{ m s}^{-1}$.
(3 marks)

(AQA 1999)

3 In an experiment (first done by Millikan) to determine the charge on an electron, a charged oil drop of known (pre-determined) mass is held stationary between two parallel plates where a uniform electric field strength exists. Figure A shows this situation for one oil drop.

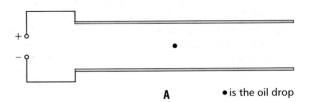

A   • is the oil drop

a i Explain what is meant by a *uniform electric field strength*.
(2 marks)

ii Sketch, on a copy of figure A, electric field lines to represent the electric field between and at the edges of the plates.
(3 marks)

b In one test an oil drop has a weight of 3.0×10^{-14} N. It is held stationary between plates 4.0 mm apart when the potential difference applied is 380 V.
i Calculate the electric field strength between the plates.
(2 marks)
ii Calculate the magnitude of the charge on the oil drop.
(2 marks)
iii State and explain whether the charge is positive or negative.
(3 marks)

c The oil drop is not isolated but has other charged oil drops nearby. Suppose that there is another drop which has an equal but opposite charge near to the drop being observed, as shown in figure B.

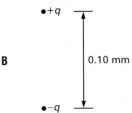

B   0.10 mm

Show that, when the two drops are separated by 0.10 mm, the magnitude of the electric force between these oil drops may be neglected in the calculations in part **b**.
The permittivity of free space, $\varepsilon_0 = 8.9 \times 10^{-12} \text{ F m}^{-1}$.
(4 marks)

(AQA 1999)

4 A small proportion of the hydrogen in air is the isotope tritium $^3_1$H. This is continually being formed in the upper atmosphere by cosmic radiation so that the tritium content of air is constant. Tritium is a beta emitter with a half-life of 12.3 years.

  a **i** Write down the symbols for the **two** isotopes of hydrogen, the atoms of which have lower masses than those of tritium.
                                                  (1 mark)

      ii Write down the nuclear equation that represents the decay of tritium using the symbol **X** for the daughter nucleus. **(2 marks)**

      iii Calculate the decay constant for tritium in year^{-1}. **(1 mark)**

  b When wine is sealed in a bottle no new tritium forms and the activity of the tritium content of the wine gradually decreases with time. At one time the activity of the tritium in an old bottle of wine is found to be 12% of that in a new bottle. Calculate the approximate age of the old wine. **(3 marks)**

  c mass of a tritium nucleus   = 3.016050 u
     mass of a proton   = 1.007277 u
     mass of a neutron   = 1.008665 u
     atomic mass unit, u   = 1.660566 × 10^{-27} kg
     speed of electromagnetic radiation in free space = 3.0×10^8 m s^{-1}
     Calculate:

      i the mass change, in kg, when a tritium nucleus is formed from its component parts; **(2 marks)**

      ii the binding energy, in J, of a tritium nucleus. **(2 marks)**
                                                (AQA 1999)

5 **a** Describe briefly the nuclear processes involved in the production of nuclear power by fission. **(3 marks)**

  b Explain briefly the purpose of the following components of a nuclear reactor:

      i the moderator; **(2 marks)**

      ii the control rods; **(2 marks)**

      iii the coolant. **(1 mark)**

  c One nuclear power station produces an average useful output power of 800 MW. The mass of uranium 235 in the fuel rods is reduced to 70% of its original value in a four year period. The average yield of each fission reaction is 200 MeV and 35% of this is converted into useful power.
     charge on an electron, e = -1.6×10^{-19} C
     Avogadro constant, N_A = 6.0×10^{23} mol^{-1}
     speed of light in a vacuum, c = 3.0×10^8 m s^{-1}
     Calculate:

      i the total number of fission reactions that occur in the four year period; **(4 marks)**

      ii the average change in the mass for each fission; **(2 marks)**

      iii the mass of uranium that was originally present in the reactor core. **(3 marks)**

  d In such a reactor about 5% of the reactions produce the strontium isotope $^{90}_{38}$Sr. This nuclide is a beta emitter with a half-life of 28 y.

      i What change occurs in the strontium nuclide when beta emission occurs? **(1 mark)**

      ii Calculate the initial rate at which strontium-90 is being formed in the reactor. **(1 mark)**

      iii Estimate the strontium-90 activity after running the reactor for one day. **(3 marks)**

      iv Discuss whether it is possible for the number of strontium-90 atoms present in the reactor to reach a constant value. **(3 marks)**
                                                  (AQA 1999)

6 ^{14}C is an *isotope* of carbon which is *radioactive* and has a *half-life* of 5730 years.

  a Explain the meanings of the terms *isotope*, *radioactive*, *half-life*. **(4 marks)**

  b Calculate the decay constant of ^{14}C, in s^{-1}. **(2 marks)**
                                                  (AQA 1998)

7 **a** The diagram shows the main features of a typical nuclear power station.

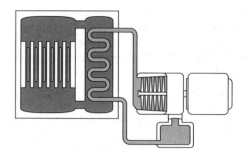

     Draw a block diagram for this power station.
     What is meant by the efficiency of a power station of this type? How could its efficiency be increased? **(6 marks)**

  b In the core of a nuclear power station one possible reaction which occurs in the fission of uranium-235 is
$$^{235}_{92}U + ^1_0n \rightarrow ^{138}_{55}Cs + ^{96}_{Z}Rb + \text{neutrons}$$

      i Write down the proton number (atomic number) Z of Rb and the number of neutrons which result from this reaction.

      ii The masses of the nuclei involved are as follows:
          U-235   235.044u
          Cs-138   137.929u
          Rb-96   95.923u
     The decrease in mass in the reaction is 3.04×10^{-28} kg.
     Calculate the mass of a neutron. Show your working. **(6 marks)**

  c The Cs and Rb nuclei repel each other immediately after the fission as both are positively charged.
     Describe a laboratory demonstration which illustrates that like charges repel.
     Explain how the bodies are charged in your experiment. **(4 marks)**
                                       (Total 16 marks)
                                            (Edexcel 1999)

8 A particle accelerator is designed to accelerate antiprotons through a potential difference of 2.0 GV and make them collide with protons of equal energy moving in the opposite direction. In such a collision, a proton–antiproton pair is created as represented by the equation
$$p + \bar{p} \rightarrow p + \bar{p} + p + \bar{p}$$
You may assume that the rest energy of the proton is 940 MeV.

  a State how an antiproton differs from a proton. **(1 mark)**

  b Give the total kinetic energy of the particles, in GeV, before collision. **(1 mark)**

  c State the rest energy of the antiproton. **(1 mark)**

  d Calculate the total kinetic energy of the particles, in GeV, after the collision. **(4 marks)**
                                            (AQA specimen)

9 **a** **i** State the difference between a hadron and a lepton in terms of the type of force experienced by each particle.

      ii Give **one** example of a hadron and **one** example of a lepton.

iii Hadrons are classified as either baryons or mesons. In terms of quark composition, explain the difference between a baryon and a meson. **(6 marks)**

b i State the quark composition of a neutron.
ii Describe, in terms of quarks, the process of β⁻ decay when a neutron changes into a proton. Sketch a Feynman diagram to represent this process. **(4 marks)**
(AQA specimen)

10 a In the photoelectric effect equation
$$hf = \phi + E_k$$
explain what is meant by hf, ϕ, E_k. **(3 marks)**

b Monochromatic light of wavelength 3.80×10^{-7} m falls with an intensity of $6.0\,\mu\text{W m}^{-2}$ on to a metallic surface whose work function is 3.2×10^{-19} J. Calculate
i the energy of a single photon of light of this wavelength,
ii the number of electrons emitted per second from $1.0 \times 10^{-6}\,\text{m}^2$ of the surface if a photon has a 1 in 1000 chance of ejecting an electron,
iii the maximum kinetic energy which one of these photoelectrons could possess. **(5 marks)**
(AQA specimen)

11 a i Explain what is meant by the *duality of electrons*.
ii State the relation between the momentum and the wavelength for a monoenergetic beam of electrons. **(3 marks)**

b The spacing of atoms in a crystal is 1.0×10^{-10} m.
mass of the electron = 9.1×10^{-31} kg
the Planck constant = 6.6×10^{-34} J s
i Estimate the speed of electrons which would give detectable diffraction effects with such crystals.
ii Give **one** piece of evidence to demonstrate that electrons have particle properties. **(5 marks)**
(AQA specimen)

12 The diagram shows the principal parts of an X-ray tube. It consists of a source of electrons C and a circular tungsten target A enclosed in a vacuum-sealed tube. The beam of electrons from C is accelerated by the 80 kV potential difference between C and A.

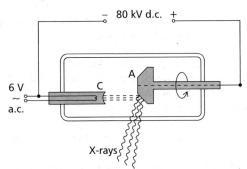

a The electron beam current in this X-ray tube is 24 mA. Calculate the power of the electron beam striking the tungsten target A. Suggest why the circular target A is made to rotate about the dashed axis as shown. **(4 marks)**

b State, in electronvolts, the energy of an electron hitting the tungsten target. Suppose all this energy becomes an X-ray photon. Calculate the wavelength of this photon. **(3 marks)**

c The X-ray beam coming from a point on the tungsten target has an intensity of $16\,\text{W m}^{-2}$ at a distance of 0.30 m from its source. Describe how the intensity varies between 0.30 m and 1.20 m from the source by sketching a graph of intensity against distance. Put numerical values on both axes. **(4 marks)**

d The hot tungsten target emits infra-red radiation as well as X-rays.
i Both infra-red waves and X-rays obey the principle of superposition and show diffraction effects. State two other properties which infra-red waves and X-rays have in common.
ii Describe an experiment to demonstrate the diffraction of waves. You may use water waves, microwaves or light. Give the approximate dimensions of the apparatus you would use. **(5 marks)**
(Total 16 marks)
(Edexcel 1999)

13 a The radioactive isotope polonium-218 has a half-life of 3.0 minutes. A pure sample initially contains 6.0×10^{15} polonium-218 nuclei.
i Show that the number of polonium nuclei remaining after 7.0 minutes is 1.2×10^{15}.
ii Calculate the activity (in Bq) of the sample of polonium after 7.0 minutes. **(4 marks)**

b In an experiment, a detector is held a fixed distance from a sample of a radioactive material and the data provided is used to plot a graph of count-rate against time.
i Explain why the data points on the graph do not lie on a smooth curve.
ii Suggest two reasons why the count-rate recorded is not the same as the activity of the sample. **(3 marks)**
(OCR specimen)

14 a An insulated zinc plate has a negative charge. When ultra-violet radiation is incident on the plate, the plate rapidly loses its negative charge. Explain what is happening to cause this effect. **(4 marks)**

b Einstein analysed the phenomenon described in **a** and derived the equation
$$hf = \phi + \tfrac{1}{2}mv^2_{max}$$
i State what each of the three terms in the equation represents. **(3 marks)**
ii Calculate the value of hf for ultra-violet light of frequency 4.7×10^{15} Hz. **(2 marks)**

c i Briefly describe how the wave nature of electrons may be demonstrated. **(4 marks)**
ii Calculate the de Broglie wavelength (m) of electrons travelling at $5.0 \times 10^7\,\text{m s}^{-1}$. **(3 marks)**
(OCR specimen)

15 The activity *A* of a radioactive isotope was measured. The graph shows how ln *A* varied with time.

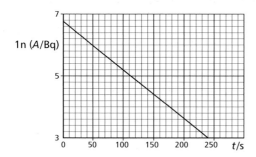

Use the graph to determine

   i the initial activity of the isotope, **(1 mark)**

   ii the decay constant of the isotope. **(2 marks)**

Calculate the half-life of the isotope. **(1 mark)**

(Total 4 marks)

(Edexcel 1999)

16 A muon is a particle which has the *same charge* as an electron but its *mass* is 207 times the mass of an electron.

An unusual atom similar to hydrogen has been created, consisting of a muon orbiting a single proton. An energy level diagram for this atom is shown.

      0 eV ——————————————

  −312 eV ——————————————

  −703 eV ——————————————

 −2810 eV ————————————— Ground state

State the ionisation energy of this atom.

Calculate the maximum possible wavelength of a photon which, when absorbed, would be able to ionise this atom.

To which part of the electromagnetic spectrum does this photon belong? **(5 marks)**

Calculate the de Broglie wavelength of a muon travelling at 11% of the speed of light. **(3 marks)**

(Total 8 marks)

(Edexcel 1999)

17 a The radius of a hydrogen nucleus is 1.3×10^{-15} m. Calculate the radius (in metres) of the nucleus of a carbon-12 atom. **(2 marks)**

  b An **atom** of carbon-12 has a mass of precisely 12 u.

   i Calculate the density (kg m^{-3}) of the nucleus of a carbon-12 atom. Assume that the nucleus is spherical. **(2 marks)**

     $1 \text{ u} = 1.66 \times 10^{-27}$ kg.

   ii State a further assumption which must be made when carrying out the calculation in **b i** above. **(1 mark)**

(OCR 1998)

18 a State the changes which occur within the nucleus of an atom when it emits a $\beta-$ particle, in terms of the quark composition of the nucleus as a whole. **(1 mark)**

  b **i** What is the nature of a $\beta+$ particle? **(1 mark)**

    ii Name another **particle** which is emitted during $\beta+$ decay. **(1 mark)**

  c The nuclei of some atoms change their composition by absorbing an orbital electron. Suggest how this process affects the particle composition of a nucleus. **(1 mark)**

(OCR 1998)

19 Lithium-5 is unstable and may emit a single proton to produce helium-4. The equation below describes the change.

$$^{5}_{3}\text{Li} \rightarrow {}^{4}_{2}\text{He} + {}^{1}_{1}\text{p} + Q$$

  a In this equation, *Q* represents the energy released. State **two** forms which this energy might take. **(2 marks)**

  b The curve on the graph below represents the binding energy per nucleon against nucleon number for most nuclei. **(2 marks)**

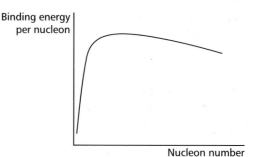

   i Define *binding energy per nucleon*. **(1 mark)**

   ii Use the letter L to indicate on a copy of the graph above the most likely position for lithium-5. **(1 mark)**

   iii The most stable nucleus is that of nickel-62. Use the letter N to mark the position of nickel-62 on your copy of the graph above. **(1 mark)**

  c Discuss the relevance of the graph to nuclear fission and to nuclear fusion. **(3 marks)**

(OCR 1998)

20 a The collision of a high energy proton with a stationary proton can produce the following interaction:

$$\text{p} + \text{p} \rightarrow \text{p} + \text{p} + \text{p} + \bar{\text{p}}$$

    Mass of proton = 1.0 GeV/c^2

    Kinetic energy of incident proton = 6.0 GeV

Calculate the initial total energy.

Calculate the momentum of the incident proton in this interaction given that $E^2 = m_0^2 c^4 + p^2 c^2$. **(4 marks)**

Describe in detail how a beam of high energy protons is produced. **(5 marks)**

  b The two decays shown below may both conserve energy and momentum.

$$\mu^+ \rightarrow \text{e}^+ + \nu_e$$
$$\mu^+ \rightarrow \text{e}^+ + \nu_e + \bar{\nu}_\mu$$

The first cannot occur but the second can.

State a further conservation law which *both* decays obey.

Which conservation law forbids the first decay?

Show how this conservation law allows the second decay. **(4 marks)**

c The diagram from a bubble chamber shows a collision between a negative pi meson and a stationary proton at A.

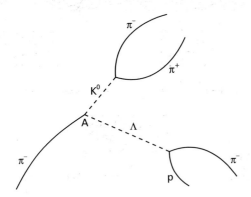

Write down the interaction at A.
The K^0 meson decays into two pi mesons, π^- and π^+. The K^0 has strangeness $+1$ and is the only strange particle in this decay. Use the data in the table to deduce the quark structure of these three mesons.

Quark	Charge	Strangeness
u	+2/3	0
d	−1/3	0
s	−1/3	−1

By which fundamental interaction does the decay of the K^0 occur? Give a reason for your answer. Suggest a value for the lifetime of the K^0. **(7 marks)**
(Total 20 marks)

(Edexcel 1999)

21 a State which interaction, strong or weak, is experienced by hadrons, and which is experienced by leptons **(2 marks)**
b Give **one** example of a hadron and **one** example of a lepton. **(2 marks)**
c Hadrons are classified as either baryons or mesons. How many quarks are there in a baryon and in a meson? **(2 marks)**
d i State the quark composition of a neutron.
ii Describe, in terms of quarks, the process of β decay when a neutron changes into a proton.
iii Sketch a Feynman diagram to represent β^- decay. **(4 marks)**

(AQA specimen)

22 a Up quarks have a charge of $+\frac{2}{3}e$ and down quarks have a charge of $-\frac{1}{3}e$.
i State the number of each type of quark in a neutron. **(2 marks)**
ii Explain in terms of charge why a neutron has this composition. **(1 mark)**
b i A neutron decays by β emission. Complete the following decay equation, naming all the particles produced in the decay.

$$\text{neutron} \rightarrow \beta \quad (\text{electron}) + \ldots..$$

(2 marks)
ii State and explain the change of quarks which occurs when this decay happens. **(2 marks)**

(AQA specimen)

23 a The radius of the Hydrogen-1 nucleus is approximately 1.3×10^{-15} m. The mass of the proton is 1.67×10^{-27} kg.
i Estimate a value for the density of the nucleus of Hydrogen-1. **(3 marks)**
ii Suggest, with a reason, whether the density of the nucleus of Uranium-235 has approximately the same value as that in **i**. **(1 mark)**
b The centres of mass of two protons in a nucleus are separated by a distance of 2.6×10^{-15} cm. Calculate
i the gravitational force (in newtons) between the two protons, **(2 marks)**
ii the electrostatic force (in newtons) between the two protons. **(2 marks)**
c Explain why your answers in **b** indicate that there must be another interaction between nucleons. **(2 marks)**
d State one physical phenomenon which may be explained by
i the strong interaction, **(1 mark)**
ii the weak interaction. **(2 marks)**

(OCR specimen)

24 a In a nuclear reactor, a uranium nucleus $^{238}_{92}\text{U}$ absorbs a neutron to form a new isotope of uranium.
i Write down a nuclear equation for this absorption process. **(1 mark)**
ii The new isotope of uranium decays by β^- emission to an isotope of neptunium (Np). Write down a nuclear equation for this decay. **(2 marks)**
b It is suggested that some radioactive waste could be stored underground in simple metal containers and would not cause damage to the environment. Comment on this suggestion. **(4 marks)**

(OCR specimen)

25 Nuclei of the element scandium (Sc) each contain 21 protons. It is found that a nucleus of one isotope of scandium contains 24 neutrons and that of another isotope contains 27 neutrons.
a What is meant by *isotopes*? **(2 marks)**
b Write down the nuclear representations of these two isotopes in the following form:

$$^{\ldots..}_{\ldots..}\text{Sc} \qquad ^{\ldots..}_{\ldots..}\text{Sc}$$

(2 marks)

(OCR 1998)

ATOMIC & NUCLEAR PHYSICS CONCEPT MAP

How to use the map

The map is a way of representing the structure of the knowledge contained in this section. It is designed to be used as you get towards the end of the section, when you should begin to see a pattern in the key concepts you have met. The map shows how one area of knowledge builds on another, so that more complex ideas develop as you go through the section.

As you study, try to think about how you learn best. Do you prefer to have understood one idea completely before going on to another? Or do you like to meet several related new ideas and then put these together rather like you might put together several pieces of a jigsaw at once?

The concept map will help you to see how ideas are related. You can use it to help you to put your knowledge and understanding in some sort of order so that you can organise your learning. You can also use it to organise your revision at the end of the section and before your examinations. Alternatively, try drawing up your own concept map as you revise.

Notes on the map

The key ideas in the section are contained in the green boxes. Solid lines with arrows between these boxes show how ideas in the section develop. Where parts of this section relate to other sections, dashed lines with arrows indicate this – the links are described in yellow boxes. Finally, some sections introduce and apply key mathematical skills – this is indicated by purple boxes, with double arrows indicating areas where the skill is applied.

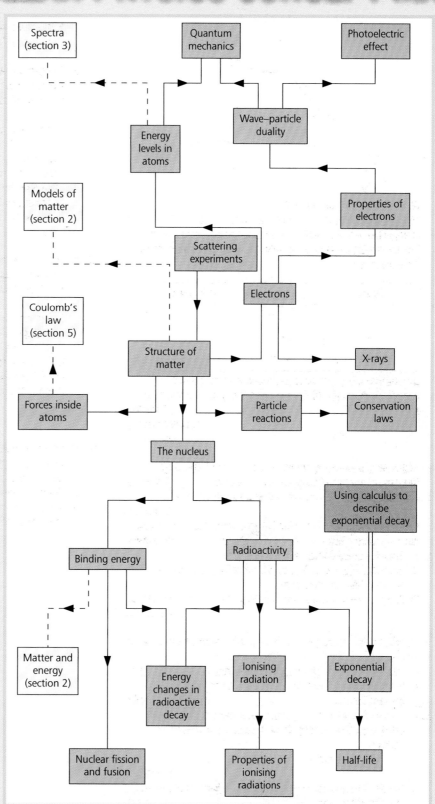

Answers

Note that numerical answers only are given.

Answers to end-of-chapter questions

1.1 Measuring and representing motion (pages 17–18)

1 **a** 0.018 s
   b 0.036 m
2 **a** 10 m s^{-2}
   b i 45 m
   ii 3 s
   c 15 s
   d 18 s
   e 371.8 m
   f 123.2 m
3 **a** 9.53 m s^{-1}
   b 10.27 m s^{-1}
4 Car travels 60 m
5 9.46×10^{12} km
6 69.95 cm, bearing S14.6°W
7 104.15 m s^{-1} at bearing N35.7°E
9 **c i** 27 m at 30 m.p.h., 45 m at 50 m.p.h., 63 m at 70 m.p.h.

1.2 Forces and their effects (pages 28–9)

5 450 men
6 160 m
7 20 m
8 **a** 6.6 s
   b Yes
9 **a** 0.6 m^2
   b 75 m^2
10 **b** ≈ 4 years
   c 6.4×10^8 m s^{-1}

1.3 Statics (pages 44–5)

1 30 N
2 **a** $T \sin \theta$
3 100 N
4 500 N
7 230 N
8 5.5×10^6 N on right-hand end, 5.25×10^6 N on left-hand end

9 5 m s^{-2}
10 **a** 2500 N
   b 4330 N

1.4 Measuring forces and their effects (pages 58–9)

1 7×10^4 N
2 **a** 5600 N
   b 2.33 times greater
3 **a** 200 N
   b 2.67×10^3 m s^{-1}
4 **a** 13.5 m s^{-2}
   b 440 m s^{-2}
5 62.5 m
6 1.8×10^{29} kg m s^{-1}
7 **a** 3.6×10^4 kg m s^{-1}
   b 8×10^4 m s^{-1}
8 0.283 m s^{-1}
9 3150 N
10 0.498 m s^{-1}, bearing of N87.1°E
11 150 N
12 **a** 7.75 m s^{-1}
   b 0.70 m s^{-1}
   c 1080 N

1.5 Energy and motion (pages 72–3)

1 **a** mgh
   b $\frac{1}{2}mv^2$
   c $\sqrt{2gh}$
   d 20 m s^{-1}
2 **a** 5000 W
   b 12 500 W
3 **a** 1.44×10^6 J
   b 1.44
4 0.667 HP
5 **a** 1.3×10^7 kg
   b 4.29×10^9 W
   c £564 million
6 **a** –20 m s^{-1}
   b 2 kg m s^{-1}
7 **a** 16 N
   b 6.4 W
   c 6.4 J
8 **a i** 4 m s^{-1}
   ii 3.2×10^4 J
   iii 1.6×10^4 J

b **i** $\Sigma mv_{\text{initial}} = \Sigma mv_{\text{final}}$
   ii $\Sigma E_{\text{k(initial)}} = \Sigma E_{\text{k(final)}}$
   iii $v_2 = 8 \text{ m s}^{-1}, v_1 = 0$
10 **b** 1.0×10^{20} J
   c 1.67×10^{-9} m s^{-1}
   d 8.33×10^6 J
   e 1.0×10^{20} J

1.6 Moving in arcs and circles (page 88)

1 **a** 1.5 s
   b 19.5 m
   c 2.81 m
2 2.4 m s^{-1}
3 14.1 m s^{-1}
4 94.3 m s^{-1}
5 **a** 6.32 s
   b 569.2 m
   c 110 m s^{-1}
6 **a** 4.2 m
7 **a** 2.41
   b 15.15 rad s^{-1}
8 **a** 2.66×10^{-6} rad s^{-1}
   b 1012 m s^{-1}
   c 2.0×10^{20} N
9 **a** 94.3 m s^{-1}
   b 148 N
10 900 N
11 15.8 m s^{-1}
12 17.3 m s^{-1}

1.7 Simple harmonic motion (pages 107–8)

1 4.66 s
2 **a** 0.1 m
   b 2.18 s
   c 0.302 N at equilibrium position
3 5.62 s
4 **a** 3.82×10^4 m s^{-2}
   b 55.3 m s^{-1}
      2.75×10^4 N
5 **a** 6.91 m s^{-1}
   b 1.91×10^4 m s^{-2}
   c 0.12 J
6 0.70 m
7 **a** 100 N m^{-1}
   b **i** 4 cm
      ii 50 N m^{-1}
   c **i** 1 cm
      ii 400 N m^{-1}
8 **a** 0.066 J
   b At $x = \pm 0.3$ m
   c At $x = \pm 0.21$ m
9 77.97 kg

10 **a** 10 000 N m^{-1}
   b 0.89 s
   c Resonance
11 0.71 Hz

2.1 Describing matter (page 120)

1 **a** 3.0×10^{23}
   b 2.4×10^{24}
   c 1.8×10^{24}
   d 191 g
5 **a** 16 units

2.2 Solids, liquids and gases (pages 149–50)

1 120 N m^{-1}
2 No
3 4.6 mm
4 6.03 m
5 2.65×10^4 N
6 5.0 cm
12 1.1×10^8 Pa
13 40 000 Pa (assuming neck length 4 m)
15 1.4×10^5 N
17 97 °C
18 $1/2.7 \times 10^{-5}$
19 26.4 lb in^{-2}
20 6.2×10^{-21} J
21 **a** 310 m s^{-1}
   b 493 m s^{-1}
   c 1300 m s^{-1}
23 **a** 1300 m s^{-1}
   b 2730 K

2.3 Energy, temperature and change of state (pages 168–9)

2 **b** 15°
4 **a** 378 kJ
   b 150 s
5 555 °C
6 60%
7 0.63 m^3
8 22.6 minutes
9 0.68 kg
10 231 kg
11 **a** 208 W m^{-2}
   b 6.23×10^{-6} m s^{-1}
   c 35 W m^{-2}, 1.05×10^{-6} m s^{-1}
12 **a** 1.6 J s^{-1}
   b 10 hours
13 12 J s^{-1} (assuming area = 0.04 m^2)

2.4 Principles of thermodynamics (page 184)

2 **a** 0
   b 98 J
   c 98 J
   d 1.56 °C higher

2.5 Applications of thermodynamics (pages 195–6)

1 0.22 J
2 **a** 1.5×10^4 N
   b 10 J
4 33 W
6 **a** $1 - (300/10^{10})$

3.1 Waves as oscillations (pages 218–19)

3 2.5 m s^{-1}
4 1.7 cm–17 m
5 300, 9.99×10^5
   3.10, 9.68×10^7
   3.08, 9.75×10^7
   4.76×10^2, 6.3×10^5
6 **a** 0.16 s
7 1:2.36
9 **a** 21 cm s^{-1}
   b 7 Hz
11 392 Hz, 588 Hz, 784 Hz
12 **a** 5.3 m
    b 0.042 m

3.2 Properties of waves in motion (pages 236–7)

1 0.97 mm
2 1.5 m
6 **b** 30 m s^{-1}
7 **b** 26 cm
9 9.5 mm
10 0.6 rad
11 1.29 mm
12 19°
13 1.8°

3.3 Light and sound (page 245)

1 6.7×10^4
2 62.5 rev s^{-1}
4 344 m s^{-1}
5 80 Hz
6 **b** 850 Hz

3.4 Using waves (pages 269–70)

2 10 cm
3 Red 1.980×10^8 m s^{-1}, blue 1.968×10^8 m s^{-1}
4 **a** 42°

5 466 Hz
6 278 Hz
7 7200 light-years
8 48.2°
9 1.9 km

4.1 Introducing electricity (page 288)

1 **a** 1.8 C
   b 0.075 W
2 **a** 4800 J
   b 40 s
3 2025 J
5 **a** Car battery: 3.02×10^6 J, torch battery: 2160 J
   b Car battery: 474.4 J cm^{-3}, torch battery 895.2 J cm^{-3}
   c Car battery: 1.44×10^5 J kg^{-1}, torch battery 8.64×10^4 J kg^{-1}
6 1.25 Ω
7 **a** 0.5 V
8 0.8 Ω
9 8.49 V
10 **a** 1.8×10^4 Ω
    b **i** 1.1×10^{-4} A
       ii 6.7×10^{-4} A
       iii 6.1×10^{-3} A
       iv 1.3×10^{-2} A
       v 1.7×10^{-1} A
11 2.38 km from one end
13 28 min 45 s

4.2 More about electricity (pages 311–12)

1 **a** A_1 0.455 A, A_2 0.273 A, A_3 0.182 A
   b A_1 0.519 A, A_2 0.259 A, A_3 0.259 A, A_4 0.148 A, A_5 0.074 A, A_6 0.296 A
2 **a** V_1 0.5 V, V_2 0.5 V, V_3 1 V
   b V_1 1.5 V; V_2, V_3 and V_4 0.5 V
3 **a** 0.6 Ω
   b 8.25 Ω
   c 2.5 Ω
5 **a** I_1 4.5 A, I_2 4 A, I_3 –0.5 A
   b I_1 –0.946 A, I_2 +0.081 A, I_3 – 0.865 A
7 10.0 V
8 **a** $I = 0.6$ A, $V = 1.2$ V
   b $I = 0.143$ A, $V = 1.43$ V
   c $I = 0.692$ A, $V = 1.154$ V
9 $I = 0.167$ A, $V = 3.5$ V
10 **a** 0.5 W
    b 50 W, low currents

4.3 Incomplete circuits and capacitors (pages 329–30)

1 **a** 6.95×10^{-11} F
   b 1.67×10^{-9} C
4 6.14 m^2

5　11.1 μF

7　5 μF: 6×10^{-5} C, 8 μF: 9.6×10^{-5} C

8　**a**　2000 J

9　1.23 K

11　200 μF

12　**a**　1.02 nF

　　b　4×10^9 Ω

　　c　3.75×10^{-9} A

　　d　2.83 s

4.4 Alternating current (pages 348–9)

3　10.6 V

4　**a**　5 V

　　b　3.54 V

　　c　100 Hz

　　d　0.5 A

5　**a**　10 A

　　b　14.14 A

　　c　24 Ω

　　d　New power = 504 W

6　**a**　1.13×10^{-3} m s^{-1}

　　b　3.58×10^{-6} m

　　c　0.354 m s^{-2}

9　**a**　160 ohms, 300 ohms

　　b　80 ohms, 260 ohms

10　450 Hz

4.5 Electronics (pages 367–8)

1　**a**　1

　　b　1

　　c　1

　　d　1

10　−4

11　−7.18 V

12　**a**　−10

5.1 Action at a distance (page 387)

1　17 N

2　**a**　4.8×10^{20} N

　　b　2.4×10^{20} N

　　c　6.4×10^{20} N

3　**a**　0.011 N kg^{-1}

　　b　8500 J kg^{-1}

4　**a**　28.6 N kg^{-1}

　　b　28.6 m s^{-2}

　　c　25.0 N kg^{-1}

　　d　12.6 km s^{-1}

　　e　2.21 N

　　f　22.8 m s^{-2}, period of 2 hours 11 minutes

6　**a**　530 m

　　b　80 m

　　c　1100 m

7　3.4×10^8 m from the centre of the Earth

5.2 Gravitational fields and energy (pages 406–7)

1　**d**　131

2　**a**　11 000 m s^{-1}

　　b　1200 km

3　2400 m s^{-1}

4　**a**　20 kJ kg^{-1}

　　b　2.25 J m^{-1} kg^{-1} radially outwards

　　c　−2.25 N kg^{-1}

5　**a**　1400 km

　　b　5.2 km s^{-1}

6　**a**　7.7 km s^{-1}

　　b　-1.4×10^{11} J

5.3 Electric fields (pages 425–6)

2　1.92 kV

3　1080 V

4　5.30×10^7 V m^{-1} in direction 3.9° from horizontal

5　**a**　**i**　−0.049 J

　　　　　ii　3×10^{-6} J

　　b　4.9×10^6 V m^{-1}

6　2×10^7 V m^{-1}

7　8.3×10^{-14} m

8　**a**　4871 N

　　b　2.44×10^{28} m s^{-2}

9　4.23×10^7 m s^{-1}

10　1.39×10^{-10} C

5.4 Magnetic fields (pages 446–7)

3　2 mm away

4　32°

5　4×10^{-4} T

6　**a**　0.80 A

　　b　1.59 A

7　**a**　0

　　b　2.4×10^{-3} N m

　　d　0

　　e　250 mA

8　**a**　1.56 mV

9　1.26×10^{11} m s^{-1}

10　8.78×10^7 m s^{-1}

11　**b**　1.6×10^{-15} N

　　c　3.13×10^7 m s^{-1}

12　5.76×10^6 V m^{-1}

5.5 Electromagnetic induction (pages 465–6)

3　4.27 V

5　222 rad s^{-1} (35.4 Hz)

6　15.9 mV

8　**a**　0.2 A

　　b　2.8 W

　　c　3.0 W

　　d　0.2 W

e 6.65 W

f 21.4 r.p.m.

9 a 1.125×10^5 W

  b 1.125×10^7 W

10 a 30.2 V

6.1 Atomic structure (page 484)

1 Na $\approx 3.4 \times 10^{-10}$ m, Mg $\approx 2.8 \times 10^{-10}$ m

2 a 8.1×10^{-15} m

  b 2.3×10^{-42} m^3

  c 1.7×10^{-29} m^3

3 b 10^8 m^3

4 a 10^{17} kg m^{-3}

  b 30 km

5 a 2.5×10^{35}

6 Alpha particle 3.2×10^{-14} m, proton 6.3×10^{-14} m

6.2 Radioactivity (page 501)

3 a 0.96 cm

  b 96 cm

4 a $\frac{1}{2}$

  b $\frac{1}{4}$

  c $\frac{1}{1024}$

5 0.49

6 1.4×10^{15} Bq

7 4300 years

6.3 The decay of the nucleus (page 521)

1 a ^{236}U

  b ^{226}Ra

  c ^{208}Pb

  d ^{237}Np

2 a ^{14}N

  b ^{8}Be

  c ^{32}S

  d ^{19}F

3 a ^{22}Ne

  b ^{56}Fe

4 8.7×10^{-13} J

5 b 7.98 MeV

  c 7.37 MeV

6 a (1) 0.93 MeV, (2) 4.98 MeV, (3) 12.9 MeV

  b 6.18 MeV per proton

  c 6.8×10^{11} kg s^{-1}

6.4 The nature of the electron (page 536)

1 a i 2.5 keV

    ii 4×10^{-16} J

  b 3×10^7 m s^{-1}

2 a 3.2×10^7 m s^{-1}

  b 4.8×10^{-3} W

3 20

4 2.84–4.98×10^{-19} J, 1.78–3.11 eV

5 a 1.21×10^{-27} kg m s^{-1}

6 290 nm

7 880 km s^{-1}

8 1.8 V

6.5 The behaviour of electrons in atoms (pages 549–50)

1 a 120 nm, 140 nm, 190 nm, 230 nm, 250 nm, 320 nm, 340 nm, 590 nm, 690 nm, 780 nm

  b 590 nm (690 nm)

2 a i 13.58 eV

    ii 2.173×10^{-18} J

  b 2.81 eV, 4.50×10^{-19} J; 0.93 eV, 1.49×10^{-19} J; 0.27 eV, 4.32×10^{-20} J

3 7.45×10^5 m s^{-1}

4 a 1.2×10^{-10} m

  b 5.0×10^{-11} m

  c 1.6×10^{-11} m

6 a 1.9×10^{16} electrons

  b 0.75 W

6.6 Probing the structure of matter (page 567)

4 a i 15 000 eV

    ii 15 keV

    iii 2.4×10^{-15} J

5 3.6×10^{-2} T

7 1.1×10^{-17} kg m s^{-1}

The author takes sole responsibility for these answers, which have not been provided by the Examinations Boards.

Section 1 (pages 109–12)

1 a i 30 s
     ii 1125 m
     iii 1125 000 J s^{-1}
2 c i 0.63 s
     ii 0.0034 J
     iii 3.45 N
     iv 2.55 N
3 c i 1.6 kg m s^{-1}
4 a 0.15 m
6 a i 30 m s^{-1}
     ii 45 m
8 c 30 000 W
  d i 460 m
     ii 1830 m
     iii 46 000 N
9 a 8.8 s
  b i 204 000 N
10 a 0.15 m s^{-1}, 0.060 m s^{-1}
   c 4.5 × 10^{-3} J, 1.8 × 10^{-3} J
11 a L: 121 N up; R: 95 N down
   b ii 1500 J
13 a i 13.9 m s^{-2}
      ii 14.2 N
   b i 10.2 N
   c i 4.0 N, 24.4 N
14 b i 1. 11 m s^{-1}
        2. 0.75 m s^{-2}
        3. 216 m
      ii 1. 57 N
        2. 33 N
      iii 90 N
   d i 152 N
15 a ii 42°
   b ii 4.5 m s^{-1}
   c i 1.8 m
      ii 1. 10 m s^{-2}
        2. 6 m s^{-1}
16 i 24 m
   ii 18 m s^{-2}
   iii 756 000 J

Section 2 (pages 197–200)

1 b i 1340 m s^{-1}
     ii 6.00 × 10^{-21} J
     iii 80 kPa
2 1.66 × 10^8 J, 18 500 s

3 6 × 10^7 m^2
4 2.5 m^2, 13 W
5 d 2460 W
  e i 0.93 W m^{-2} K^{-1}
     ii 280 W
6 d 2.1 × 10^6 J
8 b 4.6 × 10^6 J
9 b 3.89 × 10^6 J
  c 2160 s
11 c 60.5 N
12 ? iii 8.3 × 10^4 N m^{-1}
   b iii 1. 440 rad s^{-1}
        2. 264 m s^{-1}
20 c i 1.1 × 10^{-6} m^2
      ii 2.1 × 10^{11} Pa
   d 0.13 J

Section 3 (pages 271–4)

1 a i 2.5 kHz
     ii $\frac{1}{4}$
     iv 136 mm
     v 340 m s^{-1}
2 a i 0.020 m
     ii 4.4 × 10^{-4} m
4 b i 0.165 m
     ii 0.55 m
5 c i 0.25 m
     ii 0.50 m
6 b ii 1.9585 × 10^8 m s^{-1}
   c 8.8 m
7 b ii 1.29 × 10^{-5} m
9 a 5.8 × 10^5 m^{-1}
   b 6.5 × 10^{-7} m
10 c ii 1.5040, 5.5 × 10^{-15} m^2
   d 0.020
11 a 4.0 mm, 20 Hz
12 b i 37.2°, 47°
      ii 1.50
14 41.8°, 69.0°

Section 4 (pages 369–72)

1 b ii 90 J
  c i 8.0 V
     ii 8.0 Ω
     iii 4.0 V
     iv 0.8 Ω
2 a ii 30 Ω
     iii 1760 W
     iv 14.1 kWh
4 a i 1.0 A
  b i 18.0 Ω
     ii 6.0 V
     iii 1.5 Ω

5 530 Ω

7 c 1.24×10^{-5} m

d 0.017

8 b 4 A

c 4.8 A

9 i 20 V

ii 1.6×10^{-2} A

iii 250 Ω

10 a i 4.4 V

ii 7.6 V

iii 1.7×10^{-5} C

b 1.6×10^{-4} J

11 b ii 0.18 mm

c i $RC = 6.0 \times 10^{-3}$ s

ii 250 μs div^{-1}

12 b i 1900 J

ii 160 A

14 a i 6A

ii 1260 W

iii 3.3 Ω

15 a i 537 kV

ii 1.5×10^5 V m^{-1}

c i −537 kV

ii A leads C by 240°

iii zero

16 a ii 1. 10^6 Hz

2. 9 V

Section 5 (pages 467–70)

1 c 6.0×10^{-3} N

2 a 220 m

3 c 6.0 m s^{-1}

4 b ii 15 cm

c i 3.2×10^{-6} C

ii 1.7×10^{-11} F

d i 3.0×10^{-14} J

e i 0.35 m

5 a i 190 J kg^{-1}

ii 1710 J

b 4.75 N kg^{-1}

6 b i 0.035 N upwards

ii 0.012 T

8 b ii 3.8×10^7 V

11 1.89×10^{27} kg

12 1.6×10^{-6} Wb, 5.0×10^{-5} Wb, 6.2 mm s^{-1}

Section 6 (pages 568–72)

1 a 6.43×10^{-34} J s

b 5.0×10^{-19} J

2 a 4, 2

b ii 4.3×10^{-12} J

3 b i 9.5×10^4 V m^{-1}

ii 3.2×10^{-19} C

4 a iii 0.0564 year^{-1}

b 38 years

c i 1.421×10^{-27} kg

ii 1.28×10^{-12} J

5 c i 9.0×10^{27}

ii 3.56×10^{-28} kg

iii 4.6 kg

d ii 5.4×10^{-7} kg s^{-1}

iii 2.4×10^{14} Bq

6 b 3.8×10^{-12} s^{-1}

7 b i 37, 2

ii 1.675×10^{-27} kg

8 b 4.0 GeV

c 940 MeV

d 2.1 GeV

10 b i 5.2×10^{-19} J

ii 1.1×10^4 s^{-1}

iii 2.0×10^{-19} J

11 b i 7.3×10^6 m s^{-1}

12 a 1900 W

b 80 keV, 1.6×10^{-11} m

13 a ii 4.6×10^{12} Bq

14 b ii 3.1×10^{-18} J

c ii 1.5×10^{-11} m

15 i 900 Bq

ii 0.016 s^{-1}, half-life 44 s

16 2810 eV, 4.4×10^{-10} m, 1.1×10^{-13} m

17 a 3.0×10^{-15} m

b i 1.80×10^{17} kg m^{-3}

20 a 6.0 GeV, 3.16×10^{-18} kg m s^{-1}

23 a i 1.8×10^{17} kg m^{-3}

b i 2.8×10^{-35} N

ii 34 N

Useful data

Physical constants

Quantity	Symbol	Value and units	
Speed of light in a vacuum	c	$299\ 792\ 458\ \text{m s}^{-1}$	(exact)
Permeability of a vacuum	μ_0	$4\pi \times 10^{-7}\ \text{H m}^{-1}$	(exact)
Permittivity of a vacuum	ε_0	$1/\mu_0 c^2$	(exact)
		$\approx 8.854 \times 10^{-12}\ \text{F m}^{-1}$	
Gravitational constant	G	$6.673 \times 10^{-11}\ \text{m}^3\ \text{kg}^{-1}\ \text{s}^{-2}$	
Planck constant	h	$6.626 \times 10^{-34}\ \text{J s}$	
Avogadro constant	N_A	$6.022 \times 10^{23}\ \text{mol}^{-1}$	
Molar gas constant	R	$8.314\ \text{J mol}^{-1}\ \text{K}^{-1}$	
Boltzmann constant	k	$1.381 \times 10^{-23}\ \text{J K}^{-1}$	
Molar volume of ideal gas, RT/p ($T = 273.15\ \text{K}, p = 100\ \text{kPa}$)	V_m	$2.24 \times 10^{-2}\ \text{m}^3\ \text{mol}^{-1}$	
Elementary charge	e	$1.602 \times 10^{-19}\ \text{C}$	
Electron specific charge	$-e/m_e$	$-1.759 \times 10^{-11}\ \text{C kg}^{-1}$	
Electron rest mass	m_e	$9.109 \times 10^{-31}\ \text{kg}$	
Proton rest mass	m_p	$1.673 \times 10^{-27}\ \text{kg}$	
Neutron rest mass	m_n	$1.675 \times 10^{-27}\ \text{kg}$	
Atomic mass unit	u	$1.660\ 540 \times 10^{-27}\ \text{kg}$	

Other data

Quantity	Symbol	Value and units
Acceleration of free fall (at latitude 51°N)	g	$9.81\ \text{m s}^{-2}$
Mass of Earth	m_E	$5.976 \times 10^{24}\ \text{kg}$
Radius of Earth at equator	r_E	$6.371 \times 10^6\ \text{m}$
Density of air ($T = 273.15\ \text{K}, p = 100\ \text{kPa}$)	ρ_{air}	$1.247\ \text{kg m}^{-3}$
Density of water ($T = 298\ \text{K}$)	ρ_{water}	$1000\ \text{kg m}^{-3}$

INDEX

frequency of 82, 87
period of 82, 87
& SHM 103, 104
circular waves 205
classical physics 474
limitations/problems 528, 530, 544
classifying particles 559–64
classifying solids 127–31
Clausius (Rudolf Gottlieb) 172, 181–2
clock (grandfather) & energy 61–2, 63–4
clock pulse (computer) 358
closed-loop gain (op-amp) 364, 365
cloud chamber 556, 566
tracks in 489, 510
coding signals 258
coefficient of friction 22
coherent light 224, 227, 242
coil
induced in 452
magnetic field around 428
in magnetic field 433–4
collimator (spectrometer) 250, 268
collisions 68, 69–71, 72
matter & antimatter 506
of subatomic particles 86
communication & information 254–64
channels 258, 260–3
see also telecommunications
comparator (op-amp) 362
composite materials 130–1
compression (longitudinal wave) 209
compressive stress 128, 147
concept maps
atomic & nuclear physics 573
electricity 373
fields 471
forces & motion 113
matter & energy 201
waves 275
conductance 284
conduction 162–3, 167, 303–8
band theory (in solids) 307
electrical 284, 287
in insulators 305
in metals 303
model of 163–5
in semiconductors 303–5
superconductivity 156, 283, 306, 430
thermal conductivity 163, 165, 166, 167
conduction band (insulator) 307
conductors
hollow/Faraday cage 423
e.m.f. induced in 451
energy band 307
intrinsic 304
ohmic & non-ohmic 284, 287
resistance of 283
conservation laws
energy 60, 174
momentum 54–8
particles/properties 561–2, 566
conservation of charge 409
conservation of energy 175
law of 60, 174

conservation of momentum
law of 54–8
conservative fields 419
constant volume gas thermometers 154, 155, 157, 167
constants see Avogadro's; Boltzmann; decay; dielectric; gravitational; Planck's; spring constant
constructive interference 226
continuous spectra 250, 537
continuous waves 205
control rods (nuclear reactor) 513
convection 163
cooling systems/coolant (nuclear reactor) 515
Cooper pairs (superconductivity) 306
Copernicus 85
cosine waves/curves 90, 91, 94
see also sinewaves
cosmic rays 551
cosmology 253
see also galaxies; satellites; stars; universe
Coulomb, Charles Augustin 410
Coulomb's law 410–12, 424
coulombs 279
couples 41, 43
crane (equilibrium) 37, 38
Crick, Francis 232
critical angle (reflection) 224, 235
critical damping 105
critical mass (nuclear fission) 511
critical pressure 144, 148
critical temperature 144, 148
superconductivity 306
criticality (nuclear reaction) 513, 514, 517
Crookes, Sir William 473, 476
crosstalk 255
crumple zones 68
crystalline solids 129, 147
crystalline structures, modelling 130
see also diffraction
Curie, Marie 486, 487
Curie, Pierre 486
current density 310, 308
current see electric current
cyclotron 552–3, 566
synchro-cyclotron see synchrotron

da Vinci, Leonardo 238
damping 105, 207, 456
dark matter' 115
daughter nuclide (radioactivity) 503
de Broglie wavelength 533
de Broglie, Louis 239, 473, 533
decay constant (radioactivity) 496
decisions (logic gates) 353, 354
decoding signals 258
deep inelastic scattering (quarks) 564
definitions
capacitance 316
density 117
energy 63, 72
force 48, 51
gravitational field strength 26, 377

impedance 343
magnetic field strength 432
pressure 131–2
SHM 100
SI derived units
Celsius 155
joule 63, 72
newton 48, 51
radian 81, 87
weber 451
SI base units
ampere 278, 438–9
kelvin 154, 155
metre 242
mole 177
temperature 155, 173–4
velocity of light 242
weight 25, 26
see also dimensions; units
deformation 121, 124, 127
hysteresis 128, 187, 194, 463
of solids 186–7, 194
see also Hooke's law; Young modulus
Democritus 117, 238
density 119
definition/units 117
depth
& pressure 133–4, 135, 147
real & apparent 223, 224, 235
variation of g with 383
Descartes, Rene 249
destructive interference 226
detectors (particle accelerators) 556
tracks in 86, 557, 566
deuterium 481, 518
diamagnetism 430
dielectric constant (relative permittivity) 317
dielectrics (capacitors) 316, 419, 420
difference gate (EXOR gate) 354
differentiation/differential calculus 96–7, 98
diffraction 225, 235
interference patterns 228–9229–31
Rayleigh's criterion 264
slits 227, 250
simple 228–9
multiple 229–31
of ultrasound 267
X-ray 232
diffraction grating 229, 230, 233, 235
example 233
spectra 234
spectrometer 250
zero order maximum/spectra 231, 234
diffusion 176
digital signal 255, 256
digital systems/devices 350, 352, 362, 366
analogue-to-digital conversion 352
see also analogue systems
dimensions 52, 117
dimensional analysis 309
dimensionless 48
of energy 63
see also units

diodes
diode bridge 346
forward biased 345, 352
junction 344–5, 347, 352
light-emitting (LEDs) 352
reverse biased 345
direct current
& a.c. 333–4, 335
motor 435
rectification from a.c. 344
see also alternating current; electric circuits; electric current
direction 6–7, 12
electric fields/force 411, 413–14, 454
gravitation 392
SHM 98
see also vectors
discharging capacitors 321, 323, 325
disorder (chaos) 177–8
dispersion of light (prism) 248, 268
dispersive medium 268
displacement 6, 9, 10–11, 16
angular 81–2, 87
projectiles 77, 87
SHM 91, 93, 99
see also distance
displacement-time graph (oscillations) 90, 91, 93, 97, 208, 209
distance 4, 6, 9, 10, 16
see also displacement
distance-time graphs 5, 16, 96
DNA
radiation damage 488
structure 232
doped semiconductors 304
Doppler effect 250–1, 268
blood flow & ultrasound 267
example 252
& relativity 251–2
dose & dose equivalent (radiation) 491
drag coefficient 67
drag forces 21–4, 67
aerodynamic/air resistance 23, 28, 74
drift chamber 557, 566
drift tubes (particle accelerators) 552, 566
drift velocity (electrons) 303, 308
driven oscillations 206–7, 217
ductile materials 128, 147
dynamo effect 448

e.m.f. see electromotive force
Earth
earthquakes 203
gravitational field
equipotentials 397
variation of strength 375, 382–3
gravitational potential 395
ionosphere 261, 262
lightning 417, 423
magnetic field 427, 444
measurements of 375, 382
van Allen radiation belts 444
earthquakes 203
eddy currents (Lenz's law) 456

of particles 533
see also frequency
wave-particle duality 239, 245, 473, 529
waves 202, 204–5, 246–68
  circular 205
  compression 209
  concept map 275
  continuous 205
  in different media, 222, 248, 268
  & electrons 214, 533
  examples 212, 218, 236, 269
  harmonics 213, 214
  intensity of 212–13, 217
  longitudinal 240, 209, 216
  making 206–9, 214
  mechanical 204, 216
  as models 220
  nodes 213, 214, 217
  overtones 214
  & particles 528
  path difference 227
  phase of 207, 208, 217, 221, 226
  plane 205
  polarisation 210–11, 217
  progressive 204, 209, 212–13
  properties 210–11, 220
  pulse 205
  reflection 220–1, 235
  refraction 222, 235, 239
  representing 205
  speed of 205
  stationary (standing) 204, 212, 213–16, 217
  superposition 210, 214, 217
  transverse 204, 209, 213, 216
  see also electromic spectrum;
    interference; light;
    oscillations; phase; radio;
    sound
wavicles 529, 535, 544, 545
weak force 376, 377
Weber, Prof, Joseph 402
webers 449,
  definition 451
weight 28, 376
  defined 25, 26
  units 25, 26
  weightlessness' 26, 403
  see also inertia; mass
Wheatstone bridge 302
Wilkins, Maurice 232
wire & Hooke's law 124
wire spark chamber 556–7
work (energy) 62, 63, 64, 72
  & heat/temperature 152, 171
  & centripetal force 84
  by gases 187–8
  heat engines 189
work function (photoelectric effect) 531, 535
worked examples *see* examples
working agent (heat engines) 189, 194

X-rays 547–8, 549
  diffraction 232
  medical use 266

Young's experiment 225, 238
Young's modulus 124, 125, 126

zero order maximum/spectrum (diffraction) 231, 234
zero point energy 156
zeroth law of thermodynamics 172, 173
Zweig, George 562, 563
Zwicky, Fritz 115